# THEORIA

# MOTVS CORPORVM

# COELESTIVM

IN

SECTIONIBVS CONICIS SOLEM AMBIENTIVM

AVCTORE

CAROLO FRIDERICO GAVSS.

# Karl Friedrich Gauss

## Theory of the Motion of the Heavenly Bodies Moving about the Sun in Conic Sections

A Translation of

## *Theoria Motus*

Translated and with an Appendix

by Charles Henry Davis

Dover Publications, Inc., New York

This Dover edition, first published in 1963, is an unabridged and unaltered republication of the work first published by Little, Brown and Company in 1857. The publisher is grateful to the Peabody Institute Library, Baltimore, Maryland, for furnishing a copy of the first edition for reproduction purposes.

Library of Congress Catalog Card Number: 63-19953

Manufactured in the United States of America

Dover Publications, Inc.
180 Varick Street
New York 14, N.Y.

# TRANSLATOR'S PREFACE.

IN 1852, a pamphlet, entitled *The Computation of an Orbit from Three Complete Observations*, was published, under the authority of the Navy Department, for the use of the *American Ephemeris and Nautical Almanac*, the object of which was to excerpt from various parts of GAUSS's *Theoria Motus*, and to arrange in proper order the numerous details which combine to form this complicated problem. To these were added an Appendix containing the results of Professor ENCKE's investigations, *Ueber den Ausnahmefall einer doppelten Bahnbestimmung aus denselben drei geocentrischen Oertern* (*Abhandlungen der Akademie der Wissenschaften zu Berlin*, 1848), and also Professor PEIRCE's Graphic Delineations of the Curves showing geometrically the roots of GAUSS's Equation IV. Article 141.

After this pamphlet was completed, the opinion was expressed by scientific friends that a complete translation of the *Theoria Motus* should be undertaken, not only to meet the wants of the *American Ephemeris*, but those also of Astronomers generally, to whom this work (now become very rare and costly) is a standard and permanent authority. This undertaking has been particularly encouraged by the Smithsonian Institution, which has signified its high estimate of the importance of the work, by contributing to its publication. And by the authority of Hon. J. C. DOBBIN, Secretary of the Navy, this Translation is printed by the joint contributions of the Nautical Almanac and the Smithsonian Institution.

The notation of GAUSS has been strictly adhered to throughout, and the translation has been made as nearly literal as possible. No pains have been spared to secure typographical accuracy. All the errata that have been noticed in ZACH's *Monatliche Correspondenz*, the *Berliner Astronomisches Jahrbuch*, and the *Astronomische Nachrichten*, have been corrected, and in addition to these a considerable number, a list of which will be found in GOULD's *Astronomical Journal*, that were discovered by Professor CHAUVENET of the United States Naval Academy, who has examined the formulas of the body of the work with great care, not only by comparison with the original, but by independent verification. The proof-sheets have also been carefully read by Professor PHILLIPS, of Chapel Hill, North Carolina, and by Mr. RUNKLE and Professor WINLOCK of the Nautical Almanac office.

The *Appendix* contains the results of the investigations of Professor ENCKE and Professor PEIRCE, from the Appendix of the pamphlet above referred to, and other matters which, it is hoped, will be found interesting and useful to the practical computer, among which are several valuable tables: A Table for the Motion in a Parabola from LE VERRIER's *Annales de L'Observatoire Impérial de Paris*, BESSEL's and POSSELT's Tables for Ellipses and Hyperbolas closely resembling the Parabola, and a convenient Table by Professor HUBBARD for facilitating the use of GAUSS's formulas for Ellipses and Hyperbolas of which the eccentricities are nearly equal to unity. And in the form of notes on their appropriate articles, useful formulas by BESSEL, NICOLAI, ENCKE, GAUSS, and PEIRCE, and a summary of the formulas for computing the orbit of a Comet, with the accompanying Table, from OLBERS's *Abhandlung ueber die leichteste und bequemste Methode die Bahn eines Cometen zu berechnen*. Weimar, 1847.

# CONTENTS.

# CONTENTS.

# PREFACE.

AFTER the laws of planetary motion were discovered, the genius of KEPLER was not without resources for deriving from observations the elements of motion of individual planets. TYCHO BRAHE, by whom practical astronomy had been carried to a degree of perfection before unknown, had observed all the planets through a long series of years with the greatest care, and with so much perseverance, that there remained to KEPLER, the most worthy inheritor of such a repository, the trouble only of selecting what might seem suited to any special purpose. The mean motions of the planets already determined with great precision by means of very ancient observations diminished not a little this labor.

Astronomers who, subsequently to KEPLER, endeavored to determine still more accurately the orbits of the planets with the aid of more recent or better observations, enjoyed the same or even greater facilities. For the problem was no longer to deduce elements wholly unknown, but only slightly to correct those already known, and to define them within narrower limits.

The principle of universal gravitation discovered by the illustrious NEWTON opened a field entirely new, and showed that all the heavenly bodies, at least those the motions of which are regulated by the attraction of the sun, must necessarily, conform to the same laws, with a slight modification only, by which KEPLER had found the five planets to be governed. KEPLER, relying upon the evidence of observations, had announced that the orbit of every planet is an ellipse, in which the areas are described uniformly about the sun occupying one focus of the ellipse, and in such a manner that in different ellipses the times of revolution are in the sesquialteral ratio of the semi-axes-major. On the other hand, NEWTON, starting from the principle of universal gravitation, demonstrated à *priori* that all bodies controlled by the attractive force of the sun must move in conic sections, of which the planets present one form to us, namely, ellipses, while the remaining forms, parabolas and hyperbolas, must be regarded as being equally possible, provided there may be bodies encountering the force of the sun with the requisite velocity; that the sun must always occupy one focus of the conic section; that the areas which the same body describes in different times about the sun are proportional to those times; and finally, that the areas described about the sun by different bodies, in equal times, are in the subduplicate ratio of the semiparameters of the orbits: the latter of these laws, identical in elliptic motion with the last law of KEPLER, extends to the parabolic and hyperbolic motion, to which KEPLER's law cannot be applied, because the revolutions are wanting. The clue was now discovered by following which it became possible to enter the hitherto inaccessible labyrinth of the motions of the comets. And this was so successful that the single hypothesis, that their orbits were parabolas, sufficed to explain the motions of all the comets which had been accurately observed. Thus the system of universal gravitation had paved the way to new and most brilliant triumphs in analysis; and the comets, up to that time wholly unmanageable, or soon breaking from the restraints to which they seemed to be subjected, having now submitted to control, and being transformed from enemies to guests, moved on in the paths marked out by the calculus, scrupulously conforming to the same eternal laws that govern the planets.

In determining the parabolic orbits of comets from observation, difficulties arose far greater than in determining the elliptic orbits of planets, and principally from this source, that comets, seen for a brief interval, did not afford a choice of observations particularly suited to a given object: but the geometer was compelled to employ those which happened to be furnished him, so that it became necessary to make use of special methods seldom applied in planetary calculations. The great NEWTON himself, the first geometer of his age, did not disguise the difficulty of the problem: as might have been expected, he came out of this contest also the victor. Since the time of NEWTON, many geometers have labored zealously on the same problem, with various success, of course, but still in such a manner as to leave but little to be desired at the present time.

The truth, however, is not to be overlooked that in this problem the difficulty is very fortunately lessened by the knowledge of one element of the conic section, since the major-axis is put equal to infinity by the very assumption of the parabolic orbit. For, all parabolas, if position is neglected, differ among themselves only by the greater or less distance of the vertex from the focus; while conic sections, generally considered, admit of infinitely greater variety. There existed, in point of fact, no sufficient reason why it should be taken for granted that the paths of comets are exactly parabolic: on the contrary, it must be regarded as in the highest degree improbable that nature should ever have favored such an hypothesis.  Since, nevertheless, it was known, that the phenomena of a heavenly body moving in an ellipse or hyperbola, the major-axis of which is very great relatively to the parameter, differs very little near the perihelion from the motion in a parabola of which the vertex is at the same distance from the focus; and that this difference becomes the more inconsiderable the greater the ratio of the axis to the parameter: and since, moreover, experience had shown that between the observed motion and the motion computed in the parabolic orbit, there remained differences scarcely ever greater than those which might safely be attributed to errors of observation (errors quite considerable in most cases): astronomers have thought proper to retain the parabola, and very properly, because there are no means whatever of ascertaining satisfactorily what, if any, are the differences from a parabola.  We must except the celebrated comet of HALLEY, which, describing a very elongated ellipse and frequently observed at its return to the perihelion, revealed to us its periodic time; but then the major-axis being thus known, the computation of the remaining elements is to be considered as hardly more difficult than the determination of the parabolic orbit.  And we must not omit to mention that astronomers, in the case of some other comets observed for a somewhat longer time, have attempted to determine the deviation from a parabola.  However, all the methods either proposed or used for this object, rest upon the assumption that the variation from a parabola is inconsiderable, and hence in the trials referred to, the parabola itself, previously computed, furnished an approximate idea of the several elements (except the major-axis, or the time of revolution depending on it), to be corrected by only slight changes.  Besides, it must be acknowledged, that the whole of these trials hardly served in any case to settle any thing with certainty, if, perhaps, the comet of the year 1770 is excepted.

As soon as it was ascertained that the motion of the new planet, discovered in 1781, could not be reconciled with the parabolic hypothesis, astronomers undertook to adapt a circular orbit to it, which is a matter of simple and very easy calculation. By a happy accident the orbit of this planet had but a small eccentricity, in consequence of which the elements resulting from the circular hypothesis sufficed at least for an approximation on which could be based the determination of the elliptic elements. There was a concurrence of several other very favorable circumstances. For, the slow motion of the planet, and the very small inclination of the orbit to the plane of the ecliptic, not only rendered the calculations much more simple, and allowed the use of special methods not suited to other cases; but they removed the apprehension, lest the planet, lost in the rays of the sun, should subsequently elude the search of observers, (an apprehension which some astronomers might have felt, especially if its light had been less brilliant); so that the more accurate determination of the orbit might be safely deferred, until a selection could be made from observations more frequent and more remote, such as seemed best fitted for the end in view.

Thus, in every case in which it was necessary to deduce the orbits of heavenly bodies from observations, there existed advantages not to be despised, suggesting, or at any rate permitting, the application of special methods; of which advantages the chief one was, that by means of hypothetical assumptions an approximate knowledge of some elements could be obtained before the computation of the elliptic elements was commenced. Notwithstanding this, it seems somewhat strange that the general problem, —

*To determine the orbit of a heavenly body, without any hypothetical assumption, from observations not embracing a great period of time, and not allowing a selection with a view to the application of special methods,* was almost wholly neglected up to the beginning of the present century; or, at least, not treated by any one in a manner worthy of its importance; since it assuredly commended itself to mathematicians by its difficulty and elegance, even if its great utility in practice were not apparent. An opinion had universally prevailed that a complete determination from observations embracing a short interval of time was impossible, — an ill-founded opinion, — for it is now clearly shown that the orbit of a heavenly body may be determined quite nearly from good observations embracing only a few days; and this without any hypothetical assumption.

Some ideas occurred to me in the month of September of the year 1801, engaged at the time on a very different subject, which seemed to point to the solution of the great problem of which I have spoken. Under such circumstances we not unfrequently, for fear of being too much led away by an attractive investigation, suffer the associations of ideas, which, more attentively considered, might have proved most fruitful in results, to be lost from neglect. And the same fate might have befallen these conceptions, had they not happily occurred at the most propitious moment for their preservation and encouragement that could have been selected. For just about this time the report of the new planet, discovered on the first day of January of that year with the telescope at Palermo, was the subject of universal conversation;

and soon afterwards the observations made by that distinguished astronomer PIAZZI from the above date to the eleventh of February were published. Nowhere in the annals of astronomy do we meet with so great an opportunity, and a greater one could hardly be imagined, for showing most strikingly, the value of this problem, than in this crisis and urgent necessity, when all hope of discovering in the heavens this planetary atom, among innumerable small stars after the lapse of nearly a year, rested solely upon a sufficiently approximate knowledge of its orbit to be based upon these very few observations. Could I ever have found a more seasonable opportunity to test the practical value of my conceptions, than now in employing them for the determination of the orbit of the planet Ceres, which during these forty-one days had described a geocentric arc of only three degrees, and after the lapse of a year must be looked for in a region of the heavens very remote from that in which it was last seen? This first application of the method was made in the month of October, 1801, and the first clear night, when the planet was sought for* as directed by the numbers deduced from it, restored the fugitive to observation. Three other new planets, subsequently discovered, furnished new opportunities for examining and verifying the efficiency and generality of the method.

Several astronomers wished me to publish the methods employed in these calculations immediately after the second discovery of Ceres; but many things — other occupations, the desire of treating the subject more fully at some subsequent period, and, especially, the hope that a further prosecution of this investigation would raise various parts of the solution to a greater

---

* By de ZACH, December 7, 1801.

degree of generality, simplicity, and elegance, — prevented my complying at the time with these friendly solicitations. I was not disappointed in this expectation, and have no cause to regret the delay. For, the methods first employed have undergone so many and such great changes, that scarcely any trace of resemblance remains between the method in which the orbit of Ceres was first computed, and the form given in this work. Although it would be foreign to my purpose, to narrate in detail all the steps by which these investigations have been gradually perfected, still, in several instances, particularly when the problem was one of more importance than usual, I have thought that the earlier methods ought not to be wholly suppressed. But in this work, besides the solutions of the principal problems, I have given many things which, during the long time I have been engaged upon the motions of the heavenly bodies in conic sections, struck me as worthy of attention, either on account of their analytical elegance, or more especially on account of their practical utility. But in every case I have devoted greater care both to the subjects and methods which are peculiar to myself, touching lightly and so far only as the connection seemed to require, on those previously known.

The whole work is divided into two parts. In the First Book are developed the relations between the quantities on which the motion of the heavenly bodies about the sun, according to the laws of KEPLER, depends; the two first sections comprise those relations in which one place only is considered, and the third and fourth sections those in which the relations between several places are considered. The two latter contain an explanation of the common methods, and also, and more particularly, of other methods, greatly preferable to them in practice if I am not mistaken, by means of which we pass from the known elements to the phenomena; the former treat of many most important problems which prepare the way to inverse processes. Since these very phenomena result from a certain artificial and intricate complication of the elements, the nature of this texture must be thoroughly examined before we can undertake with hope of success to disentangle the threads and to resolve the fabric into its constituent parts. Accordingly, in the First Book, the means and appliances are provided, by means of which, in the second, this difficult task is accomplished; the chief part of the labor, therefore, consists in this, that these means should be properly collected together, should be suitably arranged, and directed to the proposed end.

The more important problems are, for the most part, illustrated by appropriate examples, taken, wherever it was possible, from actual observations. In this way not only is the efficacy of the methods more fully established and their use more clearly shown, but also, care, I hope, has been taken that inexperienced computers should not be deterred from the study of these subjects, which undoubtedly constitute the richest and most attractive part of theoretical astronomy.

GOTTINGEN, March 28, 1809.

# FIRST BOOK.

GENERAL RELATIONS BETWEEN THOSE QUANTITIES BY WHICH THE
MOTIONS OF HEAVENLY BODIES ABOUT THE SUN ARE DEFINED.

## FIRST SECTION.

### RELATIONS PERTAINING SIMPLY TO POSITION IN THE ORBIT.

### 1.

In this work we shall consider the motions of the heavenly bodies so far only
as they are controlled by the attractive force of the sun. All the secondary
planets are therefore excluded from our plan, the perturbations which the
primary planets exert upon each other are excluded, as is also all motion of
rotation. We regard the moving bodies themselves as mathematical points, and
we assume that all motions are performed in obedience to the following laws,
which are to be received as the basis of all discussion in this work.

I. The motion of every heavenly body takes place in the same fixed
plane in which the centre of the sun is situated.

II. The path described by a body is a conic section having its focus in the
centre of the sun.

III. The motion in this path is such that the areas of the spaces described
about the sun in different intervals of time are proportional to those intervals.
Accordingly, if the times and spaces are expressed in numbers, any space whatever divided by the time in which it is described gives a constant quotient.

IV. For different bodies moving about the sun, the squares of these quotients are.in the compound ratio of the parameters of their orbits, and of the sum of the masses of the sun and the moving bodies.

Denoting, therefore, the parameter of the orbit in which the body moves by $2p$, the mass of this body by $\mu$ (the mass of the sun being put $=1$), the area it describes about the sun in the time $t$ by $\frac{1}{2}g$, then $\frac{g}{t\sqrt{p}\sqrt{(1+\mu)}}$ will be a constant for all heavenly bodies. Since then it is of no importance which body we use for determining this number, we will derive it from the motion of the earth, the mean distance of which from the sun we shall adopt for the unit of distance; the mean solar day will always be our unit of time. Denoting, moreover, by $\pi$ the ratio of the circumference of the circle to the diameter, the area of the entire ellipse described by the earth will evidently be $\pi\sqrt{p}$, which must therefore be put $=\frac{1}{2}g$, if by $t$ is understood the sidereal year; whence, our constant becomes $=\frac{2\pi}{t\sqrt{(1+\mu)}}$. In order to ascertain the numerical value of this constant, hereafter to be denoted by $k$, we will put, according to the latest determination, the sidereal year or $t=365.2563835$, the mass of the earth, or $\mu=\frac{1}{354710}=$ 0.0000028192, whence results

$$\begin{array}{ll} \log 2\pi \quad . \quad . \quad . \quad . \quad . \quad . \quad . & 0.7981798684 \\ \text{Compl. } \log t \quad . \quad . \quad . \quad . \quad . \quad . & 7.4374021852 \\ \text{Compl. } \log. \ \sqrt{(1+\mu)} \quad . \quad . \quad . & 9.9999993878 \\ \hline \log k \ . \quad . \quad . \quad . \quad . \quad . \quad . \quad . & 8.2355814414 \\ \quad\quad k = & 0.01720209895. \end{array}$$

## 2.

The laws above stated differ from those discovered by our own Kepler in no other respect than this, that they are given in a form applicable to all kinds of conic sections, and that the action of the moving body on the sun, on which depends the factor $\sqrt{(1+\mu)}$, is taken into account. If we regard these laws as phenomena derived from innumerable and indubitable observations, geometry shows what action ought in consequence to be exerted upon bodies moving about the sun, in order that these phenomena may be continually produced.  In this way it is found that the action of the sun upon the bodies moving about it is exerted just as if an attractive force, the intensity of which is reciprocally proportional to the square of the distance, should urge the bodies towards the centre of the sun.  If now, on the other hand, we set out with the assumption of such an attractive force, the phenomena are deduced from it as necessary consequences.  It is sufficient here merely to have recited these laws, the connection of which with the principle of gravitation it will be the less necessary to dwell upon in this place, since several authors subsequently to the eminent Newton have treated this subject, and among them the illustrious La Place, in that most perfect work the Mécanique Céleste, in such a manner as to leave nothing further to be desired.

## 3.

Inquiries into the motions of the heavenly bodies, so far as they take place in conic sections, by no means demand a complete theory of this class of curves; but a single general equation rather, on which all others can be based, will answer our purpose.  And it appears to be particularly advantageous to select that one to which, while investigating the curve described according to the law of attraction, we are conducted as a characteristic equation.  If we determine any place of a body in its orbit by the distances $x, y$, from two right lines drawn in the plane of the orbit intersecting each other at right angles in the centre of the sun, that is, in one of the foci of the curve, and further, if we denote the distance of the body from the sun by $r$ (always positive), we shall have between $r, x, y$, the linear equation $r + \alpha x + \beta y = \gamma$, in which $\alpha, \beta, \gamma$ represent constant quantities, $\gamma$ being from the nature of the case always positive.  By changing the position of the right lines to which $x, y$, are referred, this position being essentially arbitrary, provided only the lines continue to intersect each other at right angles, the form of the equation and also the value of $\gamma$ will not be changed, but the values of $\alpha$ and $\beta$ will vary, and it is plain that the position may be so determined that $\beta$ shall become $= 0$, and $\alpha$, at least, not negative.  In this way by putting for $\alpha, \gamma$, respectively $e, p$, our equation takes the form $r + ex = p$.  The right line to which the distances $y$ are referred in this case, is called the *line of apsides*, $p$ is the *semi-parameter*, $e$ the *eccentricity*; finally the conic section is distinguished by the name of *ellipse, parabola*, or *hyperbola*, according as $e$ is less than unity, equal to unity, or greater than unity.

It is readily perceived that the position of the line of apsides would be fully determined by the conditions mentioned, with the exception of the single case where both $\alpha$ and $\beta$ were $= 0$; in which case $r$ is always $= p$, whatever the right lines to which $x$, $y$, are referred. Accordingly, since we have $e = 0$, the curve (which will be a circle) is according to our definition to be assigned to the class of ellipses, but it has this peculiarity, that the position of the apsides remains wholly arbitrary, if indeed we choose to extend that idea to such a case.

## 4.

Instead of the distance $x$ let us introduce the angle $v$, contained between the line of apsides and a straight line drawn from the sun to the place of the body (*the radius vector*), and this angle may commence at that part of the line of apsides at which the distances $x$ are positive, and may be supposed to increase in the direction of the motion of the body. In this way we have $x = r \cos v$, and thus our formula becomes $r = \frac{p}{1 + e \cos v}$, from which immediately result the following conclusions: —

I. For $v = 0$, the value of the radius vector $r$ becomes a minimum, that is, $= \frac{p}{1+e}$: this point is called the perihelion.

II. For opposite values of $v$, there are corresponding equal values of $r$; consequently the line of apsides divides the conic section into two equal parts.

III. In the *ellipse*, $v$ increases continuously from $v = 0$, until it attains its maximum value, $\frac{p}{1-e}$, in *aphelion*, corresponding to $v = 180°$; after aphelion, it decreases in the same manner as it had increased, until it reaches the perihelion, corresponding to $v = 360°$. That portion of the line of apsides terminated at one extremity by the perihelion and at the other by the aphelion is called the *major axis;* hence the semi-axis major, called also the *mean distance,* $= \frac{p}{1-ee}$; the distance of the middle point of the axis (*the centre of the ellipse*) from the focus will be $\frac{ep}{1-ee} = ea$, denoting by $a$ the semi-axis major.

IV. On the other hand, the aphelion in its proper sense is wanting in the parabola, but $r$ is increased indefinitely as $v$ approaches $+180°$, or $-180°$. For $v = \pm 180°$ the value of $r$ becomes infinite, which shows that the curve is not cut by the line of apsides at a point opposite the perihelion. Wherefore, we cannot, with strict propriety of language, speak of the major axis or of the centre of the curve; but by an extension of the formulas found in the ellipse, according to the established usage of analysis, an infinite value is assigned to the major axis, and the centre of the curve is placed at an infinite distance from the focus.

V. In the hyperbola, lastly, $v$ is confined within still narrower limits, in fact between $v = -(180° - \psi)$, and $v = +(180° - \psi)$, denoting by $\psi$ the angle of which the cosine $= \frac{1}{e}$. For whilst $v$ approaches these limits, $r$ increases to infinity; if, in fact, one of these two limits should be taken for $v$, the value of $r$ would result infinite, which shows that the hyperbola is not cut at all by a right line inclined to the line of apsides above or below by an angle $180° - \psi$. For the values thus excluded, that is to say, from $180° - \psi$ to $180° + \psi$, our formula assigns to $r$ a negative value. The right line inclined by such an angle to the line of apsides does not indeed cut the hyperbola, but if produced reversely, meets the other branch of the hyperbola, which, as is known, is wholly separated from the first branch and is convex towards that focus, in which the sun is situated. But in our investigation, which, as we have already said, rests upon the assumption that $r$ is taken positive, we shall pay no regard to that other branch of the hyperbola in which no heavenly body could move, except one on which the sun should, according to the same laws, exert not an attractive but a repulsive force. Accordingly, the aphelion does not exist, properly speaking, in the hyperbola also; that point of the reverse branch which lies in the line of apsides, and which corresponds to the values $v = 180°$, $r = -\frac{p}{e-1}$, might be considered as analogous to the aphelion. If now, we choose after the manner of the ellipse to call the value of the expression $\frac{p}{1-ee}$, even here where it becomes negative, the semi-axis major of the hyperbola, then this quantity indicates the distance of the point just mentioned from the perihelion, and at the same time the position opposite to that which occurs in the ellipse. In the same way $\frac{ep}{1-ee}$, that is, the distance from the focus to the middle point between these two points (the centre of the hyperbola), here obtains a negative value on account of its opposite direction.

## 5.

We call the angle $v$ the *true anomaly* of the moving body, which, in the parabola is confined within the limits $-180°$ and $+180°$, in the hyperbola between $-(180°-\psi)$ and $+(180°-\psi)$, but which in the ellipse runs through the whole circle in periods constantly renewed. Hitherto, the greater number of astronomers have been accustomed to count the true anomaly in the ellipse not from the perihelion but from the aphelion, contrary to the analogy of the parabola and hyperbola, where, as the aphelion is wanting, it is necessary to begin from the perihelion: we have the less hesitation in restoring the analogy among all classes of conic sections, that the most recent French astronomers have by their example led the way.

It is frequently expedient to change a little the form of the expression $r=\frac{p}{1+e\cos v}$; the following forms will be especially observed:—

$$r=\frac{p}{1+e-2e\sin^2\frac{1}{2}v}=\frac{p}{1-e+2e\cos^2\frac{1}{2}v}$$

$$r=\frac{p}{(1+e)\cos^2\frac{1}{2}v+(1-e)\sin^2\frac{1}{2}v}.$$

Accordingly, we have in the parabola

$$r=\frac{p}{2\cos^2\frac{1}{2}v};$$

in the hyperbola the following expression is particularly convenient,

$$r=\frac{p\cos\psi}{2\cos\frac{1}{2}(v+\psi)\cos\frac{1}{2}(v-\psi)}.$$

## 6.

Let us proceed now to the comparison of the motion with the time. Putting, as in Art. 1, the space described about the sun in the time $t = \frac{1}{2} g$, the mass of the moving body $= \mu$, that of the sun being taken $= 1$, we have $g = kt\sqrt{p}\sqrt{(1 + \mu)}$. The differential of the space $= \frac{1}{2} rr\,dv$, from which there results $kt\sqrt{p}\sqrt{(1 + \mu)} = \int rr\,dv$, this integral being so taken that it will vanish for $t = 0$. This integration must be treated differently for different kinds of conic sections, on which account, we shall now consider each kind separately, beginning with the ELLIPSE.

Since $r$ is determined from $v$ by means of a fraction, the denominator of which consists of two terms, we will remove this inconvenience by the introduction of a new quantity in the place of $v$. For this purpose we will put $\tan \frac{1}{2} v \sqrt{\frac{1 - e}{1 + e}} = \tan \frac{1}{2} E$, by which the last formula for $r$ in the preceding article gives

$$r = \frac{p \cos^2 \frac{1}{2} E}{(1 + e) \cos^2 \frac{1}{2} v} = p \left( \frac{\cos^2 \frac{1}{2} E}{1 + e} + \frac{\sin^2 \frac{1}{2} E}{1 - e} \right) = \frac{p}{1 - ee} (1 - e \cos E).$$

Moreover we have $\dfrac{dE}{\cos^2 \frac{1}{2} E} = \dfrac{dv}{\cos^2 \frac{1}{2} v} \sqrt{\dfrac{1 - e}{1 + e}}$, and consequently $dv = \dfrac{p\,dE}{r\sqrt{(1 - ee)}}$; hence

$$rr\,dv = \frac{rp\,dE}{\sqrt{(1 - ee)}} = \frac{pp}{(1 - ee)^{\frac{3}{2}}} (1 - e \cos E)\,dE,$$

and integrating,

$$kt\sqrt{p}\sqrt{(1 + \mu)} = \frac{pp}{(1 - ee)^{\frac{3}{2}}} (E - e \sin E) + \text{Constant.}$$

Accordingly, if we place the beginning of the time at the perihelion passage, where $v = 0$, $E = 0$, and thus constant $= 0$, we shall have, by reason of $\dfrac{p}{1 - ee} = a$,

$$E - e \sin E = \frac{kt\sqrt{(1 + \mu)}}{a^{\frac{3}{2}}}.$$

In this equation the auxiliary angle $E$, which is called the *eccentric anomaly*, must be expressed in parts of the radius. This angle, however, may be retained in degrees, etc., if $e \sin E$ and $\dfrac{kt\sqrt{(1 + \mu)}}{a^{\frac{3}{2}}}$ are also expressed in the same manner; these quantities will be expressed in seconds of arc if they are multiplied by the

number 206264.81. We can dispense with the multiplication by the last quantity, if we employ directly the quantity $k$ expressed in seconds, and thus put,
instead of the value before given, $k = 3548''.18761$, of which the logarithm =
3.5500065746. The quantity $\dfrac{kt \sqrt{(1+\mu)}}{a^{\frac{3}{2}}}$ expressed in this manner is called the
*mean anomaly*, which therefore increases in the ratio of the time, and indeed every
day by the increment $\dfrac{k\sqrt{(1+\mu)}}{a^{\frac{3}{2}}}$, called the *mean daily motion*. We shall denote
the mean anomaly by $M$.

## 7.

Thus, then, at the perihelion, the true anomaly, the eccentric anomaly, and the
mean anomaly are $= 0$; after that, the true anomaly increasing, the eccentric
and mean are augmented also, but in such a way that the eccentric continues to
be less than the true, and the mean less than the eccentric up to the aphelion,
where all three become at the same time $= 180°$; but from this point to
the perihelion, the eccentric is always greater than the true, and the mean
greater than the eccentric, until in the perihelion all three become $= 360°$, or,
which amounts to the same thing, all are again $= 0$. And, in general, it is
evident that if the eccentric $E$ and the mean $M$ answer to the true anomaly $v$,
then the eccentric $360° - E$ and the mean $360° - M$ correspond to the true
$360° - v$. The difference between the true and mean anomalies, $v - M$, is called
the *equation of the centre*, which, consequently, is positive from the perihelion
to the aphelion, is negative from the aphelion to the perihelion, and at the
perihelion and aphelion vanishes. Since, therefore, $v$ and $M$ run through an
entire circle from 0 to $360°$ in the same time, the time of a single revolution,
which is also called the *periodic time*, is obtained, expressed in days, by dividing
$360°$ by the mean daily motion $\dfrac{k\sqrt{(1+\mu)}}{a^{\frac{3}{2}}}$, from which it is apparent, that for different bodies revolving about the sun, the squares of the periodic times are pro-
portional to the cubes of the mean distances, so far as the masses of the bodies,
or rather the inequality of their masses, can be neglected.

## 8.

Let us now collect together those relations between the anomalies and the radius vector which deserve particular attention, the derivation of which will present no difficulties to any one moderately skilled in trigonometrical analysis. Greater elegance is attained in most of these formulas by introducing in the place of $e$ the angle the sine of which $= e$. This angle being denoted by $\varphi$, we have

$$\sqrt{(1-ee)} = \cos\varphi, \quad \sqrt{(1+e)} = \cos(45° - \tfrac{1}{2}\varphi)\sqrt{2},$$

$$\sqrt{(1-e)} = \cos(45° + \tfrac{1}{2}\varphi)\sqrt{2}, \quad \sqrt{\frac{1-e}{1+e}} = \tan(45° - \tfrac{1}{2}\varphi),$$

$$\sqrt{(1+e)} + \sqrt{(1-e)} = 2\cos\tfrac{1}{2}\varphi, \quad \sqrt{(1+e)} - \sqrt{(1-e)} = 2\sin\tfrac{1}{2}\varphi.$$

The following are the principal relations between $a, p, r, e, \varphi, v, E, M$.

I. $p = a\cos^2\varphi$

II. $r = \dfrac{p}{1 + e\cos v}$

III. $r = a(1 - e\cos E)$

IV. $\cos E = \dfrac{\cos v + e}{1 + e\cos v}$, or $\cos v = \dfrac{\cos E - e}{1 - e\cos E}$

V. $\sin\tfrac{1}{2}E = \sqrt{\tfrac{1}{2}(1 - \cos E)} = \sin\tfrac{1}{2}v\sqrt{\dfrac{1-e}{1+e\cos v}}$

$$= \sin\tfrac{1}{2}v\sqrt{\dfrac{r(1-e)}{p}} = \sin\tfrac{1}{2}v\sqrt{\dfrac{r}{a(1+e)}}$$

VI. $\cos\tfrac{1}{2}E = \sqrt{\tfrac{1}{2}(1 + \cos E)} = \cos\tfrac{1}{2}v\sqrt{\dfrac{1+e}{1+e\cos v}}$

$$= \cos\tfrac{1}{2}v\sqrt{\dfrac{r(1+e)}{p}} = \cos\tfrac{1}{2}v\sqrt{\dfrac{r}{a(1-e)}}$$

VII. $\tan\tfrac{1}{2}E = \tan\tfrac{1}{2}v\tan(45° - \tfrac{1}{2}\varphi)$

VIII. $\sin E = \dfrac{r\sin v\cos\varphi}{p} = \dfrac{r\sin v}{a\cos\varphi}$

IX. $r\cos v = a(\cos E - e) = 2a\cos(\tfrac{1}{2}E + \tfrac{1}{2}\varphi + 45°)\cos(\tfrac{1}{2}E - \tfrac{1}{2}\varphi - 45°)$

X. $\sin\tfrac{1}{2}(v - E) = \sin\tfrac{1}{2}\varphi\sin v\sqrt{\dfrac{r}{p}} = \sin\tfrac{1}{2}\varphi\sin E\sqrt{\dfrac{a}{r}}$

XI. $\sin\tfrac{1}{2}(v + E) = \cos\tfrac{1}{2}\varphi\sin v\sqrt{\dfrac{r}{p}} = \cos\tfrac{1}{2}\varphi\sin E\sqrt{\dfrac{a}{r}}$

XII. $M = E - e\sin E$.

## 9.

If a perpendicular let fall from any point whatever of the ellipse upon the line of apsides is extended in the opposite direction until it meets the circle described with the radius $a$ about the centre of the ellipse, then the inclination to the line of apsides of that radius which corresponds to the point of intersection (understood in the same way as above, in the case of the true anomaly), will be equal to the eccentric anomaly, as is inferred without difficulty from equation IX. of the preceding article. Further, it is evident that $r \sin v$ is the distance of any point of the ellipse from the line of apsides, which, since by equation VIII. it $= a \cos \varphi \sin E$, will be greatest for $E = 90°$, that is in the centre of the ellipse. This greatest distance, which $= a \cos \varphi = \dfrac{p}{\cos \varphi} = \sqrt{a\,p}$, is called the *semi-axis minor*. In the focus of the ellipse, that is for $v = 90°$, this distance is evidently $= p$, or equal the semi-parameter.

## 10.

The equations of article 8 comprise all that is requisite for the computation of the eccentric and mean anomalies from the true, or of the eccentric and true from the mean. Formula VII. is commonly employed for deriving the eccentric from the true; nevertheless it is for the most part preferable to make use of equation X. for this purpose, especially when the eccentricity is not too great, in which case $E$ can be computed with greater accuracy by means of X. than of VII. Moreover, if X. is employed, the logarithm of sine $E$ required in XII. is had immediately by means of VIII.: if VII. were used, it would be necessary to take it out from the tables; if, therefore, this logarithm is also taken from the tables in the latter method, a proof is at once obtained that the calculation has been correctly made. Tests and proofs of this sort are always to be highly valued, and therefore it will be an object of constant attention with us to provide for them in all the methods delivered in this work, where indeed it can be conveniently done. We annex an example completely calculated as a more perfect illustration.

Given $v = 310° 55' 29''.64$, $\varphi = 14° 12' 1''.87$, $\log r = 0.3307640$; $p$, $a$, $E$, $M$, are required.

$$\begin{array}{ll}
\log \sin \varphi & 9.3897262 \\
\log \cos v & 9.8162877 \\
\hline
& 9.2060139 \quad \text{whence } e \cos v = 0.1606993 \\
\log (1 + e \cos v) & 0.0647197 \\
\log r & 0.3307640 \\
\hline
\log p & 0.3954837 \\
\log \cos^2 \varphi & 9.9730448 \\
\hline
\log a & 0.4224389 \\
\log \sin v & 9.8782740 \, n* \\
\log \sqrt{\dfrac{p}{r}} & 0.0323598.5 \\
\hline
& 9.8459141.5 \, n \\
\log \sin \tfrac{1}{2} \varphi & 9.0920395 \\
\hline
\log \sin \tfrac{1}{2} (v - E) & 8.9379536.5 \, n, \text{ hence } \tfrac{1}{2} (v - E) = -4° 58' 22''.94; \\
\end{array}$$

$$v - E = -9° 56' 45''.88; \quad E = 320° 52' 15''.52.$$

Further, we have

$$\begin{array}{ll}
\log e & 9.3897262 \\
\log 206264.8 & 5.3144251 \\
\hline
\log e \text{ in seconds} & 4.7041513 \\
\log \sin E & 9.8000767 \, n \\
\hline
\end{array}$$

Calculation of $\log \sin E$ by formula VIII.

$$\begin{array}{ll}
\log \dfrac{r}{p} \sin v & 9.8135543 \, n \\
\log \cos \varphi & 9.9865224 \\
\hline
\log \sin E & 9.8000767 \, n \\
\end{array}$$

$4.5042280 \, n$, hence $e \sin E$ in seconds $= 31932''.14 = 8° 52' 12''.14$; and $M = 329° 44' 27''.66$.

The computation of $E$ by formula VII. would be as follows:—

$$\begin{array}{ll}
\tfrac{1}{2} v = 155° 27' 44''.82 & \log \tan \tfrac{1}{2} v \quad 9.6594579 \, n \\
45° - \tfrac{1}{2} \varphi = 37° 53' 59''.065 & \log \tan (45° - \tfrac{1}{2} \varphi) \quad 9.8912427 \\
& \log \tan \tfrac{1}{2} E \quad 9.5507006 \, n \\
\end{array}$$

whence $\tfrac{1}{2} E = 160° 26' 7''.76$, and $E = 320° 52' 15''.52$, as above.

---

\* The letter $n$ affixed to a logarithm signifies that the number corresponding to it is negative.

## 11.

The inverse problem, celebrated under the title of *Kepler's problem*, that of finding the true anomaly and the radius vector from the mean anomaly, is much more frequently used. Astronomers are in the habit of putting the equation of the centre in the form of an infinite series proceeding according to the sines of the angles $M$, $2M$, $3M$, etc., each one of the coefficients of these sines being a series extending to infinity according to the powers of the eccentricity. We have considered it the less necessary to dwell upon this formula for the equation of the centre, which several authors have developed, because, in our opinion, it is by no means so well suited to practical use, especially should the eccentricity not be very small, as the indirect method, which, therefore, we will explain somewhat more at length in that form which appears to us most convenient.

Equation XII., $E = M + e \sin E$, which is to be referred to the class of transcendental equations, and admits of no solution by means of direct and complete methods, must be solved by trial, beginning with any approximate value of $E$, which is corrected by suitable methods repeated often enough to satisfy the preceding equation, that is, either with all the accuracy the tables of sines admit, or at least with sufficient accuracy for the end in view. If now, these corrections are introduced, not at random, but according to a safe and established rule, there is scarcely any essential distinction between such an indirect method and the solution by series, except that in the former the first value of the unknown quantity is in a measure arbitrary, which is rather to be considered an advantage since a value suitably chosen allows the corrections to be made with remarkable rapidity. Let us suppose $\varepsilon$ to be an approximate value of $E$, and $x$ expressed in seconds the correction to be added to it, of such a value as will satisfy our equation $E = \varepsilon + x$. Let $e \sin \varepsilon$, in seconds, be computed by logarithms, and when this is done, let the change of the $\log \sin \varepsilon$ for the change of $1''$ in $\varepsilon$ itself be taken from the tables; and also the variation of $\log e \sin \varepsilon$ for the change of a unit in the number $e \sin \varepsilon$; let these changes, without regard to signs, be respectively $\lambda$, $\mu$, in which it is hardly necessary to remark that both logarithms are presumed to contain an equal number of decimals. Now, if $\varepsilon$ approaches so near the correct value of $E$

that the changes of the logarithm of the sine from $\varepsilon$ to $\varepsilon + x$, and the changes of the logarithm of the number from $e \sin \varepsilon$ to $e \sin (\varepsilon + x)$, can be regarded as uniform, we may evidently put

$$e \sin (\varepsilon + x) = e \sin \varepsilon \pm \frac{\lambda x}{\mu},$$

the upper sign belonging to the first and fourth quadrants, and the lower to the second and third.   Whence, since

$$\varepsilon + x = M + e \sin (\varepsilon + x), \text{ we have } x = \frac{\mu}{\mu + \lambda} (M + e \sin \varepsilon - \varepsilon),$$

and the correct value of $E$, or

$$\varepsilon + x = M + e \sin \varepsilon \pm \frac{\lambda}{\mu + \lambda} (M + e \sin \varepsilon - \varepsilon),$$

the signs being determined by the above-mentioned condition.

Finally, it is readily perceived that we have, without regard to the signs, $\mu : \lambda = 1 : e \cos \varepsilon$, and therefore always $\mu > \lambda$, whence we infer that in the first and last quadrant $M + e \sin \varepsilon$ lies between $\varepsilon$ and $\varepsilon + x$, and in the second and third, $\varepsilon + x$ between $\varepsilon$ and $M + e \sin \varepsilon$, which rule dispenses with paying attention to the signs.   If the assumed value $\varepsilon$ differs too much from the truth to render the foregoing considerations admissible, at least a much more suitable value will be found by this method, with which the same operation can be repeated, once, or several times if it should appear necessary.   It is very apparent, that if the difference of the first value $\varepsilon$ from the truth is regarded as a quantity of the first order, the error of the new value would be referred to the second order, and if the operation were further repeated, it would be reduced to the fourth order, the eighth order, etc.   Moreover, the less the eccentricity, the more rapidly will the successive corrections converge.

## 12.

The approximate value of $E$, with which to begin the calculation, will, in most cases, be obvious enough, particularly where the problem is to be solved for several values of $M$ of which some have been already found.   In the absence of other helps, it is at least evident that $E$ must fall between $M$ and $M \pm e$, (the eccentricity $e$ being expressed in seconds, and the upper sign being used in the first and second quadrants, the lower in the third and fourth), wherefore, either $M$, or its value increased or diminished by any estimate whatever, can be taken for the first value of $E$. It is hardly necessary to observe, that the first calculation, when it is commenced with a value having no pretension to accuracy, does not require to be strictly exact, and that the smaller tables * are abundantly sufficient. Moreover, for the sake of convenience, the values selected for $\varepsilon$ should be such that their sines can be taken from the tables without interpolation; as, for example, values to minutes or exact tens of seconds, according as the tables used proceed by differences of minutes or tens of seconds. Every one will be able to determine without assistance the modifications these precepts undergo if the angles are expressed according to the new decimal division.

## 13.

*Example.* — Let the eccentricity be the same as in article 10. $M = 332° 28'$ $54''.77$. There the log $e$ in seconds is $4.7041513$, therefore $e = 50600'' = 14° 3' 20''$. Now since $E$ here must be less than $M$, let us in the first calculation put $\varepsilon = 326°$, then we have by the smaller tables

$$\log \sin \varepsilon \quad . \quad . \quad . \quad . \quad 9.74756 n, \qquad \text{Change for } 1' \ldots 19, \text{ whence } \lambda = 0.32.$$
$$\underline{\log e \text{ in seconds} \quad . \quad . \quad 4.70415}$$
$$4.45171 n;$$

hence $e \sin \varepsilon = -28295'' = -7° 51' 35''$.   Change of logarithm for a unit of the table which is here

$M + e \sin \varepsilon$ . . . . . . 324 37 20        equal to 10 seconds . . . 16; whence $\mu = 1.6$.

differing from $\varepsilon$   . . . .    1 22 40 $= 4960''$.  Hence,

$$\frac{0.32}{1.28} \times 4960'' = 1240'' = 20' 40''.$$

Wherefore, the corrected value of $E$ becomes $324° 37' 20'' - 20' 40'' = 324° 16' 40''$, with which we repeat the calculation, making use of larger tables.

$$\log \sin \varepsilon \quad . \quad . \quad . \quad . \quad 9.7663058 n \qquad \lambda = 29.25$$
$$\underline{\log e \quad . \quad . \quad . \quad . \quad . \quad 4.7041513}$$
$$4.4704571 n \qquad\qquad \mu = 147$$

---

* Such as those which the illustrious Lalande furnished.

$$e \sin \varepsilon = - 29543''.18 = - 8° 12' 23''.18$$
$$M + e \sin \varepsilon \quad . \quad . \quad . \quad . \quad 324 \;\; 16 \;\; 31 \; .59$$
$$\text{differing from } \varepsilon \quad . \quad . \quad . \qquad\qquad 8 \; .41.$$

This difference being multiplied by $\dfrac{\lambda}{\mu - \lambda} = \dfrac{29.25}{117.75}$ gives $2''.09$, whence, finally, the corrected value of $E = 324° 16' 31''.59 - 2''.09 = 324° 16' 29''.50$, which is exact within $0''.01$.

## 14.

The equations of article 8 furnish several methods for deriving the true anomaly and the radius vector from the eccentric anomaly, the best of which we will explain.

I. By the common method $v$ is determined by equation VII., and afterwards $r$ by equation II.; the example of the preceding article treated in this way is as follows, retaining for $p$ the value given in article 10.

| | | | | |
|---|---|---|---|---|
| $\tfrac{1}{2} E = 162° 8' 14''.75$ | | $\log e$ . . . . . | 9.3897262 |
| $\log \tan \tfrac{1}{2} E$ . . . . | 9.5082198$n$ | $\log \cos v$ . . . . | 9.8496597 |
| $\log \tan (45° - \tfrac{1}{2}\varphi)$ . | 9.8912427 | | 9.2393859 |
| $\log \tan \tfrac{1}{2} v$ . . . . | 9.6169771$n$ | $e \cos v$ $\quad = 0.1735345$ | |
| $\tfrac{1}{2} v = 157° 30' 41''.50$ | | $\log p$ . . . . . | 0.3954837 |
| $v = 315 \quad 1 \;\; 23 \; .00$ | | $\log (1 + e \cos v)$ . . | 0.0694959 |
| | | $\log r$ . . . . . | 0.3259878. |

II. The following method is shorter if several places are to be computed, for which the constant logarithms of the quantities $\sqrt{a(1 + e)}$, $\sqrt{a(1 - e)}$ should be computed once for all. By equations V. and VI. we have

$$\sin \tfrac{1}{2} v \sqrt{r} = \sin \tfrac{1}{2} E \sqrt{a(1 + e)}$$
$$\cos \tfrac{1}{2} v \sqrt{r} = \cos \tfrac{1}{2} E \sqrt{a(1 - e)}$$

from which $\tfrac{1}{2} v$ and $\log \sqrt{r}$ are easily determined. It is true in general that if we have $P \sin Q = A$, $P \cos Q = B$, $Q$ is obtained by means of the formula $\tan Q = \dfrac{A}{B}$, and then $P$ by this, $P = \dfrac{A}{\sin Q}$, or by $P = \dfrac{B}{\cos Q}$: it is preferable to use the former when $\sin Q$ is greater than $\cos Q$; the latter when $\cos Q$ is greater than $\sin Q$. Commonly, the problems in which equations of this kind occur (such as present themselves most frequently in this work), involve the condition that $P$ should be a positive quantity; in this case, the doubt whether $Q$ should be taken between 0 and 180°, or between 180° and 360°, is at once removed. But if such a condition does not exist, this decision is left to our judgment.

We have in our example $e = 0.2453162$.

| | | | |
|---|---|---|---|
| $\log \sin \tfrac{1}{2} E$ . . . | 9.4867632 | $\log \cos \tfrac{1}{2} E$ . . . | 9.9785434$n$ |
| $\log \sqrt{a(1+e)}$ . . | 0.2588593 | $\log \sqrt{a(1-e)}$ . . | 0.1501020. |

Hence

| | | |
|---|---|---|
| $\log \sin \tfrac{1}{2} v \sqrt{r}$ . . | 9.7456225 | whence, $\log \tan \tfrac{1}{2} v = 9.6169771n$ |
| $\log \cos \tfrac{1}{2} v \sqrt{r}$ . . | 0.1286454$n$ | $\tfrac{1}{2} v = 157° 30' 41''.50$ |
| $\log \cos \tfrac{1}{2} v$ . . . | 9.9656515$n$ | $v = 315 \quad 1\ 23\ .00$ |
| $\log \sqrt{r}$ . . . . | 0.1629939 | |
| $\log r$ . . . . . | 0.3259878 | |

III. To these methods we add a third which is almost equally easy and expeditious, and is much to be preferred to the former if the greatest accuracy should be required. Thus, $r$ is first determined by means of equation III., and after that, $v$ by X. Below is our example treated in this manner.

| | | | |
|---|---|---|---|
| $\log e$ . . . . . | 9.3897262 | $\log \sin E$ . . . . | 9.7663366$n$ |
| $\log \cos E$ . . . | 9.9094637 | $\log \sqrt{(1 - e \cos E)}$ . | 9.9517744 |
| | 9.2991899 | | 9.8145622$n$ |
| $e \cos E =$ . . . | 0.1991544 | $\log \sin \tfrac{1}{2} \varphi$ . . . . | 9.0920395 |
| $\log a$ . . . . . | 0.4224389 | $\log \sin \tfrac{1}{2}(v - E)$ . . | 8.9066017$n$ |
| $\log (1 - e \cos E)$ . | 9.9035488 | $\tfrac{1}{2}(v - E) = -4° 37' 33''.24$ |
| $\log r$ . . . . . | 0.3259877 | $v - E = -9\ 15\ 6\ .48$ |
| | | $v = 315 \quad 1\ 23\ .02$ |

Formula VIII., or XI., is very convenient for verifying the calculation, particularly if $v$ and $r$ have been determined by the third method. Thus;

$$\log \frac{a}{r} \sin E \ .\ .\ .\ 9.8627878n \qquad\qquad \log \sin E \sqrt{\frac{a}{r}} \ .\ .\ .\ 9.8145622n$$

$$\log \cos \varphi \ .\ .\ .\ .\ 9.9865224 \qquad\qquad \log \cos \tfrac{1}{2} \varphi \ .\ .\ .\ .\ 9.9966567$$

$$\overline{\qquad\qquad\qquad\qquad 9.8493102n} \qquad\qquad \overline{\qquad\qquad\qquad\qquad 9.8112189n}$$

$$\log \sin v \ .\ .\ .\ .\ 9.8493102n \qquad\qquad \log \sin \tfrac{1}{2}(v+E) \ .\ .\ 9.8112189n$$

## 15.

Since, as we have seen, the mean anomaly $M$ is completely determined by means of $v$ and $\varphi$, in the same manner as $v$ by $M$ and $\varphi$, it is evident, that if all these quantities are regarded as variable together, an equation of condition ought to exist between their differential variations, the investigation of which will not be superfluous. By differentiating first, equation VII., article 8, we obtain

$$\frac{dE}{\sin E} = \frac{dv}{\sin v} - \frac{d\varphi}{\cos \varphi};$$

by differentiating likewise equation XII., it becomes

$$dM = (1 - e \cos E)\, dE - \sin E \cos \varphi \, d\varphi.$$

If we eliminate $dE$ from these differential equations we have

$$dM = \frac{\sin E (1 - e \cos E)}{\sin v}\, dv - \left( \sin E \cos \varphi + \frac{\sin E (1 - e \cos E)}{\cos \varphi} \right) d\varphi,$$

or by substituting for $\sin E$, $1 - e \cos E$, their values from equations VIII., III.,

$$dM = \frac{rr}{aa \cos \varphi}\, dv - \frac{r (r+p) \sin v}{aa \cos^2 \varphi}\, d\varphi,$$

or lastly, if we express both coefficients by means of $v$ and $\varphi$ only,

$$dM = \frac{\cos^3 \varphi}{(1 + e \cos v)^2}\, dv - \frac{(2 + e \cos v) \sin v \cos^2 \varphi}{(1 + e \cos v)^2}\, d\varphi.$$

Inversely, if we consider $v$ as a function of the quantities $M, \varphi$, the equation has this form: —

$$dv = \frac{aa \cos \varphi}{rr}\, dM + \frac{(2 + e \cos v) \sin v}{\cos \varphi}\, d\varphi,$$

or by introducing $E$ instead of $v$

$$dv = \frac{aa \cos \varphi}{rr}\, dM + \frac{aa}{rr} (2 - e \cos E - ee) \sin E \, d\varphi.$$

## 16.

The radius vector $r$ is not fully determined by $v$ and $\varphi$, or by $M$ and $\varphi$, but depends, besides these, upon $p$ or $a$; its differential, therefore, will consist of three parts. By differentiating equation II. of article 8, we obtain

$$\frac{\mathrm{d}\,r}{r} = \frac{\mathrm{d}\,p}{p} + \frac{e\sin v}{1 + e\cos v}\,\mathrm{d}\,v - \frac{\cos\varphi\cos v}{1 + e\cos v}\,\mathrm{d}\,\varphi.$$

By putting here

$$\frac{\mathrm{d}\,p}{p} = \frac{\mathrm{d}\,a}{a} - 2\tan\varphi\,\mathrm{d}\,\varphi$$

(which follows from the differentiation of equation I.), and expressing, in conformity with the preceding article, $\mathrm{d}\,v$ by means of $\mathrm{d}\,M$ and $\mathrm{d}\,\varphi$, we have, after making the proper reductions,

$$\frac{\mathrm{d}\,r}{r} = \frac{\mathrm{d}\,a}{a} + \frac{a}{r}\tan\varphi\sin v\,\mathrm{d}\,M - \frac{a}{r}\cos\varphi\cos v\,\mathrm{d}\,\varphi,$$

$$\mathrm{d}\,r = \frac{r}{a}\,\mathrm{d}\,a + a\tan\varphi\sin v\,\mathrm{d}\,M - a\cos\varphi\cos v\,\mathrm{d}\,\varphi.$$

Finally, these formulas, as well as those which we developed in the preceding article, rest upon the supposition that $v$, $\varphi$, and $M$, or rather $\mathrm{d}\,v$, $\mathrm{d}\,\varphi$, and $\mathrm{d}\,M$, are expressed in parts of the radius. If, therefore, we choose to express the variations of the angles $v$, $\varphi$, and $M$, in seconds, we must either divide those parts of the formulas which contain $\mathrm{d}\,v$, $\mathrm{d}\,\varphi$, or $\mathrm{d}\,M$, by 206264.8, or multiply those which contain $\mathrm{d}\,r$, $\mathrm{d}\,p$, $\mathrm{d}\,a$, by the same number. Consequently, the formulas of the preceding article, which in this respect are homogeneous, will require no change.

## 17.

It will be satisfactory to add a few words concerning the investigation of the *greatest equation of the centre*. In the first place, it is evident in itself that the difference between the eccentric and mean anomaly is a maximum for $E = 90°$, where it becomes $= e$ (expressed in degrees, etc.); the radius vector at this point $= a$, whence $v = 90° + \varphi$, and thus the whole equation of the centre $= \varphi + e$, which, nevertheless, is not a maximum here, since the difference between $v$ and $E$ may still increase beyond $\varphi$. *This last* difference becomes a maximum for $d(v - E) = 0$ or for $dv = dE$, where the eccentricity is clearly to be regarded as constant. With this assumption, since in general

$$\frac{dv}{\sin v} = \frac{dE}{\sin E},$$

it is evident that we should have $\sin v = \sin E$ at that point where the difference between $v$ and $E$ is a maximum; whence we have by equations VIII., III.,

$$r = a \cos\varphi, \; e \cos E = 1 - \cos\varphi, \text{ or } \cos E = + \tan \tfrac{1}{2}\varphi.$$

In like manner $\cos v = -\tan\tfrac{1}{2}\varphi$ is found, for which reason it will follow * that

$$v = 90° + \text{arc sin tan } \tfrac{1}{2}\varphi, \; E = 90° - \text{arc sin tan } \tfrac{1}{2}\varphi;$$

hence again

$$\sin E = \sqrt{(1 - \tan^2 \tfrac{1}{2}\varphi)} = \frac{\sqrt{\cos\varphi}}{\cos\tfrac{1}{2}\varphi},$$

so that the whole equation of the centre at this point becomes

$$2 \text{ arc sin tan } \tfrac{1}{2}\varphi + 2 \sin\tfrac{1}{2}\varphi \sqrt{\cos\varphi},$$

the second term being expressed in degrees, etc. At that point, finally, where the whole equation of the centre is a maximum, we must have $dv = dM$, and so according to article 15, $r = a\sqrt{\cos\varphi}$; hence we have

$$\cos v = -\frac{1 - \cos^{\frac{3}{2}}\varphi}{e}, \; \cos E = \frac{1 - \sqrt{\cos\varphi}}{e} = \frac{1 - \cos\varphi}{e(1 + \sqrt{\cos\varphi})} = \frac{\tan\tfrac{1}{2}\varphi}{1 + \sqrt{\cos\varphi}},$$

by which formula $E$ can be determined with the greatest accuracy. $E$ being found, we shall have, by equations X., XII.,

$$\text{equation of the centre} = 2 \text{ arc sin} \frac{\sin\tfrac{1}{2}\varphi \sin E}{\sqrt[4]{\cos\varphi}} + e \sin E.$$

We do not delay here for an expression of the greatest equation of the centre by means of a series proceeding according to the powers of the eccentricities, which several authors have given. As an example, we annex a view of the three maxima which we have been considering, for Juno, of which the eccentricity, according to the latest elements, is assumed $= 0.2554996$.

---

* It is not necessary to consider those maxima which lie between the aphelion and perihelion, because they evidently differ in the signs only from those which are situated between the perihelion and aphelion.

| Maximum. | $E$ | $E-M$ | $v-E$ | $v-M$ |
|---|---|---|---|---|
| $E-M$ | 90° 0′ 0″ | 14° 38′ 20″.57 | 14° 48′ 11″.48 | 29° 26′ 32″.05 |
| $v-E$ | 82 32 9 | 14 30 54 .01 | 14 55 41 .79 | 29 26 35 .80 |
| $v-M$ | 86 14 40 | 14 36 27 .39 | 14 53 49 .57 | 29 30 16 .96 |

## 18.

In the PARABOLA, the eccentric anomaly, the mean anomaly, and the mean motion, become $= 0$; here therefore these ideas cannot aid in the comparison of the motion with the time. In the parabola, however, there is no necessity for an auxiliary angle in integrating $r\, r\, dv$; for we have

$$r r\, dv = \frac{p\,p\,dv}{4\cos^4 \tfrac12 v} = \frac{p\,p\,d\tan\tfrac12 v}{2\cos^2 \tfrac12 v} = \tfrac12\, p\,p\,(1 + \tan^2 \tfrac12 v)\, d\tan\tfrac12 v;$$

and thus,

$$\textstyle\int r r\, dv = \tfrac12\, p\,p\,(\tan \tfrac12 v + \tfrac13 \tan^3 \tfrac12 v) + \text{Constant}.$$

If the time is supposed to commence with the perihelion passage, the Constant $= 0$; therefore we have

$$\tan \tfrac12 v + \tfrac13 \tan^3 \tfrac12 v = \frac{2\,t\,k\sqrt{(1 + \mu)}}{p^{\frac32}},$$

by means of which formula, $t$ may be derived from $v$, and $v$ from $t$, when $p$ and $\mu$ are known. In the parabolic elements it is usual, instead of $p$, to make use of the radius vector at the perihelion, which is $\tfrac12\,p$, and to neglect entirely the mass $\mu$. It will scarcely ever be possible to determine the mass of a body, the orbit of which is computed as a parabola; and indeed all comets appear, according to the best and most recent observations, to have so little density and mass, that the latter can be considered insensible and be safely neglected.

## 19.

· The solution of the problem, from the true anomaly to find the time, and, in a still greater degree, the solution of the inverse problem, can be greatly abbreviated by means of an auxiliary table, such as is found in many astronomical works.

But the Barkerian is by far the most convenient, and is also annexed to the admirable work of the celebrated OLBERS, (*Abhandlung über die leichteste und bequemste Methode die Bahn eines Cometen zu berechnen*: Weimar, 1797.) It contains, under the title of the *mean motion*, the value of the expression $75 \tan \frac{1}{2} v + 25 \tan^3 \frac{1}{2} v$, for all true anomalies for every five minutes from 0 to 180°. If therefore the time corresponding to the true anomaly $v$ is required, it will be necessary to divide the mean motion, taken from the table with the argument $v$, by $\dfrac{150\,k}{p^{\frac{3}{2}}}$, which quantity is called the *mean daily motion;* if on the contrary the true anomaly is to be computed from the time, the latter expressed in days will be multiplied by $\dfrac{150\,k}{p^{\frac{3}{2}}}$, in order to get the mean motion, with which the corresponding anomaly may be taken from the table. It is further evident that the same mean motion and time taken negatively correspond to the negative value of the $v$; the same table therefore answers equally for negative and positive anomalies. If in the place of $p$, we prefer to use the perihelion distance $\frac{1}{2} p = q$, the mean daily motion is expressed by $\dfrac{k \sqrt{2812.5}}{q^{\frac{3}{2}}}$, in which the constant factor $k \sqrt{2812.5} = 0.912279061$, and its logarithm is 9.9601277069. The anomaly $v$ being found, the radius vector will be determined by means of the formula already given,

$$r = \frac{q}{\cos^2 \frac{1}{2} v}.$$

## 20.

By the differentiation of the equation

$$\tan \tfrac{1}{2} v + \tfrac{1}{3} \tan^3 \tfrac{1}{2} v = 2\,t k p^{-\frac{3}{2}},$$

if all the quantities $v, t, p$, are regarded as variable, we have

$$\frac{dv}{2 \cos^4 \frac{1}{2} v} = 2 k p^{-\frac{3}{2}} dt - 3 t k p^{-\frac{5}{2}} dp,$$

$$dv = \frac{k \sqrt{p}}{rr} dt - \frac{3 t k}{2 r r \sqrt{p}} dp.$$

If the variations of the anomaly $v$ are wanted in seconds, both parts also of $dv$ must be expressed in this manner, that is, it is necessary to take for $k$ the value $3548''.188$ given in article 6. If, moreover, $\frac{1}{2}p = q$ is introduced instead of $p$, the formula will have the following form:

$$dv = \frac{k\sqrt{2q}}{rr}\,dt - \frac{3kt}{rr\sqrt{2q}}\,dq,$$

in which are to be used the constant logarithms

$$\log k \sqrt{2} = 3.7005215724, \quad \log 3\,k \sqrt{\tfrac{1}{2}} = 3.8766128315.$$

Moreover the differentiation of the equation

$$r = \frac{p}{2\cos^2 \frac{1}{2}v}$$

furnishes

$$\frac{dr}{r} = \frac{dp}{p} + \tan \tfrac{1}{2}v\,dv,$$

or by expressing $dv$ by means of $dt$ and $dp$,

$$\frac{dr}{r} = \left(\frac{1}{p} - \frac{3kt\tan\frac{1}{2}v}{2rr\sqrt{p}}\right) dp + \frac{k\sqrt{p}\tan\frac{1}{2}v}{rr}\,dt.$$

By substituting for $t$ its value in $v$, the coefficient of $dp$ is changed into

$$\frac{1}{p} - \frac{3p\tan^2\frac{1}{2}v}{4rr} - \frac{p\tan^4\frac{1}{2}v}{4rr} = \frac{1}{r}\left(\tfrac{1}{2} + \tfrac{1}{2}\tan^2 \tfrac{1}{2}v - \tfrac{3}{2}\sin^2 \tfrac{1}{2}v - \tfrac{1}{2}\sin^2 \tfrac{1}{2}v\tan^2 \tfrac{1}{2}v\right) = \frac{\cos v}{2r};$$

but the coefficient of $dt$ becomes $\dfrac{k\sin v}{r\sqrt{p}}$. From this there results

$$dr = \tfrac{1}{2}\cos v\,dp + \frac{k\sin v}{\sqrt{p}}\,dt,$$

or if we introduce $q$ for $p$

$$dr = \cos v\,dq + \frac{k\sin v}{\sqrt{2q}}\,dt.$$

The constant logarithm to be used here is $\log k \sqrt{\tfrac{1}{2}} = 8.0850664436$.

## 21.

In the HYPERBOLA, $\varphi$ and $E$ would become imaginary quantities, to avoid which, other auxiliary quantities must be introduced in the place of them. We have already designated by $\psi$ the angle of which the cosine $= \dfrac{1}{e}$, and we have found the radius vector

$$r = \frac{p}{2\,e\cos\frac{1}{2}(v-\psi)\cos\frac{1}{2}(v+\psi)}.$$

For $v = 0$, the factors $\cos\frac{1}{2}(v-\psi)$, and $\cos\frac{1}{2}(v+\psi)$, in the denominator of this fraction become equal, the second vanishes for the greatest positive value of $v$, and the first for the greatest negative value. Putting, therefore,

$$\frac{\cos\frac{1}{2}(v-\psi)}{\cos\frac{1}{2}(v+\psi)} = u,$$

we shall have $u = 1$ in perihelion; it will increase to infinity as $v$ approaches its limit $180° - \psi$; on the other hand it will decrease indefinitely as $v$ is supposed to return to its other limit $- (180° - \psi)$; so that reciprocal values of $u$, or, what amounts to the same thing, values whose logarithms are complementary, correspond to opposite values of $v$.

This quotient $u$ is very conveniently used in the hyperbola as an auxiliary quantity; the angle, the tangent of which is

$$\tan\tfrac{1}{2}v\sqrt{\frac{e-1}{e+1}},$$

can be made to render the same service with almost equal elegance; and in order to preserve the analogy with the ellipse, we will denote this angle by $\frac{1}{2}F$. In this way the following relations between the quantities $v, r, u, F$ are easily brought together, in which we put $a = - b$, so that $b$ becomes a positive quantity.

I. $\quad b = p\cot^2\psi$

II. $\quad r = \dfrac{p}{1 + e\cos v} = \dfrac{p\cos\psi}{2\cos\frac{1}{2}(v-\psi)\cos\frac{1}{2}(v+\psi)}$

III. $\quad \tan\tfrac{1}{2}F = \tan\tfrac{1}{2}v\sqrt{\dfrac{e-1}{e+1}} = \tan\tfrac{1}{2}v\tan\tfrac{1}{2}\psi = \dfrac{u-1}{u+1}$

IV. $\quad u = \dfrac{\cos\frac{1}{2}(v-\psi)}{\cos\frac{1}{2}(v+\psi)} = \dfrac{1+\tan\frac{1}{2}F}{1-\tan\frac{1}{2}F} = \tan(45° + \tfrac{1}{2}F)$

V. $\quad \dfrac{1}{\cos F} = \tfrac{1}{2}\left(u + \dfrac{1}{u}\right) = \dfrac{1+\cos\psi\cos v}{2\cos\frac{1}{2}(v-\psi)\cos\frac{1}{2}(v+\psi)} = \dfrac{e+\cos v}{1+e\cos v}.$

By subtracting 1 from both sides of equation V. we get,

VI. $\quad \sin\tfrac{1}{2}v\sqrt{r} = \sin\tfrac{1}{2}F\sqrt{\dfrac{p}{(e-1)\cos F}} = \sin\tfrac{1}{2}F\sqrt{\dfrac{(e+1)\,b}{\cos F}}$

$$= \tfrac{1}{2}(u-1)\sqrt{\dfrac{p}{(e-1)\,u}} = \tfrac{1}{2}(u-1)\sqrt{\dfrac{(e+1)\,b}{u}}.$$

In the same manner, by adding 1 to both sides, it becomes

VII. $\cos \frac{1}{2} v \sqrt{r} = \cos \frac{1}{2} F \sqrt{\dfrac{p}{(e+1) \cos F}} = \cos \frac{1}{2} F \sqrt{\dfrac{(e-1) b}{\cos F}}$

$\qquad = \frac{1}{2} (u+1) \sqrt{\dfrac{p}{(e+1) u}} = \frac{1}{2} (u+1) \sqrt{\dfrac{(e-1) b}{u}}.$

By dividing VI. by VII. we should reproduce III.: the multiplication produces

VIII. $r \sin v = p \cotan \psi \tan F = b \tan \psi \tan F$

$\qquad = \frac{1}{2} p \cotan \psi \left(u - \dfrac{1}{u}\right) = \frac{1}{2} b \tan \psi \left(u - \dfrac{1}{u}\right).$

From the combination of the equations II. V. are easily derived

IX. $r \cos v = b \left(e - \dfrac{1}{\cos F}\right) = \frac{1}{2} b \left(2 e - u - \dfrac{1}{u}\right),$

X. $r = b \left(\dfrac{e}{\cos F} - 1\right) = \frac{1}{2} b \left(e \left(u + \dfrac{1}{u}\right) - 2\right).$

## 22.

By the differentiation of the formula IV. (regarding $\psi$ as a constant quantity) we get

$$\frac{d u}{u} = \frac{1}{2} \left(\tan \frac{1}{2} (v + \psi) - \tan \frac{1}{2} (v - \psi)\right) d v = \frac{r \tan \psi}{p} d v;$$

hence,

$$r r \, d v = \frac{p r}{u \tan \psi} d u,$$

or by substituting for $r$ the value taken from X.

$$r r \, d v = b b \tan \psi \left(\frac{1}{2} e \left(1 + \frac{1}{u u}\right) - \frac{1}{u}\right) d u.$$

Afterwards by integrating in such a manner that the integral may vanish at the perihelion, it becomes

$$\int r r \, d v = b b \tan \psi \left(\frac{1}{2} e \left(u - \frac{1}{u}\right) - \log u\right) = k t \sqrt{p} \sqrt{(1 + \mu)} = k t \tan \psi \sqrt{b} \sqrt{(1 + \mu)}.$$

The logarithm here is the hyperbolic; if we wish to use the logarithm from Brigg's system, or in general from the system of which the modulus $= \lambda$, and the mass $\mu$ (which we can assume to be indeterminable for a body moving in an hyperbola) is neglected, the equation assumes the following form:—

XI.   $\frac{1}{2}\lambda e\dfrac{uu-1}{u} - \log u = \dfrac{\lambda k t}{b^{\frac{3}{2}}},$

or by introducing $F$,

$$\lambda e \tan F - \log \tan(45° + \tfrac{1}{2}F) = \frac{\lambda k t}{b^{\frac{3}{2}}}.$$

Supposing Brigg's logarithms to be used, we have

$$\log \lambda = 9.6377843113, \quad \log \lambda k = 7.8733657527;$$

but a little greater precision can be attained by the immediate application of the hyperbolic logarithms. The hyperbolic logarithms of the tangents are found in several collections of tables, in those, for example, which Schulze edited, and still more extensively in the *Magnus Canon Triangulor. Logarithmicus* of Benjamin Ursin, Cologne, 1624, in which they proceed by tens of seconds.

Finally, formula XI. shows that opposite values of $t$ correspond to reciprocal values of $u$, or opposite values of $F$ and $v$, on which account equal parts of the hyperbola, at equal distances from the perihelion on both sides, are described in equal times.

## 23.

If we should wish to make use of the auxiliary quantity $u$ for finding the time from the true anomaly, its value is most conveniently determined by means of equation IV.; afterwards, formula II. gives directly, without a new calculation, $p$ by means of $r$, or $r$ by means of $p$. Having found $u$, formula XI. will give the quantity $\dfrac{\lambda k t}{b^{\frac{3}{2}}}$, which is analogous to the mean anomaly in the ellipse and will be denoted by $N$, from which will follow the elapsed time after the perihelion transit. Since the first term of $N$, that is $\dfrac{\lambda e(uu-1)}{2u}$ may, by means of formula VIII. be made $= \dfrac{\lambda r \sin v}{b \sin \psi}$, the double computation of this quantity will answer for testing its accuracy, or, if preferred, $N$ can be expressed without $u$, as follows:—

XII.   $N = \dfrac{\lambda \tan \psi \sin v}{2 \cos \frac{1}{2}(v+\psi) \cos \frac{1}{2}(v-\psi)} - \log \dfrac{\cos \frac{1}{2}(v-\psi)}{\cos \frac{1}{2}(v+\psi)}.$

*Example.* — Let $e = 1.2618820$, or $\psi = 37° 35' 0''$, $v = 18° 51' 0''$, $\log r = 0.0333585$. Then the computation for $u, p, b, N, t$, is as follows: —

| | | |
|---|---|---|
| $\log \cos \frac{1}{2} (v - \psi)$ . . | 9.9941706 ⎱ | hence, $\log u$ . . .    0.0491129 |
| $\log \cos \frac{1}{2} (v + \psi)$ . . | 9.9450577 ⎰ | $u =$    1.1197289 |
| $\log r$ . . . . . . | 0.0333585 | $uu =$    1.2537928 |
| $\log 2 e$ . . . . . | 0.4020488 | |

| | |
|---|---|
| $\log p$ . . . . . . | 0.3746356 |
| $\log \cotan^2 \psi$ . . . | 0.2274244 |

| | |
|---|---|
| $\log b$ . . . . . . | 0.6020600 |
| $\log \dfrac{r}{b}$ . . . . . . | 9.4312985 |
| $\log \sin v$ . . . . | 9.5093258 |
| $\log \lambda$ . . . . . | 9.6377843 |
| Compl. $\log \sin \psi$ . . | 0.2147309 |
| | 8.7931395 |
| First term of $N =$ . | 0.0621069 |
| $\log u =$ | 0.0491129 |
| $N =$ | 0.0129940 |
| $\log \lambda k$ . . . . . | 7.8733658 ⎱ |
| $\frac{3}{2} \log b$ . . . . . | 0.9030900 ⎰ |

The other calculation.

| | |
|---|---|
| $\log (uu - 1)$ . . . | 9.4044793 |
| Compl. $\log u$ . . . | 9.9508871 |
| $\log \lambda$ . . . . . . | 9.6377843 |
| $\log \frac{1}{2} e$ . . . . . | 9.7999888 |
| | 8.7931395 |
| $\log N$ . . . . . | 8.1137429 |
| Difference . . . . | 6.9702758 |
| $\log t$ . . . . . . | 1.1434671 |
| $t =$ | 13.91448 |

## 24.

If it has been decided to carry out the calculation with hyperbolic logarithms, it is best to employ the auxiliary quantity $F$, which will be determined by equation III., and thence $N$ by XI.; the semi-parameter will be computed from the radius vector, or inversely the latter from the former by formula VIII.; the second part of $N$ can, if desired, be obtained in two ways, namely, by means of the formula hyp. $\log \tan (45° + \frac{1}{2} F)$, and by this, hyp. $\log \cos \frac{1}{2} (v - \psi) -$ hyp. $\log \cos \frac{1}{2} (v + \psi)$. Moreover it is apparent that here where $\lambda = 1$ the quantity $N$

will come out greater in the ratio $1 : \lambda$, than if Brigg's logarithms were used. Our example treated according to this method is as follows: —

$\log \tan \tfrac{1}{2} \psi$ . . . . 9.5318179
$\log \tan \tfrac{1}{2} v$ . . . . . 9.2201009

$\log \tan \tfrac{1}{2} F$ . . . . 8.7519188        $\tfrac{1}{2} F = 3° 13' 58''.12$

$\log e$ . . . . . . . 0.1010188
$\log \tan F$ . . . . . 9.0543366

9.1553554        C. hyp. log cos $\tfrac{1}{2} (v - \psi) = 0.01342266$
$e \tan F =$ . . . . . 0.14300638        C. hyp. log cos $\tfrac{1}{2} (v + \psi) = 0.12650930$
hyp. log tan $(45° + \tfrac{1}{2} F) = 0.11308666$        Difference . . . . $= 0.11308664$

$N =$ . . . . . . 0.02991972        $\log N$ . . . . . . . 8.4759575
$\log k$ . . . . . . 8.2355814 ⎱        Difference . . . . . 7.3324914
$\tfrac{3}{2} \log b$ . . . . . . 0.9030900 ⎰        $\log t$ . . . . . . . 1.1434661
                $t =$        13.91445

## 25.

For the solution of the inverse problem, that of determining the true anomaly and the radius vector from the time, the auxiliary quantity $u$ or $F$ must be first derived from $N = \lambda k b^{-\frac{3}{2}} t$ by means of equation XI. The solution of this transcendental equation will be performed by trial, and can be shortened by devices analogous to those we have described in article 11. But we suffer these to pass without further explanation; for it does not seem worth while to elaborate as carefully the precepts for the hyperbolic motion, very rarely perhaps to be exhibited in celestial space, as for the elliptic motion, and besides, all cases that can possibly occur may be solved by another method to be given below. Afterwards $F$ or $u$ will be found, thence $v$ by formula III., and subsequently $r$ will be determined either by II. or VIII.; $v$ and $r$ are still more conveniently obtained by means of formulas VI. and VII.; some one of the remaining formulas can be called into use at pleasure, for verifying the calculation.

## 26.

*Example.* — Retaining for $e$ and $b$ the same values as in the preceding example, let $t = 65.41236$: $v$ and $r$ are required. Using Briggs's logarithms we have

$\log t$ . . . . . . 1.8156598

$\log \lambda\, k\, b^{-\frac{3}{2}}$ . . . . 6.9702758

$\log N$ . . . . . . 8.7859356, whence $N = 0.06108514$. From this it is seen that the equation $N = \lambda\, e \tan F - \log \tan (45° + \tfrac{1}{2} F)$ is satisfied by $F = 25° 24' 27''.66$, whence we have, by formula III.,

$\log \tan \tfrac{1}{2} F$ . . . . 9.3530120

$\log \tan \tfrac{1}{2} \psi$ . . . . 9.5318179

$\log \tan \tfrac{1}{2} v$ . . . . 9.8211941,    and thus $\tfrac{1}{2} v = 33° 31' 29''.89$, and $v = 67° 2' 59''.78$. Hence, there follows,

C. $\log \cos \tfrac{1}{2} (v + \psi)$ . 0.2137476 ⎫

C. $\log \cos \tfrac{1}{2} (v - \psi)$ . 0.0145197 ⎭    difference . . . . . . . 0.1992279

$\log \dfrac{p}{2\,e}$ . . . . . . 9.9725868    $\log \tan (45° + \tfrac{1}{2} F)$ . . . 0.1992280

$\log r\mathfrak{t}$ . . . . . . 0.2008541.

## 27.

If equation IV. is differentiated, considering $u$, $v$, $\psi$, as variable at the same time, there results,

$$\frac{d u}{u} = \frac{\sin \psi \, d v + \sin v \, d \psi}{2 \cos \tfrac{1}{2} (v - \psi) \cos \tfrac{1}{2} (v + \psi)} = \frac{r \tan \psi}{p} \, d v + \frac{r \sin v}{p \cos \psi} \, d \psi.$$

By differentiating in like manner equation XI., the relation between the differential variations of the quantities $u$, $\psi$, $N$, becomes,

$$\frac{d N}{\lambda} = \left( \tfrac{1}{2} e \left(1 + \frac{1}{u u}\right) - \frac{1}{u} \right) d u + \frac{(u u - 1) \sin \psi}{2 u \cos^2 \psi} \, d \psi,$$

or

$$\frac{d N}{\lambda} = \frac{r}{b u} \, d u + \frac{r \sin v}{b \cos \psi} \, d \psi.$$

Hence, by eliminating $d\,u$ by means of the preceding equation we obtain

$$\frac{d\,N}{\lambda} = \frac{rr}{b\,b\tan\psi}\,d\,v + \left(1+\frac{r}{p}\right)\frac{r\sin v}{b\cos\psi}\,d\,\psi,$$

or

$$d\,v = \frac{b\,b\tan\psi}{\lambda rr}\,d\,N - \left(\frac{b}{r}+\frac{b}{p}\right)\frac{\sin v\tan\psi}{\cos\psi}\,d\,\psi$$

$$= \frac{b\,b\tan\psi}{\lambda rr}\,d\,N - \left(1+\frac{p}{r}\right)\frac{\sin v}{\sin\psi}\,d\,\psi.$$

## 28.

By differentiating equation X., all the quantities $r, b, e, u$, being regarded as variables, by substituting

$$d\,e = \frac{\sin\psi}{\cos^2\psi}\,d\,\psi,$$

and eliminating $d\,u$ with the help of the equation between $dN$, $d\,u$, $d\,\psi$, given in the preceding article, there results,

$$d\,r = \frac{r}{b}\,d\,b + \frac{b\,b\,e\,(u\,u-1)}{2\,\lambda\,u\,r}\,d\,N + \frac{b}{2\cos^2\psi}\left\{\left(u+\frac{1}{u}\right)\sin\psi - \left(u-\frac{1}{u}\right)\sin v\right\}d\,\psi.$$

The coefficient of $d\,N$ is transformed, by means of equation VIII., into $\frac{b\sin v}{\lambda\sin\psi}$; but the coefficient of $d\,\psi$, by substituting from equation IV.,

$$u\,(\sin\psi - \sin v) = \sin(\psi - v), \quad \frac{1}{u}\,(\sin\psi + \sin v) = \sin(\psi + v),$$

is changed into

$$\frac{b\sin\psi\cos v}{\cos^2\psi} = \frac{p\cos v}{\sin\psi};$$

so that we have

$$d\,r = \frac{r}{b}\,d\,b + \frac{b\sin v}{\lambda\sin\psi}\,d\,N + \frac{p\cos v}{\sin\psi}\,d\,\psi.$$

So far, moreover, as $N$ is considered a function of $b$ and $t$, we have

$$d\,N = \frac{N}{t}\,d\,t - \frac{3}{2}\frac{N}{b}\,d\,b,$$

which value being substituted, we shall have $d\,r$, and also $d\,v$ in the preceding article, expressed by means of $d\,t$, $d\,b$, $d\,\psi$. Finally, we have here to repeat our previous injunction, that, if the variations of the angles $v$ and $\psi$ are conceived to be expressed, not in parts of the radius, but in seconds, either all the terms containing $d\,v$, $d\,\psi$, must be divided by 206264.8, or all the remaining terms must be multiplied by this number.

## 29.

Since the auxiliary quantities $\varphi$, $E$, $M$, employed in the ellipse obtain imaginary values in the hyperbola, it will not be out of place to investigate their connection with the real quantities of which we have made use: we add therefore the principal relations, in which we denote by $i$ the imaginary quantity $\sqrt{-1}$.

$$\sin \varphi = e = \frac{1}{\cos \psi}$$

$$\tan (45° - \tfrac{1}{2}\varphi) = \sqrt{\frac{1-e}{1+e}} = i\sqrt{\frac{e-1}{e+1}} = i \tan \tfrac{1}{2}\psi$$

$$\tan \varphi = \tfrac{1}{2} \cotan (45° - \tfrac{1}{2}\varphi) - \tfrac{1}{2}\tan (45° - \tfrac{1}{2}\varphi) = -\frac{i}{\sin \psi}$$

$$\cos \varphi = i \tan \psi$$

$$\varphi = 90° + i \log (\sin \varphi + i \cos \varphi) = 90° - i \log \tan (45° + \tfrac{1}{2}\psi)$$

$$\tan \tfrac{1}{2}E = i \tan \tfrac{1}{2}F = \frac{i(u-1)}{u+1}$$

$$\frac{1}{\sin E} = \tfrac{1}{2} \cotan \tfrac{1}{2}E + \tfrac{1}{2}\tan \tfrac{1}{2}E = -i \cotan F,$$

or

$$\sin E = i \tan F = \frac{i(uu-1)}{2u}$$

$$\cotan E = \tfrac{1}{2} \cotan \tfrac{1}{2}E - \tfrac{1}{2}\tan \tfrac{1}{2}E = -\frac{i}{\sin F},$$

or

$$\tan E = i \sin F = \frac{i(uu-1)}{uu+1}$$

$$\cos E = \frac{1}{\cos F} = \frac{uu+1}{2u}$$

$$iE = \log (\cos E + i \sin E) = \log \frac{1}{u},$$

or

$$E = i \log u = i \log (45° + \tfrac{1}{2}F)$$

$$M = E - e \sin E = i \log u - \frac{ie(uu-1)}{2u} = -\frac{iN}{\lambda}.$$

The logarithms in these formulas are hyperbolic.

## 30.

Since none of the numbers which we take out from logarithmic and trigo-nometrical tables admit of absolute precision, but are all to a certain extent approximate only, the results of all calculations performed by the aid of these numbers can only be approximately true. In most cases, indeed, the common tables, which are exact to the seventh place of decimals, that is, never deviate from the truth either in excess or defect beyond half of an unit in the seventh figure, furnish more than the requisite accuracy, so that the unavoidable errors are evidently of no consequence: nevertheless it may happen, that in special cases the effect of the errors of the tables is so augmented that we may be obliged to reject a method, otherwise the best, and substitute another in its place. Cases of this kind can occur in those computations which we have just explained; on which account, it will not be foreign to our purpose to introduce here some inquiries concerning the degree of precision allowed in these computations by the common tables. Although this is not the place for a thorough examination of this subject, which is of the greatest importance to the practical computer, yet we will conduct the investigation sufficiently far for our own object, from which point it may be further perfected and extended to other operations by any one requiring it.

## 31.

Any logarithm, sine, tangent, etc. whatever, (or, in general, any irrational quantity whatever taken from the tables,) is liable to an error which may amount to a half unit in the last figure : we will designate this limit of error by $\omega$, which therefore is in the common tables $= 0.00000005$. If now, the logarithm, etc., cannot be taken directly from the tables, but must be obtained by means of inter-polation, this error may be slightly increased from two causes. *In the first place*, it is usual to take for the proportional part, when (regarding the last figure as unity) it is not an integer, the next greatest or least integer ; and in this way, it is easily perceived, this error may be increased to just within twice its actual amount. But we shall pay no attention to this augmentation of the error, since there is no objection to our affixing one more than another decimal figure to the proportional part, and it is very evident that, if the proportional part is exact, the interpolated logarithm is not liable to a greater error than the logarithms given directly in the tables, so far indeed as we are authorized to consider the changes in the latter as uniform. Thence arises *another* increase of the error, that this last assumption is not rigorously true; but this also we pretermit, because the effect of the second and higher differences (especially where the superior tables computed by Taylor are used for trigonometrical functions) is evidently of no importance, and may readily be taken into account, if it should happen to turn out a little too great. In all cases, therefore, we will put the maximum unavoidable error of the tables $= \omega$, assuming that the argument (that is, the number the logarithm of which, or the angle the sine etc. of which, is sought) is given with strict accuracy. But if the argument itself is only approximately known, and the variation $\omega'$ of the logarithm, etc. (which may be defined by the method of differentials) is supposed to correspond to the greatest error to which it is liable, then the maximum error of the logarithm, computed by means of the tables, can amount to $\omega + \omega'$.

Inversely, if the argument corresponding to a given logarithm is computed by the help of the tables, the greatest error is equal to that change in the argument which corresponds to the variation $\omega$ in the logarithm, if the latter is correctly given, or to that which corresponds to the variation $\omega + \omega'$ in the logarithm, if the logarithm can be erroneous to the extent of $\omega'$. It will hardly be necessary to remark that $\omega$ and $\omega'$ must be affected by the same sign.

If several quantities, correct within certain limits only, are added together, the greatest error of the sum will be equal to the sum of the greatest individual errors affected by the same sign; wherefore, in the subtraction also of quantities approximately correct, the greatest error of the difference will be equal to the sum of the greatest individual errors. In the multiplication or division of a quantity not strictly correct, the maximum error is increased or diminished in the same ratio as the quantity itself.

## 32.

Let us proceed now to the application of these principles to the most useful of the operations above explained.

I. If $\varphi$ and $E$ are supposed to be exactly given in using the formula VII., article 8, for computing the true anomaly from the eccentric anomaly in the elliptic motion, then in $\log \tan (45° - \frac{1}{2}\varphi)$ and $\log \tan \frac{1}{2} E$, the error $\omega$ may be committed, and thus in the difference $= \log \tan \frac{1}{2} v$, the error $2\omega$; therefore the greatest error in the determination of the angle $\frac{1}{2} v$ will be

$$\frac{3\,\omega\,\mathrm{d}\frac{1}{2}v}{\mathrm{d}\log\tan\frac{1}{2}v} = \frac{3\,\omega\sin v}{2\lambda},$$

$\lambda$ denoting the modulus of the logarithms used in this calculation. The error, therefore, to which the true anomaly $v$ is liable, expressed in seconds, becomes

$$\frac{3\,\omega\sin v}{\lambda}\,206265 = 0''.0712\sin v,$$

if Brigg's logarithms to seven places of decimals are employed, so that we may be assured of the value of $v$ within $0''.07$; if smaller tables to five places only, are used, the error may amount to $7''.12$.

II. If $e \cos E$ is computed by means of logarithms, an error may be committed to the extent of

$$\frac{3\,\omega\,e\cos E}{\lambda};$$

therefore the quantity

$$1 - e \cos E, \text{ or } \frac{r}{a},$$

will be liable to the same error. In computing, accordingly, the logarithm of this quantity, the error may amount to $(1 + \delta)\,\omega$, denoting by $\delta$ the quantity

$$\frac{3\,e\cos E}{1 - e\cos E}$$

taken positively: the possible error in $\log r$ goes up to the same limit, $\log a$ being assumed to be correctly given. If the eccentricity is small, the quantity $\delta$ is always confined within narrow limits; but when $e$ differs but little from 1, $1 - e \cos E$ remains very small as long as $E$ is small; consequently, $\delta$ may increase to an amount not to be neglected: for this reason formula III., article 8, is less suitable in this case.   The quantity $\delta$ may be expressed thus also,

$$\frac{3\,(a-r)}{r} = \frac{3\,e\,(\cos v + e)}{1 - e\,e},$$

which formula shows still more clearly when the error $(1 + \delta)\,\omega$ may be neglected.

III. In the use of formula X., article 8, for the computation of the true from the mean anomaly, the $\log\sqrt{\dfrac{a}{r}}$ is liable to the error $(\tfrac{1}{2} + \tfrac{1}{2}\,\delta)\,\omega$, and so the log $\sin\tfrac{1}{2}\,\varphi\sin E\sqrt{\dfrac{a}{r}}$ to that of $(\tfrac{5}{2} + \tfrac{1}{2}\,\delta)\,\omega$; hence the greatest possible error in the determination of the angles $v - E$ or $v$ is

$$\frac{\omega}{\lambda}\,(7 + \delta)\tan\tfrac{1}{2}\,(v - E),$$

or expressed in seconds, if seven places of decimals are employed,

$$(0''.166 + 0''.024\,\delta)\tan\tfrac{1}{2}\,(v - E).$$

When the eccentricity is not great, $\delta$ and $\tan\tfrac{1}{2}\,(v - E)$ will be small quantities, on account of which, this method admits of greater accuracy than that which we have considered in I.: the latter, on the other hand, will be preferable when the eccentricity is very great and approaches nearly to unity, where $\delta$ and $\tan\tfrac{1}{2}\,(v - E)$ may acquire very considerable values.   It will always be easy to decide, by means of our formulas, which of the two methods is to be preferred.

IV. In the determination of the mean anomaly from the eccentric by means of formula XII., article 8, the error of the quantity $e\sin E$, computed by the help of logarithms, and therefore of the anomaly itself, $M$, may amount to

$$\frac{3\,\omega\,e\sin E}{\lambda},$$

which limit of error is to be multiplied by $206265''$ if wanted expressed in seconds.   Hence it is readily inferred, that in the inverse problem where $E$ is to be determined from $M$ by trial, $E$ may be erroneous by the quantity

$$\frac{3\,\omega\,e\sin E}{\lambda}\cdot\frac{d\,E}{d\,M}\cdot 206265'' = \frac{3\,\omega\,e\,a\sin E}{\lambda\,r}\cdot 206265'',$$

even if the equation $E - e\sin E = M$ should be satisfied with all the accuracy which the tables admit.

The true anomaly therefore computed from the mean may be incorrect in two ways, if we consider the mean as given accurately; first, on account of the error committed in the computation of $v$ from $E$, which, as we have seen, is of slight importance; second, because the value of the eccentric anomaly itself may be erroneous. The effect of the latter cause will be expressed by the product of the error committed in $E$ into $\frac{dv}{dE}$, which product becomes

$$\frac{3 \omega e \sin E}{\lambda} \cdot \frac{dv}{dM} \cdot 206265'' = \frac{3 \omega e a \sin v}{\lambda r} \cdot 206265'' = \left( \frac{e \sin v + \frac{1}{2} e e \sin 2 v}{1 - e e} \right) 0''.0712,$$

if seven places of decimals are used. This error, always small for small values of $e$, may become very large when $e$ differs but little from unity, as is shown by the following table, which exhibits the maximum value of the preceding expression for certain values of $e$.

| $e$ | maximum error. | $e$ | maximum error. | $e$ | maximum error. |
|------|------|------|------|------|------|
| 0.90 | 0''.42 | 0.94 | 0''.73 | 0.98 | 2''.28 |
| 0.91 | 0 .48 | 0.95 | 0 .89 | 0.99 | 4 .59 |
| 0.92 | 0 .54 | 0.96 | 1 .12 | 0.999 | 46 .23 |
| 0.93 | 0 .62 | 0.97 | 1 .50 | | |

V. In the hyperbolic motion, if $v$ is determined by means of formula III., article 21, from $F$ and $\psi$ accurately known, the error may amount to

$$\frac{3 \omega \sin v}{\lambda} \cdot 206265'';$$

but if it is computed by means of the formula

$$\tan \tfrac{1}{2} v = \frac{(u - 1) \tan \tfrac{1}{2} \psi}{u + 1},$$

$u$ and $\psi$ being known precisely, the limit of the error will be one third greater, that is,

$$\frac{4 \omega \sin v}{\lambda} \cdot 206265'' = 0''.09 \sin v$$

for seven places.

VI. If the quantity

$$\frac{\lambda k t}{b^{\frac{3}{2}}} = N$$

is computed by means of formula XI., article 22, with the aid of Briggs's logarithms, assuming $e$ and $u$ or $e$ and $F$ to be known exactly, the first part will be liable to the error

$$\frac{5\,(u\,u-1)\,e\,\omega}{2\,u},$$

if it has been computed in the form

$$\frac{\lambda\,e\,(u-1)\,(u+1)}{2\,u};$$

or to the error

$$\frac{3\,(u\,u+1)\,e\,\omega}{2\,u};$$

if computed in the form

$$\tfrac{1}{2}\,\lambda\,e\,u-\frac{\lambda\,e}{2\,u};$$

or to the error $3\,e\,\omega\,\tan F$ if computed in the form $\lambda\,e\,\tan F$, provided we neglect the error committed in $\log \lambda$ or $\log \tfrac{1}{2}\lambda$. In the first case the error can be expressed also by $5\,e\,\omega\,\tan F$, in the second by $\dfrac{3\,e\,\omega}{\cos F}$, whence it is apparent that the error is the least of all in the third case, but will be greater in the first or second, according as $u$ or $\dfrac{1}{u} > 2$ or $< 2$, or according as $\pm F > 36° 52'$ or $< 36° 52'$. But, in any case, the second part of $N$ will be liable to the error $\omega$.

VII. On the other hand, it is evident that if $u$ or $F$ is derived from $N$ by trial, $u$ would be liable to the error

$$(\omega \pm 5\,e\,\omega\,\tan F)\frac{d\,u}{d\,N},$$

or to

$$\left(\omega + \frac{3\,e\,\omega}{\cos F}\right)\frac{d\,u}{d\,N},$$

according as the first term in the value of $N$ is used separated into factors, or into terms; $F$, however, is liable to the error

$$(\omega \pm 3\,e\,\omega\,\tan F)\frac{d\,F}{d\,N}.$$

The upper signs serve after perihelion, the lower before perihelion. Now if $\dfrac{d\,v}{d\,N}$ is substituted here for $\dfrac{d\,u}{d\,N}$ or for $\dfrac{d\,F}{d\,N}$, the effect of this error appears in the determination of $v$, which therefore will be

$$\frac{b\,b\tan\psi\,(1\pm 3\,e\tan F)\,\omega}{\lambda\,r\,r}\quad \text{or}\quad \frac{b\,b\tan\psi\,(1+3\,e\sec F)\,\omega}{\lambda\,r\,r},$$

if the auxiliary quantity $u$ has been employed; on the other hand, if $F$ has been used, this effect becomes,

$$\frac{b\,b\tan\psi\,(1\pm 3\,e\tan F)\,\omega}{\lambda\,r\,r}=\frac{\omega}{\lambda}\left\{\frac{(1+e\cos v)^2}{\tan^3\psi}\pm\frac{3\,e\sin v(1+e\cos v)}{\tan^2\psi}\right\}.$$

If the error is to be expressed in seconds, it is necessary to apply the factor $206265''$. It is evident that this error can only be considerable when $\psi$ is a small angle, or $e$ a little greater than 1. The following are the greatest values of this third expression, for certain values of $e$, if seven places of decimals are employed:

| $e$ | maximum error. |
|-------|----------------|
| 1.3   | $0''.34$       |
| 1.2   | $0\ .54$       |
| 1.1   | $1\ .31$       |
| 1.05  | $3\ .03$       |
| 1.01  | $34\ .41$      |
| 1.001 | $1064\ .65$    |

To this error arising from the erroneous value of $F$ or $u$ it is necessary to apply the error determined in V. in order to have the total uncertainty of $v$.

VIII. If the equation XI., article 22, is solved by the use of hyperbolic logarithms, $F$ being employed as an auxiliary quantity, the effect of the possible error in this operation in the determination of $v$, is found by similar reasoning to be,

$$\frac{(1+e\cos v)^2\,\omega'}{\tan^3\psi}\pm\frac{3\,e\sin v\,(1+e\cos v)\,\omega}{\lambda\tan^2\psi},$$

where by $\omega'$ we denote the greatest uncertainty in the tables of hyperbolic logarithms. The second part of this expression is identical with the second part of the expression given in VII.; but the first part in the latter is less than the first in the former, in the ratio $\lambda\omega':\omega$, that is, in the ratio $1:23$, if it be admissible to assume that the table of Ursin is everywhere exact to eight figures, or

$$\omega'=0.000000005.$$

## 33.

The methods above treated, both for the determination of the true anomaly from the time and for the determination of the time from the true anomaly,* do not admit of all the precision that might be required in those conic sections of which the eccentricity differs but little from unity, that is, in ellipses and hyperbolas which approach very near to the parabola; indeed, unavoidable errors, increasing as the orbit tends to resemble the parabola, may at length exceed all limits. Larger tables, constructed to more than seven figures would undoubtedly diminish this uncertainty, but they would not remove it, nor would they prevent its surpassing all limits as soon as the orbit approached too near the parabola. Moreover, the methods given above become in this case very troublesome, since a part of them require the use of indirect trials frequently repeated, of which the tediousness is even greater if we work with the larger tables. It certainly, therefore, will not be superfluous, to furnish a peculiar method by means of which the uncertainty in this case may be avoided, and sufficient precision may be obtained with the help of the common tables.

## 34.

The common method, by which it is usual to remedy these inconveniences, rests upon the following principles. In the ellipse or hyperbola of which $e$ is the eccentricity, $p$ the semi-parameter, and therefore the perihelion distance

$$\frac{p}{1+e} = q,$$

let the true anomaly $v$ correspond to the time $t$ after the perihelion; in the parabola of which the semi-parameter $= 2q$, or the perihelion distance $= q$, let the true anomaly $w$ correspond to the same time, supposing in each case the mass $\mu$ to be either neglected or equal. It is evident that we then have

---

* Since the time contains the factor $a^{\frac{3}{2}}$ or $b^{\frac{3}{2}}$, the greater the values of $a = \dfrac{p}{1-ee}$, or $b = \dfrac{p}{e^2-1}$, the more the error in $M$ or $N$ will be increased.

$$\int \frac{p\,p\,d\,v}{(1+e\cos v)^2} : \int \frac{4\,q\,q\,d\,w}{(1+\cos w)^2} = \sqrt{p} : \sqrt{2\,q},$$

the integrals commencing from $v = 0$ and $w = 0$, or

$$\int \frac{(1+e)^{\frac{3}{2}}d\,v}{(1+e\cos v)^2\sqrt{2}} = \int \frac{2\,d\,w}{(1+\cos w)^2}.$$

Denoting $\frac{1-e}{1+e}$ by $\alpha$, $\tan \frac{1}{2} v$ by $\theta$, the former integral is found to be

$$\sqrt{(1+\alpha)}.\ \left(\theta + \tfrac{1}{3}\theta^3(1-2\alpha) - \tfrac{1}{5}\theta^5(2\alpha - 3\alpha\alpha) + \tfrac{1}{7}\theta^7(3\alpha\alpha - 4\alpha^3) - \text{etc.}\right),$$

the latter, $\tan \frac{1}{2} w + \frac{1}{3}\tan^3 \frac{1}{2} w$.  From this equation it is easy to determine $w$ by $\alpha$ and $v$, and also $v$ by $\alpha$ and $w$ by means of infinite series: instead of $\alpha$ may be introduced, if preferred,

$$1 - e = \frac{2\,\alpha}{1+\alpha} = \delta.$$

Since evidently for $\alpha = 0$, or $\delta = 0$, we have $v = w$, these series will have the following form : —

$$w = v + \delta\,v' + \delta\,\delta\,v'' + \delta^3\,v''' + \text{etc.}$$
$$v = w + \delta\,w' + \delta\,\delta\,w'' + \delta^3\,w''' + \text{etc.}$$

where $v'$, $v''$, $v'''$, etc. will be functions of $v$, and $w'$, $w''$, $w'''$, functions of $w$.  When $\delta$ is a very small quantity, these series converge rapidly, and few terms suffice for the determination of $w$ from $v$, or of $v$ from $w$.  $t$ is derived from $w$, or $w$ from $t$, by the method we have explained above for the parabolic motion.

## 35.

Our BESSEL has developed the analytical expressions of the three first coefficients of the second series $w'$, $w''$, $w'''$, and at the same time has added a table constructed with a single argument $w$ for the numerical values of the two first $w'$ and $w''$, ( *Von Zach Monatliche Correspondenz*, vol. XII., p. 197).  A table for the first coefficient $w'$, computed by SIMPSON, was already in existence, and was annexed to the work of the illustrious OLBERS above commended.  By the use of this method, with the help of BESSEL's table, it is possible in most cases to determine the true anomaly from the time with sufficient precision; what remains to be desired is reduced to nearly the following particulars : —

I. In the inverse problem, the determination of the time, that is, from the true anomaly, it is requisite to have recourse to a somewhat indirect method, and to derive $w$ from $v$ by trial. In order to meet this inconvenience, the first series should be treated in the same manner as the second: and since it may be readily perceived that $-v'$ is the same function of $v$ as $w'$ of $w$, so that the table for $w'$ might answer for $v'$ the sign only being changed, nothing more is required than a table for $v''$, by which either problem may be solved with equal precision.

Sometimes, undoubtedly, cases may occur, where the eccentricity differs but little from unity, such that the general methods above explained may not appear to afford sufficient precision, not enough at least, to allow the effect of the third and higher powers of $\delta$ in the peculiar method just sketched out, to be safely neglected. Cases of this kind are possible in the hyperbolic motion especially, in which, whether the former methods are chosen or the latter one, an error of several seconds is inevitable, if the common tables, constructed to seven places of figures only, are employed. Although, in truth, such cases rarely occur in practice, something might appear to be wanting if it were not possible in *all* cases to determine the true anomaly within $0''.1$, or at least $0''.2$, without consulting the larger tables, which would require a reference to books of the rarer sort. We hope, therefore, that it will not seem wholly superfluous to proceed to the exposition of a peculiar method, which we have long had in use, and which will also commend itself on this account, that it is not limited to eccentricities differing but little from unity, but in this respect admits of general application.

## 36.

Before we proceed to explain this method, it will be proper to observe that the uncertainty of the general methods given above, in orbits approaching the form of the parabola, ceases of itself, when $E$ or $F$ increase to considerable magnitude, which indeed can take place only in large distances from the sun. To show which, we give to

$$\frac{3\,\omega\,e\,a \sin v}{\lambda\,r} \cdot\ 206265'',$$

the greatest possible error in the ellipse, which we find in article 32, IV., the following form,

$$\frac{3\,\omega\,e\sqrt{(1-e\,e)}.\sin E}{\lambda\,(1-e\cos E)^2}.\ 206265'';$$

from which is evident of itself that the error is always circumscribed within narrow limits when $E$ acquires considerable value, or when $\cos E$ recedes further from unity, however great the eccentricity may be. This will appear still more distinctly from the following table, in which we have computed the greatest numerical value of that formula for certain given values of $E$, for seven decimal places.

| $E=10°$ | maximum error $=3''.04$ |
|---|---|
| 20 | 0 .76 |
| 30 | 0 .34 |
| 40 | 0 .19 |
| 50 | 0 .12 |
| 60 | 0 .08 |

The same thing takes place in the hyperbola, as is immediately apparent, if the expression obtained in article 32, VII., is put into this form,

$$\frac{\omega\cos F\,(\cos F+3\,e\sin F)\sqrt{(e\,e-1)}}{\lambda\,(e-\cos F)^2}\ 206265''.$$

The following table exhibits the greatest values of this expression for certain given values of $F$.

| $F$ | $u$ | | maximum error. |
|---|---|---|---|
| 10° | 1.192 | 0.839 | 8''.66 |
| 20 | 1.428 | 0.700 | 1 .38 |
| 30 | 1.732 | 0.577 | 0 .47 |
| 40 | 2.144 | 0.466 | 0 .22 |
| 50 | 2.747 | 0.364 | 0 .11 |
| 60 | 3.732 | 0.268 | 0 .06 |
| 70 | 5.671 | 0.176 | 0 .02 |

When, therefore, $E$ or $F$ exceeds 40° or 50° (which nevertheless does not easily occur in orbits differing but little from the parabola, because heavenly bodies moving in such orbits at such great distances from the sun are for the most part withdrawn from our sight) there will be no reason for forsaking the general method. For the rest, in such a case even the series which we treated in article

34 might converge too slowly; and therefore it is by no means to be regarded as a defect of the method about to be explained, that it is specially adapted to those cases in which $E$ or $F$ has not yet increased beyond moderate values.

### 37.

Let us resume in the elliptic motion the equation between the eccentric anomaly and the time,

$$E - e \sin E = \frac{k t \sqrt{(1+\mu)}}{a^{\frac{3}{2}}},$$

where we suppose $E$ to be expressed in parts of the radius. Henceforth, we shall leave out the factor $\sqrt{(1+\mu)}$; if a case should occur where it is worth while to take it into account, the symbol $t$ would not express the time itself after perihelion, but this time multiplied by $\sqrt{(1+\mu)}$. We designate in future by $q$ the perihelion distance, and in the place of $E$ and $\sin E$, we introduce the quantities

$$E - \sin E, \text{ and } E - \tfrac{1}{10}(E - \sin E) = \tfrac{9}{10}E + \tfrac{1}{10}\sin E:$$

the careful reader will readily perceive from what follows, our reason for selecting particularly these expressions. In this way our equation assumes the following form: —

$$(1 - e)\left(\tfrac{9}{10}E + \tfrac{1}{10}\sin E\right) + \left(\tfrac{1}{10} + \tfrac{9}{10}e\right)(E - \sin E) = k t \left(\frac{1-e}{q}\right)^{\frac{3}{2}}.$$

As long as $E$ is regarded as a quantity of the first order,

$$\tfrac{9}{10}E + \tfrac{1}{10}\sin E = E - \tfrac{1}{60}E^3 + \tfrac{1}{1200}E^5 - \text{etc.}$$

will be a quantity of the first order, while

$$E - \sin E = \tfrac{1}{6}E^3 - \tfrac{1}{120}E^5 + \tfrac{1}{5040}E^7 - \text{etc.},$$

will be a quantity of the third order. Putting, therefore,

$$\frac{6(E - \sin E)}{\tfrac{9}{10}E + \tfrac{1}{10}\sin E} = 4A, \quad \frac{\tfrac{9}{10}E + \tfrac{1}{10}\sin E}{2\sqrt{A}} = B,$$

$$4A = E^2 - \tfrac{1}{30}E^4 - \tfrac{1}{5040}E^6 - \text{etc.}$$

will be a quantity of the second order, and

$$B = 1 + \tfrac{3}{2800}E^4 - \text{etc.}$$

will differ from unity by a quantity of the fourth order. But hence our equation becomes

$$B\left(2\left(1-e\right)A^{\frac{1}{2}}+\tfrac{2}{15}\left(1+9\,e\right)A^{\frac{3}{2}}\right)=k\,t\left(\frac{1-e}{q}\right)^{\frac{3}{2}} \quad . \quad . \quad . \quad . \quad [1]$$

By means of the common trigonometrical tables, $\tfrac{9}{10}E+\tfrac{1}{10}\sin E$ may be computed with sufficient accuracy, but not $E-\sin E$ when $E$ is a small angle; in this way therefore it would not be possible to determine correctly enough the quantities $A$ and $B$. A remedy for this difficulty would be furnished by an appropriate table, from which we could take out with the argument $E$, either $B$ or the logarithm of $B$; the means necessary to the construction of such a table will readily present themselves to any one even moderately versed in analysis. By the aid of the equation

$$\frac{9\,E+\sin E}{20\,B}=\sqrt{A},$$

$\sqrt{A}$ can be determined, and hence $t$ by formula [1] with all desirable precision.

The following is a specimen of such a table, which will show the slow increase of $\log B$; it would be superfluous to take the trouble to extend this table, for further on we are about to describe tables of a much more convenient form.

| $E$ | $\log B$ | $E$ | $\log B$ | $E$ | $\log B$ |
|---|---|---|---|---|---|
| 0° | 0.0000000 | 25° | 0.0000168 | 50° | 0.0002675 |
| 5 | 00 | 30 | 0349 | 55 | 3910 |
| 10 | 04 | 35 | 0645 | 60 | 5526 |
| 15 | 22 | 40 | 1099 | | |
| 20 | 69 | 45 | 1758 | | |

### 38.

It will not be useless to illustrate by an example what has been given in the preceding article. Let the proposed true anomaly $= 100°$, the eccentricity $= 0.96764567$, $\log q = 9.7656500$. The following is the calculation for $E$, $B$, $A$, and $t$:—

$$\log \tan \tfrac{1}{2} v \quad . \quad . \quad . \quad . \quad . \quad 0.0761865$$

$$\log \sqrt{\frac{1-e}{1+e}} \quad . \quad . \quad . \quad . \quad 9.1079927$$

$$\log \tan \tfrac{1}{2} E \quad . \quad . \quad . \quad . \quad 9.1841792, \quad \text{whence } \tfrac{1}{2}E = 8°\,41'\,19''.32, \text{ and } E =$$

$17°\,22'\,38''.64$. To this value of $E$ corresponds $\log B = 0.0000040$; next is found in parts of the radius, $E = 0.3032928$, $\sin E = 0.2986643$, whence $\frac{9}{20}E + \frac{1}{20}\sin E = 0.1514150$, the logarithm of which $= 9.1801689$, and so $\log A^{\frac{1}{2}} = 9.1801649$. Thence is derived, by means of formula [1] of the preceding article,

$$\log \frac{2\,B q^{\frac{3}{2}}}{k\sqrt{(1-e)}} \;\cdot\;\cdot\;\cdot\; 2.4589614 \qquad \log \frac{2\,B\,(1+9\,e)}{15\,k}\left(\frac{q}{1-e}\right)^{\frac{3}{2}} \cdot\;\cdot\;\cdot\; 3.7601038$$

$$\log A^{\frac{1}{2}} \;\cdot\;\cdot\;\cdot\;\cdot\; 9.1801649 \qquad \log A^{\frac{3}{2}} \;\cdot\;\cdot\;\cdot\;\cdot\;\cdot\;\cdot\; 7.5404947$$

$$\overline{\log 43.56386 = \;\cdot\;\cdot\; 1.6391263} \qquad \overline{\log 19.98014 = \;\cdot\;\cdot\;\cdot\;\cdot\; 1.3005985.}$$

$$\frac{19.98014}{63.54400 = t.}$$

If the same example is treated according to the common method, $e \sin E$ in seconds is found $= 59610''.79 = 16°\,33'\,30''.79$, whence the mean anomaly $= 49'\,7''.85 = 2947''.85$. And hence from

$$\log k\left(\frac{1-e}{q}\right)^{\frac{3}{2}} = 1.6664302$$

is derived $t = 63.54410$. The difference, which is here only $\frac{1}{10000}$ part of a day, might, by the errors concurring, easily come out three or four times greater. It is further evident, that with the help of such a table for $\log B$ even the inverse problem can be solved with all accuracy, $E$ being determined by repeated trials, so that the value of $t$ calculated from it may agree with the proposed value. But this operation would be very troublesome: on account of which, we will now show how an auxiliary table may be much more conveniently arranged, indefinite trials be altogether avoided, and the whole calculation reduced to a numerical operation in the highest degree neat and expeditious, which seems to leave nothing to be desired.

### 39.

It is obvious that almost one half the labor which those trials would require, could be saved, if there were a table so arranged that $\log B$ could be immediately taken out with the argument $A$. Three operations would then remain; the first indirect, namely, the determination of $A$ so as to satisfy the equation

[1], article 37; the second, the determination of $E$ from $A$ and $B$, which may be done directly, either by means of the equation

$$E = 2\,B\,(A^{\frac{1}{2}} + \tfrac{1}{15}\,A^{\frac{3}{2}}),$$

or by this,

$$\sin E = 2\,B\,(A^{\frac{1}{2}} - \tfrac{3}{5}\,A^{\frac{3}{2}});$$

the third, the determination of $v$ from $E$ by means of equation VII., article 8. The first operation, we will bring to an easy calculation free from vague trials; the second and third, we will really abridge into one, by inserting a new quantity $C$ in our table by which means we shall have no need of $E$, and at the same time we shall obtain an elegant and convenient formula for the radius vector. Each of these subjects we will follow out in its proper order.

First, we will change the form of equation [1] so that the Barkerian table may be used in the solution of it. For this purpose we will put

$$A^{\frac{1}{2}} = \tan \tfrac{1}{2} w \sqrt{\frac{5 - 5\,e}{1 + 9\,e}},$$

from which comes

$$75 \tan \tfrac{1}{2} w + 25 \tan \tfrac{1}{2} w^3 = \frac{75\,kt\sqrt{(\tfrac{1}{5} + \tfrac{9}{5}\,e)}}{2\,B\,q^{\frac{3}{2}}} = \frac{\alpha\,t}{B},$$

denoting by $\alpha$ the constant

$$\frac{75\,k\sqrt{(\tfrac{1}{5} + \tfrac{9}{5}\,e)}}{2\,q^{\frac{3}{2}}}.$$

If therefore $B$ should be known, $w$ could be immediately taken from the Barkerian table containing the true anomaly to which answers the mean motion $\frac{\alpha\,t}{B}$; $A$ will be deduced from $w$ by means of the formula

$$A = \beta \tan^2 \tfrac{1}{2} w,$$

denoting the constant

$$\frac{5 - 5\,e}{1 + 9\,e} \quad \text{by } \beta.$$

Now, although $B$ may be finally known from $A$ by means of our auxiliary table, nevertheless it can be foreseen, owing to its differing so little from unity, that if the divisor $B$ were wholly neglected from the beginning, $w$ and $A$ would be affected with a slight error only. Therefore, we will first determine roughly $w$ and $A$, putting $B = 1$; with the approximate value of $A$, we will find $B$ in our auxiliary table, with which we will repeat more exactly the same calculation; most frequently, precisely the same value of $B$ that had been found from the approximate value of $A$ will correspond to the value of $A$ thus corrected, so that a second repetition of the operation would be superfluous, those cases excepted in which the value of $E$ may have been very considerable.

Finally, it is hardly necessary to observe that, if the approximate value of $B$ should in any other way whatever be known from the beginning, (which may always occur, when of several places to be computed, not very distant from each other, some few are already obtained,) it is better to make use of this at once in the first approximation: in this manner the expert computer will very often not have occasion for even a single repetition. We have arrived at this most rapid approximation from the fact that $B$ differs from unity, only by a difference of the fourth order, and is multiplied by a very small numerical coefficient, which advantage, as will now be perceived, was secured by the introduction of the quantities $E - \sin E$, $\frac{9}{10} E + \frac{1}{10} \sin E$, in the place of $E$ and $\sin E$.

## 40.

Since, for the third operation, that is, the determination of the true anomaly, the angle $E$ is not required, but the $\tan \frac{1}{2} E$ only, or rather the $\log \tan \frac{1}{2} E$, that operation could be conveniently joined with the second, provided our table supplied directly the logarithm of the quantity

$$\frac{\tan \frac{1}{2} E}{\sqrt{A}},$$

which differs from unity by a quantity of the second order. We have preferred, however, to arrange our table in a somewhat different manner, by which, notwithstanding the small extension, we have obtained a much more convenient interpolation. By writing, for the sake of brevity, $T$ instead of the $\tan^2 \frac{1}{2} E$, the value of $A$, given in article 37,

$$\frac{15 (E - \sin E)}{9 E + \sin E},$$

is easily changed to

$$A = \frac{T - \frac{6}{8} T^2 + \frac{9}{7} T^3 - \frac{12}{9} T^4 + \frac{15}{11} T^5 - \text{etc.}}{1 - \frac{6}{15} T + \frac{7}{25} T^2 - \frac{8}{35} T^3 + \frac{9}{45} T^4 - \text{etc.}},$$

in which the law of progression is obvious. Hence is deduced, by the inversion of the series,

$$\frac{A}{T} = 1 - \tfrac{4}{5}A + \tfrac{8}{175}A^2 + \tfrac{8}{525}A^3 + \tfrac{1896}{336875}A^4 + \tfrac{28744}{13138125}A^5 + \text{etc.}$$

Putting, therefore,

$$\frac{A}{T} = 1 - \tfrac{4}{5}A + C,$$

$C$ will be a quantity of the fourth order, which being included in our table, we can pass directly to $v$ from $A$ by means of the formula,

$$\tan \tfrac{1}{2} v = \sqrt{\frac{1+e}{1-e}} \sqrt{\frac{A}{1 - \tfrac{4}{5}A + C}} = \frac{\gamma \tan \tfrac{1}{2} w}{\sqrt{(1 - \tfrac{4}{5}A + C)}},$$

denoting by $\gamma$ the constant

$$\sqrt{\frac{5 + 5e}{1 + 9e}}.$$

In this way we gain at the same time a very convenient computation for the radius vector. It becomes, in fact, (article 8, VI.),

$$r = \frac{q \cos^2 \tfrac{1}{2} E}{\cos^2 \tfrac{1}{2} v} = \frac{q}{(1 + T) \cos^2 \tfrac{1}{2} v} = \frac{(1 - \tfrac{4}{5}A + C) q}{(1 + \tfrac{1}{5}A + C) \cos^2 \tfrac{1}{2} v}.$$

## 41.

Nothing now remains but to reduce the inverse problem also, that is, the determination of the time from the true anomaly, to a more expeditious form of computation: for this purpose we have added to our table a new column for $T$. $T$, therefore, will be computed first from $v$ by means of the formula

$$T = \frac{1 - e}{1 + e} \tan^2 \tfrac{1}{2} v;$$

then $A$ and $\log B$ are taken from our table with the argument $T$, or, (which is more accurate, and even more convenient also), $C$ and $\log B$, and hence $A$ by the formula

$$A = \frac{(1 + C) T}{1 + \tfrac{4}{5}T};$$

finally $t$ is derived from $A$ and $B$ by formula [1], article 37. If it is desired to call into use the Barkerian table here also, which however in this inverse problem has less effect in facilitating the calculation, it is not necessary to pay any regard to $A$, but we have at once

$$\tan \tfrac{1}{2} w = \tan \tfrac{1}{2} v \sqrt{\frac{1 + C}{\gamma (1 + \tfrac{1}{3} T)}},$$

and hence the time $t$, by multiplying the mean motion corresponding to the true anomaly, $w$, in the Barkerian table, by $\dfrac{B}{a}$.

## 42.

We have constructed with sufficient fulness a table, such as we have just described, and have added it to this work, (Table I.). Only the first part pertains to the ellipse; we will explain, further on, the other part, which includes the hyperbolic motion. The argument of the table, which is the quantity $A$, proceeds by single thousandths from 0 to 0.300; the log $B$ and $C$ follow, which quantities it must be understood are given in ten millionths, or to seven places of decimals, the ciphers preceding the significant figures being suppressed; lastly, the fourth column gives the quantity $T$ computed first to five, then to six figures, which degree of accuracy is quite sufficient, since this column is only needed to get the values of log $B$ and $C$ corresponding to the argument $T$, whenever $t$ is to be determined from $v$ by the precept of the preceding article. As the inverse problem which is much more frequently employed, that is, the determination of $v$ and $r$ from $t$, is solved altogether without the help of $T$, we have preferred the quantity $A$ for the argument of our table rather than $T$, which would otherwise have been an almost equally suitable argument, and would even have facilitated a little the construction of the table. It will not be unnecessary to mention, that all the numbers of the table have been calculated from the beginning to ten places, and that, therefore, the seven places of figures which we give can be safely relied upon; but we cannot dwell here upon the analytical methods used for this work, by a full explanation of which we should be too much diverted from our plan. Finally, the extent of the table is abundantly sufficient for all cases in which it is advantageous to pursue the method just explained, since beyond the limit $A = 0.3$, to which answers $T = 0.392374$, or $E = 64°\,7'$, we may, as has been shown before, conveniently dispense with artificial methods.

### 43.

We add, for the better illustration of the preceding investigations, an example of the complete calculation for the true anomaly and radius vector from the time, for which purpose we will resume the numbers in article 38. We put then $e = 0.9674567$, $\log q = 9.7656500$, $t = 63.54400$, whence, we first derive the constants $\log \alpha = 0.03052357$, $\log \beta = 8.2217364$, $\log \gamma = 0.0028755$.

Hence we have $\log \alpha t = 2.1083102$, to which corresponds in Barker's table the approximate value of $w = 99° 6'$ whence is obtained $A = 0.022926$, and from our table $\log B = 0.0000040$. Hence, the correct argument with which Barker's table must be entered, becomes $\log \frac{\alpha t}{B} = 2.1083062$, to which answers $w = 99° 6'$ $13''.14$; after this, the subsequent calculation is as follows: —

| | | |
|---|---|---|
| $\log \tan^2 \tfrac{1}{2} w$ . . . | 0.1385934 | |
| $\log \beta$ . . . . . | 8.2217364 | |
| $\log A$ . . . . . | 8.3603298 | |
| $A =$ . . . . . | 0.02292608 | |

hence $\log B$ in the same manner as before;

| | | |
|---|---|---|
| $C =$ . | 0.0000242 | |
| $1 - \tfrac{4}{5} A + C =$ . | 0.9816833 | |
| $1 + \tfrac{1}{5} A + C =$ . | 1.0046094 | |

| | | |
|---|---|---|
| $\log \tan \tfrac{1}{2} w$ . . . . . . | 0.0692967 |
| $\log \gamma$ . . . . . . . . | 0.0028755 |
| $\tfrac{1}{2}$ Comp. $\log(1 - \tfrac{4}{5} A + C)$ . | 0.0040143 |
| $\log \tan \tfrac{1}{2} v$ . . . . . . | 0.0761865 |
| $\tfrac{1}{2} v =$ . . . . . | 50° 0' 0'' |
| $v =$ . . . . . | 100  0  0 |
| $\log q$ . . . . . . . . | 9.7656500 |
| 2 Comp. $\log \cos \tfrac{1}{2} v$ . . . | 0.3838650 |
| $\log(1 - \tfrac{4}{5} A + C)$ . . . . | 9.9919714 |
| C. $\log(1 + \tfrac{1}{5} A + C)$ . . . | 9.9980028 |
| $\log r$ . . . . . . . . | 0.1394892 |

If the factor $B$ had been wholly neglected in this calculation, the true anomaly would have come out affected with a very slight error (in excess) of $0''.1$ only.

### 44.

It will be in our power to despatch the hyperbolic motion the more briefly, because it is to be treated in a manner precisely analogous to that which we have thus far expounded for the elliptic motion.

We present the equation between the time $t$ and the auxiliary quantity $u$ in the following form : —

$$(e-1)\left(\tfrac{1}{20}(u-\tfrac{1}{u})+\tfrac{9}{10}\log u\right)+(\tfrac{1}{10}+\tfrac{9}{10}e)\left(\tfrac{1}{3}(u-\tfrac{1}{u})-\log u\right)=kt\left(\tfrac{e-1}{q}\right)^{\frac{3}{2}},$$

in which the logarithms are hyperbolic, and

$$\tfrac{1}{20}(u-\tfrac{1}{u})+\tfrac{9}{10}\log u$$

is a quantity of the first order,

$$\tfrac{1}{3}(u-\tfrac{1}{u})-\log u$$

a quantity of the third order, when $\log u$ may be considered as a small quantity of the first order. Putting, therefore,

$$\frac{6\left(\tfrac{1}{3}(u-\tfrac{1}{u})-\log u\right)}{\tfrac{1}{20}(u-\tfrac{1}{u})+\tfrac{9}{10}\log u}=4A, \qquad \frac{\tfrac{1}{20}(u-\tfrac{1}{u})+\tfrac{9}{10}\log u}{2\sqrt{A}}=B,$$

$A$ will be a quantity of the second order, but $B$ will differ from unity by a difference of the fourth order. Our equation will then assume the following form : —

$$B\left(2(e-1)A^{\frac{1}{2}}+\tfrac{2}{15}(1+9e)A^{\frac{3}{2}}\right)=kt\left(\tfrac{e-1}{q}\right)^{\frac{3}{2}} \quad \cdots \cdots \quad [2]$$

which is entirely analogous to equation [1] of article 37. Putting moreover,

$$\left(\tfrac{u-1}{u+1}\right)^{2}=T,$$

$T$ will be a quantity of the second order, and by the method of infinite series will be found

$$\frac{A}{T}=1+\tfrac{4}{5}A+\tfrac{8}{175}A^2-\tfrac{8}{525}A^3+\tfrac{1896}{336875}A^4-\tfrac{28744}{13138125}A^5+\text{etc.}$$

Wherefore, putting

$$\frac{A}{T}=1+\tfrac{4}{5}A+C,$$

$C$ will be a quantity of the fourth order, and

$$A=\frac{(1+C)T}{1-\tfrac{4}{5}T}.$$

Finally, for the radius vector, there readily follows from equation VII., article 21,

$$r=\frac{q}{(1-T)\cos^2\tfrac{1}{2}v}=\frac{(1+\tfrac{4}{5}A+C)q}{(1-\tfrac{1}{5}A+C)\cos^2\tfrac{1}{2}v}.$$

## 45.

The latter part of the table annexed to this work belongs, as we have remarked above, to the hyperbolic motion, and gives for the argument $A$ (common to both parts of the table), the logarithm of $B$ and the quantity $C$ to seven places of decimals, (the preceding ciphers being omitted), and the quantity $T$ to five and afterwards to six figures. The latter part is extended in the same manner as the former to $A = 0.300$, corresponding to which is $T = 0.241207$, $u = 2.930$, or $= 0.341$, $F = \pm 52° 19'$; to extend it further would have been superfluous, (article 36).

The following is the arrangement of the calculation, not only for the determination of the time from the true anomaly, but for the determination of the true anomaly from the time. In the former problem, $T$ will be got by means of the formula

$$T = \frac{e-1}{e+1} \tan^2 \tfrac{1}{2} v ;$$

with $T$ our table will give log $B$ and $C$, whence will follow

$$A = \frac{(1+C)\, T}{1 - \tfrac{4}{3}T} ;$$

finally $t$ is then found from the formula [2] of the preceding article. In the last problem, will first be computed, the logarithms of the constants

$$\alpha = \frac{75\, k \sqrt{(\tfrac{1}{5} + \tfrac{2}{5} e)}}{2\, q^{\frac{3}{2}}}$$

$$\beta = \frac{5\, e - 5}{1 + 9\, e}$$

$$\gamma = \sqrt{\frac{5\, e + 5}{1 + 9\, e}}.$$

$A$ will then be determined from $t$ exactly in the same manner as in the elliptic motion, so that in fact the true anomaly $w$ may correspond in Barker's table to the mean motion $\frac{\alpha\, t}{B}$, and that we may have

$$A = \beta \tan^2 \tfrac{1}{2} w ;$$

the approximate value of $A$ will be of course first obtained, the factor $B$ being either neglected, or, if the means are at hand, being estimated; our table will then furnish the approximate value of $B$, with which the work will be repeated; the new value of $B$ resulting in this manner will scarcely ever suffer sensible correction, and thus a second repetition of the calculation will not be necessary. $C$ will be taken from the table with the corrected value of $A$, which being done we shall have,

$$\tan \tfrac{1}{2} v = \frac{\gamma \tan \tfrac{1}{2} w}{\sqrt{(1 + \tfrac{4}{5} A + C)}}, \quad r = \frac{(1 + \tfrac{4}{5} A + C)q}{(1 - \tfrac{1}{5} A + C)\cos^2 \tfrac{1}{2} v}.$$

From this it is evident, that no difference can be perceived between the formulas for elliptic and hyperbolic motions, provided that we consider $\beta$, $A$, and $T$, in the hyperbolic motion as negative quantities.

## 46.

It will not be unprofitable to elucidate the hyperbolic motion also by some examples, for which purpose we will resume the numbers in articles 23, 26.

I. The data are $e = 1.2618820$, $\log q = 0.0201657$, $v = 18°\,51'\,0''$: $t$ is required. We have

| | | |
|---|---|---|
| $2 \log \tan \tfrac{1}{2} v$ . . . . . | 8.4402018 | |
| $\log \dfrac{e-1}{e+1}$ . . . . . | 9.0636357 | |
| $\log T$ . . . . . . | 7.5038375 | |
| $T =$ . . . . . . | 0.00319034 | |
| $\log B =$ . . . . . . | 0.0000001 | |
| $C =$ . . . . . . | 0.0000005 | |

| | |
|---|---|
| $\log T$ . . . . . | 7.5038375 |
| $\log (1 + C)$ . . . | 0.0000002 |
| C. $\log (1 - \tfrac{4}{5} T)$ . | 0.0011099 |
| $\log A$ . . . . . | 7.5049476 |

| | |
|---|---|
| $\log \dfrac{2 B q^{\frac{3}{2}}}{k \sqrt{(e-1)}}$ . . . | 2.3866444 |
| $\log A^{\frac{1}{2}}$ . . . . . | 8.7524738 |
| $\log 13.77584 =$ . . | 1.1391182 |
| 0.13861 | |
| 13.91445 $= t$. | |

| | |
|---|---|
| $\log \dfrac{2 B (1 + 9 e)}{15 k}\left(\dfrac{q}{e-1}\right)^{\frac{3}{2}}$ . . . | 2.8843582 |
| $\log A^{\frac{3}{2}}$ . . . . . . . . | 6.2574214 |
| $\log 0.138605 =$ . . . . . | 9.1417796 |

II. $e$ and $q$ remaining as before, there is given $t = 65.41236$; $v$ and $r$ are required. We find the logarithms of the constants,

$$\log \alpha = 9.9758345$$
$$\log \beta = 9.0251649$$
$$\log \gamma = 9.9807646.$$

Next we have $\log \alpha t = 1.7914943$, whence by Barker's table the approximate value of $w = 70° 31' 44''$, and hence $A = 0.052983$. To this $A$ in our table answers $\log B = 0.0000207$; from which, $\log \frac{\alpha t}{B} = 1.7914736$, and the corrected value of $w = 70° 31' 36''.86$. The remaining operations of the calculation are as follows: —

| | | | | |
|---|---|---|---|---|
| $2 \log \tan \frac{1}{2} w$ . . . | 9.6989398 | $\log \tan \frac{1}{2} w$ . . . . . | 9.8494699 |
| $\log \beta$ . . . . . . | 9.0251649 | $\log \gamma$ . . . . . . . | 9.9807646 |
| $\log A$ . . . . . . | 8.7241047 | $\frac{1}{2}$ C. $\log (1 + \frac{4}{5} A + C)$ . | 9.9909602 |
| $A =$ . . . . . . | 0.05297911 | $\log \tan \frac{1}{2} v$ . . . . . | 9.8211947 |
| $\log B$ as before, | | $\frac{1}{2} v =$ . . . | 33° 31' 30''.02 |
| $C =$ . . | 0.0001252 | $v =$ . . . | 67  3  0 .04 |
| $1 + \frac{4}{5} A + C =$ . . | 1.0425085 | $\log q$ . . . . . . . | 0.0201657 |
| $1 - \frac{1}{5} A + C =$ . . | 0.9895294 | $2$ C. $\log \cos \frac{1}{2} v$ . . . . | 0.1580378 |
| | | $\log (1 + \frac{4}{5} A + C)$ . . | 0.0180796 |
| | | C. $\log (1 - \frac{1}{5} A + C)$ . . | 0.0045713 |
| | | $\log r$ . . . . . . . | 0.2008544 |

Those which we found above (article 26), $v = 67° 2' 59''.78$, $\log r = 0.2008541$, are less exact, and $v$ should properly have resulted $= 67° 3' 0''.00$, with which assumed value, the value of $t$ had been computed by means of the larger tables.

# SECOND SECTION.

---

## 47.

In the first section, the motion of heavenly bodies in their orbits is treated without regard to the position of these orbits in space. For determining this position, by which the relation of the places of the heavenly body to any other point of space can be assigned, there is manifestly required, not only the position of the plane in which the orbit lies with reference to a certain known plane (as, for example, the plane of the orbit of the earth, the *ecliptic*), but also the position of the apsides in that plane. Since these things may be referred, most advantageously, to spherical trigonometry, we conceive a spherical surface described with an arbitrary radius, about the sun as a centre, on which any plane passing through the sun will mark a great circle, and any right line drawn from the sun, a point. For planes and right lines not passing through the sun, we draw through the sun parallel planes and right lines, and we conceive the great circles and points in the surface of the sphere corresponding to the latter to represent the former. The sphere may also be supposed to be described with a radius infinitely great, in which parallel planes, and also parallel right lines, are represented in the same manner.

Except, therefore, the plane of the orbit coincide with the plane of the ecliptic, the great circles corresponding to those planes (which we will simply call the orbit and the ecliptic) cut each other in two points, which are called *nodes;* in one of these nodes, the body, seen from the sun, will pass from the southern, through the ecliptic, to the northern hemisphere, in the other, it will return from the latter to the former; the former is called the *ascending*, the latter the *descending* node. We

(54)

fix the positions of the nodes in the ecliptic by means of their distance from the mean vernal equinox (*longitude*) counted in the order of the signs. Let, in fig. 1, ☊ be the ascending node, $A$ ☊ $B$ part of the ecliptic, $C$ ☊ $D$ part of the orbit; let the motions of the earth and of the heavenly body be in the directions from $A$ towards $B$ and from $C$ towards $D$, it is evident that the spherical angle which ☊ $D$ makes with ☊ $B$ can increase from 0 to 180°, but not beyond, without ☊ ceasing to be the ascending node: this angle we call the *inclination of the orbit* to the ecliptic. The situation of the plane of the orbit being determined by the longitude of the node and the inclination of the orbit, nothing further is wanted except the distance of the perihelion from the ascending node, which we reckon in the direction of the motion, and therefore regard it as negative, or between 180° and 360°, whenever the perihelion is south of the ecliptic. The following expressions are yet to be observed. The longitude of any point whatever in the circle of the orbit is counted from that point which is distant just so far back from the ascending node in the orbit as the vernal equinox is back from the same point in the ecliptic: hence, the *longitude of the perihelion* will be the sum of the longitude of the node and the distance of the perihelion from the node; also, the *true longitude in orbit* of the body will be the sum of the true anomaly and the longitude of the perihelion. Lastly, the sum of the mean anomaly and longitude of the perihelion is called the *mean longitude:* this last expression can evidently only occur in elliptic orbits.

## 48.

In order, therefore, to be able to assign the place of a heavenly body in space for any moment of time, the following things must be known.

I. The mean longitude for any moment of time taken at will, which is called the *epoch:* sometimes the longitude itself is designated by the same name. For the most part, the beginning of some year is selected for the epoch, namely, noon of January 1 in the bissextile year, or noon of December 31 preceding, in the common year.

II. The mean motion in a certain interval of time, for example, in one mean solar day, or in 365, 365¼, or 36525 days.

III. The semi-axis major, which indeed might be omitted when the mass of the body is known or can be neglected, since it is already given by the mean motion, (article 7); both, nevertheless, are usually given for the sake of convenience.

IV. Eccentricity. V. Longitude of the perihelion. VI. Longitude of the ascending node. VII. Inclination of the orbit.

These seven things are called the *elements* of the motion of the body.

In the parabola and hyperbola, the time of passage through the perihelion serves in place of the first element; instead of II., are given what in these species of conic sections are analogous to the mean daily motion, (see article 19; in the hyperbolic motion the quantity $\lambda\,k\,b^{-\frac{3}{2}}$, article 23). In the hyperbola, the remaining elements may be retained the same, but in the parabola, where the major axis is infinite and the eccentricity $= 1$, the perihelion distance alone will be given in place of the elements III. and IV.

## 49.

According to the common mode of speaking, the inclination of the orbit, which we count from 0 to 180°, is only extended to 90°, and if the angle made by the orbit with the arc $\Omega\,B$ exceeds a right angle, the angle of the orbit with the arc $\Omega\,A$, which is its complement to 180°, is regarded as the inclination of the orbit; in this case then it will be necessary to add that the motion is *retrograde* (as if, in our fiigure, $E\,\Omega\,F$ should represent a part of the orbit), in order that it may be distinguished from the other case where the motion is called *direct*. The longitude in orbit is then usually so reckoned that in $\Omega$ it may agree with the longitude of this point in the ecliptic, but *decrease* in the direction $\Omega\,F$; the initial point, therefore, from which longitudes are counted contrary to the order of motion in the direction $\Omega\,F$, is just so far distant from $\Omega$, as the vernal equinox from the same $\Omega$ in the direction $\Omega\,A$. Wherefore, in this case the longitude of the perihelion will be the longitude of the node diminished by the distance of the perihelion from the node. In this way either form of expression is easily converted into the other, but we have preferred our own, for the reason that we might do away with the distinction between the direct and retrograde motion, and use always the same formulas for both, while the common form may frequently require double precepts.

## 50.

The most simple method of determining the position, with respect to the ecliptic, of any point whatever on the surface of the celestial sphere, is by means of its distance from the ecliptic (*latitude*), and the distance from the equinox of the point at which the ecliptic is cut by a perpendicular let fall upon it, (*longitude*). The latitude, counted both ways from the ecliptic up to 90°, is regarded as positive in the northern hemisphere, and as negative in the southern. Let the longitude $\lambda$, and the latitude $\beta$, correspond to the heliocentric place of a celestial body, that is, to the projection upon the celestial sphere of a right line drawn from the sun to the body; let, also, $u$ be the distance of the heliocentric place from the ascending node (which is called the *argument of the latitude*), $i$ be the inclination of the orbit, $\Omega$ the longitude of the ascending node; there will exist between $i$, $u$, $\beta$, $\lambda - \Omega$, which quantities will be parts of a right-angled spherical triangle, the following relations, which, it is easily shown, hold good without any restriction : —

I.   $\tan (\lambda - \Omega) = \cos i \tan u$

II.  $\tan \beta = \tan i \sin (\lambda - \Omega)$

III. $\sin \beta = \sin i \sin u$

IV.  $\cos u = \cos \beta \cos (\lambda - \Omega)$.

When the quantities $i$ and $u$ are given, $\lambda - \Omega$ will be determined from them by means of equation I., and afterwards $\beta$ by II. or by III., if $\beta$ does not approach too near to $\pm$ 90°; formula IV. can be used at pleasure for confirming the calculation. Formulas I. and IV. show, moreover, that $\lambda - \Omega$ and $u$ always lie in the same quadrant when $i$ is between 0° and 90°; $\lambda - \Omega$ and 360° $- u$, on the other hand, will belong to the same quadrant when $i$ is between 90° and 180°, or, according to the common usage, when the motion is retrograde : hence the ambiguity which remains in the determination of $\lambda - \Omega$ by means of the tangent according to formula I., is readily removed.

The following formulas are easily deduced from the combination of the preceding : —

V.   $\sin(u - \lambda + \Omega) = 2 \sin^2 \frac{1}{2} i \sin u \cos(\lambda - \Omega)$

VI.   $\sin(u - \lambda + \Omega) = \tan \frac{1}{2} i \sin \beta \cos(\lambda - \Omega)$

VII.   $\sin(u - \lambda + \Omega) = \tan \frac{1}{2} i \tan \beta \cos u$

VIII.   $\sin(u + \lambda - \Omega) = 2 \cos^2 \frac{1}{2} i \sin u \cos(\lambda - \Omega)$

IX.   $\sin(u + \lambda - \Omega) = \cotan \frac{1}{2} i \sin \beta \cos(\lambda - \Omega)$

X.   $\sin(u + \lambda - \Omega) = \cotan \frac{1}{2} i \tan \beta \cos u.$

The angle $u - \lambda + \Omega$, when $i$ is less than 90°, or $u + \lambda - \Omega$, when $i$ is more than 90°, called, according to common usage, the *reduction to the ecliptic*, is, in fact, the difference between the heliocentric longitude $\lambda$ and the longitude in orbit, which last is by the former usage $\Omega \pm u$, by ours $\Omega + u$. When the inclination is small or differs but little from 180°, the same reduction may be regarded as a quantity of the second order, and in this case it will be better to compute first $\beta$ by the formula III., and afterwards $\lambda$ by VII. or X., by which means a greater precision will be attained than by formula I.

If a perpendicular is let fall from the place of the heavenly body in space upon the plane of the ecliptic, the distance of the point of intersection from the sun is called the *curtate distance*. Designating this by $r'$, the radius vector likewise by $r$, we shall have

XI.   $r' = r \cos \beta.$

## 51.

As an example, we will continue further the calculations commenced in articles 13 and 14, the numbers of which the planet Juno furnished. We had found above, the true anomaly $315° 1' 23''.02$, the logarithm of the radius vector $0.3259877$ : now let $i = 13° 6' 44''.10$, the distance of the perihelion from the node $= 241° 10' 20''.57$, and consequently $u = 196° 11' 43''.59$ ; finally let $\Omega = 171° 7' 48''.73$.   Hence we have : —

| | | | | |
|---|---|---|---|---|
| log tan $u$ . . . . | 9.4630573 | log sin $(\lambda - \Omega)$ . . . . | 9.4348691$n$ |
| log cos $i$ . . . . | 9.9885266 | log tan $i$ . . . . . . | 9.3672305 |
| log tan $(\lambda - \Omega)$ . . | 9.4515839 | log tan $\beta$ . . . . . . | 8.8020996$n$ |

| | | | |
|---|---|---|---|
| $\lambda - \Omega =$ | $195°\,47'\,40''.25$ | $\beta =$ | $-3°\,37'\,40''.02$ |
| $\lambda =$ | $6\ \ 55\ \ 28\ .98$ | $\log \cos \beta$ . . . . . | $9.9991289$ |
| $\log r$ . . . . . . | $0.3259877$ | $\log \cos \lambda - \Omega$ . . . | $9.9832852n$ |
| $\log \cos \beta$ . . . . . | $9.9991289$ | | $9.9824141n$ |
| $\log r'$ . . . . . . | $0.3251166$ | $\log \cos u$ . . . . . | $9.9824141n.$ |

The calculation by means of formulas III., VII. would be as follows: —

| | | | |
|---|---|---|---|
| $\log \sin u$ . . . . | $9.4454714n$ | $\log \tan \tfrac{1}{2} i$ . . . . . | $9.0604259$ |
| $\log \sin i$ . . . . . | $9.3557570$ | $\log \tan \beta$ . . . . . | $8.8020995n$ |
| $\log \sin \beta$ . . . . | $8.8012284n$ | $\log \cos u$ . . . . . | $9.9824141n$ |
| $\beta =$ | $-3°\,37'\,40''.02$ | $\log \sin (u - \lambda + \Omega)$ . | $7.8449395$ |
| | | $u - \lambda + \Omega =$ | $0°\,24'\ \ 3''.34$ |
| | | $\lambda - \Omega =$ | $195\ \ 47\ \ 40\ .25.$ |

## 52.

Regarding $i$ and $u$ as variable quantities, the differentiation of equation III., article 50, gives

$$\operatorname{cotan} \beta \, d\beta = \operatorname{cotan} i \, di + \operatorname{cotan} u \, du,$$

or

XII.  $d\beta = \sin (\lambda - \Omega) \, di + \sin i \cos (\lambda - \Omega) \, du.$

In the same manner, by differentiation of equation I. we get

XIII.  $d (\lambda - \Omega) = -\tan \beta \cos (\lambda - \Omega) \, di + \frac{\cos i}{\cos^2 \beta} \, du.$

Finally, from the differentiation of equation XI. comes

$$dr' = \cos \beta \, dr - r \sin \beta \, d\beta,$$

or

XIV.  $dr' = \cos \beta \, dr - r \sin \beta \sin (\lambda - \Omega) \, di - r \sin \beta \sin i \cos (\lambda - \Omega) \, du.$

In this last equation, either the parts that contain $di$ and $du$ are to be divided by $206265''$, or the remaining ones are to be multiplied by this number, if the changes of $i$ and $u$ are supposed to be expressed in minutes and seconds.

## 53.

The position of any point whatever in space is most conveniently determined by means of its distances from three planes cutting each other at right angles. Assuming the plane of the ecliptic to be one of these planes, and denoting the distance of the heavenly body from this plane by $z$, taken positively on the north side, negatively on the south, we shall evidently have $z = r' \tan \beta = r \sin \beta = r \sin i \sin u$. The two remaining planes, which we also shall consider drawn through the sun, will project great circles upon the celestial sphere, which will cut the ecliptic at right angles, and the poles of which, therefore, will lie in the ecliptic, and will be at the distance of 90° from each other. We call that pole of each plane, lying on the side from which the positive distances are counted, the *positive pole*. Let, accordingly, $N$ and $N + 90°$ be the longitudes of the positive poles, and let distances from the planes to which they respectively belong be denoted by $x$ and $y$. Then it will be readily perceived that we have

$$x = r' \cos (\lambda - N)$$
$$= r \cos \beta \cos (\lambda - \Omega) \cos (N - \Omega) + r \cos \beta \sin (\lambda - \Omega) \sin (N - \Omega)$$
$$y = r' \sin (\lambda - N)$$
$$= r \cos \beta \sin (\lambda - \Omega) \cos (N - \Omega) - r \cos \beta \cos (\lambda - \Omega) \sin (N - \Omega),$$

which values are transformed into

$$x = r \cos (N - \Omega) \cos u + r \cos i \sin (N - \Omega) \sin u$$
$$y = r \cos i \cos (N - \Omega) \sin u - r \sin (N - \Omega) \cos u.$$

If now the positive pole of the plane of $x$ is placed in the ascending node, so that $N = \Omega$, we shall have the most simple expressions of the coördinates $x, y, z,$ —

$$x = r \cos u$$
$$y = r \cos i \sin u$$
$$z = r \sin i \sin u.$$

But, if this supposed condition does not occur, the formulas given above will still acquire a form almost equally convenient, by the introduction of four auxiliary quantities, $a$, $b$, $A$, $B$, so determined as to have

$$\cos(N - ☊) = a \sin A$$
$$\cos i \sin(N - ☊) = a \cos A$$
$$- \sin(N - ☊) = b \sin B$$
$$\cos i \cos(N - ☊) = b \cos B,$$

(see article 14, II.).   We shall then evidently have

$$x = r a \sin(u + A)$$
$$y = r b \sin(u + B)$$
$$z = r \sin i \sin u.$$

## 54.

The relations of the motion to the ecliptic explained in the preceding article, will evidently hold equally good, even if some other plane should be substituted for the ecliptic, provided, only, the position of the plane of the orbit in respect to this plane be known; but in this case the expressions longitude and latitude must be suppressed.   The problem, therefore, presents itself: *From the known position of the plane of the orbit and of another new plane in respect to the ecliptic, to derive the position of the plane of the orbit in respect to the new plane.*   Let $n$ ☊, ☊ ☊′, $n$ ☊′ be parts of the great circles which the plane of the ecliptic, the plane of the orbit, and the new plane, project upon the celestial sphere, (fig. 2).   In order that it may be possible to assign, without ambiguity, the inclination of the second circle to the third, and the place of the ascending node, one direction or the other must be chosen in the third circle, analogous, as it were, to that in the ecliptic which is in the order of the signs; let this direction in our figure be from $n$ toward ☊′.   Moreover, of the two hemispheres, separated by the circle $n$ ☊′, it will be necessary to regard one as analogous to the northern hemisphere, the other to the southern ; these hemispheres, in fact, are already distinct in themselves, since that is always regarded as the northern, which is on the right hand to one moving forward* in the circle according to the order of the signs.   In our figure, then, ☊, $n$, ☊′, are the ascending nodes of the second circle upon the first, the third upon the first, the second upon the third; $180° - n$ ☊ ☊′, ☊ $n$ ☊′, $n$ ☊′ ☊ the inclina-

---

* In the *inner* surface, that is to say, of the sphere represented by our figure.

tions of the second to the first, the third to the first, the second to the third.
Our problem, therefore, depends upon the solution of a spherical triangle, in
which, from one side and the adjacent angles, the other parts are to be deduced.
We omit, as sufficiently well known, the common precepts for this case given
in spherical trigonometry : another method, derived from certain equations, which
are sought in vain in our works on trigonometry, is more conveniently employed.
The following are these equations, which we shall make frequent use of in future:
$a$, $b$, $c$, denote the sides of the spherical triangle, and $A$, $B$, $C$, the angles opposite to them respectively : —

$$\text{I.} \quad \frac{\sin\frac{1}{2}(b-c)}{\sin\frac{1}{2}a} = \frac{\sin\frac{1}{2}(B-C)}{\cos\frac{1}{2}A}$$

$$\text{II.} \quad \frac{\sin\frac{1}{2}(b+c)}{\sin\frac{1}{2}a} = \frac{\cos\frac{1}{2}(B-C)}{\sin\frac{1}{2}A}$$

$$\text{III.} \quad \frac{\cos\frac{1}{2}(b-c)}{\cos\frac{1}{2}a} = \frac{\sin\frac{1}{2}(B+C)}{\cos\frac{1}{2}A}$$

$$\text{IV.} \quad \frac{\cos\frac{1}{2}(b+c)}{\cos\frac{1}{2}a} = \frac{\cos\frac{1}{2}(B+C)}{\sin\frac{1}{2}A}.$$

Although it is necessary, for the sake of brevity, to omit here the demonstration
of these propositions, any one can easily verify them in triangles of which neither
the sides nor the angles exceed 180°. But if the idea of the spherical triangle is
conceived in its greatest generality, so that neither the sides nor the angles are
confined within any limits whatever (which affords several remarkable advantages, but requires certain preliminary explanations), cases may exist in which it
is necessary to change the signs in all the preceding equations; since the former
signs are evidently restored as soon as one of the angles or one of the sides is
increased or diminished 360°, it will always be safe to retain the signs as we
have given them, whether the remaining parts are to be determined from a side
and the adjacent angles, or from an angle and the adjacent sides ; for, either
the values of the quantities sought, or those differing by 360° from the true values, and, therefore, equivalent to them, will be obtained by our formulas. We
reserve for another occasion a fuller elucidation of this subject: because, in the
meantime, it will not be difficult, by a rigorous induction, that is, by a complete
enumeration of all the cases, to prove, that the precepts which we shall base upon

these formulas, both for the solution of our present problem, and for other purposes, hold good in all cases generally.

## 55.

Designating as above, the longitude of the ascending node of the orbit upon
the ecliptic by $\Omega$, the inclination by $i$; also, the longitude of the ascending node
of the new plane upon the ecliptic by $n$, the inclination by $\varepsilon$; the distance of the
ascending node of the orbit upon the new plane from the ascending node of the
new plane upon the ecliptic (the arc $n\,\Omega'$ in fig. 2) by $\Omega'$, the inclination of the
orbit to the new plane by $i'$; finally, the arc from $\Omega$ to $\Omega'$ in the direction of the
motion by $\varDelta$: the sides of our spherical triangle will be $\Omega - n$, $\Omega'$, $\varDelta$, and the
opposite angles, $i'$, $180° - i$, $\varepsilon$.   Hence, according to the formulas of the preceding
article, we shall have

$$\sin \tfrac{1}{2} i' \sin \tfrac{1}{2} (\Omega' + \varDelta) = \sin \tfrac{1}{2} (\Omega - n) \sin \tfrac{1}{2} (i + \varepsilon).$$
$$\sin \tfrac{1}{2} i' \cos \tfrac{1}{2} (\Omega' + \varDelta) = \cos \tfrac{1}{2} (\Omega - n) \sin \tfrac{1}{2} (i - \varepsilon).$$
$$\cos \tfrac{1}{2} i' \sin \tfrac{1}{2} (\Omega' - \varDelta) = \sin \tfrac{1}{2} (\Omega - n) \cos \tfrac{1}{2} (i + \varepsilon).$$
$$\cos \tfrac{1}{2} i' \cos \tfrac{1}{2} (\Omega' - \varDelta) = \cos \tfrac{1}{2} (\Omega - n) \cos \tfrac{1}{2} (i - \varepsilon).$$

The two first equations will furnish $\tfrac{1}{2} (\Omega' + \varDelta)$ and $\sin \tfrac{1}{2} i'$; the remaining two,
$\tfrac{1}{2} (\Omega' - \varDelta)$ and $\cos \tfrac{1}{2} i'$; from $\tfrac{1}{2} (\Omega' + \varDelta)$ and $\tfrac{1}{2} (\Omega' - \varDelta)$ will follow $\Omega'$ and $\varDelta$;
from $\sin \tfrac{1}{2} i'$ and $\cos \tfrac{1}{2} i'$ (the agreement of which will serve to prove the calcula-
tion) will result $i'$.   The uncertainty, whether $\tfrac{1}{2} (\Omega' + \varDelta)$ and $\tfrac{1}{2} (\Omega' - \varDelta)$ should
be taken between 0 and 180° or between 180° and 360°, will be removed in this
manner, that both $\sin \tfrac{1}{2} i'$, $\cos \tfrac{1}{2} i'$, are positive, since, from the nature of the case, $i'$
must fall below 180°.

## 56.

It will not prove unprofitable to illustrate the preceding precepts by an
example.   Let $\Omega = 172° 28' 13''.7$, $i = 34° 38' 1''.1$; let also the new plane be
parallel to the equator, so that $n = 180°$; we put the angle $\varepsilon$, which will be the
obliquity of the ecliptic $= 23° 27' 55''.8$.   We have, therefore,

$$\text{☋} - n = \qquad -7°\ 31'\ 46''.3 \qquad\qquad \tfrac{1}{2}(\text{☋} - n) = \qquad -3°\ 45'\ 53''.15$$
$$i + \varepsilon = \qquad 58\ \ 5\ 56\ .9 \qquad\qquad \tfrac{1}{2}(i + \varepsilon) = \qquad 29\ \ 2\ 58\ .45$$
$$i - \varepsilon = \qquad 11\ 10\ \ 5\ .3 \qquad\qquad \tfrac{1}{2}(i - \varepsilon) = \qquad 5\ 35\ \ 2\ .65$$

$$\log \sin \tfrac{1}{2}(\text{☋} - n) \ \ . \ \ . \ \ 8.8173026n \qquad \log \cos \tfrac{1}{2}(\text{☋} - n) \ \ . \ \ . \ \ 9.9990618$$
$$\log \sin \tfrac{1}{2}(i + \varepsilon) \ \ . \ \ . \ \ . \ \ 9.6862484 \qquad \log \sin \tfrac{1}{2}(i - \varepsilon) \ \ . \ \ . \ \ . \ \ 8.9881405$$
$$\log \cos \tfrac{1}{2}(i + \varepsilon) \ \ . \ \ . \ \ . \ \ 9.9416108 \qquad \log \cos \tfrac{1}{2}(i - \varepsilon) \ \ . \ \ . \ \ . \ \ 9.9979342.$$

Hence we have

$$\log \sin \tfrac{1}{2} i' \sin \tfrac{1}{2}(\text{☋}' + \varDelta) \ \ 8.5035510n \qquad \log \cos \tfrac{1}{2} i' \sin \tfrac{1}{2}(\text{☋}' - \varDelta) \ \ 8.7589134n$$
$$\log \sin \tfrac{1}{2} i' \cos \tfrac{1}{2}(\text{☋}' + \varDelta) \ \ 8.9872023 \qquad \log \cos \tfrac{1}{2} i' \cos \tfrac{1}{2}(\text{☋}' - \varDelta) \ \ 9.9969960$$

whence $\tfrac{1}{2}(\text{☋}' + \varDelta) = 341°\ 49'\ 19''.01$     whence $\tfrac{1}{2}(\text{☋}' - \varDelta) = 356°\ 41'\ 31''.43$

$$\log \sin \tfrac{1}{2} i' \ \ . \ \ . \ \ . \ \ . \ \ 9.0094368 \qquad \log \cos \tfrac{1}{2} i' \ \ . \ \ . \ \ . \ \ . \ \ 9.9977202.$$

Thus we obtain $\tfrac{1}{2} i' = 5°\ 51'\ 56''.445$, $i' = 11°\ 43'\ 52''.89$, $\text{☋}' = 338°\ 30'\ 50''.43$, $\varDelta = -14°\ 52'\ 12''.42$. Finally, the point $n$ evidently corresponds in the celestial sphere to the autumnal equinox; for which reason, the distance of the ascending node of the orbit on the equator from the vernal equinox (its *right ascension*) will be $158°\ 30'\ 50''.43$.

In order to illustrate article 53, we will continue this example still further, and will develop the formulas for the coördinates with reference to the three planes passing through the sun, of which, let one be parallel to the equator, and let the positive poles of the two others be situated in right ascension $0°$ and $90°$: let the distances from these planes be respectively $z$, $x$, $y$. If now, moreover, the distances of the heliocentric place in the celestial sphere from the points $\text{☋}$, $\text{☋}'$, are denoted respectively by $u$, $u'$, we shall have $u' = u - \varDelta = u + 14°\ 52'\ 12''.42$, and the quantities which in article 53 were represented by $i$, $N - \text{☋}$, $u$, will here be $i'$, $180° - \text{☋}'$, $u'$. Thus, from the formulas there given, follow,

$$\log a \sin A \ \ . \ \ . \ \ . \ \ . \ \ 9.9687197n \qquad \log b \sin B \ \ . \ \ . \ \ . \ \ . \ \ 9.5638058$$
$$\log a \cos A \ \ . \ \ . \ \ . \ \ . \ \ 9.5546380n \qquad \log b \cos B \ \ . \ \ . \ \ . \ \ . \ \ 9.9595519n$$

whence $A = 248°\ 55'\ 22''.97$        whence $B = 158°\ 5'\ 54''.97$

$$\log a \ \ . \ \ . \ \ . \ \ . \ \ . \ \ 9.9987923 \qquad \log b \ \ . \ \ . \ \ . \ \ . \ \ . \ \ 9.9920848.$$

We have therefore,

$$x = ar \sin (u' + 248° 55' 22''.97) = ar \sin (u + 263° 47' 35''.39)$$
$$y = br \sin (u' + 158 \quad 5 \; 54 \; .97) = br \sin (u + 172 \; 58 \quad 7 \; .39)$$
$$z = cr \sin u' \qquad\qquad\quad = cr \sin (u + \quad 14 \; 52 \; 12 \; .42)$$

in which $\log c = \log \sin i' = 9.3081870$.

Another solution of the problem here treated is found in *Von Zach's Monatliche Correspondenz*, B. IX. p. 385.

## 57.

Accordingly, the distance of a heavenly body from any plane passing through the sun can be reduced to the form $kr \sin (v + K)$, $v$ denoting the true anomaly; $k$ will be the sine of the inclination of the orbit to this plane, $K$ the distance of the perihelion from the ascending node of the orbit in the same plane. So far as the position of the plane of the orbit, and of the line of apsides in it, and also the position of the plane to which the distances are referred, can be regarded as constant, $k$ and $K$ will also be constant. In such a case, however, that method will be more frequently called into use in which the third assumption, at least, is not allowed, even if the perturbations should be neglected, which always affect the first and second to a certain extent. This happens as often as the distances are referred to the equator, or to a plane cutting the equator at a right angle in given right ascension: for since the position of the equator is variable, owing to the precession of the equinoxes and moreover to the nutation (if the true and not the mean position should be in question), in this case also $k$ and $K$ will be subject to changes, though undoubtedly slow. The computation of these changes can be made by means of differential formulas obtained without difficulty: but here it may be, for the sake of brevity, sufficient to add the differential variations of $i'$, $\Omega'$ and $\Delta$, so far as they depend upon the changes of $\Omega - n$ and $\varepsilon$.

$$d\,i' = \sin \varepsilon \sin \Omega' d\,(\Omega - n) - \cos \Omega' d\,\varepsilon$$
$$d\Omega' = \frac{\sin i \cos \Delta}{\sin i'} d\,(\Omega - n) + \frac{\sin \Omega'}{\tan i'} d\,\varepsilon$$
$$d\Delta = \frac{\sin \varepsilon \cos \Omega'}{\sin i'} d\,(\Omega - n) + \frac{\sin \Omega'}{\sin i'} d\,\varepsilon.$$

Finally, when the problem only is, that several places of a celestial body with respect to such variable planes may be computed, which places embrace a moderate interval of time (one year, for example), it will generally be most convenient to calculate the quantities $a$, $A$, $b$, $B$, $c$, $C$, for the two epochs between which they fall, and to derive from them by simple interpolation the changes for the particular times proposed.

## 58.

Our formulas for distances from given planes involve $v$ and $r$; when it is necessary to determine these quantities first from the time, it will be possible to abridge part of the operations still more, and thus greatly to lighten the labor. These distances can be immediately derived, by means of a very simple formula, from the eccentric anomaly in the ellipse, or from the auxiliary quantity $F$ or $u$ in the hyperbola, so that there will be no need of the computation of the true anomaly and radius vector. The expression $kr \sin(v + K)$ is changed;

I. For the *ellipse*, the symbols in article 8 being retained, into

$$ak \cos \varphi \cos K \sin E + ak \sin K (\cos E - e).$$

Determining, therefore, $l$, $L$, $\lambda$, by means of the equations

$$ak \sin K = l \sin L$$
$$ak \cos \varphi \cos K = l \cos L$$
$$- eak \sin K = - el \sin L = \lambda,$$

our expression passes into $l \sin(E + L) + \lambda$, in which $l$, $L$, $\lambda$ will be constant, so far as it is admissible to regard $k$, $K$, $e$ as constant; but if not, the same precepts which we laid down in the preceding article will be sufficient for computing their changes.

We add, for the sake of an example, the transformation of the expression for $x$ found in article 56, in which we put the longitude of the perihelion $= 121° 17' 34''.4$, $\varphi = 14° 13' 31''.97$, $\log a = 0.4423790$. The distance of the perihelion from the ascending node in the ecliptic, therefore, $= 308° 49' 20''.7 = u - v$; hence $K = 212° 36' 56''.09$. Thus we have,

| | | | |
|---|---|---|---|
| $\log a\,k$ . . . . . | 0.4411713 | $\log l \sin L$ . . . . | 0.1727600$n$ |
| $\log \sin K$ . . . . | 9.7315887$n$ | $\log l \cos L$ . . . . | 0.3531154$n$ |
| $\log a\,k \cos \varphi$ . . . | 0.4276456 | whence $L =$ | 213° 25′ 51″.30 |
| $\log \cos K$ . . . . | 9.9254698$n$ | $\log l =$ | 0.4316627 |
| | | $\log \lambda =$ | 9.5632352 |
| | | $\lambda =$ | $+$ 0.3657929. |

II. In the hyperbola the formula $k\,r \sin (v + K)$, by article 21, passes into $\lambda + \mu \tan F + \nu \sec F$, if we put $e\,b\,k \sin K = \lambda$, $b\,k \tan \psi \cos K = \mu$, $- b\,k \sin K = \nu$; it is also, evidently, allowable to bring the same expression under the form

$$\frac{n \sin (F + N) + \nu}{\cos F}.$$

If the auxiliary quantity $u$ is used in the place of $F$, the expression $k\,r \sin (v + K)$ will pass, by article 21, into

$$\alpha + \beta u + \frac{\gamma}{u},$$

in which $\alpha$, $\beta$, $\gamma$, are determined by means of the formulas

$$\alpha = \lambda = e\,b\,k \sin K$$
$$\beta = \tfrac{1}{2} (\nu + \mu) = - \tfrac{1}{2} e\,b\,k \sin (K - \psi)$$
$$\gamma = \tfrac{1}{2} (\nu - \mu) = - \tfrac{1}{2} e\,b\,k \sin (K + \psi).$$

III. In the parabola, where the true anomaly is derived directly from the time, nothing would remain but to substitute for the radius vector its value. Thus, denoting the perihelion distance by $q$, the expression $k\,r \sin (v + K)$ becomes

$$\frac{q\,k \sin (v + K)}{\cos^2 \tfrac{1}{2} v}.$$

## 59.

The precepts for determining distances from planes passing through the sun may, it is evident, be applied to distances from the earth; here, indeed, only the most simple cases usually occur. Let $R$ be the distance of the earth from the sun, $L$ the heliocentric longitude of the earth (which differs 180° from the geocentric longitude of the sun), lastly, $X$, $Y$, $Z$, the distances of the earth from three planes cutting each other in the sun at right angles. Now if

I. The plane of $Z$ is the ecliptic itself, and the longitudes of the poles of the remaining planes, the distances from which are $X$, $Y$, are respectively $N$, and $N + 90°$; then

$$X = R \cos (L - N), \quad Y = R \sin (L - N), \quad Z = 0.$$

II. If the plane of $Z$ is parallel to the equator, and the right ascensions of the poles of the remaining planes, from which the distances are $X$, $Y$, are respectively $0°$ and $90°$, we shall have, denoting by $\varepsilon$ the obliquity of the ecliptic,

$$X = R \cos L, \quad Y = R \cos \varepsilon \sin L, \quad Z = R \sin \varepsilon \sin L.$$

The editors of the most recent solar tables, the illustrious VON ZACH and DE LAMBRE, first began to take account of the latitude of the sun, which, produced by the perturbations of the other planets and of the moon, can scarcely amount to one second. Denoting by $B$ the heliocentric latitude of the earth, which will always be equal to the latitude of the sun but affected with the opposite sign, we shall have,

<table>
<tr><td align="center">In Case I.</td><td align="center">In Case II.</td></tr>
<tr><td>$X = R \cos B \cos (L - N)$</td><td>$X = R \cos B \cos L$</td></tr>
<tr><td>$Y = R \cos B \sin (L - N)$</td><td>$Y = R \cos B \cos \varepsilon \sin L - R \sin B \sin \varepsilon$</td></tr>
<tr><td>$Z = R \sin B$</td><td>$Z = R \cos B \sin \varepsilon \sin L + R \sin B \cos \varepsilon.$</td></tr>
</table>

It will always be safe to substitute 1 for $\cos B$, and the angle expressed in parts of the radius for $\sin B$.

The coördinates thus found are referred to the *centre* of the earth. If $\xi$, $\eta$, $\zeta$, are the distances of any point whatever on the *surface* of the earth from three planes drawn through the centre of the earth, parallel to those which were drawn through the sun, the distances of this point from the planes passing through the sun, will evidently be $X + \xi$, $Y + \eta$, $Z + \zeta$: the values of the coördinates $\xi$, $\eta$, $\zeta$, are easily determined in both cases by the following method. Let $\varrho$ be the radius of the terrestrial globe, (or the sine of the mean horizontal parallax of the sun,) $\lambda$ the longitude of the point at which the right line drawn from the centre of the earth to the point on the surface meets the celestial sphere, $\beta$ the latitude of the same point, $\alpha$ the right ascension, $\delta$ the declination, and we shall have,

| In Case I. | In Case II. |
|---|---|

$$\xi = \varrho \cos \beta \cos (\lambda - N) \qquad \xi = \varrho \cos \delta \cos \alpha$$
$$\eta = \varrho \cos \beta \sin (\lambda - N) \qquad \eta = \varrho \cos \delta \sin \alpha$$
$$\zeta = \varrho \sin \beta \qquad\qquad\quad \zeta = \varrho \sin \delta.$$

This point of the celestial sphere evidently corresponds to the zenith of the place on the surface (if the earth is regarded as a sphere), wherefore, its right ascension agrees with the right ascension of the mid-heaven, or with the sidereal time converted into degrees, and its declination with the elevation of the pole; if it should be worth while to take account of the spheroidal figure of the earth, it would be necessary to adopt for $\delta$ the *corrected* elevation of the pole, and for $\varrho$ the true distance of the place from the centre of the earth, which are deduced by means of known rules. The longitude and latitude $\lambda$ and $\beta$ will be derived from $\alpha$ and $\delta$ by known rules, also to be given below: it is evident that $\lambda$ coincides with the longitude of the *nonagesimal*, and $90° - \beta$ with its altitude.

## 60.

If $x, y, z$, denote the distances of a heavenly body from three planes cutting each other at right angles at the sun; $X, Y, Z$, the distances of the earth (either of the centre or a point on the surface), it is apparent that $x - X, y - Y, z - Z$, would be the distances of the heavenly body from three planes drawn through the earth parallel to the former; and these distances would have the same relation to the distance of the body from the earth and its *geocentric place*,[*] (that is, the place of its projection in the celestial sphere, by a right line drawn to it from the earth), which $x, y, z$, have to its distance from the sun and the heliocentric place. Let $\varDelta$ be the distance of the celestial body from the earth; suppose a perpendicular in the celestial sphere let fall from the geocentric place on the great circle which corresponds to the plane of the distances $z$, and let $a$ be the distance of the intersection from the positive pole of the great circle which corresponds to the

---

[*] In the broader sense: for properly this expression refers to that case in which the right line is drawn from the centre of the earth.

plane of the distances $x$; and, finally, let $b$ be the length of this perpendicular, or the distance of the geocentric place from the great circle corresponding to the distances $z$. Then $b$ will be the geocentric latitude or declination, according as the plane of the distances $z$ is the ecliptic or the equator; on the other hand, $a + N$ will be the geocentric longitude or right ascension, if $N$ denotes, in the former case, the longitude, in the latter, the right ascension, of the pole of the plane of the distances $x$. Wherefore, we shall have

$$x - X = \varDelta \cos b \cos a$$
$$y - Y = \varDelta \cos b \sin a$$
$$z - Z = \varDelta \sin b.$$

The two first equations will give $a$ and $\varDelta \cos b$; the latter quantity (which must be positive) combined with the third equation, will give $b$ and $\varDelta$.

## 61.

We have given, in the preceding articles, the easiest method of determining the geocentric place of a heavenly body with respect to the ecliptic or equator, either free from parallax or affected by it, and in the same manner, either free from, or affected by, nutation. In what pertains to the nutation, all the difference will depend upon this, whether we adopt the mean or true position of the equator; as in the former case, we should count the longitudes from the mean equinox, in the latter, from the true, just as, in the one, the mean obliquity of the ecliptic is to be used, in the other, the true obliquity. It appears at once, that the greater the number of abbreviations introduced into the computation of the coördinates, the more the preliminary operations which are required; on which account, the superiority of the method above explained, of deriving the coördinates immediately from the eccentric anomaly, will show itself especially when it is necessary to determine many geocentric places. But when one place only is to be computed, or very few, it would not be worth while to undertake the labor of calculating so many auxiliary quantities. It will be preferable in such a case not to depart from the common method, according to which the true anomaly and radius vector are deduced from the eccentric anomaly; hence, the heliocentric place with respect to the ecliptic; hence, the geocentric longitude and latitude; and hence, finally, the right ascension and declination. Lest any thing should seem to be wanting, we will in addition briefly explain the two last operations.

## 62.

Let $\lambda$ be the heliocentric longitude of the heavenly body, $\beta$ the latitude; $l$ the geocentric longitude, $b$ the latitude, $r$ the distance from the sun, $\Delta$ the distance from the earth; lastly, let $L$ be the heliocentric longitude of the earth, $B$ the latitude, $R$ its distance from the sun. When we cannot put $B = 0$, our formulas may also be applied to the case in which the heliocentric and geocentric places are referred, not to the ecliptic, but to any other plane whatever; it will only be necessary to suppress the terms longitude and latitude: moreover, account can be immediately taken of the parallax, if only, the heliocentric place of the earth is referred, not to the centre, but to a point on the surface. Let us put, moreover,

$$r \cos \beta = r', \ \Delta \cos b = \Delta', \ R \cos B = R'.$$

Now by referring the place of the heavenly body and of the earth in space to three planes, of which one is the ecliptic, and the second and third have their poles in longitude $N$ and $N + 90°$, the following equations immediately present themselves:—

$$r' \cos (\lambda - N) - R' \cos (L - N) = \Delta' \cos (l - N)$$
$$r' \sin (\lambda - N) - R' \sin (L - N) = \Delta' \sin (l - N)$$
$$r' \tan \beta \qquad - R' \tan B \qquad = \Delta' \tan b,$$

in which the angle $N$ is wholly arbitrary. The first and second equations will determine directly $l - N$ and $\Delta'$, whence $b$ will follow from the third; from $b$ and $\Delta'$ you will have $\Delta$. That the labor of calculation may be as convenient as possible, we determine the arbitrary angle $N$ in the three following ways:—

I. By putting $N = L$, we shall make

$$\frac{r'}{R'} \sin (\lambda - L) = P, \ \frac{r'}{R'} \cos (\lambda - L) - 1 = Q,$$

and $l - L$, $\frac{\Delta'}{R'}$, and $b$, will be found by the formulas

$$\tan (l - L) = \frac{P}{Q}$$

$$\frac{\varDelta'}{R'} = \frac{P}{\sin (l - L)} = \frac{Q}{\cos (l - L)}$$

$$\tan b = \frac{\frac{r'}{R'} \tan \beta - \tan B}{\frac{\varDelta'}{R'}}$$

II. By putting $N = \lambda$, we shall make

$$\frac{R'}{r'} \sin (\lambda - L) = P, \; 1 - \frac{R'}{r'} \cos (\lambda - L) = Q,$$

and we shall have,

$$\tan (l - \lambda) = \frac{P}{Q}$$

$$\frac{\varDelta'}{r'} = \frac{P}{\sin (l - \lambda)} = \frac{Q}{\cos (l - \lambda)}$$

$$\tan b = \frac{\tan \beta - \frac{R'}{r'} \cdot \tan B}{\frac{\varDelta'}{r'}}.$$

III. By putting $N = \frac{1}{2} (\lambda + L)$, $l$ and $\varDelta'$ will be found by means of the equations

$$\tan \left( l - \tfrac{1}{2} (\lambda + L) \right) = \frac{r' + R'}{r' - R'} \tan \tfrac{1}{2} (\lambda - L)$$

$$\varDelta' = \frac{(r' + R') \sin \tfrac{1}{2} (\lambda - L)}{\sin \left( l - \tfrac{1}{2} (\lambda + L) \right)} = \frac{(r' - R') \cos \tfrac{1}{2} (\lambda - L)}{\cos \left( l - \tfrac{1}{2} (\lambda + L) \right)},$$

and afterwards $b$, by means of the equation given above. The logarithm of the fraction

$$\frac{r' + R'}{r' - R'}$$

is conveniently computed if $\frac{R'}{r'}$ is put $= \tan \zeta$, whence we have

$$\frac{r' + R'}{r' - R'} = \tan (45° + \zeta).$$

In this manner the method III. for the determination of $l$ is somewhat shorter than I. and II.; but, for the remaining operations, we consider the two latter preferable to the former.

## 63.

For an example, we continue. further the calculation carried to the helio-centric place in article 51. Let the heliocentric longitude of the earth, $24° 19' 49''.05 = L$, and $\log R = 9.9980979$, correspond to that place; we put the latitude $= 0$. We have, therefore, $\lambda - L = -17° 24' 20''.07$, $\log R' = R$, and thus, according to method II.,

| | | | |
|---|---|---|---|
| $\log \frac{R'}{r'}$ . . . . | 9.6729813 | $\log(1-Q)$ . . . . | 9.6526258 |
| $\log \sin(\lambda - L)$ . | 9.4758653$n$ | $1 - Q =$ | 0.4493925 |
| $\log \cos(\lambda - L)$ . | 9.9796445 | $Q =$ | 0.5506075 |

| | | | |
|---|---|---|---|
| $\log P$ . . . . | 9.1488466$n$ | | |
| $\log Q$ . . . . | 9.7408421 | | |

| | | | |
|---|---|---|---|
| Hence $l - \lambda = -14° 21' 6''.75$ | | whence $l =$ | $352° 34' 22''.23$ |
| $\log \frac{\Delta'}{r'}$ . . . . | 9.7546117 | whence $\log \Delta'$ . . . | 0.0797283 |
| $\log \tan \beta$ . . . | 8.8020996$n$ | $\log \cos b$ . . . . . . | 9.9973144 |

| | | | |
|---|---|---|---|
| $\log \tan b$ . . . | 9.0474879$n$ | $\log \Delta$ . . . . . . . | 0.0824139 |
| $b = -$ | $6° 21' 55''.07$ | | |

According to method III., from $\log \tan \zeta = 9.6729813$, we have $\zeta = 25° 13' 6''.31$, and thus,

| | |
|---|---|
| $\log \tan(45° + \zeta)$ . . . | 0.4441091 |
| $\log \tan \frac{1}{2}(\lambda - L)$ . . . | 9.1848938$n$ |
| $\log \tan(l - \frac{1}{2}\lambda - \frac{1}{2}L)$ . | 9.6290029$n$ |

$\left. \begin{array}{l} l - \frac{1}{2}\lambda - \frac{1}{2}L = - \quad 23° \ 3' 16''.79 \\ \frac{1}{2}\lambda + \frac{1}{2}L = \quad 15 \ 37 \ 39 \ .015 \end{array} \right\}$ whence $l = 352° 34' 22''.225$.

## 64.

We further add the following remarks concerning the problem of article 62.

I. By putting, in the second equation there given,

$$N = \lambda, \ N = L, \ N = l,$$

there results

$$R' \sin (\lambda - L) = \varDelta' \sin (l - \lambda)$$
$$r' \sin (\lambda - L) = \varDelta' \sin (l - L)$$
$$r' \sin (l - \lambda) = R' \sin (l - L).$$

The first or the second equation can be conveniently used for the proof of the calculation, if the method I. or II. of article 62 has been employed. In our example it is as follows: —

$$\log \sin (\lambda - L) \quad . \quad . \quad . \quad 9.4758653 n \qquad l - L = - 31° 45' 26''.82$$
$$\log \frac{\varDelta'}{r'} . \quad . \quad . \quad . \quad . \quad . \quad 9.7546117$$
$$\overline{\phantom{\log \sin (\lambda - L) \quad . \quad . \quad . \quad} 9.7212536 n}$$
$$\log \sin (l - L) \quad . \quad . \quad . \quad 9.7212536 n$$

II. The sun, and the two points in the plane of the ecliptic which are the projections of the place of the heavenly body and the place of the earth form a plane triangle, the sides of which are $\varDelta'$, $R'$, $r'$, and the opposite angles, either $\lambda - L, l - \lambda, 180° - l + L,$ or $L - \lambda, \lambda - l,$ and $180° - L + l;$ from this the relations given in I. readily follow.

III. The sun, the true place of the heavenly body in space, and the true place of the earth will form another triangle, of which the sides will be $\varDelta, R, r:$ if, therefore, the angles opposite to them respectively be denoted by

$$S, T, 180° - S - T,$$

we shall have

$$\frac{\sin S}{\varDelta} = \frac{\sin T}{R} = \frac{\sin (S + T)}{r}.$$

The plane of this triangle will project a great circle on the celestial sphere, in which will be situated the heliocentric place of the earth, the heliocentric place of the heavenly body, and its geocentric place, and in such a manner that the distance of the second from the first, of the third from the second, of the third from the first, counted in the same direction, will be respectively, $S, T, S + T$.

IV. The following differential equations are derived from known differential variations of the parts of a plane triangle, or with equal facility from the formulas of article 62: —

$$d\,l = \frac{r' \cos(\lambda - l)}{\varDelta'}\, d\,\lambda + \frac{\sin(\lambda - l)}{\varDelta'}\, d\,r'$$

$$d\,\varDelta' = -r' \sin(\lambda - l)\, d\,\lambda + \cos(\lambda - l)\, d\,r'$$

$$d\,b = \frac{r' \cos b \sin b \sin(\lambda - l)}{\varDelta'}\, d\,\lambda + \frac{r' \cos^2 b}{\varDelta' \cos^2 \beta}\, d\,\beta + \frac{\cos^2 b}{\varDelta'} (\tan\beta - \cos(\lambda - l) \tan b)\, d\,r',$$

in which the terms which contain $d\,r'\ d\,\varDelta'$ are to be multiplied by 206265, or the rest are to be divided by 206265, if the variations of the angles are expressed in seconds.

V. The inverse problem, that is, the determination of the heliocentric from the geocentric place, is entirely analogous to the problem solved above, on which account it would be superfluous to pursue it further. For all the formulas of article 62 answer also for that problem, if, only, all the quantities which relate to the heliocentric place of the body being changed for analogous ones referring to the geocentric place, $L + 180°$ and $-B$ are substituted respectively for $L$ and $B$, or, which is the same thing, if the geocentric place of the sun is taken instead of the heliocentric place of the earth.

## 65.

Although in that case where only a very few geocentric places are to be determined from given elements, it is hardly worth while to employ all the devices above given, by means of which we can pass directly from the eccentric anomaly to the geocentric longitude and latitude, and so also to the right ascension and declination, because the saving of labor therefrom would be lost in the preliminary computation of the multitude of auxiliary quantities; still, the combination of the reduction to the ecliptic with the computation of the geocentric longitude and latitude will afford an advantage not to be despised. For if the ecliptic itself is assumed for the plane of the coördinates $z$, and the poles of the planes of the coördinates $x, y$, are placed in $\Omega$, $90° + \Omega$, the coördinates are very easily determined without any necessity for auxiliary quantities. We have,

| | | |
|---|---|---|
| $x = r \cos u$ | $X = R' \cos(L - \Omega)$ | $x - X = \varDelta' \cos(l - \Omega)$ |
| $y = r \cos i \sin u$ | $Y = R' \sin(L - \Omega)$ | $y - Y = \varDelta' \sin(l - \Omega)$ |
| $z = r \sin i \sin u$ | $Z = R' \tan B$ | $z - Z = \varDelta' \tan b.$ |

When $B = 0$, then $R' = R$, $Z = 0$. According to these formulas our example is solved as follows: —

$$L - \Omega = 213° 12' 0''.32.$$

| | | | |
|---|---|---|---|
| $\log r$ . . . . . . | 0.3259877 | $\log R'$ . . . . . | 9.9980979 |
| $\log \cos u$ . . . . . | 9.9824141$n$ | $\log \cos (L - \Omega)$ . . | 9.9226027$n$ |
| $\log \sin u$ . . . . . | 9.4454714$n$ | $\log \sin (L - \Omega)$ . . | 9.7384353$n$ |
| $\log x$ . . . . . . | 0.3084018$n$ | $\log X$ . . . . . | 9.9207006$n$ |
| $\log r \sin u$ . . . . | 9.7714591$n$ | | |
| $\log \cos i$ . . . . . | 9.9885266 | | |
| $\log \sin i$ . . . . . | 9.3557570 | | |
| $\log y$ . . . . . . | 9.7599857$n$ | $\log Y$ . . . . . . | 9.7365332$n$ |
| $\log z$ . . . . . . | 9.1272161$n$ | $Z =$ | 0 |

Hence follows

$\log (x - X)$ . . . 0.0795906$n$

$\log (y - Y)$ . . . 8.4807165$n$

whence $(l - \Omega) =$ 181° 26' 33''.49     $l =$     352° 34' 22''.22

$\log \varDelta'$ . . . . . . 0.0797283

$\log \tan b$ . . . . . 9.0474878$n$     $b =$     — 6 21 55 .06

## 66.

The right ascension and declination of any point whatever in the celestial sphere are derived from its longitude and latitude by the solution of the spherical triangle which is formed by that point and by the north poles of the ecliptic and equator. Let $\varepsilon$ be the obliquity of the ecliptic, $l$ the longitude, $b$ the latitude, $\alpha$ the right ascension, $\delta$ the declination, and the sides of the triangle will be $\varepsilon$, $90° - b$, $90° - \delta$; it will be proper to take for the angles opposite the second and third sides, $90° + \alpha$, $90° - l$, (if we conceive the idea of the spherical triangle in its utmost generality); the third angle, opposite $\varepsilon$, we will put $= 90° - E$. We shall have, therefore, by the formulas, article 54,

$$\sin (45° - \tfrac{1}{2} \delta) \sin \tfrac{1}{2} (E + \alpha) = \sin (45° + \tfrac{1}{2} l) \sin \left(45° - \tfrac{1}{2} (\varepsilon + b)\right)$$
$$\sin (45° - \tfrac{1}{2} \delta) \cos \tfrac{1}{2} (E + \alpha) = \cos (45° + \tfrac{1}{2} l) \cos \left(45° - \tfrac{1}{2} (\varepsilon - b)\right)$$
$$\cos (45° - \tfrac{1}{2} \delta) \sin \tfrac{1}{2} (E - \alpha) = \cos (45° + \tfrac{1}{2} l) \sin \left(45° - \tfrac{1}{2} (\varepsilon - b)\right)$$
$$\cos (45° - \tfrac{1}{2} \delta) \cos \tfrac{1}{2} (E - \alpha) = \sin (45° + \tfrac{1}{2} l) \cos \left(45° - \tfrac{1}{2} (\varepsilon + b)\right)$$

The first two equations will give $\tfrac{1}{2} (E + \alpha)$ and $\sin (45° - \tfrac{1}{2} \delta)$; the last two, $\tfrac{1}{2} (E - \alpha)$ and $\cos (45° - \tfrac{1}{2} \delta)$; from $\tfrac{1}{2} (E + \alpha)$ and $\tfrac{1}{2} (E - \alpha)$ will be had $\alpha$, and, at the same time, $E$; from $\sin (45° - \tfrac{1}{2} \delta)$ or $\cos (45° - \tfrac{1}{2} \delta)$, the agreement of which will serve for proving the calculation, will be determined $45° - \tfrac{1}{2} \delta$, and hence $\delta$. The determination of the angles $\tfrac{1}{2} (E + \alpha)$, $\tfrac{1}{2} (E - \alpha)$ by means of their tangents is not subject to ambiguity, because both the sine and cosine of the angle $45° - \tfrac{1}{2} \delta$ must be positive.

The differentials of the quantities $\alpha$, $\delta$, from the changes of $l$, $b$, are found according to known principles to be,

$$d\alpha = \frac{\sin E \cos b}{\cos \delta} \, dl - \frac{\cos E}{\cos \delta} \, db$$
$$d\delta = \cos E \cos b \, dl + \sin E \, db.$$

## 67.

Another method is required of solving the problem of the preceding article from the equations

$$\cos \varepsilon \sin l = \sin \varepsilon \tan b + \cos l \tan \alpha$$
$$\sin \delta = \cos \varepsilon \sin b + \sin \varepsilon \cos b \sin l$$
$$\cos b \cos l = \cos \alpha \cos \delta.$$

The auxiliary angle $\theta$ is determined by the equation

$$\tan \theta = \frac{\tan b}{\sin l},$$

and we shall have

$$\tan \alpha = \frac{\cos (\varepsilon + \theta) \tan l}{\cos \theta}$$
$$\tan \delta = \sin \alpha \tan (\varepsilon + \theta),$$

to which equations may be added, to test the calculation,

$$\cos \delta = \frac{\cos b \cos l}{\cos \alpha}, \text{ or } \cos \delta = \frac{\cos (\varepsilon + \theta) \cos b \sin l}{\cos \theta \sin \alpha}.$$

This ambiguity in the determination of $\alpha$ by the second equation is removed by this consideration, that $\cos \alpha$ and $\cos l$ must have the same sign.

This method is less expeditious, if, besides $\alpha$ and $\delta$, $E$ also is required: the most convenient formula for determining this angle will then be

$$\cos E = \frac{\sin \varepsilon \cos \alpha}{\cos b} = \frac{\sin \varepsilon \cos l}{\cos \delta}.$$

But $E$ cannot be correctly computed by this formula when $\pm \cos E$ differs but little from unity; moreover, the ambiguity remains whether $E$ should be taken between 0 and 180°, or between 180° and 360°. The inconvenience is rarely of any importance, particularly, since extreme precision in the value of $E$ is not required for computing differential ratios; but the ambiguity is easily removed by the help of the equation

$$\cos b \cos \delta \sin E = \cos \varepsilon - \sin b \sin \delta,$$

which shows that $E$ must be taken between 0 and 180°, or between 180° and 360°, according as $\cos \varepsilon$ is greater or less than $\sin b \sin \delta$: this test is evidently not necessary when either one of the angles $b$, $\delta$, does not exceed the limit 66° 32'; for in that case $\sin E$ is always positive. Finally, the same equation, in the case above pointed out, can be applied to the more exact determination of $E$, if it appears worth while.

## 68.

The solution of the inverse problem, that is, the determination of the longitude and latitude from the right ascension and declination, is based upon the same spherical triangle; the formulas, therefore, above given, will be adapted to this purpose by the mere interchange of $b$ with $\delta$, and of $l$ with $-\alpha$. It will not be unacceptable to add these formulas also, on account of their frequent use:

According to the method of article 66, we have,

$$\sin (45° - \tfrac{1}{2} b) \sin \tfrac{1}{2} (E - l) = \cos (45° + \tfrac{1}{2} \alpha) \sin (45° - \tfrac{1}{2} (\varepsilon + \delta))$$
$$\sin (45° - \tfrac{1}{2} b) \cos \tfrac{1}{2} (E - l) = \sin (45° + \tfrac{1}{2} \alpha) \cos (45° - \tfrac{1}{2} (\varepsilon - \delta))$$
$$\cos (45° - \tfrac{1}{2} b) \sin \tfrac{1}{2} (E + l) = \sin (45° + \tfrac{1}{2} \alpha) \sin (45° - \tfrac{1}{2} (\varepsilon - \delta))$$
$$\cos (45° - \tfrac{1}{2} b) \cos \tfrac{1}{2} (E + l) = \cos (45° + \tfrac{1}{2} \alpha) \cos (45° - \tfrac{1}{2} (\varepsilon + \delta)).$$

As in the other method of article 67, we will determine the auxiliary angle $\zeta$ by the equation

$$\tan \zeta = \frac{\tan \delta}{\sin \alpha},$$

and we shall have

$$\tan l = \frac{\cos (\zeta - \varepsilon) \tan \alpha}{\cos \zeta}$$

$$\tan b = \sin l \tan (\zeta - \varepsilon).$$

For proving the calculation, may be added,

$$\cos b = \frac{\cos \delta \cos \alpha}{\cos l} = \frac{\cos (\zeta - \varepsilon) \cos \delta \sin \alpha}{\cos \zeta \sin l}.$$

For the determination of $E$, in the same way as in the preceding article, the following equations will answer: —

$$\cos E = \frac{\sin \varepsilon \cos \alpha}{\cos b} = \frac{\sin \varepsilon \cos l}{\cos \delta}$$

$$\cos b \cos \delta \sin E = \cos \varepsilon - \sin b \sin \delta.$$

The differentials of $l$, $b$, will be given by the formulas

$$d\, l = \frac{\sin E \cos \delta}{\cos b} d\, \alpha + \frac{\cos E}{\cos b} d\, \delta$$

$$d\, b = - \cos E \cos \delta\, d\, \alpha + \sin E\, d\, \delta.$$

## 69.

We will compute, for an example, the longitude and latitude from the right ascension $355° 43' 45''.30 = \alpha$, the declination $- 8° 47' 25'' = \delta$, and the obliquity of the ecliptic $23° 27' 59''.26 = \varepsilon$. We have, therefore, $45° + \frac{1}{2} \alpha = 222° 51' 52''.65$, $45° - \frac{1}{2} (\varepsilon + \delta) = 37° 39' 42''.87$, $45° - \frac{1}{2} (\varepsilon - \delta) = 28° 52' 17''.87$; hence also,

| | | | |
|---|---|---|---|
| $\log \cos (45° + \frac{1}{2} \alpha)$ . . | $9.8650820n$ | $\log \sin (45° + \frac{1}{2} \alpha)$ . . | $9.8326803n$ |
| $\log \sin (45° - \frac{1}{2} (\varepsilon + \delta))$ | $9.7860418$ | $\log \sin (45° - \frac{1}{2} (\varepsilon - \delta))$ | $9.6838112$ |
| $\log \cos (45° - \frac{1}{2} (e + \delta))$ | $9.8985222$ | $\log \cos (45° - \frac{1}{2} (\varepsilon - \delta))$ | $9.9423572$ |

$\log \sin (45° - \frac{1}{2} b) \sin \frac{1}{2} (E - l)$ . . $9.6511238n$

$\log \sin (45° - \frac{1}{2} b) \cos \frac{1}{2} (E - l)$ . . $9.7750375n$

whence $\frac{1}{2} (E - l) = 216° 56' 5''.39$; $\log \sin (45° - \frac{1}{2} b) = 9.8723171$

$\log \cos (45° — \tfrac{1}{2} b) \sin \tfrac{1}{2} (E + l)$ . . $9.5164915n$
$\log \cos (45° — \tfrac{1}{2} b) \cos \tfrac{1}{2} (E + l)$ . . $9.7636042n$

whence $\tfrac{1}{2} (E + l) = 209° 30' 49''.94$ : $\log \cos (45° — \tfrac{1}{2} b) = 9.8239669.$

Therefore, we have $E = 426° 26' 55''.33$, $l = — 7° 25' 15''.45$, or, what amounts to the same thing, $E = 66° 26' 55''.33$, $l = 352° 34' 44''.55$; the angle $45° — \tfrac{1}{2} b$, obtained from the logarithm of the sine, is $48° 10' 58''.12$, from the logarithm of the cosine, $48° 10' 58''.17$, from the tangent, the logarithm of which is their difference, $48° 10' 58''.14$; hence $b = — 6° 21' 56''.28.$

According to the other method, the calculation is as follows:—

| | | | |
|---|---|---|---|
| $\log \tan \delta$ . . . . | $9.1893062n$ | C. $\log \cos \zeta$ . . . . | $0.3626190$ |
| $\log \sin \alpha$ . . . . | $8.8719792n$ | $\log \cos (\zeta — \varepsilon)$ . . | $9.8789703$ |
| $\log \tan \zeta$ . . . . | $0.3173270$ | $\log \tan \alpha$ . . . . | $8.8731869n$ |
| $\zeta =$ | $64° 17' 6''.83$ | $\log \tan l$ . . . . . | $9.1147762n$ |
| $\zeta — \varepsilon =$ | $40\ 49\ 7\ .57$ | $l =$ | $352° 34' 44''.50$ |
| | | $\log \sin l$ . . . . . | $9.1111232n$ |
| | | $\log \tan (\zeta — \varepsilon)$ . . | $9.9363874$ |
| | | $\log \tan b$ . . . . . | $9.0475106n$ |
| | | $b =$ | $— 6° 21' 56''.26.$ |

For determining the angle $E$ we have the double calculation

| | | | |
|---|---|---|---|
| $\log \sin \varepsilon$ . . . . | $9.6001144$ | $\log \sin \varepsilon$ . . . . . | $6.6001144$ |
| $\log \cos \alpha$ . . . . | $9.9987924$ | $\log \cos l$ . . . . . | $9.9963470$ |
| C. $\log \cos b$ . . . | $0.0026859$ | C. $\log \cos \delta$ . . . . | $0.0051313$ |
| $\log \cos E$ . . . | $9.6015927$ | $\log \cos E$ . . . . . | $9.6015927$ |
| whence $E =$ | $66° 26' 55''.35.$ | | |

## 70.

Something is still to be added concerning the *parallax* and *aberration*, that nothing requisite for the computation of geocentric places may be wanting. We have already described, above, a method, according to which, the place affected by parallax, that is, corresponding to any point on the surface of the earth, can be determined directly with the greatest facility; but as in the common method, given in article 62 and the following articles, the geocentric place is commonly referred to the centre of the earth, in which case it is said to be free from parallax, it will be necessary to add a particular method for determining the parallax, which is the difference between the two places.

Let the geocentric longitude and latitude of the heavenly body with reference to the centre of the earth be $\lambda, \beta$; the same with respect to any point whatever on the surface of the earth be $l, b$; the distance of the body from the centre of the earth, $r$; from the point on the surface, $\Delta$; lastly, let the longitude $L$, and the latitude $B$, correspond to the zenith of this point in the celestial sphere, and let the radius of the earth be denoted by $R$. Now it is evident that all the equations of article 62 will be applicable to this place also, but they can be materially abridged, since in this place $R$ expresses a quantity which nearly vanishes in comparison with $r$ and $\Delta$. The same equations evidently will hold good if $\lambda, l, L$ denote right ascensions instead of longitudes, and $\beta, b, B,$ declinations instead of latitudes. In this case $l - \lambda, b - \beta$, will be the parallaxes in right ascension and declination, but in the other, parallaxes in longitude and latitude. If, accordingly, $R$ is regarded as a quantity of the first order, $l - \lambda, b - \beta, \Delta - r$, will be quantities of the same order; and the higher orders being neglected, from the formulas of article 62 will be readily derived:—

I.  $\quad l - \lambda = \dfrac{R \cos B \sin (\lambda - L)}{r \cos \beta}$

II. $\quad b - \beta = \dfrac{R \cos B \cos \beta}{r} \left( \tan \beta \cos (\lambda - L) - \tan B \right)$

III. $\quad \Delta - r = - R \cos B \sin \beta \left( \cotan \beta \cos (\lambda - L) + \tan B \right).$

The auxiliary angle $\theta$ being so taken that

$$\tan \theta = \frac{\tan B}{\cos (\lambda - L)},$$

the equations II. and III. assume the following form:—

II. $\quad b - \beta = \dfrac{R \cos B \cos (\lambda - L) \sin (\beta - \theta)}{r \cos \theta} = \dfrac{R \sin B \sin (B - \theta)}{r \sin \theta}$

III. $\quad \Delta - r = - \dfrac{R \cos B \cos (\lambda - L) \cos (\beta - \theta)}{\cos \theta} = - \dfrac{R \sin B \cos (\beta - \theta)}{\sin \theta}.$

Further, it is evident, that in I. and II., in order that $l - \lambda$ and $b - \beta$ may be had in seconds, for $R$, must be taken the mean parallax of the sun in seconds; but in III., for $R$, must be taken the same parallax divided by $206265''$. Finally, when it is required to determine in the inverse problem, the place free from parallax from the place affected by it, it will be admissible to use $\varDelta, l, b$, instead of $r, \lambda, \beta$, in the values of the parallaxes, without loss of precision.

*Example.* — Let the right ascension of the sun for the centre of the earth be $220°\,46'\,44''.65 = \lambda$, the declination, $-15°\,49'\,43''.94 = \beta$, the distance, $0.9904311 = r$: and the sidereal time at any point on the surface of the earth expressed in degrees, $78°\,20'\,38'' = L$, the elevation of the pole of the point, $45°\,27'57'' = B$, the mean solar parallax, $8''.6 = R$. The place of the sun as seen from this point, and its distance from the same, are required.

| | | | | |
|---|---|---|---|---|
| $\log R$ . . . . . . | $0.93450$ | $\log R$ . . . . . . | $0.93450$ |
| $\log \cos B$ . . . . . | $9.84593$ | $\log \sin B$ . . . . . | $9.85299$ |
| $C. \log r$ . . . . . . | $0.00418$ | $C. \log r$ . . . . . . | $0.00418$ |
| $C. \log \cos \beta$ . . . . | $0.01679$ | $C. \log \sin \theta$ . . . . . | $0.10317$ |
| $\log \sin (\lambda - L)$ . . . | $9.78508$ | $\log \sin (\beta - \theta)$ . . . | $9.77152n$ |
| $\log (l - \lambda)$ . . . . | $0.58648$ | $\log (b - \beta)$ . . . . | $0.66636n$ |
| $l - \lambda =$ | $+ 3''.86$ | $b - \beta =$ | $- 4''.64$ |
| $l =$ | $220°\,46'\,48''.51$ | $b =$ | $-15°\,49'\,48''.58$ |
| $\log \tan B$ . . . . . | $0.00706$ | $\log (b - \beta)$ . . . . | $0.66636n$ |
| $\log \cos (\lambda - L)$ . . . | $9.89909n$ | $\log \cot (\beta - \theta)$ . . . | $0.13522$ |
| $\log \tan \theta$ . . . . . . | $0.10797n$ | $\log r$ . . . . . . . | $9.99582$ |
| $\theta =$ | $127°\,57'\ \ 0''$ | $\log 1''$ . . . . . . | $4.68557$ |
| $\beta - \theta =$ | $-143\ 46\ 44$ | $\log (r - \varDelta)$ . . . . | $5.48297n$ |
| | | $r - \varDelta =$ | $-0.0000304$ |
| | | $\varDelta =$ | $0.9904615$ |

## 71.

The aberration of the fixed stars, and also that part of the aberration of comets and planets due to the motion of the earth alone, arises from the fact, that the telescope is carried along with the earth, while the ray of light is passing along its optical axis. The observed place of a heavenly body (which is called the apparent, or affected by aberration), is determined by the direction of the optical axis of the telescope set in such a way, that a ray of light proceeding from the body on its path may impinge upon both extremities of its axis: but this direction differs from the true direction of the ray of light in space. Let us consider two moments of time $t$, $t'$, when the ray of light touches the anterior extremity (the centre of the object-glass), and the posterior (the focus of the object-glass); let the position of these extremities in space be for the first moment $a$, $b$; for the last moment $a'$, $b'$. Then it is evident that the straight line $ab'$ is the true direction of the ray in space, but that the straight line $ab$ or $a'b'$ (which may be regarded as parallel) corresponds to the apparent place: it is perceived without difficulty that the apparent place does not depend upon the length of the tube. The difference in direction of the right lines $b'a$, $ba$, is the aberration such as exists for the fixed stars: we shall pass over the mode of calculating it, as well known. This difference is still not the entire aberration for the wandering stars: the planet, for example, whilst the ray which left it is reaching the earth, itself changes its place, on which account, the direction of this ray does not correspond to the true geocentric place at the time of observation. Let us suppose the ray of light which impinges upon the tube at the time $t$ to have left the planet at the time $T$; and let the position of the planet in space at the time $T$ be denoted by $P$, and at the time $t$ by $p$; lastly, let $A$ be the place of the anterior extremity of the axis of the tube at the time $T$. Then it is evident that,—

1st. The right line $AP$ shows the true place of the planet at the time $T$;

2d. The right line $ap$ the true place at the time $t$;

3d. The right line $ba$ or $b'a'$ the apparent place at the time $t$ or $t'$ (the difference of which may be regarded as an infinitely small quantity);

4th. The right line $b'a$ the same apparent place freed from the aberration of the fixed stars.

Now the points $P$, $a$, $b'$, lie in a straight line, and the parts $Pa$, $ab'$, will be proportional to the intervals of time $t — T$, $t' — t$, if light moves with an uniform velocity. The interval of time $t' — T$ is always very small on account of the immense velocity of light; within it, it is allowable to consider the motion of the earth as rectilinear and its velocity as uniform: so also $A$, $a$, $a'$ will lie in a straight line, and the parts $Aa$, $aa'$ will likewise be proportional to the intervals $t - T$, $t' - t$. Hence it is readily inferred, that the right lines $AP$, $b'a'$ are parallel, and therefore that the first and third places are identical.

The time $t - T$, within which the light traverses the mean distance of the earth from the sun which we take for unity, will be the product of the distance $Pa$ into 493$^s$. In this calculation it will be proper to take, instead of the distance $Pa$, either $PA$ or $pa$, since the difference can be of no importance.

From these principles follow three methods of determining the apparent place of a planet or comet for any time $t$, of which sometimes one and sometimes another may be preferred.

I. The time in which the light is passing from the planet to the earth may be subtracted from the given time; thus we shall have the reduced time $T$, for which the true place, computed in the usual way, will be identical with the apparent place for $t$. For computing the reduction of the time $t - T$, it is requisite to know the distance from the earth; generally, convenient helps will not be wanting for this purpose, as, for example, an ephemeris hastily calculated, otherwise it will be sufficient to determine, by a preliminary calculation, the true distance for the time $t$ in the usual manner, avoiding an unnecessary degree of precision.

II. The true place and distance may be computed for the instant $t$, and, from this, the reduction of the time $t - T$, and hence, with the help of the daily motion (in longitude and latitude, or in right ascension and declination), the reduction of the true place to the time $T$.

III. The heliocentric place of the earth may be computed for the time $t$; and the heliocentric place of the planet for the time $T$: then, from the combination of these in the usual way, the geocentric place of the planet, which, increased by the aberration of the fixed stars (to be obtained by a well-known method, or to be taken from the tables), will furnish the apparent place sought.

The second method, which is commonly used, is preferable to the others, because there is no need of a double calculation for determining the distance, but it labors under this inconvenience, that it cannot be used except several places near each other are calculated, or are known from observation; otherwise it would not be admissible to consider the diurnal motion as given.

The disadvantage with which the first and third methods are incumbered, is evidently removed when several places near each other are to be computed. For, as soon as the distances are known for some, the distances next following may be deduced very conveniently and with sufficient accuracy by means of familiar methods. If the distance is known, the first method will be generally preferable to the third, because it does not require the aberration of the fixed stars; but if the double calculation is to be resorted to, the third is recommended by this, that the place of the earth, at least, is retained in the second calculation.

What is wanted for the inverse problem, that is, when the true is to be derived from the apparent place, readily suggests itself. According to method I., you will retain the place itself unchanged, but will convert the time $t$, to which the given place corresponds as the apparent place, into the reduced time $T$, to which the same will correspond as the true place. According to method II., you will retain the time $t$, but you will add to the given place the motion in the time $t - T$, as you would wish to reduce it to the time $t + (t - T)$. According to the method III., you will regard the given place, free from the aberration of the fixed stars, as the true place for the time $T$, but the true place of the earth, answering to the time $t$, is to be retained as if it also belonged to $T$. The utility of the third method will more clearly appear in the second book.

Finally, that nothing may be wanting, we observe that the place of the sun is affected in the same manner by aberration, as the place of a planet: but since both the distance from the earth and the diurnal motion are nearly constant, the aberration itself has an almost constant value equal to the mean motion of the sun in $493^{s}$, and so $= 20''.25$; which quantity is to be subtracted from the true to obtain the mean longitude. The exact value of the aberration is in the compound ratio of the distance and the diurnal motion, or what amounts to the same thing, in the inverse ratio of the distance; whence, the mean value must be diminished in apogee by $0''.34$, and increased by the same amount in perigee. Our solar tables already include the constant aberration $- 20''.25$; on which account, it will be necessary to add $20''.25$ to the tabular longitude to obtain the true.

## 72.

Certain problems, which are in frequent use in the determination of the orbits of planets and comets, will bring this section to a close. And first, we will revert to the parallax, from which, in article 70, we showed how to free the observed place. Such a reduction to the centre of the earth, since it supposes the distance of the planet from the earth to be at least approximately known, cannot be made when the orbit of the planet is wholly unknown. But, even in this case, it is possible to reach the object on account of which the reduction to the centre of the earth is made, since several formulas acquire greater simplicity and neatness from this centre lying, or being supposed to lie, in the plane of the ecliptic, than they would have if the observation should be referred to a point out of the plane of the ecliptic. In this regard, it is of no importance whether the observation be reduced to the centre of the earth, or to any other point in the plane of the ecliptic. Now it is apparent, that if the point of intersection of the plane of the ecliptic with a straight line drawn from the planet through the true place of observation be chosen, the observation requires no reduction whatever, since the planet may be seen in the same way from all points of this line:* wherefore, it will be admissible to substitute this point as a fictitious place of observation instead of the true place. We determine the situation of this point in the following manner:—

Let $\lambda$ be the longitude of the heavenly body, $\beta$ the latitude, $\varDelta$ the distance, all referred to the true place of observation on the surface of the earth, to the zenith of which corresponds the longitude $l$, and the latitude $b$; let, moreover, $\pi$ be the semidiameter of the earth, $L$ the heliocentric longitude of the centre of the earth, $B$ its latitude, $R$ its distance from the sun; lastly, let $L'$ be the heliocentric longitude of the fictitious place, $R'$ its distance from the sun, $\varDelta + \delta$.

---

* If the nicest accuracy should be wanted, it would be necessary to add to or subtract from the given time, the interval of time in which light passes from the true place of observation to the fictitious, or from the latter to the former, if we are treating of places affected by aberration: but this difference can scarcely be of any importance unless the latitude should be very small.

its distance from the heavenly body. Then, $N$ denoting an arbitrary angle, the following equations are obtained without any difficulty : —

$$R' \cos (L' - N) + \delta \cos \beta \cos (\lambda - N) = R \cos B \cos (L - N) + \pi \cos b \cos (l - N)$$
$$R' \sin (L' - N) + \delta \cos \beta \sin (\lambda - N) = R \cos B \sin (L - N) + \pi \cos b \sin (l - N)$$
$$\delta \sin \beta = R \sin B + \pi \sin b.$$

Putting, therefore,

I.  $(R \sin B + \pi \sin b) \cotan \beta = \mu,$

we shall have

II.  $R' \cos (L' - N) = R \cos B \cos (L - N) + \pi \cos b \cos (l - N) - \mu \cos (\lambda - N)$

III.  $R' \sin (L' - N) = R \cos B \sin (L - N) + \pi \cos b \sin (l - N) - \mu \sin (\lambda - N)$

IV.  $\delta = \dfrac{\mu}{\cos \beta}.$

From equations II. and III., can be determined $R'$ and $L'$, from IV., the interval of time to be added to the time of observation, which in seconds will be $= 493 \, \delta.$

These equations are exact and general, and will be applicable therefore when, the plane of the equator being substituted for the plane of the ecliptic, $L$, $L'$, $l$, $\lambda$, denote right ascensions, and $B$, $b$, $\beta$ declinations. But in the case which we are specially treating, that is, when the fictitious place must be situated in the ecliptic, the smallness of the quantities $B$, $\pi$, $L' - L$, still allows some abbreviation of the preceding formulas. The mean solar parallax may be taken for $\pi$; $B$, for $\sin B$; 1, for $\cos B$, and also for $\cos (L' - L)$; $L' - L$, for $\sin (L' - L)$. In this way, making $N = L$, the preceding formulas assume the following form : —

I.  $\mu = (RB + \pi \sin b) \cotan \beta$

II.  $R' = R + \pi \cos b \cos (l - L) - \mu \cos (\lambda - L)$

III.  $L' - L = \dfrac{\pi \cos b \sin (l - L) - \mu \sin (\lambda - L)}{R'}.$

Here $B$, $\pi$, $L' - L$ are, properly, to be expressed in parts of the radius; but it is evident, that if those angles are expressed in seconds, the equations I., III. can be retained without alteration, but for II. must be substituted

$$R' = R + \frac{\pi \cos b \cos (l - L) - \mu \cos (\lambda - L)}{206265''}.$$

Lastly, in the formula III., $R$ may always be used in place of the denominator $R'$ without sensible error. The reduction of the time, the angles being expressed in seconds, becomes

$$\frac{493^s.\,\mu}{206265''.\,\cos\beta}.$$

## 73.

*Example.* — Let $\lambda = 354° 44' 54''$, $\beta = -4° 59' 32''$, $l = 24° 29'$, $b = 46° 53'$, $L' = 12° 28' 54''$, $B = +0''.49$, $R = 0.9988839$, $\pi = 8''.60$. The calculation is as follows: —

| | | | |
|---|---|---|---|
| $\log R$ . . . . . . | 9.99951 | $\log \pi$ . . . . . . | 0.93450 |
| $\log B$ . . . . . . | 9.69020 | $\log \sin b$ . . . . . | 9.86330 |
| $\log BR$ . . . . . | 9.68971 | $\log \pi \sin b$ . . . . | 0.79780 |
| Hence $\log(BR + \pi \sin b)$ . | 0.83040 | | |
| $\log \cotan \beta$ . . . . | 1.05873n | | |
| $\log \mu$ . . . . . . | 1.88913n | | |
| $\log \pi$ . . . . . . | 0.93450 | $\log \mu$ . . . . . . | 1.88913n |
| $\log \cos b$ . . . . . | 9.83473 | $\log 1''$ . . . . . . | 4.68557 |
| $\log 1''$ . . . . . . | 4.68557 | $\log \cos(\lambda - L)$ . . . | 9.97886 |
| $\log \cos(l - L)$ . . . | 9.99040 | | 6.55356n |
| | 5.44520 | number — 0.0003577 | |
| number + 0.0000279 | | | |

Hence is obtained $R' = R + 0.0003856 = 0.9992695$. Moreover, we have

| | | | |
|---|---|---|---|
| $\log \pi \cos b$ . . . . . | 0.76923 | $\log \mu$ . . . . . . | 1.88913n |
| $\log \sin(l - L)$ . . . | 9.31794 | $\log \sin(\lambda - L)$ . . | 9.48371n |
| C. $\log R'$ . . . . . | 0.00032 | C. $\log R'$ . . . . . | 0.00032 |
| | 0.08749 | | 1.37316 |
| number + 1''.22 | | number + 23''.61 | |

Whence is obtained $L' = L - 22''.39$.   Finally we have

$\log \mu$ . . . . . . . .   1.88913$n$
C. $\log 206265$ . . . .   4.68557
$\log 493$ . . . . . . .   2.69285
C. $\log \cos \beta$ . . . . .   0.00165
_____
9.26920$n$,

whence the reduction of time $= - 0^s.186$, and thus is of no importance.

## 74.

The other problem, *to deduce the heliocentric place of a heavenly body in its orbit from the geocentric place and the situation of the plane of the orbit,* is thus far similar to the preceding, that it also depends upon the intersection of a right line drawn between the earth and the heavenly body with the plane given in position.   The solution is most conveniently obtained from the formulas of article 65, where the meaning of the symbols was as follows: —

$L$ the longitude of the earth, $R$ the distance from the sun, the latitude $B$ we put $= 0$, — since the case in which it is not $= 0$, can easily be reduced to this by article 72, — whence $R' = R$, $l$ the geocentric longitude of the heavenly body, $b$ the latitude, $\varDelta$ the distance from the earth, $r$ the distance from the sun, $u$ the argument of the latitude, $\Omega$ the longitude of the ascending node, $i$ the inclination of the orbit.   Thus we have the equations

I.   $r \cos u - R \cos (L - \Omega) = \varDelta \cos b \cos (l - \Omega)$

II.   $r \cos i \sin u - R \sin (L - \Omega) = \varDelta \cos b \sin (l - \Omega)$

III.   $r \sin i \sin u = \varDelta \sin b$.

Multiplying equation I. by $\sin (L - \Omega) \sin b$, II. by $- \cos (L - \Omega) \sin b$, III. by $- \sin (L - l) \cos b$, and adding together the products, we have

$\cos u \sin (L - \Omega) \sin b - \sin u \cos i \cos (L - \Omega) \sin b - \sin u \sin i \sin (L - l) \cos b = 0$,

whence

IV.   $\tan u = \dfrac{\sin (L - \Omega) \sin b}{\cos i \cos (L - \Omega) \sin b + \sin i \sin (L - l) \cos b}.$

Multiplying likewise I. by $\sin(l - \Omega)$, II. by $-\cos(l - \Omega)$, and adding together the products, we have

$$\text{V.} \quad r = \frac{R \sin(L - l)}{\sin u \cos i \cos(l - \Omega) - \cos u \sin(l - \Omega)}.$$

The ambiguity in the determination of $u$ by means of equation IV., is removed by equation III., which shows that $u$ is to be taken between 0 and 180°, or between 180° and 360° according as the latitude $b$ may be positive or negative; but if $b = 0$, equation V. teaches us that we must put $u = 180°$, or $u = 0$, according as $\sin(L - l)$ and $\sin(l - \Omega)$ have the same or different signs.

The numerical computation of the formulas IV. and V. may be abbreviated in various ways by the introduction of auxiliary angles. For example, putting

$$\frac{\tan b \cos(L - \Omega)}{\sin(L - l)} = \tan A,$$

we have

$$\tan u = \frac{\sin A \tan(L - \Omega)}{\sin(A + i)};$$

putting

$$\frac{\tan i \sin(L - l)}{\cos(L - \Omega)} = \tan B,$$

we have

$$\tan u = \frac{\cos B \sin b \tan(L - \Omega)}{\sin(B + b) \cos i}.$$

In the same manner the equation V. obtains a neater form by the introduction of the angle, the tangent of which is equal to

$$\cos i \tan u, \text{ or } \frac{\tan(l - \Omega)}{\cos i}.$$

Just as we have obtained formula V. by the combination of I., II., so by a combination of the equations II., III., we arrive at the following: —

$$r = \frac{R \sin(L - \Omega)}{\sin u (\cos i - \sin i \sin(l - \Omega) \cotan b)};$$

and in the same manner, by the combination of equations I., III., at this;

$$r = \frac{R \cos(L - \Omega)}{\cos u - \sin u \sin i \cos(l - \Omega) \cotan b};$$

both of which, in the same manner as V., may be rendered more simple by the introduction of auxiliary angles. The solutions resulting from the preceding equations are met with in VON ZACH *Monatliche Correspondenz*, Vol. V. p. 540, collected and illustrated by an example, wherefore we dispense with their further development in this place. If, besides $u$ and $r$, the distance $\varDelta$ is also wanted, it can be determined by means of equation III.

## 75.

Another solution of the preceding problem rests upon the truth asserted in article 64, III.,— that the heliocentric place of the earth, the geocentric place of the heavenly body and its heliocentric place are situated in one and the same great circle of the sphere. In fig. 3 let these places be respectively $T$, $G$, $H$; further, let $\Omega$ be the place of the ascending node; $\Omega T$, $\Omega H$, parts of the ecliptic and orbit; $GP$ the perpendicular let fall upon the ecliptic from $G$, which, therefore, will be $= b$. Hence, and from the arc $PT = L - l$ will be determined the angle $T$ and the arc $TG$. Then in the spherical triangle $\Omega HT$ are given the angle $\Omega = i$, the angle $T$, and the side $\Omega T = L - \Omega$, whence will be got the two remaining sides $\Omega H = u$ and $TH$. Finally we have $HG = TG - TH$, and

$$r = \frac{R \sin TG}{\sin HG}, \quad \varDelta = \frac{R \sin TH}{\sin HG}.$$

## 76.

In article 52 we have shown how to express the differentials of the heliocentric longitude and latitude, and of the curtate distance for changes in the argument of the latitude $u$, the inclination $i$, and the radius vector $r$, and subsequently (article 64, IV.) we have deduced from these the variations of the geocentric longitude and latitude, $l$ and $b$: therefore, by a combination of these formulas, $dl$ and $db$ will be had expressed by means of $du$, $di$, $d\Omega$, $dr$. But it will be worth while to show, how, in this calculation, the reduction of the heliocentric place to the ecliptic, may be omitted in the same way as in article 65 we have deduced the geocentric place immediately from the heliocentric place in orbit. That the formulas may become more simple, we will neglect the latitude of the earth, which of course can have no sensible effect in differential formulas. The following formulas accordingly are at hand, in which, for the sake of brevity, we write $\omega$ instead of $l - \Omega$, and also, as above, $\Delta'$ in the place of $\Delta \cos b$.

$$\Delta' \cos \omega = r \cos u - R \cos (L - \Omega) = \xi$$
$$\Delta' \sin \omega = r \cos i \sin u - R \sin (L - \Omega) = \eta$$
$$\Delta' \tan b = r \sin i \sin u = \zeta;$$

from the differentiation of which result

$$\cos \omega . d \Delta' - \Delta' \sin \omega . d \omega = d \xi$$
$$\sin \omega . d \Delta' + \Delta' \cos \omega . d \omega = d \eta$$
$$\tan b . d \Delta' + \frac{\Delta}{\cos b} d b = d \zeta.$$

Hence by elimination,

$$d \omega = \frac{- \sin \omega . d \xi + \cos \omega . d \eta}{\Delta'}$$
$$d b = \frac{- \cos \omega . \sin b . d \xi - \sin \omega \sin b . d \eta + \cos b . d \zeta}{\Delta}$$

If in these formulas, instead of $\xi$, $\eta$, $\zeta$, their values are substituted, $d \omega$ and $d b$ will appear represented by $dr$, $du$, $di$, $d \Omega$; after this, on account of $d l = d \omega + d \Omega$, the partial differentials of $l$ and $b$ will be as follows :—

I.   $\Delta' \left( \frac{d l}{d r} \right) = - \sin \omega \cos u + \cos \omega \sin u \cos i$

II.  $\frac{\Delta'}{r} \left( \frac{d l}{d u} \right) = \sin \omega \sin u + \cos \omega \cos u \cos i$

III. $\frac{\Delta'}{r} \left( \frac{d l}{d i} \right) = - \cos \omega \sin u \sin i$

IV.  $\left( \frac{d l}{d \Omega} \right) = 1 + \frac{R}{\Delta'} \cos (L - \Omega - \omega) = 1 + \frac{R}{\Delta'} \cos (L - l)$

V.   $\Delta \left( \frac{d b}{d r} \right) = - \cos \omega \cos u \sin b - \sin \omega \sin u \cos i \sin b + \sin u \sin i \cos b$

VI.  $\frac{\Delta}{r} \left( \frac{d b}{d u} \right) = \cos \omega \sin u \sin b - \sin \omega \cos u \cos i \sin b + \cos u \sin i \cos b$

VII. $\frac{\Delta}{r} \left( \frac{d b}{d i} \right) = \sin \omega \sin u \sin i \sin b + \sin u \cos i \cos b$

VIII. $\frac{\Delta}{R} \left( \frac{d b}{d \Omega} \right) = \sin b \sin (L - \Omega - \omega) = \sin b \sin (L - l).$

The formulas IV. and VIII. already appear in the most convenient form for calculation; but the formulas I., III., V., are reduced to a more elegant form by obvious substitutions, as

I.*  $\left(\dfrac{d\,l}{d\,r}\right) = \dfrac{R}{r\varDelta'}\sin{(L-l)}$

III.*  $\left(\dfrac{d\,l}{d\,i}\right) = -\cos\omega\tan b$

V.*  $\left(\dfrac{d\,b}{d\,r}\right) = -\dfrac{R}{r\varDelta}\cos{(L-l)}\sin b = -\dfrac{R}{r\varDelta'}\cos{(L-l)}\sin b\cos b.$

Finally, the remaining formulas II., VI., VII., are changed into a more simple form by the introduction of certain auxiliary angles: which may be most conveniently done in the following manner. The auxiliary angles $M$, $N$, may be determined by means of the formulas

$$\tan M = \frac{\tan\omega}{\cos i}, \ \ \tan N = \sin\omega\tan i = \tan M\cos\omega\sin i.$$

Then at the same time we have

$$\frac{\cos^2 M}{\cos^2 N} = \frac{1+\tan^2 N}{1+\tan^2 M} = \frac{\cos^2 i + \sin^2\omega\sin^2 i}{\cos^2 i + \tan^2\omega} = \cos^2\omega :$$

now, since the doubt remaining in the determination of $M$, $N$, by their tangents, may be settled at pleasure, it is evident that this can be done so that we may have

$$\frac{\cos M}{\cos N} = +\cos\omega,$$

and thence

$$\frac{\sin N}{\sin M} = +\sin i.$$

These steps being taken, the formulas II., VI., VII., are transformed into the following:—

II.*  $\left(\dfrac{d\,l}{d\,u}\right) = \dfrac{r\sin\omega\cos{(M-u)}}{\varDelta'\sin M}$

VI.*  $\left(\dfrac{d\,b}{d\,u}\right) = \dfrac{r}{\varDelta}\left(\cos\omega\sin i\cos{(M-u)}\cos{(N-b)}+\sin{(M-u)}\sin{(N-b)}\right)$

VII.*  $\left(\dfrac{d\,b}{d\,i}\right) = \dfrac{r\sin u\cos i\cos{(N-b)}}{\varDelta\cos N}.$

These transformations, so far as the formulas II. and VII. are concerned, will detain no one, but in respect to formula VI., some explanation will not be superfluous. From the substitution, in the first place, of $M-(M-u)$ for $u$, in formula VI., there results

$$\frac{\mathit{\Delta}}{r}\left(\frac{d\,b}{d\,u}\right) = \cos\left(M-u\right)\left(\cos\omega\sin M\sin b - \sin\omega\cos i\cos M\sin b + \sin i\cos M\cos b\right)$$
$$- \sin\left(M-u\right)\left(\cos\omega\cos M\sin b + \sin\omega\cos i\sin M\sin b - \sin i\sin M\cos b\right).$$

Now we have

$$\cos\omega\sin M = \cos^2 i\cos\omega\sin M + \sin^2 i\cos\omega\sin M$$
$$= \sin\omega\cos i\cos M + \sin^2 i\cos\omega\sin M;$$

whence the former part of that expression is transformed into

$$\sin i\cos\left(M-u\right)\left(\sin i\cos\omega\sin M\sin b + \cos M\cos b\right)$$
$$= \sin i\cos\left(M-u\right)\left(\cos\omega\sin N\sin b + \cos\omega\cos N\cos b\right)$$
$$= \cos\omega\sin i\cos\left(M-u\right)\cos\left(N-b\right).$$

Likewise,

$$\cos N = \cos^2\omega\cos N + \sin^2\omega\cos N = \cos\omega\cos M + \sin\omega\cos i\sin M;$$

whence the latter part of the expression is transformed into

$$- \sin\left(M-u\right)\left(\cos N\sin b - \sin N\cos b\right) = \sin\left(M-u\right)\sin\left(N-b\right).$$

The expression VI.* follows directly from this.

The auxiliary angle $M$ can also be used in the transformation of formula I., which, by the introduction of $M$, assumes the form

$$\text{I.**}\quad \left(\frac{d\,l}{d\,r}\right) = -\frac{\sin\omega\sin\left(M-u\right)}{\mathit{\Delta}'\sin M}$$

from the comparison of which with formula I.* is derived

$$- R\sin\left(L-l\right)\sin M = r\sin\omega\sin\left(M-u\right);$$

hence also a somewhat more simple form may be given to formula II.*, that is,

$$\text{II.**}\quad \left(\frac{d\,l}{d\,u}\right) = -\frac{R}{\mathit{\Delta}'}\sin\left(L-l\right)\cotan\left(M-u\right).$$

That formula VI.* may be still further abridged, it is necessary to introduce a new auxiliary angle, which can be done in two ways, that is, either by putting

$$\tan P = \frac{\tan (M-u)}{\cos \omega \sin i}, \text{ or } \tan Q = \frac{\tan (N-b)}{\cos \omega \sin i};$$

from which results

$$\text{VI.**} \quad \left(\frac{db}{du}\right) = \frac{r \sin (M-u) \cos (N-b-P)}{\varDelta \sin P} = \frac{r \sin (N-b) \cos (M-u-Q)}{\varDelta \sin Q}.$$

The auxiliary angles $M, N, P, Q$, are, moreover, not merely fictitious, and it would be easy to designate what may correspond to each one of them in the celestial sphere; several of the preceding equations might even be exhibited in a more elegant form by means of arcs and angles on the sphere, on which we are less inclined to dwell in this place, because they are not sufficient to render superfluous, in numerical calculation, the formulas above given.

## 77.

What has been developed in the preceding article, together with what we have given in articles 15, 16, 20, 27, 28, for the several kinds of conic sections, will furnish all which is required for the computation of the differential variations in the geocentric place caused by variations in the individual elements. For the better illustration of these precepts, we will resume the example treated above in articles 13, 14, 51, 63, 65. And first we will express $dl$ and $db$ in terms of $dr, du, di, d\Omega$, according to the method of the preceding article; which calculation is as follows: —

| | | | | | |
|---|---|---|---|---|---|
| $\log \tan \omega$ | . | 8.40113 | $\log \sin \omega$ . | 8.40099$n$ | $\log \tan (M-u)$    9.41932$n$ |
| $\log \cos i$ | | 9.98853 | $\log \tan i$ . | 9.36723 | $\log \cos \omega \sin i$  .   9.35562$n$ |
| $\log \tan M$ | . | 8.41260 | $\log \tan N$ . | 7.76822$n$ | $\log \tan P$   .   .   0.06370 |
| $M$ | = | 1° 28′ 52″ | $N = 179° 39′ 50″$ | | $P = $   49° 11′ 13″ |
| $M-u =$ | | 165 17 8 | $N-b = 186$   1 45 | | $N-b-P = $   136 50 32 |

### I.*

| | | |
|---|---|---|
| $\log \sin(L-l)$ | | 9.72125 |
| $\log R$ | . . | 9.99810 |
| C. $\log \varDelta'$ | . | 9.92027 |
| (*) | . . . | 9.63962 |
| C. $\log r$ | . | 9.67401 |
| $\log \left(\dfrac{\mathrm{d}\,l}{\mathrm{d}\,r}\right)$ | . | 9.31363 |

### II.**

| | | |
|---|---|---|
| (*) | . . . | 9.63962 |
| $\log \cot(M-u)$ | | 0.58068n |
| $\log \left(\dfrac{\mathrm{d}\,l}{\mathrm{d}\,u}\right)$ | . | 0.22030 |

### III.*

| | | |
|---|---|---|
| $\log \cos \omega$ | . . | 9.99986n |
| $\log \tan b$ | . . | 9.04749n |
| $\log \left(\dfrac{\mathrm{d}\,l}{\mathrm{d}\,i}\right)$ | . . | 9.04735n |

### IV.

| | | |
|---|---|---|
| $\log \dfrac{R}{\varDelta'}$ | . . | 9.91837 |
| $\log \cos(L-l)$ | | 9.92956 |
| (**) | . . | 9.84793 |
| $= \log \left(\dfrac{\mathrm{d}\,l}{\mathrm{d}\,\Omega} - 1\right)$ | | |

### V.*

| | | |
|---|---|---|
| (**) | . . . | 9.84793 |
| $\log \sin b \cos b$ | | 9.04212n |
| C. $\log r$ | . . | 9.67401 |
| $\log \left(\dfrac{\mathrm{d}\,b}{\mathrm{d}\,r}\right)$ | . . | 8.56406 |

### VI.**

| | | |
|---|---|---|
| $\log \dfrac{r}{\varDelta}$ | . . . | 0.24357 |
| $\log \sin(M-u)$ | | 9.40484 |
| $\log \cos(N-b-P)$ | | 9.86301n |
| C. $\log \sin P$ | . | 0.12099 |
| $\log \left(\dfrac{\mathrm{d}\,b}{\mathrm{d}\,u}\right)$ | . . | 9.63241n |

### VII.*

| | | |
|---|---|---|
| $\log r \sin u \cos i$ | | 9.75999n |
| $\log \cos(N-b)$ | | 9.99759n |
| C. $\log \varDelta$ | . . | 9.91759 |
| C. $\log \cos N$ | | 0.00001n |
| $\log \left(\dfrac{\mathrm{d}\,b}{\mathrm{d}\,i}\right)$ | . | 9.67518n |

### VIII.

| | | |
|---|---|---|
| (*) | . . . | 9.63962 |
| $\log \sin b \cos b$ | | 9.04212n |
| $\log \left(\dfrac{\mathrm{d}\,b}{\mathrm{d}\,\Omega}\right)$ | . | 8.68174n |

These values collected give

$$\mathrm{d}l = +\ 0.20589\ \mathrm{d}r + 1.66073\ \mathrm{d}u - 0.11152\ \mathrm{d}i + 1.70458\ \mathrm{d}\Omega$$
$$\mathrm{d}b = +\ 0.03665\ \mathrm{d}r - 0.42895\ \mathrm{d}u - 0.47335\ \mathrm{d}i - 0.04805\ \mathrm{d}\Omega.$$

It will hardly be necessary to repeat here what we have often observed, namely, that either the variations $\mathrm{d}l$, $\mathrm{d}b$, $\mathrm{d}u$, $\mathrm{d}i$, $\mathrm{d}\Omega$, are to be expressed in parts of the radius, or the coefficients of $\mathrm{d}r$ are to be multiplied by $206265''$, if the former are supposed to be expressed in seconds.

Denoting now the longitude of the perihelion (which in our example is

$52° 18' 9''.30$) by $\Pi$, and the true anomaly by $v$, the longitude in orbit will be $u + \Omega = v + \Pi$, and therefore $du = dv + d\Pi - d\Omega$, which value being substituted in the preceding formulas, $dl$ and $db$ will be expressed in terms of $dr$, $dv$, $d\Pi$, $d\Omega$, $di$. Nothing, therefore, now remains, except to express $dr$ and $dv$, according to the method of articles 15, 16, by means of the differential variations of the elliptic elements.*

We had in our example, article 14,

$$\log\frac{r}{a} = 9.90355 = \log\left(\frac{dr}{da}\right)$$

| | | | | | |
|---|---|---|---|---|---|
| $\log\frac{aa}{rr}$ . . . . . | 0.19290 | $\log a$ . . . . . | 0.42244 |
| $\log\cos\varphi$ . . . . | 9.98652 | $\log\tan\varphi$ . . . . | 9.40320 |
| | | $\log\sin v$ . . . . | $9.84931n$ |
| $\log\left(\frac{dv}{dM}\right)$ . . . . | 0.17942 | $\log\left(\frac{dr}{dM}\right)$ . . . . | $9.67495n$ |
| $2 - e\cos E =$ | 1.80085 | | |
| $ee =$ | 0.06018 | $\log a$ . . . . . | 0.42244 |
| | 1.74067 | $\log\cos\varphi$ . . . . | 9.98652 |
| $\log$ . . . . . . | 0.24072 | $\log\cos v$ . . . . | 9.84966 |
| $\log\frac{aa}{rr}$ . . . . . | 0.19290 | $\log\left(\frac{dr}{d\varphi}\right)$ . . . . | $0.25862n$ |
| $\log\sin E$ . . . . | $9.76634n$ | | |
| $\log\left(\frac{dv}{d\varphi}\right)$ . . . . | $0.19996n$ | | |

Hence is collected

$$dv = + 1.51154\, dM - 1.58475\, d\varphi$$
$$dr = - 0.47310\, dM - 1.81393\, d\varphi + 0.80085\, da;$$

which values being substituted in the preceding formulas, give

$$dl = + 2.41287\, dM - 3.00531\, d\varphi + 0.16488\, da + 1.66073\, d\Pi$$
$$- 0.11152\, di + 0.04385\, d\Omega$$
$$db = - 0.66572\, dM + 0.61331\, d\varphi + 0.02925\, da - 0.42895\, d\Pi$$
$$- 0.47335\, di + 0.38090\, d\Omega.$$

---

* It will be perceived, at once, that the symbol $M$, in the following calculation, no longer expresses our auxiliary angle, but (as in section 1) the mean anomaly.

If the time, to which the computed place corresponds, is supposed to be distant $n$ days from the epoch, and the mean longitude for the epoch is denoted by $N$, the daily motion by $\tau$, we shall have $M = N + n\tau - \Pi$, and thus $dM = dN + n\, d\tau - d\Pi$. In our example, the time answering to the computed place is October 17.41507 days, of the year 1804, at the meridian of Paris: if, accordingly, the beginning of the year 1805 is taken for the epoch, then $n = -74.58493$; the mean longitude for that epoch was $41° 52' 21''.61$, and the diurnal motion, $824''.7988$. Substituting now in the place of $dM$ its value in the formulas just found, the differential changes of the geocentric place, expressed by means of the changes of the elements alone, are as follows:—

$$dl = 2.41287\, dN - 179.96\, d\tau - 0.75214\, d\Pi - 3.00531\, d\varphi + 0.16488\, da$$
$$- 0.11152\, di + 0.04385\, d\Omega,$$

$$db = -0.66572\, dN + 49.65\, d\tau + 0.23677\, d\Pi + 0.61331\, d\varphi + 0.02935\, da$$
$$- 0.47335\, di + 0.38090\, d\Omega.$$

If the mass of the heavenly body is either neglected, or is regarded as known, $\tau$ and $a$ will be dependent upon each other, and so either $d\tau$ or $da$ may be eliminated from our formulas. Thus, since by article 6 we have

$$\tau a^{\frac{3}{2}} = k \sqrt{(1 + \mu)},$$

we have also

$$\frac{d\tau}{\tau} = -\tfrac{3}{2} \frac{da}{a},$$

in which formula, if $d\tau$ is to be expressed in parts of the radius, it will be necessary to express $\tau$ in the same manner. Thus in our example we have

$$
\begin{array}{llll}
\log \tau & . \quad . \quad . \quad . \quad . & 2.91635 \\
\log 1'' & . \quad . \quad . \quad . \quad . & 4.68557 \\
\log \tfrac{3}{2} & . \quad . \quad . \quad . \quad . & 0.17609 \\
\mathrm{C.}\log a & . \quad . \quad . \quad . & 9.57756 \\
\hline
\log \dfrac{d\tau}{da} & . \quad . \quad . \quad . \quad . & 7.35557n,
\end{array}
$$

or, $d\tau = -0.0022676\, da$, and $da = -440.99\, d\tau$, which value being substituted in our formulas, the final form at length becomes:—

$$\mathrm{d}l = 2.41287\,\mathrm{d}N - 252.67\,\mathrm{d}\tau - 0.75214\,\mathrm{d}\varPi - 3.00531\,\mathrm{d}\varphi$$
$$- 0.11152\,\mathrm{d}i + 0.04385\,\mathrm{d}\Omega,$$
$$\mathrm{d}b = -\,0.66572\,\mathrm{d}N + 36.71\,\mathrm{d}\tau + 0.23677\,\mathrm{d}\varPi + 0.61331\,\mathrm{d}\varphi$$
$$- 0.47335\,\mathrm{d}i + 0.38090\,\mathrm{d}\Omega.$$

In the development of these formulas we have supposed all the differentials $\mathrm{d}l$, $\mathrm{d}b$, $\mathrm{d}N$, $\mathrm{d}\tau$, $\mathrm{d}\varPi$, $\mathrm{d}\varphi$, $\mathrm{d}i$, $\mathrm{d}\Omega$ to be expressed in parts of the radius, but, manifestly, by reason of the homogeneity of all the parts, the same formulas will answer, if all those differentials are expressed in seconds.

# THIRD SECTION.

---

## 78.

THE discussion of the relations of two or more places of a heavenly body in its orbit as well as in space, furnishes an abundance of elegant propositions, such as might easily fill an entire volume. But our plan does not extend so far as to exhaust this fruitful subject, but chiefly so far as to supply abundant facilities for the solution of the great problem of the determination of unknown orbits from observations: wherefore, neglecting whatever might be too remote from our purpose, we will the more carefully develop every thing that can in any manner conduce to it. We will preface these inquiries with some trigonometrical propositions, to which, since they are more commonly used, it is necessary more frequently to recur.

I. Denoting by $A$, $B$, $C$, any angles whatever, we have

$$\sin A \sin(C-B) + \sin B \sin(A-C) + \sin C \sin(B-A) = 0$$
$$\cos A \sin(C-B) + \cos B \sin(A-C) + \cos C \sin(B-A) = 0.$$

II. If two quantities $p$, $P$, are to be determined by equations such as

$$p \sin(A-P) = a$$
$$p \sin(B-P) = b,$$

it may generally be done by means of the formulas

$$p \sin(B-A) \sin(H-P) = b \sin(H-A) - a \sin(H-B)$$
$$p \sin(B-A) \cos(H-P) = b \cos(H-A) - a \cos(H-B),$$

in which $H$ is an arbitrary angle. Hence are derived (article 14, II.) the angle $H-P$, and $p \sin(B-A)$; and hence $P$ and $p$. The condition added is gen-

(100)

erally that $p$ must be a positive quantity, whence the ambiguity in the determination of the angle $H — P$ by means of its tangent is decided; but without that condition, the ambiguity may be decided at pleasure. In order that the calculation may be as convenient as possible, it will be expedient to put the arbitrary angle $H$ either $= A$ or $= B$ or $= \frac{1}{2}(A + B)$. In the first case the equations for determining $P$ and $p$ will be

$$p \sin (A — P) = a,$$

$$p \cos (A — P) = \frac{b — a \cos (B — A)}{\sin (B — A)}.$$

In the second case the equations will be altogether analogous; but in the third case,

$$p \sin (\tfrac{1}{2} A + \tfrac{1}{2} B — P) = \frac{b + a}{2 \cos \frac{1}{2} (B — A)}$$

$$p \cos (\tfrac{1}{2} A + \tfrac{1}{2} B — P) = \frac{b — a}{2 \sin \frac{1}{2} (B — A)}.$$

And thus if the auxiliary angle $\zeta$ is introduced, the tangent of which $= \frac{a}{b}$, $P$ will be found by the formula

$$\tan (\tfrac{1}{2} A + \tfrac{1}{2} B — P) = \tan (45° + \zeta) \tan \tfrac{1}{2} (B — A),$$

and afterwards $p$ by some one of the preceding formulas, in which

$$\tfrac{1}{2} (b + a) = \sin (45° + \zeta) \sqrt{\frac{ab}{\sin 2 \zeta}} = \frac{a \sin (45° + \zeta)}{\sin \zeta \sqrt 2} = \frac{b \sin (45° + \zeta)}{\cos \zeta \sqrt 2}$$

$$\tfrac{1}{2} (b — a) = \cos (45° + \zeta) \sqrt{\frac{ab}{\sin 2 \zeta}} = \frac{a \cos (45° + \zeta)}{\sin \zeta \sqrt 2} = \frac{b \cos (45° + \zeta)}{\cos \zeta \sqrt 2}.$$

III. If $p$ and $P$ are to be determined from the equations

$$p \cos (A — P) = a,$$

$$p \cos (B — P) = b,$$

every thing said in II. could be immediately applied provided, only, $90° + A$ $90° + B$ were written there throughout instead of $A$ and $B$: that their use may be more convenient, we can, without trouble, add the developed formulas. The general formulas will be

$$p \sin (B — A) \sin (H — P) = — b \cos (H — A) + a \cos (H — B)$$

$$p \sin (B — A) \cos (H — P) = \quad b \sin (H — A) — a \sin (H — B).$$

Thus for $H = A$, they change into

$$p \sin (A - P) = \frac{a \cos (B - A) - b}{\sin (B - A)}$$
$$p \cos (A - P) = a.$$

For $H = B$, they acquire a similar form; but for $H = \frac{1}{2} (A + B)$ they become

$$p \sin (\tfrac{1}{2} A + \tfrac{1}{2} B - P) = \frac{a - b}{2 \sin \frac{1}{2} (B - A)}$$
$$p \cos (\tfrac{1}{2} A + \tfrac{1}{2} B - P) = \frac{a + b}{2 \cos \frac{1}{2} (B - A)},$$

so that the auxiliary angle $\zeta$ being introduced, of which the tangent $= \frac{a}{b}$, it becomes

$$\tan (\tfrac{1}{2} A + \tfrac{1}{2} B - P) = \tan (\zeta - 45°) \, \cotan \tfrac{1}{2} (B - A).$$

Finally, if we desire to determine $p$ immediately from $a$ and $b$ without previous computation of the angle $P$, we have the formula

$$p \sin (B - A) = \sqrt{(aa + bb - 2ab \cos (B - A))},$$

as well in the present problem as in II.

## 79.

For the complete determination of the conic section in its plane, *three* things are required, the place of the perihelion, the eccentricity, and the semi-parameter. If these are to be deduced from given quantities depending upon them, there must be data enough to be able to form three equations independent of each other. Any radius vector whatever given in magnitude and position furnishes one equation: wherefore, three radii vectores given in magnitude and position are requisite for the determination of an orbit; but if two only are had, either one of the elements themselves must be given, or at all events some other quantity, with which to form the third equation. Thence arises a variety of problems which we will now investigate in succession.

Let $r, r'$, be two radii vectores which make, with a right line drawn at pleasure from the sun in the plane of the orbit, the angles $N, N'$, in the direction of the motion; further, let $\Pi$ be the angle which the radius vector at perihelion makes with the same straight line, so that the true anomalies $N - \Pi$, $N' - \Pi$ may answer to the radii vectores $r, r'$; lastly, let $e$ be the eccentricity, and $p$ the semi-parameter. Then we have the equations

$$\frac{p}{r} = 1 + e \cos(\overset{\cdot}{N} - \Pi)$$

$$\frac{p}{r'} = 1 + e \cos(N' - \Pi),$$

from which, if one of the quantities $p$, $e$, $\Pi$, is also given, it will be possible to determine the two remaining ones.

Let us first suppose the semi-parameter $p$ to be given, and it is evident that the determination of the quantities $e$ and $\Pi$ from the equations

$$e \cos(N - \Pi) = \frac{p}{r} - 1$$

$$e \cos(N' - \Pi) = \frac{p}{r'} - 1,$$

can be performed by the rule of lemma III. in the preceding article. We have accordingly

$$\tan(N - \Pi) = \cot(N' - N) - \frac{r(p - r')}{r'(p - r)\sin(N' - N)}$$

$$\tan(\tfrac{1}{2} N + \tfrac{1}{2} N' - \Pi) = \frac{(r' - r)\cot\tfrac{1}{2}(N' - N)}{r' + r - \dfrac{2rr'}{p}}.$$

## 80.

If the angle $\Pi$ is given, $p$ and $e$ will be determined by means of the equations

$$p = \frac{rr'\left(\cos(N - \Pi) - \cos(N' - \Pi)\right)}{r\cos(N - \Pi) - r'\cos(N' - \Pi)}$$

$$e = \frac{r' - r}{r\cos(N - \Pi) - r'\cos(N' - \Pi)}.$$

It is possible to reduce the common denominator in these formulas to the form $a \cos(A - \Pi)$, so that $a$ and $A$ may be independent of $\Pi$. Thus letting $H$ denote an arbitrary angle, we have

$$r\cos(N - \Pi) - r'\cos(N' - \Pi) = (r\cos(N - H) - r'\cos(N' - H))\cos(H - \Pi)$$
$$- (r\sin(N - H) - r'\sin(N' - H))\sin(H - \Pi)$$

and so

$$= a\cos(A - \Pi),$$

if $a$ and $A$ are determined by the equations

$$r\cos(N - H) - r'\cos(N' - H) = a\cos(A - H)$$
$$r\sin(N - H) - r'\sin(N' - H) = a\sin(A - H).$$

**In** this way we have

$$p = \frac{2\,r r' \sin \frac{1}{2}\,(N'-N)\sin\left(\frac{1}{2}\,N + \frac{1}{2}\,N' - \Pi\right)}{a \cos\,(A - \Pi)}$$

$$e = \frac{r' - r}{a \cos\,(A - \Pi)}.$$

These formulas are especially convenient when $p$ and $e$ are to be computed for several values of $\Pi$; $r$, $r'$, $N$, $N'$ continuing the same. Since for the calculation of the auxiliary quantities $a$, $A$, the angle $H$ may be taken at pleasure, it will be of advantage to put $H = \frac{1}{2}\,(N + N')$, by which means the formulas are changed into these, —

$$(r' - r)\cos\tfrac{1}{2}\,(N' - N) = - a \cos\,(A - \tfrac{1}{2}\,N - \tfrac{1}{2}\,N')$$
$$(r' + r)\sin\tfrac{1}{2}\,(N' - N) = - a \sin\,(A - \tfrac{1}{2}\,N - \tfrac{1}{2}\,N').$$

And so the angle $A$ being determined by the equation

$$\tan\,(A - \tfrac{1}{2}\,N - \tfrac{1}{2}\,N') = \frac{r' + r}{r' - r}\tan\tfrac{1}{2}\,(N' - N),$$

we have immediately

$$e = - \frac{\cos\,(A - \frac{1}{2}\,N - \frac{1}{2}\,N')}{\cos\frac{1}{2}\,(N' - N)\cos\,(A - \Pi)}.$$

The computation of the logarithm of the quantity $\frac{r' + r}{r' - r}$ may be abridged by a method already frequently explained.

## 81.

If the eccentricity $e$ is given, the angle $\Pi$ will be found by means of the equation

$$\cos\,(A - \Pi) = - \frac{\cos\,(A - \frac{1}{2}\,N - \frac{1}{2}\,N')}{e \cos\frac{1}{2}\,(N' - N)},$$

afterwards the auxiliary angle $A$ is determined by the equation

$$\tan\,(A - \tfrac{1}{2}\,N - \tfrac{1}{2}\,N') = \frac{r' + r}{r' - r}\tan\tfrac{1}{2}\,(N' - N).$$

The ambiguity remaining in the determination of the angle $A - \Pi$ by its cosine is founded in the nature of the case, so that the problem can be satisfied by two different solutions; which of these is to be adopted, and which rejected, must be decided in some other way; and for this purpose the approximate value at least of $\varPi$ must be already known. After $\varPi$ is found, $p$ will be computed by the formulas

$$p = r\,(1 + e \cos\,(N - \varPi)) = r'\,(1 + e \cos\,(N' - \varPi)),$$

or by this,

$$p = \frac{2\,rr'\,e \sin \tfrac{1}{2}\,(N' - N) \sin\,(\tfrac{1}{2}\,N' + \tfrac{1}{2}\,N - \varPi)}{r' - r}.$$

### 82.

Finally, let us suppose that there are given three radii vectores $r,\ r',\ r''$, which make, with the right line drawn from the sun in the plane of the orbit at pleasure, the angles $N,\ N',\ N''$. We shall have, accordingly, the remaining symbols being retained, the equations

(I.)
$$\frac{p}{r} = 1 + e \cos\,(N - \varPi)$$

$$\frac{p}{r'} = 1 + e \cos\,(N' - \varPi)$$

$$\frac{p}{r''} = 1 + e \cos\,(N'' - \varPi),$$

from which $p,\ \varPi,\ e$, can be derived in several different ways. If we wish to compute the quantity $p$ before the rest, the three equations (I.) may be multiplied respectively by $\sin\,(N'' - N')$, $-\sin\,(N'' - N)$, $\sin\,(N' - N)$, and the products being added, we have by lemma I., article 78,

$$p = \frac{\sin\,(N'' - N') - \sin\,(N'' - N) + \sin\,(N' - N)}{\dfrac{1}{r} \sin\,(N'' - N') - \dfrac{1}{r'} \sin\,(N'' - N) + \dfrac{1}{r''} \sin\,(N' - N)}.$$

This expression deserves to be considered more closely. The numerator evidently becomes

$2 \sin \tfrac{1}{2}\,(N'' - N') \cos \tfrac{1}{2}\,(N'' - N') - 2 \sin \tfrac{1}{2}\,(N'' - N') \cos\,(\tfrac{1}{2}\,N'' + \tfrac{1}{2}\,N' - N)$
$= 4 \sin \tfrac{1}{2}\,(N'' - N') \sin \tfrac{1}{2}\,(N'' - N) \sin \tfrac{1}{2}\,(N' - N).$

Putting, moreover,

$$r'\,r'' \sin\,(N'' - N') = n,\ \ rr'' \sin\,(N'' - N) = n',\ \ r\,r' \sin\,(N' - N) = n'',$$

it is evident that $\tfrac{1}{2}\,n,\ \tfrac{1}{2}\,n'\ \tfrac{1}{2}\,n''$, are areas of triangles between the second and third radius vector, between the first and third, and between the first and second.

Hence it will readily be perceived, that in the new formula,

$$p = \frac{4 \sin \frac{1}{2} (N'' - N') \sin \frac{1}{2} (N'' - N) \sin \frac{1}{2} (N' - N) \cdot r \, r' \, r''}{n - n' + n''}$$

the denominator is double the area of the triangle contained between the extremities of the three radii vectores, that is, between the three places of the heavenly body in space. When these places are little distant from each other, this area will always be a very small quantity, and, indeed, of the third order, if $N' - N$, $N'' - N'$ are regarded as small quantities of the first order. Hence it is readily inferred, that if one or more of the quantities $r$, $r'$, $r''$, $N$, $N'$, $N''$, are affected by errors never so slight, a very great error may thence arise in the determination of $p$; on which account, this manner of obtaining the dimensions of the orbit can never admit of great accuracy, except the three heliocentric places are distant from each other by considerable intervals.

As soon as the semi-parameter $p$ is found, $e$ and $\mathit{\Pi}$ will be determined by the combination of any two whatever of the equations I. by the method of article 79.

## 83.

If we prefer to commence the solution of this problem by the computation of the angle $\mathit{\Pi}$, we make use of the following method. From the second of equations I. we subtract the third, from the first the third, from the first the second, in which manner we obtain the three following new equations: —

$$\text{(II.)} \qquad \frac{\frac{1}{r'} - \frac{1}{r''}}{2 \sin \frac{1}{2} (N'' - N')} = \frac{e}{p} \sin \left( \tfrac{1}{2} N' + \tfrac{1}{2} N'' - \mathit{\Pi} \right)$$

$$\frac{\frac{1}{r} - \frac{1}{r''}}{2 \sin \frac{1}{2} (N'' - N)} = \frac{e}{p} \sin \left( \tfrac{1}{2} N + \tfrac{1}{2} N'' - \mathit{\Pi} \right)$$

$$\frac{\frac{1}{r} - \frac{1}{r'}}{2 \sin \frac{1}{2} (N' - N)} = \frac{e}{p} \sin \left( \tfrac{1}{2} N + \tfrac{1}{2} N' - \mathit{\Pi} \right).$$

Any two of these equations, according to lemma II., article 78, will give $\mathit{\Pi}$ and $\frac{e}{p}$, whence by either of the equations (I.) will be obtained likewise $e$ and $p$. If we select the third solution given in article 78, II., the combination of the first equation with the third gives rise to the following mode of proceeding. The auxiliary angle $\zeta$ may be determined by the equation

$$\tan \zeta = \frac{\frac{r'}{r} - 1}{1 - \frac{r'}{r''}} \cdot \frac{\sin \frac{1}{2} (N'' - N')}{\sin \frac{1}{2} (N' - N)}$$

and we shall have

$$\tan (\tfrac{1}{4} N + \tfrac{1}{2} N' + \tfrac{1}{4} N'' - \mathit{\Pi}) = \tan (45° + \zeta) \tan \tfrac{1}{4} (N'' - N).$$

Two other solutions wholly analogous to this will result from changing the second place with the first or third. Since the formulas for $\frac{e}{p}$ become more complicated by the use of this method, it will be better to deduce $e$ and $p$, by the method of article 80, from two of the equations (I.). The uncertainty in the determination of $\mathit{\Pi}$ by the tangent of the angle $\tfrac{1}{4} N + \tfrac{1}{2} N' + \tfrac{1}{4} N'' - \mathit{\Pi}$ must be so decided that $e$ may become a positive quantity: for it is manifest that if values 180° different were taken for $\mathit{\Pi}$, opposite values would result for $e$. The sign of $p$, however, is free from this uncertainty, and the value of $p$ cannot become negative, unless the three given points lie in the part of the hyperbola away from the sun, a case contrary to the laws of nature which we do not consider in this place.

That which, after the more difficult substitutions, would arise from the application of the first method in article 78, II., can be more conveniently obtained in the present case in the following manner. Let the first of equations II. be multiplied by $\cos \tfrac{1}{2} (N'' - N')$, the third by $\cos \tfrac{1}{2} (N' - N)$, and let the product of the latter be subtracted from the former. Then, lemma I. of article 78 being properly applied,* will follow the equation

$$\tfrac{1}{2} \left( \frac{1}{r'} - \frac{1}{r''} \right) \cotan \tfrac{1}{2} (N'' - N') - \tfrac{1}{2} \left( \frac{1}{r} - \frac{1}{r'} \right) \cotan \tfrac{1}{2} (N' - N)$$

$$= \frac{e}{p} \sin \tfrac{1}{2} (N'' - N) \cos (\tfrac{1}{2} N + \tfrac{1}{2} N'' - \mathit{\Pi}).$$

By combining which with the second of equations II. $\mathit{\Pi}$ and $\frac{e}{p}$ will be found; thus, $\mathit{\Pi}$ by the formula

---

* Putting, that is, in the second formula, $A = \tfrac{1}{2} (N'' - N')$, $B = \tfrac{1}{2} N + \tfrac{1}{2} N'' - \mathit{\Pi}$, $C = \tfrac{1}{2} (N - N')$.

$$\tan\left(\tfrac{1}{2}N + \tfrac{1}{2}N'' - \mathbf{\Pi}\right)$$

$$= \frac{\dfrac{r'}{r} - \dfrac{r'}{r''}}{\left(1 - \dfrac{r'}{r''}\right)\cotan \tfrac{1}{2}\left(N'' - N\right) - \left(\dfrac{r'}{r} - 1\right)\cotan \tfrac{1}{2}\left(N' - N\right)}.$$

Hence, also, two other wholly analogous formulas are obtained by interchanging the second place with the first or third.


## 84.

Since it is possible to determine the whole orbit by two radii vectores given in magnitude and position together with one element of the orbit, the *time* also in which the heavenly body moves from one radius vector to another, may be determined, if we either neglect the mass of the body, or regard it as known: we shall adhere to the former case, to which the latter is easily reduced. Hence, inversely, it is apparent that two radii vectores given in magnitude and position, together with the time in which the heavenly body describes the intermediate space, determine the whole orbit. But this problem, to be considered among the most important in the theory of the motions of the heavenly bodies, is not so easily solved, since the expression of the time in terms of the elements is transcendental, and, moreover, very complicated. It is so much the more worthy of being carefully investigated; we hope, therefore, it will not be disagreeable to the reader, that, besides the solution to be given hereafter, which seems to leave nothing further to be desired, we have thought proper to preserve also the one of which we have made frequent use before the former suggested itself to me. It is always profitable to approach the more difficult problems in several ways, and not to despise the good although preferring the better. We begin with explaining this older method.


## 85.

We will retain the symbols $r$, $r'$, $N$, $N'$, $p$, $e$, $\mathbf{\Pi}$ with the same meaning, with which they have been taken above; we will denote the difference $N' - N$ by $\mathit{\Delta}$, and the time in which the heavenly body moves from the former place to the latter by $t$. Now it is evident that if the approximate value of any one of the quantities $p, e, \varPi$, is known, the two remaining ones can be determined from them, and afterwards, by the methods explained in the first section, the time corresponding to the motion from the first place to the second. If this proves to be equal to the given time $t$, the assumed value of $p$, $e$, or $\varPi$, is the true one, and the orbit is found; but if not, the calculation repeated with another value differing a little from the first, will show how great a change in the value of the time corresponds to a small change in the values of $p$, $e$, $\varPi$; whence the correct value will be discovered by simple interpolation. And if the calculation is repeated anew with this, the resulting time will either agree exactly with that given, or at least differ very little from it, so that, by applying new corrections, as perfect an agreement can be attained as our logarithmic and trigonometrical tables allow.

The problem, therefore, is reduced to this, — for the case in which the orbit is still wholly unknown, to determine an approximate value of any one of the quantities $p$, $e$, $\varPi$. We will now give a method by which the value of $p$ is obtained with such accuracy that for small values of $\varDelta$ it will require no further correction; and thus the whole orbit will be determined by the first computation with all the accuracy the common tables allow. This method, however, can hardly ever be used, except for moderate values of $\varDelta$, because the determination of an orbit wholly unknown, on account of the very intricate complexity of the problem, can only be undertaken with observations not very distant from each other, or rather with such as do not involve very considerable heliocentric motion.

## 86.

Denoting the indefinite or variable radius vector corresponding to the true anomaly $v - \varPi$ by $\varrho$, the area of the sector described by the heavenly body in the time $t$ will be $\tfrac{1}{2}\int \varrho \varrho \, dv$, this integral being extended from $v = N$ to $v = N'$, and thus, ($k$ being taken in the meaning of article 6), $k\, t\, \sqrt{p} = \int \varrho \varrho \, dv$. Now it is evident from the fomulas developed by Cotes, that if $\varphi x$ expresses any function whatever of $x$, the continually approximating value of the integral $\int \varphi x \,.\, dx$ taken from $x = u$ to $x = u + \varDelta$ is given by the formulas

$$\tfrac{1}{2} \varDelta \left( \varphi u + \varphi \left( u + \varDelta \right) \right)$$

$$\tfrac{1}{6} \varDelta \left( \varphi u + 4 \varphi \left( u + \tfrac{1}{2} \varDelta \right) + \varphi \left( u + \varDelta \right) \right)$$

$$\tfrac{1}{8} \varDelta \left( \varphi u + 3 \varphi \left( u + \tfrac{1}{3} \varDelta \right) + 3 \varphi \left( u + \tfrac{2}{3} \varDelta \right) + \varphi \left( u + \varDelta \right) \right), \text{ etc.}$$

It will be sufficient for our purpose to stop at the two first formulas.

By the first formula we have in our problem,

$$\int \varrho \varrho \, d\nu = \tfrac{1}{2} \varDelta \left( r r + r' r' \right) = \frac{\varDelta r r'}{\cos 2 \omega},$$

if we put

$$\frac{r'}{r} = \tan \left( 45^\circ + \omega \right).$$

Wherefore, the first approximate value of $\sqrt{p}$, which we will put $= 3 \, \alpha$, will be

$$\sqrt{p} = \frac{\varDelta r r'}{k t \cos 2 \omega} = 3 \, \alpha.$$

By the second formula we have more exactly

$$\int \varrho \varrho \, d\nu = \tfrac{1}{6} \varDelta \left( r r + r' r' + 4 R R \right),$$

denoting by $R$ the radius vector corresponding to the middle anomaly

$$\tfrac{1}{2} N + \tfrac{1}{2} N' - \mathit{\Pi}.$$

Now expressing $p$ by means of $r, R, r', N, N + \tfrac{1}{2} \varDelta, N + \varDelta$ according to the for mula given in article 82, we find

$$p = \frac{4 \sin^2 \tfrac{1}{4} \varDelta \sin \tfrac{1}{2} \varDelta}{\left( \dfrac{1}{r} + \dfrac{1}{r'} \right) \sin \tfrac{1}{2} \varDelta - \dfrac{1}{R} \sin \varDelta},$$

and hence

$$\frac{\cos \tfrac{1}{2} \varDelta}{R} = \tfrac{1}{2} \left( \frac{1}{r} + \frac{1}{r'} \right) - \frac{2 \sin^2 \tfrac{1}{4} \varDelta}{p} = \frac{\cos \omega}{\sqrt{\left( r r' \cos 2 \omega \right)}} - \frac{2 \sin^2 \tfrac{1}{4} \varDelta}{p}.$$

By putting, therefore,

$$\frac{2 \sin^2 \tfrac{1}{4} \varDelta \sqrt{\left( r r' \cos 2 \omega \right)}}{\cos \omega} = \delta,$$

we have

$$R = \frac{\cos \tfrac{1}{2} \varDelta \sqrt{\left( r r' \cos 2 \omega \right)}}{\cos \omega \left( 1 - \dfrac{\delta}{p} \right)},$$

whence is obtained the second approximate value of $\sqrt{p}$,

$$\sqrt{p} = \alpha + \frac{2\,\alpha \cos^2\frac{1}{2}\varDelta \cos^2 2\,\omega}{\cos^2\omega\,(1-\frac{\delta}{p})^2} = \alpha + \frac{\varepsilon}{(1-\frac{\delta}{p})^2},$$

if we put

$$2\,\alpha\left(\frac{\cos\frac{1}{2}\varDelta \cos 2\,\omega}{\cos\omega}\right)^2 = \varepsilon.$$

Writing, therefore, $\pi$ for $\sqrt{p}$, $\pi$ will be determined by the equation

$$(\pi - \alpha)\,(1 - \frac{\delta}{\pi\,\pi})^2 = \varepsilon,$$

which properly developed would ascend to the fifth degree. We may put $\pi = q + \mu$, so that $q$ is the approximate value of $\pi$, and $\mu$ a very small quantity, the square and higher powers of which may be neglected: from which substitution proceeds

$$(q - \alpha)\,(1 - \frac{\delta}{q\,q})^2 + \mu\left((1 - \frac{\delta}{q\,q})^2 + \frac{4\,\delta\,(q-\alpha)}{q^3}\,(1-\frac{\delta}{q\,q})\right) = \varepsilon,$$

or

$$\mu = \frac{\varepsilon\,q^5 - (q\,q - \alpha\,q)\,(q\,q - \delta)^2}{(q\,q - \delta)\,(q^3 + 3\,\delta\,q - 4\,\alpha\,\delta)},$$

and so

$$\pi = \frac{\varepsilon\,q^5 + (q\,q - \delta)\,(\alpha\,q\,q + 4\,\delta\,q - 5\,\alpha\,\delta)\,q}{(q\,q - \delta)\,(q^3 + 3\,\delta\,q - 4\,\alpha\,\delta)}.$$

Now we have in our problem the approximate value of $\pi$, namely, $3\,\alpha$, which being substituted in the preceding formula for $q$, the corrected value becomes

$$\pi = \frac{243\,\alpha^4\varepsilon + 3\,\alpha\,(9\,\alpha\,\alpha - \delta)\,(9\,\alpha\,\alpha + 7\,\delta)}{(9\,\alpha\,\alpha - \delta)\,(27\,\alpha\,\alpha + 5\,\delta)}.$$

Putting, therefore,

$$\frac{\delta}{27\,\alpha\,\alpha} = \beta, \quad \frac{\varepsilon}{(1 - 3\,\beta)\,\alpha} = \gamma,$$

the formula assumes this form,

$$\pi = \frac{\alpha\,(1 + \gamma + 21\,\beta)}{1 + 5\,\beta},$$

and all the operations necessary to the solution of the problem are comprehended in these five formulas: —

I. $\dfrac{r'}{r} = \tan(45° + \omega)$

II.    $\dfrac{\varDelta\, r\, r'}{3\, k\, t \cos 2\,\omega} = \alpha$

III.    $\dfrac{2 \sin^2 \frac{1}{4}\, \varDelta\, \sqrt{(r\, r' \cos 2\,\omega)}}{27\,\alpha\,\alpha \cos \omega} = \beta$

IV.    $\dfrac{2 \cos^2 \frac{1}{2}\, \varDelta \cos^2 2\,\omega}{(1 - 3\,\beta)\cos^2 \omega} = \gamma$

V.    $\dfrac{\alpha\,(1 + \gamma + 21\,\beta)}{1 + 5\,\beta} = \sqrt{p}.$

If we are willing to relinquish something of the precision of these formulas, it will be possible to develop still more simple expressions. Thus, by making $\cos \omega$ and $\cos 2\,\omega = 1$, and developing the value of $\sqrt{p}$ in a series proceeding according to the powers of $\varDelta$, the fourth and higher powers being neglected, we have,

$$\sqrt{p} = \alpha \left(3 - \tfrac{1}{2}\varDelta\varDelta + \frac{\varDelta\varDelta\sqrt{r r'}}{18\, a\, a}\right),$$

in which $\varDelta$ is to be expressed in parts of the radius. Wherefore, by making

$$\frac{\varDelta\, r\, r'}{k t} = \sqrt{p'},$$

we have

VI.    $p = p' \left(1 - \tfrac{1}{3}\varDelta\varDelta + \dfrac{\varDelta\varDelta\sqrt{r r'}}{3\, p'}\right).$

In like manner, by developing $\sqrt{p}$ in a series proceeding according to the powers of $\sin \varDelta$, putting

$$\frac{r\, r' \sin \varDelta}{k t} = \sqrt{p''},$$

we have

VII.    $\sqrt{p} = \left(1 + \dfrac{\sin^2 \varDelta \sqrt{r r'}}{6\, p''}\right) \sqrt{p''},$

or

VIII.    $p = p'' + \tfrac{1}{3}\sin^2 \varDelta \sqrt{r r'}.$

The formulas VII. and VIII. agree with those which the illustrious Euler has given in the *Theoria motus planetarum et cometarum*, but formula VI., with that which has been introduced in the *Recherches et calculs sur la vraie orbite elliptique de la comete de* 1769, p. 80.

## 87.

The following examples will illustrate the use of the preceding precepts, while from them the degree of precision can be estimated.

I. Let $\log r = 0.3307640$, $\log r' = 0.3222239$, $\varDelta = 7° 34' 53''.73 = 27293''.73$, $t = 21.93391$ days. Then is found $\omega = -33' 47''.90$, whence the further computation is as follows: —

| | | | | | |
|---|---|---|---|---|---|
| $\log \varDelta$ . . . . | 4.4360629 | | $\frac{1}{2} \log r r' \cos 2\,\omega$ . | 0.3264519 |
| $\log r r'$ . . . . | 0.6529879 | | $2 \log \sin \frac{1}{4} \varDelta$ . . | 7.0389972 |
| C. $\log 3\,k$ . . . | 5.9728722 | | $\log \frac{2}{27}$ . . . . | 8.8696662 |
| C. $\log t$ . . . . | 8.6588840 | | C. $\log \alpha\,\alpha$ . . . | 0.5582180 |
| C. $\log \cos 2\,\omega$ . | 0.0000840 | | C. $\log \cos \omega$ . . . | 0.0000210 |
| $\log \alpha$ . . . . | 9.7208910 | | $\log \beta$ . . . . . | 6.7933543 |
| | | | $\beta =$ | 0.0006213757 |
| $\log 2$ . . . . | 0.3010300 | | | |
| $2 \log \cos \frac{1}{2} \varDelta$ . | 9.9980976 | | $1 + \gamma + 21\,\beta =$ | 3.0074471 |
| $2 \log \cos 2\,\omega$ . | 9.9998320 | | $\log$ . . . . . . | 0.4781980 |
| C. $\log (1 - 3\,\beta)$ | 0.0008103 | | $\log \alpha$ . . . . | 9.7208910 |
| $2$ C. $\log \cos \omega$ . | 0.0000420 | | C. $\log (1 + 5\,\beta)$ . | 9.9986528 |
| $\log \gamma$ . . . . | 0.2998119 | | $\log \sqrt{p}$ . . . . | 0.1977418 |
| $\gamma =$ | 1.9943982 | | $\log p$ . . . . | 0.3954836 |
| $21\,\beta =$ | 0.0130489 | | | |

This value of $\log p$ differs from the true value by scarcely a single unit in the seventh place: formula VI., in this example, gives $\log p = 0.3954822$; formula VII. gives $0.3954780$; finally, formula VIII., $0.3954754$.

II. Let $\log r = 0.4282792$, $\log r' = 0.4062033$, $\varDelta = 62° 55' 16''.64$, $t = 259.88477$ days. Hence is derived $\omega = -1° 27' 20''.14$, $\log \alpha = 9.7482348$, $\beta = 0.04535216$, $\gamma = 1.681127$, $\log \sqrt{p} = 0.2198027$, $\log p = 0.4396054$, which is less than the true value by 183 units in the seventh place. For, the true value in this example is $0.4396237$; it is found to be, by formula VI., $0.4368730$; from formula VII. it results 0.4159824 ; lastly, it is deduced from formula VIII., 0.4051103 : the two last values differ so much from the truth that they cannot even be used as approximations.

88.

The exposition of the *second* method will afford an opportunity for treating fully a great many new and elegant relations; which, as they assume different forms in the different kinds of conic sections, it will be proper to treat separately; we will begin with the ELLIPSE.

Let the eccentric anomalies $E$, $E'$, and the radii vectores $r$, $r'$, correspond to two places of the true anomaly $v$, $v'$, (of which $v$ is first in time); let also $p$ be the semi-parameter, $e = \sin \varphi$ the eccentricity, $a$ the semi-axis major, $t$ the time in which the motion from the first place to the second is completed; finally let us put

$$v' - v = 2f, \quad v' + v = 2F, \quad E' - E = 2g, \quad E' + E = 2G, \quad a \cos \varphi = \frac{p}{\cos \varphi} = b.$$

Then, the following equations are easily deduced from the combination of formulas V., VI., article 8 : —

[1]  $b \sin g = \sin f . \sqrt{r r'}$,

[2]  $b \sin G = \sin F . \sqrt{r r'}$,

$p \cos g = \left( \cos \tfrac{1}{2} v \cos \tfrac{1}{2} v' . (1 + e) + \sin \tfrac{1}{2} v \sin \tfrac{1}{2} v' . (1 - e) \right) \sqrt{r r'}$, or

[3]  $p \cos g = (\cos f + e \cos F) \sqrt{r r'}$, and in the same way,

[4]  $p \cos G = (\cos F + e \cos f) \sqrt{r r'}$.

From the combination of the equations 3 and 4 arise,

[5]  $\cos f . \sqrt{r r'} = (\cos g - e \cos G) a$,

[6]  $\cos F . \sqrt{r r'} = (\cos G - e \cos g) a$.

From formula III., article 8, we obtain

[7]  $r' - r = 2 a e \sin g \sin G$,

$r' + r = 2 a - 2 a e \cos g \cos G = 2 a \sin^2 g + 2 \cos f \cos g \sqrt{r r'}$ ;

whence,

[8]  $a = \dfrac{r + r' - 2 \cos f \cos g \sqrt{r r'}}{2 \sin^2 g}$ .

Let us put

[9] $\quad \dfrac{\sqrt{\frac{r'}{r}}+\sqrt{\frac{r}{r'}}}{2\cos f}=1+2l,$

and then will

[10] $\quad a=\dfrac{2\,(l+\sin^2\frac{1}{2}g)\,\cos f\sqrt{r\,r'}}{\sin^2 g};$

also

$$\sqrt{a}=\pm\,\dfrac{\sqrt{(2\,(l+\sin^2\frac{1}{2}g)\,\cos f\sqrt{rr'})}}{\sin g},$$

in which the upper or lower sign must be taken, as $\sin g$ is positive or negative. Formula XII., article 8, furnishes us the equation

$$\frac{k\,t}{a^{\frac{3}{2}}}=E'-e\sin E'-E+e\sin E=2\,g-2\,e\sin g\cos G$$

$$=2\,g-\sin 2\,g+2\cos f\sin g\,\frac{\sqrt{rr'}}{a}.$$

If now we substitute in this equation instead of $a$ its value from 10, and put, for the sake of brevity,

[11] $\quad \dfrac{k\,t}{2^{\frac{3}{2}}\cos f^{\frac{3}{2}}\,(r\,r')^{\frac{3}{4}}}=m,$

we have, after the proper reductions,

[12] $\quad \pm\,m=(l+\sin^2\tfrac{1}{2}\,g)^{\frac{1}{2}}+(l+\sin^2\tfrac{1}{2}\,g)^{\frac{3}{2}}\Big(\dfrac{2\,g-\sin 2\,g}{\sin^3 g}\Big),$

in which the upper or lower sign is to be prefixed to $m$, as $\sin g$ is positive or negative.

When the heliocentric motion is between 180° and 360°, or, more generally, when $\cos f$ is negative, the quantity $m$ determined by formula 11 becomes imaginary, and $l$ negative; in order to avoid which we will adopt in this case, instead of the equations 9, 11, the following:—

[9*] $\quad \dfrac{\sqrt{\frac{r'}{r}}+\sqrt{\frac{r}{r'}}}{2\cos f}=1-2L,$

[11*] $\quad \dfrac{k\,t}{2^{\frac{3}{2}}\,(-\cos f)^{\frac{3}{2}}\,(r\,r')^{\frac{3}{4}}}=M,$

whence for 10, 12, we shall obtain these,—

$$[10^*] \quad a = \frac{-2\,(L - \sin^2\tfrac{1}{2}\,g)\cos f \sqrt{rr'}}{\sin^2 g},$$

$$[12^*] \quad \pm M = -(L - \sin^2\tfrac{1}{2}\,g)^{\frac{1}{2}} + (L - \sin^2\tfrac{1}{2}\,g)^{\frac{3}{2}}\left(\frac{2\,g - \sin 2\,g}{\sin^3 g}\right),$$

in which the doubtful sign is to be determined in the same manner as before.

## 89.

We have now two things to accomplish; first, to derive the unknown quantity $g$ as conveniently as possible from the transcendental equation 12, since it does not admit of a direct solution; second, to deduce the elements themselves from the angle $g$ thus found. Before we proceed to these, we will obtain a certain transformation, by the help of which the computation of the auxiliary quantity $l$ or $L$ is more expeditiously performed, and also several formulas afterwards to be developed are reduced to a more elegant form.

By introducing the auxiliary angle $\omega$, to be determined by means of the formula

$$\sqrt[4]{\frac{r'}{r}} = \tan\,(45^\circ + \omega),$$

we have

$$\sqrt{\frac{r'}{r}} + \sqrt{\frac{r}{r'}} = 2 + (\tan\,(45^\circ + \omega) - \cotan\,(45^\circ + \omega))^2 = 2 + 4\tan^2 2\,\omega;$$

whence are obtained

$$l = \frac{\sin^2\tfrac{1}{2}f}{\cos f} + \frac{\tan^2 2\,\omega}{\cos f}, \quad L = -\frac{\sin^2\tfrac{1}{2}f}{\cos f} - \frac{\tan^2 2\,\omega}{\cos f}.$$

## 90.

We will consider, in the first place, the case in which a value of $g$ not very great, is obtained from the solution of the equation 12, so that

$$\frac{2\,g - \sin 2\,g}{\sin^3 g}$$

may be developed in a series arranged according to the powers of $\sin \tfrac{1}{2}\,g$. The numerator of this expression, which we shall denote by $X$, becomes

$$\tfrac{3\,2}{3}\sin^3 \tfrac{1}{2}\,g - \tfrac{1\,6}{5}\sin^5 \tfrac{1}{2}\,g - \tfrac{4}{7}\sin^7 \tfrac{1}{2}\,g - \text{etc.};$$

and the denominator,

$$8 \sin^3 \tfrac{1}{2} g - 12 \sin^5 \tfrac{1}{2} g + 3 \sin^7 \tfrac{1}{2} g + \text{etc.}$$

Whence $X$ obtains the form

$$\tfrac{4}{3} + \tfrac{8}{5} \sin^2 \tfrac{1}{2} g + \tfrac{64}{35} \sin^4 \tfrac{1}{2} g + \text{etc.}$$

But in order to obtain the law of progression of the coefficients, let us differentiate the equation

$$X \sin^3 g = 2 g - \sin 2 g,$$

whence results

$$3 X \cos g \sin^2 g + \sin^3 g \frac{d X}{d g} = 2 - 2 \cos 2 g = 4 \sin^2 g;$$

putting, moreover,

$$\sin^2 \tfrac{1}{2} g = x,$$

We have

$$\frac{d x}{d g} = \tfrac{1}{2} \sin g,$$

whence is deduced

$$\frac{d X}{d x} = \frac{8 - 6 X \cos g}{\sin^2 g} = \frac{4 - 3 X (1 - 2 x)}{2 x (1 - x)},$$

and next,

$$(2 x - 2 x x) \frac{d X}{d x} = 4 - (3 - 6 x) X.$$

If, therefore, we put

$$X = \tfrac{4}{3}(1 + \alpha x + \beta x x + \gamma x^3 + \delta x^4 + \text{etc.})$$

we obtain the equation

$$\tfrac{8}{3} \left( \alpha x + (2 \beta - \alpha) x x + (3 \gamma - 2 \beta) x^3 + (4 \delta - 3 \gamma) x^4 + \text{etc.} \right)$$
$$= (8 - 4 \alpha) x + (8 \alpha - 4 \beta) x x + (8 \beta - 4 \gamma) x^3 + (8 \gamma - 4 \delta) x^4 + \text{etc.}$$

which should be identical. Hence we get

$$\alpha = \tfrac{6}{5}, \ \beta = \tfrac{8}{7} \alpha, \ \gamma = \tfrac{10}{9} \beta, \ \delta = \tfrac{12}{11} \gamma \ \text{etc.,}$$

in which the law of progression is obvious. We have, therefore,

$$X = \tfrac{4}{3} + \frac{4 \cdot 6}{3 \cdot 5} x + \frac{4 \cdot 6 \cdot 8}{3 \cdot 5 \cdot 7} x x + \frac{4 \cdot 6 \cdot 8 \cdot 10}{3 \cdot 5 \cdot 7 \cdot 9} x^3 + \frac{4 \cdot 6 \cdot 8 \cdot 10 \cdot 12}{3 \cdot 5 \cdot 7 \cdot 9 \cdot 11} x^4 + \text{etc.}$$

This series may be transformed into the following continuous fraction: —

$$X = \cfrac{\frac{1}{3}}{1 - \cfrac{\frac{6}{5}x}{1 + \cfrac{\frac{2}{5.7}x}{1 - \cfrac{\frac{5.8}{7.9}x}{1 - \cfrac{\frac{1.4}{9.11}x}{1 - \cfrac{\frac{7.10}{11.13}x}{1 - \cfrac{\frac{3.6}{13.15}x}{1 - \cfrac{\frac{9.12}{15.17}x}{1 - \text{etc.}}}}}}}}}$$

The law according to which the coefficients

$$\frac{6}{5}, \; -\frac{2}{5.7}, \; \frac{5.8}{7.9}, \; \frac{1.4}{9.11}, \; \text{etc.}$$

proceed is obvious; in truth, the $n^{th}$ term of this series is, when $n$ is even,

$$\frac{n-3.n}{2n+1.2n+3},$$

when $n$ is odd,

$$\frac{n+2.n+5}{2n+1.2n+3}:$$

the further development of this subject would be too foreign from our purpose.
If now we put

$$\cfrac{x}{1 + \cfrac{\frac{2}{5.7}x}{1 - \cfrac{\frac{5.8}{7.9}x}{1 - \cfrac{\frac{1.4}{9.11}x}{1 - \text{etc.}}}}} = x - \xi$$

we have

$$X = \frac{1}{\frac{1}{3} - \frac{9}{10}(x - \xi)},$$

and

$$\xi = x - \tfrac{5}{6} + \frac{10}{9\,X},$$

or

$$\xi = \frac{\sin^3 g - \tfrac{3}{4}(2g - \sin 2g)(1 - \tfrac{6}{5}\sin^2\tfrac{1}{2}g)}{\tfrac{9}{10}(2g - \sin 2g)}.$$

The numerator of this expression is a quantity of the seventh order, the denominator of the third order, and $\xi$, therefore, of the fourth order, if $g$ is regarded as a quantity of the first order, and $x$ as of the second order. Hence it is inferred that this formula is not suited to the exact numerical computation of $\xi$ when $g$ does not denote a very considerable angle: then the following formulas are conveniently used for this purpose, which differ from each other in the changed order of the numerators in the fractional coefficients, and the first of which is derived without difficulty from the assumed value of $x - \xi$.*

$$[13]\quad \xi = \cfrac{\tfrac{2}{35}\,xx}{1 + \tfrac{2}{35}\,x - \cfrac{\tfrac{40}{63}\,x}{1 - \cfrac{\tfrac{4}{99}\,x}{1 - \cfrac{\tfrac{70}{143}\,x}{1 - \cfrac{\tfrac{18}{195}\,x}{1 - \cfrac{\tfrac{108}{255}\,x}{1 - \text{etc.,}}}}}}$$

or,

$$\xi = \cfrac{\tfrac{2}{35}\,xx}{1 - \tfrac{18}{35}\,x - \cfrac{\tfrac{4}{63}\,x}{1 - \cfrac{\tfrac{40}{99}\,x}{1 - \cfrac{\tfrac{18}{143}\,x}{1 - \cfrac{\tfrac{70}{195}\,x}{1 - \cfrac{\tfrac{40}{255}\,x}{1 - \text{etc.}}}}}}$$

In the third table annexed to this work are found, for all values of $x$ from 0 to 0.3, and for every thousandth, corresponding values of $\xi$ computed to seven places of decimals. This table shows at first sight the smallness of $\xi$ for

---

* The derivation of the latter supposes some less obvious transformations, to be explained on another occasion.

moderate values of $g$; thus, for example, for $E' - E = 10°$, or $g = 5°$, when $x = 0.00195$, is $\xi = 0.0000002$. It would be superfluous to continue the table further, since to the last term $x = 0.3$ corresponds $g = 66° 25'$, or $E' - E = 132° 50'$. The third column of the table, which contains values of $\xi$ corresponding to negative values of $x$, will be explained further on in its proper place.

## 91.

Equation 12, in which, in the case we are treating, the upper sign must evidently be adopted, obtains by the introduction of the quantity $\xi$ the form

$$m = (l + x)^{\frac{1}{2}} + \frac{(l+x)^{\frac{3}{2}}}{\frac{3}{4} - \frac{9}{10}(x - \xi)}.$$

Putting, therefore,

$$\sqrt{(l + x)} = \frac{m}{y},$$

and

[14] $\quad \dfrac{mm}{\frac{5}{6} + l + \xi} = h,$ $\qquad\qquad$ 0——

the proper reductions being made, we have

[15] $\quad h = \dfrac{(y-1)\,yy}{y + \frac{1}{6}}.$

If, accordingly, $h$ may properly be regarded as a known quantity, $y$ can be determined from it by means of a cubic equation, and then we shall have

[16] $\quad x = \dfrac{mm}{yy} - l.$

Now, although $h$ involves the quantity $\xi$, still unknown, it will be allowable to neglect it in the first approximation, and for $h$ to take

$$\frac{mm}{\frac{5}{6} + l},$$

since $\xi$ is undoubtedly a very small quantity in the case we are discussing. Hence $y$ and $x$ will be deduced by means of equations 15, 16; $\xi$ will be got from $x$ by table III., and with its aid the corrected value of $h$ will be obtained by formula 14, with which the same calculation repeated will give corrected values of $y$ and $x$: for the most part these will differ so little from the preceding, that $\xi$

taken again from table III., will not differ from the first value; otherwise it would be necessary to repeat the calculation anew until it underwent no further change. When the quantity $x$ shall be found, $g$ will be got by the formula $\sin^2 \frac{1}{2} g = x$.

These precepts refer to the first case, in which $\cos f$ is positive; in the other case, where it is negative, we put

$$\sqrt{(L-x)} = \frac{M}{Y}$$

and

[14*]   $\dfrac{MM}{L-\frac{5}{6}-\xi} = H,$

whence equation 12* properly reduced passes into this,

[15*]   $H = \dfrac{(Y+1)\,YY}{Y-\frac{1}{3}}.$

$Y$ and $H$ can be determined, accordingly, by this cubic equation, whence again $x$ will be derived from the equation

[16*]   $x = L - \dfrac{MM}{YY}.$

In the first approximation

$$\frac{MM}{L-\frac{5}{6}}$$

will be taken for $H$; $\xi$ will be taken from table III. with the value of $x$ derived from $H$ by means of the equations 15*, 16*; hence, by formula 14*, will be had the corrected value of $H$, with which the calculation will be repeated in the same manner. Finally, the angle $g$ will be determined from $x$ in the same way as in the first case.

## 92.

Although the equations 15, 15*, can have three real roots in certain cases, it will, notwithstanding, never be doubtful which should be selected in our problem. Since $h$ is evidently a positive quantity, it is readily inferred from the theory of equations, that equation 15 has one positive root with two imaginary or two negative. Now since

$$y = \frac{m}{\sqrt{(l+x)}}$$

must necessarily be a positive quantity, it is evident that no uncertainty remains here. So far as relates to equation 15*, we observe, in the first place, that $L$ is necessarily greater than 1; which is easily proved, if the equation given in article 89 is put under the form

$$L = 1 + \frac{\cos^2 \frac{1}{2} f}{-\cos f} + \frac{\tan^2 2 \omega}{-\cos f}.$$

Moreover, by substituting, in equation 12*, $Y \sqrt{(L - x)}$ in the place of $M$, we have

$$Y + 1 = (L - x) X,$$

and so

$$Y + 1 > (1 - x) X > \frac{4}{3} + \frac{4}{3.5} x + \frac{4.6}{3.5.7} x x + \frac{4.6.8}{3.5.7.9} x^3 + \text{etc.} > \frac{4}{3},$$

and therefore $Y > \frac{1}{3}$. Putting, therefore, $Y = \frac{1}{3} + Y'$, $Y'$ will necessarily be a positive quantity; hence also equation 15* passes into this,

$$Y'^3 + 2 Y' Y' + (1 - H) Y' + \frac{4}{27} - \frac{2}{9} H = 0,$$

which, it is easily proved from the theory of equations, cannot have several positive roots. Hence it is concluded that equation 15* would have only one root greater than $\frac{1}{3}$,[†] which, the remaining ones being neglected, it will be necessary to adopt in our problem.

## 93.

In order to render the solution of equation 15 the most convenient possible in cases the most frequent in practice, we append to this work a special table (Table II.), which gives for values of $h$ from 0 to 0.6 the corresponding logarithms computed with great care to seven places of decimals. The argument $h$, from 0 to 0.04, proceeds by single ten thousandths, by which means the second differences vanish, so that simple interpolation suffices in this part of the table. But since the table, if it were equally extended throughout, would be very voluminous, from $h = 0.04$ to the end it was necessary to proceed by single thousandths only; on which account, it will be necessary in this latter part to have regard to second differences, if we wish to avoid errors of some units

---

† If in fact we suppose that our problem admits of solution.

in the seventh figure. The smaller values, however, of $h$ are much the more frequent in practice.

The solution of equation 15, when $h$ exceeds the limit of the table, as also the solution of 15*, can be performed without difficulty by the indirect method, or by other methods sufficiently known. But it will not be foreign to the purpose to remark, that a small value of $g$ cannot coexist with a negative value of $\cos f$, except in an orbit considerably eccentric, as will readily appear from equation 20 given below in article 95.†

## 94.

The treatment of equations 12, 12*, explained in articles 91, 92, 93, rests upon the supposition that the angle $g$ is not very large, certainly within the limit $66°\,25'$, beyond which we do not extend table III. When this supposition is not correct, these equations do not require so many artifices; they can be most securely and conveniently solved by trial *without a change of form*. *Securely*, since the value of the expression

$$\frac{2\,g - \sin 2\,g}{\sin^3 g},$$

in which it is evident that $2\,g$ is to be expressed in parts of the radius, can, for greater values of $g$, be computed with *perfect accuracy* by means of the trigonometrical tables, which certainly cannot be done as long as $g$ is a small angle : *conveniently*, because heliocentric places distant from each other by so great an interval will scarcely ever be used for the determination of an orbit wholly unknown, while by means of equation 1 or 3 of article 88, an approximate value of $g$ follows with almost no labor, from any knowledge whatever of the orbit : lastly, from an approximate value of $g$, a corrected value will always be derived with few trials, satisfying with sufficient precision equation 12 or 12*. For the rest, when two given heliocentric places embrace more than one entire revolution, it is necessary to remember that just as many revolutions will have been completed by the eccentric anomaly, so that the angles $E' - E$, $v' - v$, either both lie between 0 and 360°,

---

† That equation shows, that if $\cos f$ is negative, $\varphi$ must, at least, be greater than $90° - g$.

or both between similar multiples of the whole circumference, and also $f$ and $g$ together, either between 0 and 180°, or between similar multiples of the semicircumference. If, finally, the orbit should be wholly unknown, and it should not appear whether the heavenly body, in passing from the first radius vector to the second, had described a part only of a revolution or, in addition, one entire revolution, or several, our problem would sometimes admit several different solutions: however, we do not dwell here on this case, which can rarely occur in practice.

## 95.

We pass to the second matter, that is, the determination of the elements from the angle $g$ when found. The major semiaxis is had here immediately by the formulas 10, 10*, instead of which the following can also be used:—

$$[17] \quad a = \frac{2\,m\,m \cos f \sqrt{r\,r'}}{y\,y \sin^2 g} = \frac{k\,k\,t\,t}{4\,y\,y\,r\,r \cos^2 f \sin^2 g}$$

$$[17^*] \quad a = \frac{-2\,M\,M \cos f \sqrt{r\,r'}}{Y\,Y \sin^2 g} = \frac{k\,k\,t\,t}{4\,Y\,Y\,r\,r' \cos^2 f \sin^2 g}.$$

The minor semiaxis $b = \sqrt{ap}$ is got by means of equation 1, which being combined with the preceding, there results

$$[18] \quad p = \left(\frac{y\,r\,r' \sin 2f}{k\,t}\right)^2$$

$$[18^*] \quad p = \left(\frac{Y\,r\,r' \sin 2f}{k\,t}\right)^2.$$

Now the elliptic sector contained between two radii vectores and the elliptic arc is $\tfrac{1}{2}k\,t\sqrt{p}$, also the triangle between the same radii vectores and the chord $\tfrac{1}{2}r\,r' \sin 2f$: wherefore, the ratio of the sector to the triangle is as $y$: 1 or $Y$: 1. This remark is of the greatest importance, and elucidates in a beautiful manner both the equations 12, 12*: for it is apparent from this, that in equation 12 the parts $m$, $(l+x)^{\frac{1}{2}}$, $X(l+x)^{\frac{3}{2}}$, and in equation 12* the parts $M$, $(L-x)^{\frac{1}{2}}$, $X(L-x)^{\frac{3}{2}}$, are respectively proportional to the area of the sector (between the radii vectores and the elliptic arc), the area of the triangle (between the radii vectores and the chord), the area of the segment (between the arc and the chord), because the first area is evidently equal to the sum or difference of the other two, according as $v' - v$ lies between 0 and 180°, or between 180° and 360°. In the case where $v' - v$ is greater than 360° we must conceive the area of the whole ellipse added to the area of the sector and the area of the segment just as many times as the motion comprises entire revolutions.

Moreover, since $b = a \cos \varphi$, from the combination of equations 1, 10, 10*, follow

[19]　$\cos \varphi = \dfrac{\sin g \tan f}{2\,(l + \sin^2 \frac{1}{2} g)}$

[19*]　$\cos \varphi = \dfrac{-\sin g \tan f}{2\,(L - \sin^2 \frac{1}{2} g)}$,

whence, by substituting for $l$, $L$, their values from article 89, we have

[20]　$\cos \varphi = \dfrac{\sin f \sin g}{1 - \cos f \cos g + 2 \tan^2 2\,\omega}$.

This formula is not adapted to the exact computation of the eccentricity when the latter is not great: but from it is easily deduced the more suitable formula

[21]　$\tan^2 \frac{1}{2} \varphi = \dfrac{\sin^2 \frac{1}{2}(f - g) + \tan^2 2\,\omega}{\sin^2 \frac{1}{2}(f + g) + \tan^2 2\,\omega}$.

to which the following form can likewise be given (by multiplying the numerator and denominator by $\cos^2 2\,\omega$)

[22]　$\tan^2 \frac{1}{2} \varphi = \dfrac{\sin^2 \frac{1}{2}(f - g) + \cos^2 \frac{1}{2}(f - g) \sin^2 2\,\omega}{\sin^2 \frac{1}{2}(f + g) + \cos^2 \frac{1}{2}(f - g) \sin^2 2\,\omega}$.

The angle $\varphi$ can always be determined with all accuracy by either formula, using, if thought proper, the auxiliary angles of which the tangents are

$$\dfrac{\tan 2\,\omega}{\sin \frac{1}{2}(f - g)}, \quad \dfrac{\tan 2\,\omega}{\sin \frac{1}{2}(f + g)}$$

for the former, or

$$\dfrac{\sin 2\,\omega}{\tan \frac{1}{2}(f - g)}, \quad \dfrac{\sin 2\,\omega}{\tan \frac{1}{2}(f + g)}$$

for the latter.

The following formula can be used for the determination of the angle $G$, which readily results from the combination of equations 5, 7, and the following one not numbered,

[23]　$\tan G = \dfrac{(r' - r) \sin g}{(r' + r) \cos g - 2 \cos f \sqrt{rr'}}$,

from which, by introducing $\omega$, is easily derived

$$[24] \quad \tan G = \frac{\sin g \sin 2\,\omega}{\cos^2 2\,\omega \sin \frac{1}{2}(f-g) \sin \frac{1}{2}(f+g) + \sin^2 2\,\omega \cos g}.$$

The ambiguity here remaining is easily decided by means of equation 7, which shows, that $G$ must be taken between 0 and 180°, or between 180° and 360°, as the numerator in these two formulas is positive or negative.

By combining equation 3 with these, which flow at once from equation II. article 8,

$$\frac{1}{r} - \frac{1}{r'} = \frac{2\,e}{p} \sin f \sin F$$

$$\frac{1}{r} + \frac{1}{r'} = \frac{2}{p} + \frac{2\,e}{p} \cos f \cos F,$$

the following will be derived without trouble,

$$[25] \quad \tan F = \frac{(r'-r)\sin f}{2 \cos g \sqrt{rr' - (r'+r)\cos f}};$$

from which, the angle $\omega$ being introduced, results

$$[26] \quad \tan F = \frac{\sin f \sin 2\,\omega}{\cos^2 2\,\omega \sin \frac{1}{2}(f-g) \sin \frac{1}{2}(f+g) - \sin^2 2\,\omega \cos f}.$$

The uncertainty here is removed in the same manner as before. — As soon as the angles $F$ and $G$ shall have been found, we shall have $v = F - f$, $v' = F + f$, whence the position of the perihelion will be known; also $E = G - g$, $E' = G + g$. Finally the mean motion in the time $t$ will be

$$\frac{k\,t}{a^{\frac{3}{2}}} = 2\,g - 2\,e \cos G \sin g,$$

the agreement of which expressions will serve to confirm the calculation; also, the epoch of the mean anomaly, corresponding to the middle time between the two given times, will be $G - e \sin G \cos g$, which can be transferred at pleasure to any other time. It is somewhat more convenient to compute the mean anomalies for the two given times by the formulas $E - e \sin E$, $E' - e \sin E'$, and to make use of their difference for a proof of the calculation, by comparing it with

$$\frac{k\,t}{a^{\frac{3}{2}}}.$$

## 96.

The equations in the preceding article possess so much neatness, that there may seem nothing more to be desired. Nevertheless, we can obtain certain other formulas, by which the elements of the orbit are determined much more elegantly and conveniently; but the development of these formulas is a little more abstruse.

We resume the following equations from article 8, which, for convenience, we distinguish by new numbers : —

$$\text{I.} \quad \sin\tfrac{1}{2}v\sqrt{\tfrac{r}{a}} = \sin\tfrac{1}{2}E\sqrt{(1+e)}$$

$$\text{II.} \quad \cos\tfrac{1}{2}v\sqrt{\tfrac{r}{a}} = \cos\tfrac{1}{2}E\sqrt{(1-e)}$$

$$\text{III.} \quad \sin\tfrac{1}{2}v'\sqrt{\tfrac{r'}{a}} = \sin\tfrac{1}{2}E'\sqrt{(1+e)}$$

$$\text{IV.} \quad \cos\tfrac{1}{2}v'\sqrt{\tfrac{r'}{a}} = \cos\tfrac{1}{2}E'\sqrt{(1-e)}.$$

We multiply I. by $\sin\tfrac{1}{2}(F+g)$, II. by $\cos\tfrac{1}{2}(F+g)$, whence, the products being added, we obtain

$$\cos\tfrac{1}{2}(f+g)\sqrt{\tfrac{r}{a}} = \sin\tfrac{1}{2}E\sin\tfrac{1}{2}(F+g)\sqrt{(1+e)} + \cos\tfrac{1}{2}E\cos\tfrac{1}{2}(F+g)\sqrt{(1-e)}$$

or, because

$$\sqrt{(1+e)} = \cos\tfrac{1}{2}\varphi + \sin\tfrac{1}{2}\varphi, \quad \sqrt{(1-e)} = \cos\tfrac{1}{2}\varphi - \sin\tfrac{1}{2}\varphi,$$

$$\cos\tfrac{1}{2}(f+g)\sqrt{\tfrac{r}{a}} = \cos\tfrac{1}{2}\varphi\cos(\tfrac{1}{2}F - \tfrac{1}{2}G + g) - \sin\tfrac{1}{2}\varphi\cos\tfrac{1}{2}(F+G).$$

In exactly the same way, by multiplying III. by $\sin\tfrac{1}{2}(F-g)$, IV. by $\cos\tfrac{1}{2}(F-g)$, the products being added, appears

$$\cos\tfrac{1}{2}(f+g)\sqrt{\tfrac{r'}{a}} = \cos\tfrac{1}{2}\varphi\cos(\tfrac{1}{2}F - \tfrac{1}{2}G - g) - \sin\tfrac{1}{2}\varphi\cos\tfrac{1}{2}(F+G).$$

The subtraction of the preceding from this equation gives

$$\cos\tfrac{1}{2}(f+g)\left(\sqrt{\tfrac{r'}{a}} - \sqrt{\tfrac{r}{a}}\right) = 2\cos\tfrac{1}{2}\varphi\sin g\sin\tfrac{1}{2}(F-G),$$

or, by introducing the auxiliary angle $\omega$,

$$[27] \quad \cos\tfrac{1}{2}(f+g)\tan 2\omega = \sin\tfrac{1}{2}(F-G)\cos\tfrac{1}{2}\varphi\sin g\sqrt[4]{\tfrac{aa}{rr'}}.$$

By transformations precisely similar, the development of which we leave to the skilful reader, are found

[28]  $\dfrac{\sin\frac{1}{2}(f+g)}{\cos 2\,\omega} = \cos\frac{1}{2}(F-G)\cos\frac{1}{2}\varphi\sin g\sqrt[4]{\dfrac{a\,a}{r\,r'}},$

[29]  $\cos\frac{1}{2}(f-g)\tan 2\,\omega = \sin\frac{1}{2}(F+G)\sin\frac{1}{2}\varphi\sin g\sqrt[4]{\dfrac{a\,a}{r\,r'}},$

[30]  $\dfrac{\sin\frac{1}{2}(f-g)}{\cos 2\,\omega} = \cos\frac{1}{2}(F+G)\sin\frac{1}{2}\varphi\sin g\sqrt[4]{\dfrac{a\,a}{r\,r'}}.$

When the first members of these four equations are known, $\frac{1}{2}(F-G)$ and

$$\cos\tfrac{1}{2}\varphi\sin g\sqrt[4]{\dfrac{a\,a}{r\,r'}} = P$$

will be determined from 27 and 29; and also, from 29 and 30, in the same manner, $\frac{1}{2}(F+G)$ and

$$\sin\tfrac{1}{2}\varphi\sin g\sqrt[4]{\dfrac{a\,a}{r\,r'}} = Q;$$

the doubt in the determination of the angles $\frac{1}{2}(F-G)$, $\frac{1}{2}(F+G)$, is to be so decided that $P$ and $Q$ may have the same sign as $\sin g$. Then $\frac{1}{2}\varphi$ and

$$\sin g\sqrt[4]{\dfrac{a\,a}{r\,r'}} = R$$

will be derived from $P$ and $Q$. From $R$ can be deduced

$$a = \frac{R\,R\sqrt{r\,r'}}{\sin^2 g},$$

and also

$$p = \frac{\sin^2 f\sqrt{r\,r'}}{R\,R},$$

unless we prefer to use the former quantity, which must be

$$\pm\sqrt{(2\,(l+\sin^2\tfrac{1}{2}g)\cos f)} = \pm\sqrt{(-2\,(L-\sin^2\tfrac{1}{2}g)\cos f)},$$

for a proof of the computation chiefly, in which case $a$ and $p$ are most conveniently determined by the formulas

$$b = \frac{\sin f\sqrt{r\,r'}}{\sin g},\quad a = \frac{b}{\cos\varphi},\quad p = b\cos\varphi.$$

Several of the equations of articles 88 and 95 can be employed for proving the calculation, to which we further add the following:—

$$\frac{2\tan 2\,\omega}{\cos 2\,\omega}\sqrt{\dfrac{r\,r'}{a\,a}} = e\sin G\sin g$$

$$\frac{2\tan 2\,\omega}{\cos 2\,\omega}\sqrt{\frac{p\,p}{r\,r'}}=e\sin F\sin f$$

$$\frac{2\tan 2\,\omega}{\cos 2\,\omega}=\tan\varphi\sin G\sin f=\tan\varphi\sin F\sin g.$$

Lastly, the mean motion and the epoch of the mean anomaly will be found in the same manner as in the preceding article.

## 97.

We will resume the two examples of article 87 for the illustration of the method explained in the 88th, and subsequent articles: it is hardly necessary to say that the meaning of the auxiliary angle $\omega$ thus far adhered to is not to be confounded with that with which the same symbol was taken in articles 86, 87.

I.  In the first example we have $f = 3°\ 47'\ 26''.865$, also

$$\log\frac{r'}{r}=9.9914599,\ \log\tan(45°+\omega)=9.997864975,\ \omega=-8'\ 27''.006.$$

Hence, by article 89,

| | | | | |
|---|---|---|---|---|
| $\log\sin^2\tfrac12 f$ . . . | 7.0389972 | $\log\tan^2 2\,\omega$ . . | 5.3832428 |
| $\log\cos f$ . . . . | 9.9990488 | $\log\cos f$ . . . | 9.9990488 |
| | 7.0399484 | | 5.3841940 |
| $=\log 0.0010963480$ | | $=\log 0.0000242211$ | |

and thus $l = 0.0011205691$, $\tfrac56+l = 0.8344539$.  Further we have

| | |
|---|---|
| $\log k\,t$ . . . . | 9.5766974 |
| $2\log k\,t$ . . . . | 9.1533948 |
| $C.\tfrac32\log r\,r'$ . . . | 9.0205181 |
| $C.\log 8\cos^3 f$ . . | 9.0997636 |
| $\log m\,m$ . . . | 7.2736765 |
| $\log(\tfrac56+l)$ . . . | 9.9214023 |
| | 7.3522742 |

The approximate value, therefore, of $h$ is $0.00225047$, to which in our table II. corresponds $\log y\,y = 0.0021633$.  We have, accordingly,

$$\log\frac{m\,m}{y\,y}=7.2715132,\ \text{or}\ \frac{m\,m}{y\,y}=0.001868587,$$

whence, by formula 16, $x = 0.0007480179$: wherefore, since $\xi$ is, by table III., wholly insensible, the values found for $h, y, x$, do not need correction. Now, the determination of the elements is as follows:—

$\log x$ . . . . . 6.8739120

$\log \sin \frac{1}{2} g$ . . . 8.4369560, $\frac{1}{2} g = 1° 34' 2''.0286$, $\frac{1}{2}(f+g) = 3° 27' 45''.4611$,
$\frac{1}{2}(f-g) = 19' 41''.4039$. Wherefore, by the formulas 27, 28, 29, 30, is had

| | | | | |
|---|---|---|---|---|
| $\log \tan 2\omega$ . . . | 7.6916214 $n$ | C. $\log \cos 2\omega$ . . . | 0.0000052 |
| $\log \cos \frac{1}{2}(f+g)$ . | 9.9992065 | $\log \sin \frac{1}{2}(f+g)$ . . | 8.7810188 |
| $\log \cos \frac{1}{2}(f-g)$ . | 9.9999929 | $\log \sin \frac{1}{2}(f-g)$ . . | 7.7579709 |
| $\log P \sin \frac{1}{2}(F-G)$ | 7.6908279 $n$ | $\log Q \sin \frac{1}{2}(F+G)$ . | 7.6916143 $n$ |
| $\log P \cos \frac{1}{2}(F-G)$ | 8.7810240 | $\log Q \cos \frac{1}{2}(F+G)$ . | 7.7579761 |
| $\frac{1}{2}(F-G) =$ | $-4° 38' 41''.54$ | $\log P = \log R \cos \frac{1}{2}\varphi$ | 8.7824527 |
| $\frac{1}{2}(F+G) =$ | 319 21 38 .05 | $\log Q = \log R \sin \frac{1}{2}\varphi$ | 7.8778355 |
| $F =$ | 314 42 56 .51 | Hence $\frac{1}{2}\varphi =$ | 7° 6' 0''.935 |
| $v =$ | 310 55 29 .64 | $\varphi =$ | 14 12 1 .87 |
| $v' =$ | 318 30 23 .37 | $\log R$ . . . . . . | 8.7857960 |
| $G =$ | 324 0 19 .59 | For proving the calculation. | |
| $E =$ | 320 52 15 .53 | $\frac{1}{2}\log 2 \cos f$ . . . . | 0.1500394 |
| $E' =$ | 327 8 23 .65 | $\frac{1}{2}\log(l+x) = \log \frac{m}{y}$ | 8.6357566 |
| | | | 8.7857960 |
| $\frac{1}{2}\log r r'$ . . . . | 0.3264939 | $\log \sin \varphi$ . . . . | 9.3897262 |
| $\log \sin f$ . . . . | 8.8202909 | $\log 206265$ . . . . | 5.3144251 |
| C. $\log \sin g$ . . . | 1.2621765 | $\log e$ in seconds . . | 4.7041513 |
| $\log b$ . . . . . | 0.4089613 | $\log \sin E$ . . . . . | 9.8000767 $n$ |
| $\log \cos \varphi$ . . . . | 9.9865224 | $\log \sin E'$ . . . . | 9.7344714 $n$ |
| $\log p$ . . . . . | 0.3954837 | $\log e \sin E$ . . . . | 4.5042280 $n$ |
| $\log a$ . . . . . | 0.4224389 | $\log e \sin E'$ . . . . | 4.4386227 $n$ |

| | | |
|---|---|---|
| $\log k$ . . . | 3.5500066 | $e \sin E = -31932''.14 = -8° 52' 12''.14$ |
| $\frac{3}{2} \log a$ . . . | 0.6336584 | $e \sin E' = -27455.08 = -7\ 37\ 35\ .08$ |
| | 2.9163482 | Hence the mean anomaly for the |
| $\log t$ . . . | 1.3411160 | first place $=$ $329° 44' 27''.67$ |
| | 4.2574642 | for the second $=$ $334\ 45\ 58\ .73$ |
| | | Difference $=$ $5\ \ 1\ 31\ .06$ |

Therefore, the mean daily motion is $824''.7989$. The mean motion in the time $t$ is $18091''.07 = 5° 1'31''.07$.

II. In the other example we have

$$f = 31° 27' 38''.32,\ \omega = -21' 50''.565,\ l = 0.08635659,\ \log mm = 9.3530651,$$

$$\frac{mm}{\frac{2}{3}+l},\ \text{or the approximate value of } h = 0.2451454\ ;$$

to this, in table II., corresponds $\log yy = 0.1722663$, whence is deduced

$$\frac{mm}{yy} = 0.15163477,\ x = 0.06527818,$$

hence from table III. is taken $\xi = 0.0002531$. Which value,being used, the corrected values become

$$h = 0.2450779,\ \log yy = 0.1722303,\ \frac{mm}{yy} = 0.15164737,\ x = 0.06529078,$$
$$\xi = 0.0002532.$$

If the calculation should be repeated with this value of $\xi$, differing, by a single unit only, in the seventh place, from the first; $h$, $\log yy$, and $x$ would not suffer sensible change, wherefore the value of $x$ already found is the true one, and we may proceed from it at once to the determination of the elements. We shall not dwell upon this here, as it differs in nothing from the preceding example.

III. It will not be out of place, to elucidate by an example the other case also in which $\cos f$ is negative. Let $v' - v = 224°\ 0'\ 0''$, or $f = 112°\ 0'\ 0''$, $\log r = 0.1394892$, $\log r' = 0.3978794$, $t = 206.80919$ days. Here we find $\omega = +4° 14' 43'' 78$, $L = 1.8942298$, $\log MM = 0.6724333$, the first approximate value of $\log H = 0.6467603$, whence by the solution of equation 15* is obtained $Y = 1.591432$, and afterwards $x = 0.037037$, to which, in table III., corresponds $\xi = 0.0000801$. Hence are derived the corrected values $\log H = 0.6467931$, $Y = 1.5915107$, $x = 0.0372195$, $\xi = 0.0000809$. The calculation being repeated with this value of $\xi$, we have $x = 0.0372213$, which value requires no further correction, since $\xi$ is not thereby changed. Afterwards is found $\frac{1}{2} g = 11°\ 7' 25''.40$, and hence in the same manner as in example I.

| | | | |
|---|---|---|---|
| $\frac{1}{2} (F — G) =$ | $3° 33' 53''.59$ | $\log P = \log R \cos \frac{1}{2} \varphi$ | $9.9700507$ |
| $\frac{1}{2} (F + G) =$ | $8\ 26\ \ 6\ .38$ | $\log Q = \log R \sin \frac{1}{2} \varphi\ \ .$ | $9.8580552$ |
| $F =$ | $11\ 59\ 59\ .97$ | $\frac{1}{2} \varphi =$ | $37° 41' 34''.27$ |
| $v =$ | $-100\ \ 0\ \ 0\ .03$ | $\varphi =$ | $75\ 23\ \ 8\ .54$ |
| $v' =$ | $+123\ 59\ 59\ .97$ | $\log R\ \ .\ .\ .\ .\ .\ .$ | $0.0717096$ |
| $G =$ | $4\ 52\ 12\ .79$ | For proving the calculation. | |
| $E =$ | $-17\ 22\ 38\ .01$ | $\log \dfrac{M}{Y} \sqrt{-2 \cos f}\ \ .\ \ .$ | $0.0717097$ |
| $E' =$ | $+27\ \ 7\ \ 3\ .59$ | | |

The angle $\varphi$ in such eccentric orbits is computed a little more exactly by formula 19*, which gives in our example $\varphi = 75° 23'\ 8''.57$; likewise the eccentricity $e$ is determined with greater precision by the formula

$$e = 1 — 2 \sin^2 (45° — \tfrac{1}{2} \varphi),$$

than by $e = \sin \varphi$; according to the former, $e = 0.96764630$.

By formula 1, moreover, is found $\log b = 0.6576611$, whence $\log p = 0.0595967$, $\log a = 1.2557255$, and the logarithm of the perihelion distance

$$\log \frac{p}{1 + e} = \log a\, (1 — e) = \log b \tan (45° — \tfrac{1}{2} \varphi) = 9.7656496.$$

It is usual to give the time of passage through the perihelion in place of the epoch of the mean anomaly in orbits approaching so nearly the form of the parabola; the intervals between this time and the times corresponding to the two given places can be determined from the known elements by the method given in article 41, of which intervals the difference or sum (according as the perihelion lies without or between the two given places), since it must agree with the time $t$, will serve to prove the computation. The numbers of this third example were based upon the assumed elements in the example of articles 38, 43, as indeed that very example had furnished our first place: the trifling differences of the elements obtained here owe their origin to the limited accuracy of the logarithmic and trigonometrical tables.

## 98.

The solution of our problem for the ellipse in the preceding article, might be rendered applicable also to the parabola and hyperbola, by considering the parabola as an ellipse, in which $a$ and $b$ would be infinite quantities, $\varphi = 90°$, finally $E, E', g,$ and $G = 0$; and in a like manner, the hyperbola as an ellipse, in which $a$ would be negative, and $b, E, E', g, G, \varphi$, imaginary: we prefer, however, not to employ these hypotheses, and to treat the problem for each of the conic sections separately. In this way a remarkable analogy will readily show itself between all three kinds.

Retaining in the PARABOLA the symbols $p, v, v', F, f, r, r', t$ with the same signification with which they had been taken above, we have from the theory of the parabolic motion:—

[1] $\sqrt{\dfrac{p}{2r}} = \cos \tfrac{1}{2}(F-f)$

[2] $\sqrt{\dfrac{p}{2r'}} = \cos \tfrac{1}{2}(F+f)$

$$\frac{2kt}{p^{\frac{3}{2}}} = \tan \tfrac{1}{2}(F+f) - \tan \tfrac{1}{2}(F-f) + \tfrac{1}{3}\tan^3 \tfrac{1}{2}(F+f) - \tfrac{1}{3}\tan^3 \tfrac{1}{2}(F-f)$$

$$= \Big(\tan \tfrac{1}{2}(F+f) - \tan \tfrac{1}{2}(F-f)\Big)\Big(1 + \tan \tfrac{1}{2}(F+f)\tan \tfrac{1}{2}(F-f) +$$

$$\tfrac{1}{3}\big(\tan \tfrac{1}{2}(F+f) - \tan \tfrac{1}{2}(F-f)\big)^2\Big)$$

$$= \frac{2\sin f\sqrt{rr'}}{p}\Big(\frac{2\cos f\sqrt{rr'}}{p} + \frac{4\sin^2 f r r'}{3pp}\Big),$$

whence

[3] $\quad kt = \dfrac{2\sin f \cos f . rr'}{\sqrt{p}} + \dfrac{4\sin^3 f (rr')^{\frac{3}{2}}}{3 p^{\frac{3}{2}}}$

Further, by the multiplication of the equations 1, 2, is derived

[4] $\quad \dfrac{p}{\sqrt{rr'}} = \cos F + \cos f$

and by the addition of the squares,

[5] $\quad \dfrac{p(r+r')}{2rr'} = 1 + \cos F \cos f.$

Hence, cos $F$ being eliminated,

$$[6] \quad p = \frac{2\,rr'\sin^2 f}{r + r' - 2\cos f\sqrt{rr'}}.$$

If, accordingly, we adopt here also the equations 9, 9*, article 88, the first for $\cos f$ positive, the second for $\cos f$ negative, we shall have,

$$[7] \quad p = \frac{\sin^2 f\sqrt{nr'}}{2\,l\cos f}$$

$$[7^*] \quad p = \frac{\sin^2 f\sqrt{rr'}}{-2\,L\cos f},$$

which values being substituted in equation 3, preserving the symbols $m$, $M$, with the meaning established by the equations 11, 11*, article 88, there result

$$[8] \quad m = l^{\frac{1}{2}} + \tfrac{4}{3}\,l^{\frac{3}{2}},$$

$$[8^*] \quad M = -L^{\frac{1}{2}} + \tfrac{4}{3}\,L^{\frac{3}{2}}.$$

These equations agree with 12, 12*, article 88, if we there put $g = 0$. Hence it is concluded that, if two heliocentric places which are satisfied by the parabola, are treated as if the orbit were elliptic, it must follow directly from the application of the rules of article 19, that $x = 0$; and vice versa, it is readily seen that, if by these rules we have $x = 0$, the orbit must come out a parabola instead of an ellipse, since by equations 1, 16, 17, 19, 20 we should have $b = \infty$, $a = \infty$, $\varphi = 90$. After this, the determination of the elements is easily effected. Instead of $p$, either equation 7 of the present article, or equation 18 of article 95 † might be employed: but for $F$ we have from equations 1, 2, of this article

$$\tan \tfrac{1}{2}\,F = \frac{\sqrt{r'} - \sqrt{r}}{\sqrt{r'} + \sqrt{r}}\,\cotan \tfrac{1}{2}\,f = \sin 2\,\omega \cotan \tfrac{1}{2}\,f,$$

if the auxiliary angle is taken with the same meaning as in article 89.

We further observe just here, that if in equation 3 we substitute instead of $p$ its value from 6, we obtain the well-known equation

$$kt = \tfrac{1}{3}\,(r + r' + \cos f \cdot \sqrt{rr'})\,(r + r' - 2\cos f \cdot \sqrt{rr'})^{\frac{1}{2}}\sqrt{2}.$$

---

† Whence it is at once evident that $y$ and $Y$ express the same ratios in the parabola as in the ellipse. See article 95.

## 99.

We retain, in the HYPERBOLA also, the symbols $p$, $v$, $v'$, $f$, $F$, $r$, $r'$, $t$ with the same meaning, but instead of the major semiaxis $a$, which is here negative, we shall write $-\alpha$; we shall put the eccentricity $e = \frac{1}{\cos \psi}$ in the same manner as above, article 21, etc. The auxiliary quantity there represented by $u$, we shall put for the first place $= \frac{C}{c}$, for the second $= Cc$, whence it is readily inferred that $c$ is always greater than 1, but that it differs less from one, other things being equal, in proportion as the two given places are less distant from each other. Of the equations developed in article 21, we transfer here the sixth and seventh slightly changed in form,

[1] $\quad \cos \frac{1}{2} v = \frac{1}{2} \left( \sqrt{\frac{C}{c}} + \sqrt{\frac{c}{C}} \right) \sqrt{\frac{(e-1)\alpha}{r}}$

[2] $\quad \sin \frac{1}{2} v = \frac{1}{2} \left( \sqrt{\frac{C}{c}} - \sqrt{\frac{c}{C}} \right) \sqrt{\frac{(e+1)\alpha}{r}}$

[3] $\quad \cos \frac{1}{2} v' = \frac{1}{2} \left( \sqrt{Cc} + \sqrt{\frac{1}{Cc}} \right) \sqrt{\frac{(e-1)\alpha}{r'}}$

[4] $\quad \sin \frac{1}{2} v' = \frac{1}{2} \left( \sqrt{Cc} - \sqrt{\frac{1}{Cc}} \right) \sqrt{\frac{(e+1)\alpha}{r'}}$.

From these result directly the following: —

[5] $\quad \sin F = \frac{1}{2} \alpha \left( C - \frac{1}{C} \right) \sqrt{\frac{ee-1}{rr'}}$

[6] $\quad \sin f = \frac{1}{2} \alpha \left( c - \frac{1}{c} \right) \sqrt{\frac{ee-1}{rr'}}$

[7] $\quad \cos F = \left( e \left( c + \frac{1}{c} \right) - \left( C + \frac{1}{C} \right) \right) \frac{\alpha}{2\sqrt{rr'}}$

[8] $\quad \cos f = \left( e \left( C + \frac{1}{C} \right) - \left( c + \frac{1}{c} \right) \right) \frac{\alpha}{2\sqrt{rr'}}$.

Again, by equation X. article 21, we have

$$\frac{r}{\alpha} = \frac{1}{2} e \left( \frac{C}{c} + \frac{c}{C} \right) - 1,$$

$$\frac{r'}{\alpha} = \frac{1}{2} e \left( Cc + \frac{1}{Cc} \right) - 1,$$

and hence,

[9] $\dfrac{r'-r}{\alpha} = \tfrac{1}{2} e \left( C - \dfrac{1}{C} \right) \left( c - \dfrac{1}{c} \right),$

[10] $\dfrac{r'+r}{\alpha} = \tfrac{1}{2} e \left( C + \dfrac{1}{C} \right) \left( c + \dfrac{1}{c} \right) - 2.$

This equation 10 combined with 8 gives

[11] $\alpha = \dfrac{r'+r - \left( c + \dfrac{1}{c} \right) \cos f . \sqrt{rr'}}{\tfrac{1}{2} \left( c - \dfrac{1}{c} \right)^2}.$

Putting, therefore, in the same manner as in the ellipse

$$\dfrac{\sqrt{\dfrac{r'}{r}} + \sqrt{\dfrac{r}{r'}}}{2 \cos f} = 1 + 2\, l, \text{ or } = 1 - 2\, L,$$

according as $\cos f$ is positive or negative, we have

[12] $\alpha = \dfrac{8 \left( l - \tfrac{1}{4} \left( \sqrt{c} - \sqrt{\dfrac{1}{c}} \right)^2 \right) \cos f . \sqrt{rr'}}{\left( c - \dfrac{1}{c} \right)^2},$

[12*] $\alpha = \dfrac{-8 \left( L + \tfrac{1}{4} \left( \sqrt{c} - \sqrt{\dfrac{1}{c}} \right)^2 \right) \cos f . \sqrt{rr'}}{\left( c - \dfrac{1}{c} \right)^2}.$

The computation of the quantity $l$ or $L$ is here made with the help of the auxiliary angle $\omega$ in the same way as in the ellipse. Finally, we have from equation XI. article 22, (using the hyperbolic logarithms),

$$\dfrac{kt}{a^{\frac{3}{2}}} = \tfrac{1}{2} e \left( Cc - \dfrac{1}{Cc} - \dfrac{C}{c} + \dfrac{c}{C} \right) - \log Cc + \log \dfrac{C}{c}$$

$$= \tfrac{1}{2} e \left( C + \dfrac{1}{C} \right) \left( c - \dfrac{1}{c} \right) - 2 \log c,$$

or, $C$ being eliminated by means of equation 8,

$$\dfrac{kt}{a^{\frac{3}{2}}} = \dfrac{\left( c - \dfrac{1}{c} \right) \cos f . \sqrt{rr'}}{\alpha} + \tfrac{1}{2} \left( cc - \dfrac{1}{cc} \right) - 2 \log c.$$

In this equation we substitute for $\alpha$ its value from 12, 12*; we then introduce the symbol $m$ or $M$, with the same meaning that formulas 11, 11*, article 88 give it; and finally, for the sake of brevity, we write

$$\tfrac{1}{4}\left(\sqrt{c}-\sqrt{\tfrac{1}{c}}\right)^2 = z, \qquad \frac{cc-\dfrac{1}{cc}-4\log c}{\tfrac{1}{4}\left(c-\dfrac{1}{c}\right)^3} = Z;$$

from which result the equations

[13]  $m = (l-z)^{\frac{1}{2}} + (l-z)^{\frac{3}{2}}\,Z,$

[13*]  $M = -(L+z)^{\frac{1}{2}} + (L+z)^{\frac{3}{2}}\,Z,$

which involve only one unknown quantity, $z$, since $Z$ is evidently a function of $z$ expressed by the following formula,

$$Z = \frac{(1+2z)\sqrt{(z+zz)} - \log\left(\sqrt{(1+z)}+\sqrt{z}\right)}{2\,(z+zz)^{\frac{3}{2}}}.$$

## 100.

In solving the equation 13 or 13*, we will first consider, by itself, that case in which the value of $z$ is not great, so that $Z$ can be expressed by a series proceeding according to the powers of $z$ and converging rapidly. Now we have

$$(1+2z)\sqrt{(z+zz)} = z^{\frac{1}{2}} + \tfrac{5}{2}z^{\frac{3}{2}} + \tfrac{7}{8}z^{\frac{5}{2}} \dots,$$

$$\log\left(\sqrt{(1+z)}+\sqrt{z}\right) = z^{\frac{1}{2}} - \tfrac{1}{6}z^{\frac{3}{2}} + \tfrac{3}{40}z^{\frac{5}{2}} \dots,$$

and so the numerator of $Z$ is $\tfrac{8}{3}z^{\frac{3}{2}} + \tfrac{4}{5}z^{\frac{5}{2}} \dots;$

and the denominator, $2\,z^{\frac{3}{2}} + 3\,z^{\frac{5}{2}} \dots,$

whence,

$$Z = \tfrac{4}{3} - \tfrac{8}{5}z \dots.$$

In order to discover the law of progression, we differentiate the equation

$$2\,(z+zz)^{\frac{3}{2}}\,Z = (1+2z)\sqrt{(z+zz)} - \log\left(\sqrt{(1+z)}+\sqrt{z}\right),$$

whence results, all the reductions being properly made,

$$2\,(z+zz)^{\frac{3}{2}}\frac{dZ}{dz} + 3\,Z(1+2z)\sqrt{(z+zz)} = 4\sqrt{(z+zz)},$$

or

$$(2z + 2zz)\frac{dZ}{dz} = 4 - (3 + 6z)\,Z,$$

whence, in the same manner as in article 90, is deduced

$$Z = \tfrac{4}{3} - \frac{4.6}{3.5}z + \frac{4.6.8}{3.5.7}zz - \frac{4.6.8.10}{3.5.7.9}z^3 + \frac{4.6.8.10.12}{3.5.7.9.11}z^4 - \text{etc.}$$

It is evident, therefore, that $Z$ depends upon $- z$ in axactly the same manner as $X$ does upon $x$ above in the ellipse ; wherefore, if we put

$$Z = \frac{1}{\tfrac{3}{4} + \tfrac{9}{10}(z + \zeta)},$$

$\zeta$ also will be determined in the same manner by $- z$ as $\xi$, above, by $x$, so that we have

[14]  $\zeta = \cfrac{\tfrac{2}{35}zz}{1 - \tfrac{2}{35}z + \cfrac{\tfrac{40}{63}z}{1 + \cfrac{\tfrac{4}{99}z}{1 + \cfrac{\tfrac{70}{143}z}{1 + \text{etc.,}}}}}$

or,

$\zeta = \cfrac{\tfrac{2}{35}zz}{1 + \tfrac{18}{35}z + \cfrac{\tfrac{4}{63}z}{1 + \cfrac{\tfrac{40}{99}z}{1 + \cfrac{\tfrac{18}{143}z}{1 + \text{etc.}}}}}$

In this way the values of $\zeta$ are computed for $z$ to single thousandths, from $z = 0$ up to $z = 0.3$, which values are given in the third column of table III.

## 101.

By introducing the quantity $\zeta$ and putting

$$\sqrt{(l - z)} = \frac{m}{y} \text{ or } \sqrt{(L + z)} = \frac{M}{Y},$$

also

[15]  $\dfrac{mm}{\tfrac{5}{6} + l + \zeta} = h$, or

[15*]  $\dfrac{MM}{L - \tfrac{5}{6} - \zeta} = H,$

equations 13, 13* assume the form,

[16] $\dfrac{(y-1)\,yy}{y+\frac{1}{9}} = h,$

[16*] $\dfrac{(Y+1)\,YY}{Y-\frac{1}{9}} = H,$

and so, are wholly identical with those at which we arrived in the ellipse (15, 15*, article 91). Hence, therefore, so far as $h$ or $H$ can be considered as known, $y$ or $Y$ can be deduced, and afterwards we shall have

[17] $z = l - \dfrac{mm}{yy},$

[17*] $z = \dfrac{MM}{YY} - L.$

From these we gather, that all the operations directed above for the ellipse serve equally for the hyperbola, up to the period when $y$ or $Y$ shall have been deduced from $h$ or $H$; but after that, the quantity

$$\frac{mm}{yy} - l, \text{ or } L - \frac{MM}{YY},$$

which, in the ellipse, should become positive, and in the parabola, 0, must in the hyperbola become negative: the nature of the conic section will be defined by this criterion. Our table will give $\zeta$ from $z$ thus found, hence will arise the corrected value of $h$ or $H$, with which the calculation is to be repeated until all parts exactly agree.

After the true value of $z$ is found, $c$ might be derived from it by means of the formula

$$c = 1 + 2z + 2\sqrt{(z+zz)},$$

but it is preferable, for subsequent uses, to introduce also the auxiliary angle $n$, to be determined by the equation

$$\tan 2n = 2\sqrt{(z+zz)};$$

hence we have

$$c = \tan 2n + \sqrt{(1 + \tan^2 2n)} = \tan(45° + n).$$

## 102.

Since $y$ must necessarily be positive, as well in the hyperbola as in the ellipse, the solution of equation 16 is, here also, free from ambiguity:[†] but with respect to equation 16*, we must adopt a method of reasoning somewhat different from that employed in the case of the ellipse. It is easily demonstrated, from the theory of equations, that, for a positive value of $H$[‡], this equation (if indeed it has any positive real root) has, with one negative, two positive roots, which will either both be equal, that is, equal to

$$\tfrac{1}{6}\sqrt{5} - \tfrac{1}{6} = 0.20601,$$

or one will be greater, and the other less, than this limit. We demonstrate in the following manner, that, in our problem (assuming that $z$ is not a large quantity, at least not greater than 0.3, that we may not abandon the use of the third table) the greater root is always, of necessity, to be taken. If in equation 13*, in place of $M$, is substituted $Y\sqrt{(L+z)}$, we have

$$Y + 1 = (L + z)\,Z > (1 + z)\,Z, \text{ or}$$

$$Y > \tfrac{1}{3} - \frac{4}{3.5}z + \frac{4.6}{3.5.7}zz - \frac{4.6.8}{3.5.7.9}z^3 + \text{ etc.}$$

whence it is readily inferred that, for such small values of $z$ as we here suppose, $Y$ must always be $> 0.20601$. In fact, we find, on making the calculation, that $z$ must be equal to 0.79858 in order that $(1 + z)\,Z$ may become equal to this limit: but we are far from wishing to extend our method to such great values of $z$.

## 103.

When $z$ acquires a greater value, exceeding the limits of table III., the equations 13, 13* are always safely and conveniently solved by trial in their unchanged form; and, in fact, for reasons similar to those which we have explained

---

† It will hardly be necessary to remark, that our table II. can be used, in the hyperbola, as well as in the ellipse, for the solution of this equation, as long as $h$ does not exceed its limit.

‡ The quantity $H$ evidently cannot become negative, unless $\zeta > \tfrac{1}{6}$; but to such a value of $\zeta$ would correspond a value of $z$ greater than 2.684, thus, far exceeding the limits of this method.

in article 94 for the ellipse. In such a case, it is admissible to suppose the elements of the orbit, roughly at least, known: and then an approximate value of $n$ is immediately had by the formula

$$\tan 2\,n = \frac{\sin f \sqrt{r r'}}{a \sqrt{(e e - 1')}}$$

which readily follows from equation 6, article 99. $z$ also will be had from $n$ by the formula

$$z = \frac{1 - \cos 2\,n}{2 \cos 2\,n} = \frac{\sin^2 n}{\cos 2\,n};$$

and from the approximate value of $z$, that value will be deduced with a few trials which exactly satisfies the equation 13, 13*. These equations can also be exhibited in this form,

$$m = \left(l - \frac{\sin^2 n}{\cos 2 n}\right)^{\frac{1}{2}} + 2\left(l - \frac{\sin^2 n}{\cos 2 n}\right)^{\frac{3}{2}} \left\{ \frac{\frac{\tan 2 n}{\cos 2 n} - \text{hyp.} \log \tan\left(45° + n\right)}{\tan^3 2\,n} \right\}$$

$$M = -\left(L + \frac{\sin^2 n}{\cos 2 n}\right)^{\frac{1}{2}} + 2\left(L + \frac{\sin^2 n}{\cos 2 n}\right)^{\frac{3}{2}} \left\{ \frac{\frac{\tan 2 n}{\cos 2 n} - \text{hyp.} \log \tan\left(45° + n\right)}{\tan^3 2\,n} \right\}$$

and thus, $z$ being **neglected**, the true value of $n$ can be deduced.

## 104.

It remains to determine the elements themselves from $z$, $n$, or $c$. Putting $a \sqrt{(e e - 1)} = \beta$, we shall have from equation 6, article 99,

[18]  $\beta = \dfrac{\sin f \sqrt{r r'}}{\tan 2\,n}.$

combining this formula with 12, 12*, article 99, we derive,

[19]  $\sqrt{(e e - 1)} = \tan \psi = \dfrac{\tan f \tan 2\,n}{2\,(l - z)},$

[19*]  $\tan \psi = - \dfrac{\tan f \tan 2\,n}{2\,(L + z)},$

whence the eccentricity is conveniently and accurately computed; $a$ will result from $\beta$ and $\sqrt{(e e - 1)}$ by division, and $p$ by multiplication, so that we have,

$$\alpha = \frac{2\,(l-z)\cos f.\sqrt{r\,r'}}{\tan^2 2\,n} = \frac{2\,m\,m\cos f.\sqrt{r\,r'}}{y\,y\tan^2 2\,n} = \frac{k\,k\,t\,t}{4\,y\,y\,r\,r'\cos^2 f\tan^2 2\,n}$$

$$= \frac{-2\,(L+z)\cos f.\sqrt{r\,r'}}{\tan^2 2\,n} = \frac{-2\,M\,M\cos f.\sqrt{r\,r'}}{Y\,Y\tan^2 2\,n} = \frac{k\,k\,t\,t}{4\,Y\,Y\,r\,r'\cos^2 f\tan^2 2\,n},$$

$$p = \frac{\sin f.\tan f.\sqrt{r\,r'}}{2\,(l-z)} = \frac{y\,y\sin f.\tan f.\sqrt{r\,r'}}{2\,m\,m} = \left(\frac{y\,r\,r'\sin 2f}{k\,t}\right)^2$$

$$= \frac{-\sin f.\tan f.\sqrt{r\,r'}}{2\,(L+z)} = \frac{-Y\,Y\sin f.\tan f.\sqrt{r\,r'}}{2\,M\,M} = \left(\frac{Y\,r\,r'\sin 2f}{k\,t}\right)^2.$$

The third and sixth expressions for $p$, which are wholly identical with the formulas 18, 18*, article 95, show that what is there said concerning the meaning of the quantities $y$, $Y$, holds good also for the hyperbola.

From the combination of the equations 6, 9, article 99, is derived

$$(r'-r)\sqrt{\frac{e\,e-1}{r\,r'}} = e\sin f.\left(C-\frac{1}{C}\right);$$

by introducing therefore $\psi$ and $\omega$, and by putting $C = \tan(45° + N)$, we have

[20] $\quad \tan 2\,N = \dfrac{2\sin\psi\tan 2\,\omega}{\sin f\cos 2\,\omega}.$

$C$ being hence found, the values of the quantity expressed by $u$ in article 21, will be had for both places; after that, we have by equation III., article 21,

$$\tan \tfrac{1}{2}\,v = \frac{C-c}{(C+c)\tan\tfrac{1}{2}\,\psi}$$

$$\tan \tfrac{1}{2}\,v' = \frac{Cc-1}{(Cc+1)\tan\tfrac{1}{2}\,\psi},$$

or, by introducing for $C, c$, the angles $N, n$,

[21] $\quad \tan \tfrac{1}{2}\,v = \dfrac{\sin(N-n)}{\cos(N+n)\tan\tfrac{1}{2}\,\psi}$

[22] $\quad \tan \tfrac{1}{2}\,v' = \dfrac{\sin(N+n)}{\cos(N-n)\tan\tfrac{1}{2}\,\psi}.$

Hence will be determined the true anomalies $v, v'$, the difference of which compared with $2f$ will serve at once for proving the calculation.

Finally, the interval of time from the perihelion to the time corresponding to the first place, is readily determined by formula XI., article 22, to be

$$\frac{\alpha^{\frac{3}{2}}}{k}\left(\frac{2\,e\cos(N+n)\sin(N-n)}{\cos 2\,N\cos 2\,n} - \text{hyp.}\log\frac{\tan(45°+N)}{\tan(45°+n)}\right),$$

and, in the same manner, the interval of time from the perihelion to the time corresponding to the second place,

$$\frac{\alpha^{\frac{3}{2}}}{k}\left(\frac{2\,e\cos\,(N-n)\sin\,(N+n)}{\cos 2\,N\cos 2\,n} - \text{hyp.log} \tan\,(45^{\circ} + N)\tan\,(45^{\circ} + n)\right).$$

If, therefore, the first time is put $= T - \frac{1}{2}\,t$, and, therefore, the second $= T + \frac{1}{2}\,t$, we have

[23]  $$T = \frac{\alpha^{\frac{3}{2}}}{k}\left(\frac{e\tan 2\,N}{\cos 2\,n} - \log\tan\,(45^{\circ} + N)\right),$$

whence the time of perihelion passage will be known; finally,

[24]  $$t = \frac{2\,\alpha^{\frac{3}{2}}}{k}\left(\frac{e\tan 2\,n}{\cos 2\,N} - \log\tan\,(45^{\circ} + n)\right),$$

which equation, if it is thought proper, can be applied to the final proof of the calculation.

## 105.

To illustrate these precepts, we will make an example from the two places in articles 23, 24, 25, 46, computed for the same hyperbolic elements. Let, accordingly,

$v' - v = 48^{\circ}\,12'\ 0''$, or $f = 24^{\circ}\ 6'\ 0''$, $\log r = 0.0333585$, $\log r' = 0.2008541$,
$t = 51.49788$ days.

Hence is found

$$\omega = 2^{\circ}\,45'\,28''.47,\ l = 0.05796039,$$

$\frac{m\,m}{\frac{1}{4}+l}$ or the approximate value of $h = 0.0644371$; hence, by table II.,

$$\log y\,y = 0.0560848,\ \frac{m\,m}{y\,y} = 0.05047454,\ z = 0.00748585,$$

to which in table III. corresponds $\zeta = 0.0000032$. Hence the corrected value of $h$ is $0.06443691$,

$$\log y\,y = 0.0560846,\ \frac{m\,m}{y\,y} = 0.05047456,\ z = 0.00748583,$$

which values require no further correction, because $\zeta$ is not changed by them. The computation of the elements is as follows: —

| | |
|---|---|
| $\log z$ . . . . . | 7.8742399 |
| $\log (1 + z)$ . . . | 0.0032389 |
| $\log \sqrt{(z + zz)}$ . . | 8.9387394 |
| $\log 2$ . . . . . | 0.3010300 |
| $\log \tan 2n$ . . . | 9.2397694 |
| $2n =$ | $9° 51' 11''.816$ |
| $n =$ | 4 55 35 .908 |
| $\log \sin f$ . . . . | 9.6110118 |
| $\log \sqrt{r r'}$ . . . . | 0.1171063 |
| C. $\log \tan 2n$ . . | 0.7602306 |
| $\log \beta$ . . . . . | 0.4883487 |
| $\log \tan \psi$ . . . . | 9.8862868 |
| $\log \alpha$ . . . . . | 0.6020619 |
| $\log p$ . . . . . | 0.3746355 |

(they should be 0.6020600 and 0.3746356)

| | |
|---|---|
| $\log \sin (N - n)$ . | 8.7406274 |
| C. $\log \cos (N + n)$ . | 0.0112902 |
| $\log \cot \tfrac{1}{2} \psi$ . . . | 0.4681829 |
| $\log \tan \tfrac{1}{2} v$ . . . | 9.2201005 |
| $\tfrac{1}{2} v =$ | $9° 25' 29''.97$ |
| $v =$ | 18 50 59 .94 |

(it should be $18° 51' 0''$)

| | |
|---|---|
| $\log e$ . . . . . | 0.1010184 |
| $\log \tan 2N$ . . . | 9.4621341 |
| C. $\log \cos 2n$ . . | 0.0064539 |
| | 9.5696064 |
| number = | 0.37119863 |
| hyp $\log \tan (45° + N) =$ | 0.28591251 |
| Difference = | 0.08528612 |

| | |
|---|---|
| $\log \tan f$ . . . . . | 9.6506199 |
| $\log \tfrac{1}{2} \tan 2n$ . . . . | 8.9387394 |
| C. $\log (l - z)$ . . . | 1.2969275 |
| $\log \tan \psi$ . . . . | 9.8862868 |
| $\psi =$ | $37° 34' 59''.77$ |

(it should be $37° 35' 0''$)

| | |
|---|---|
| C. $\log \tfrac{1}{2} \sin f$ . . . | 0.6900182 |
| $\log \tan 2\omega$ . . . . | 8.9848318 |
| C. $\log \cos 2\omega$ . . . | 0.0020156 |
| $\log \sin \psi$ . . . . . | 9.7852685 |
| $\log \tan 2N$ . . . . | 9.4621341 |
| $2N =$ | $16° 9' 46''.253$ |
| $N =$ | 8 4 53 .127 |
| $N - n =$ | 3 9 17 .219 |
| $N + n =$ | 13 0 29 .035 |

| | |
|---|---|
| $\log \sin (N + n)$ . . | 9.3523527 |
| C. $\log \cos (N - n)$ . . | 0.0006587 |
| $\log \cot \tfrac{1}{2} \psi$ . . . . | 0.4681829 |
| $\log \tan \tfrac{1}{2} v'$ . . . . | 9.8211943 |
| $\tfrac{1}{2} v' =$ | $33° 31' 29''.93$ |
| $v' =$ | 67 2 59 .86 |

(it should be $67° 3' 0''$)

| | |
|---|---|
| $\log e$ . . . . . . | 0.1010184 |
| $\log \tan 2n$ . . . . | 9.2397694 |
| C. $\log \cos 2N$ . . . | 0.0175142 |
| | 9.3583020 |
| number = | 0.22819284 |
| hyp $\log \tan (45° + n) =$ | 0.17282621 |
| Difference = | 0.05536663 |

| | | | | |
|---|---|---|---|---|
| log ;  . . . . . . | 8.9308783 | log  . . . . . . | 8.7432480 |
| $\frac{3}{2}\log\alpha$  . . . . . | 0.9030928 | $\frac{3}{2}\log\alpha$  . . . . . | 0.9030928 |
| C. log $k$ . . . . . | 1.7644186 | C. log $k$ . . . . . | 1.7644186 |
| log $T$  . . . . . | 1.5983897 | log 2 . . . . . . | 0.3010300 |
| $T=$ | 39.66338 | log $t$ . . . . . . | 1.7117894 |
| | | $t=$ | 51.49788 |

Therefore, the perihelion passage is 13.91444 days distant from the time corresponding to the first place, and 65.41232 days from the time corresponding to the second place. Finally, we must attribute to the limited accuracy of the tables, the small differences of the elements here obtained, from those, according to which, the given places had been computed.

## 106.

In a treatise upon the most remarkable relations pertaining to the motion of heavenly bodies in conic sections, we cannot pass over in silence the elegant expression of the time by means of the major semiaxis, the sum $r + r'$, and the chord joining the two places. This formula appears to have been first discovered, for the parabola, by the illustrious EULER, (Miscell. Berolin, T. VII. p. 20,) who nevertheless subsequently neglected it, and did not extend it to the ellipse and hyperbola: they are mistaken, therefore, who attribute the formula to the illustrious LAMBERT, although the merit cannot be denied this geometer, of having independently obtained this expression when buried in oblivion, and of having extended it to the remaining conic sections. Although this subject is treated by several geometers, still the careful reader will acknowledge that the following explanation is not superfluous. We begin with the elliptic motion.

We observe, in the first place, that the angle $2f$ described about the sun (article 88, from which we take also the other symbols) may be assumed to be less than $360°$; for it is evident that if this angle is increased by $360°$, the time is increased by one revolution, or

$$\frac{a^{\frac{3}{2}}.360°}{k} = a^{\frac{3}{2}} \times 365.25 \text{ days.}$$

Now, if we denote the chord by $\varrho$, we shall evidently have

$$\varrho\varrho = (r' \cos v' - r \cos v)^2 + (r' \sin v' - r \sin v)^2,$$

and, therefore, by equations VIII., IX., article 8,

$$\varrho\varrho = a\,a\,(\cos E' - \cos E)^2 + a\,a\,\cos^2 \varphi\,(\sin E' - \sin E)^2$$
$$= 4\,a\,a\,\sin^2 g\,(\sin^2 G + \cos^2 \varphi \cos^2 G) = 4\,a\,a\,\sin^2 g\,(1 - e\,e\,\cos^2 G).$$

We introduce the auxiliary angle $h$ such, that $\cos h = e \cos G$; at the same time, that all ambiguity may be removed, we suppose $h$ to be taken between $0°$ and $180°$, whence $\sin h$ will be a positive quantity. Therefore, as $g$ lies between the same limits (for if $2\,g$ should amount to $360°$ or more, the motion would attain to, or would surpass an entire revolution about the sun), it readily follows from the preceding equation that $\varrho = 2\,a \sin g \sin h$, if the chord is considered a positive quantity. Since, moreover, we have

$$r + r' = 2\,a\,(1 - e \cos g \cos G) = 2\,a\,(1 - \cos g \cos h),$$

it is evident that, if we put $h - g = \delta$, $h + g = \varepsilon$, we have,

[1]  $r + r' - \varrho = 2\,a\,(1 - \cos \delta) = 4\,a \sin^2 \tfrac{1}{2}\,\delta,$

[2]  $r + r' + \varrho = 2\,a\,(1 - \cos \varepsilon) = 4\,a \sin^2 \tfrac{1}{2}\,\varepsilon.$

Finally, we have

$$k\,t = a^{\frac{3}{2}}(2\,g - 2\,e \sin g \cos G) = a^{\frac{3}{2}}(2\,g - 2 \sin g \cos h),$$

or

[3]  $k\,t = a^{\frac{3}{2}}\Big(\varepsilon - \sin \varepsilon - (\delta - \sin \delta)\Big).$

Therefore, the angles $\delta$ and $\varepsilon$ can be determined by equations 1, 2, from $r + r'$, $\varrho$, and $a$; wherefore, the time $t$ will be determined, from the same equations, by equation 3. If it is preferred, this formula can be expressed thus:

$$k\,t = a^{\frac{3}{2}}\Big(\text{arc} \cos \frac{2\,a - (r + r') - \varrho}{2\,a} - \sin \text{arc} \cos \frac{2\,a - (r + r') - \varrho}{2\,a}$$
$$- \text{arc} \cos \frac{2\,a - (r + r') + \varrho}{2\,a} + \sin \text{arc} \cos \frac{2\,a - (r + r') + \varrho}{2\,a}\Big).$$

But an uncertainty remains in the determination of the angles $\delta, \varepsilon$, by their cosines, which must be examined more closely. It appears at once, that $\delta$ must lie between $-180°$ and $+180°$, and $\varepsilon$ between $0°$ and $360°$: but thus both angles seem to admit of a double, and the resulting time, of a quadruple, determination. We have, however, from equation 5, article 88,

$$\cos f . \sqrt{r\, r'} = a\, (\cos g - \cos h) = 2\, a \sin \tfrac{1}{2}\, \delta \sin \tfrac{1}{2}\, \varepsilon :$$

now, $\sin \tfrac{1}{2}\, \varepsilon$ is of necessity a positive quantity, whence we conclude, that $\cos f$ and $\sin \tfrac{1}{2}\, \delta$ are necessarily affected by the same sign; and, for this reason, that $\delta$ is to be taken between $0°$ and $180°$, or between $-180°$ and $0°$ according as $\cos f$ happens to be positive or negative, that is, according as the heliocentric motion happens to be less or more than $180°$. Moreover, it is evident that $\delta$ must necessarily be $0°$, for $2f = 180°$. In this manner $\delta$ is completely determined. But the determination of the angle $\varepsilon$ continues, of necessity, doubtful, so that two values are obtained for the time, of which it is impossible to determine the true one, unless it is known from some other source. Finally, the reason of this phenomenon is readily seen: for it is known that, through two given points, it is possible to describe *two* different ellipses, both of which can have their focus in the same given point and, at the same time, the same major semiaxis;* but the motion from the first place to the second in these ellipses is manifestly performed in unequal times.

## 107.

Denoting by $\chi$ any arc whatever between $-180°$ and $+180°$, and by $s$ the sine of the arc $\tfrac{1}{2}\,\chi$, it is known that,

$$\tfrac{1}{2}\chi = s + \tfrac{1}{3} \cdot \tfrac{1}{2} s^3 + \tfrac{1}{5} \cdot \frac{1.3}{2.4} s^5 + \tfrac{1}{7} \cdot \frac{1.3.5}{2.4.6} s^7 + \text{etc.}$$

Moreover, we have

$$\tfrac{1}{2} \sin \chi = s \sqrt{(1 - s\,s)} = s - \tfrac{1}{2} s^3 - \frac{1.1}{2.4} s^5 - \frac{1.1.3}{2.4.6} s^7 - \text{etc.}$$

and thus,

$$\chi - \sin \chi = 4\,(\tfrac{1}{3} s^3 + \tfrac{1}{5} \cdot \tfrac{1}{2} s^5 + \tfrac{1}{7} \cdot \frac{1.3}{2.4} s^7 + \tfrac{1}{9} \cdot \frac{1.3.5}{2.4.6} s^9 + \text{etc.}$$

---

* A circle being described from the first place, as a centre, with the radius $2\, a - r$, and another, from the second place, with the radius $2\, a - r'$, it is manifest that the other focus of the ellipse lies in the intersection of these circles. Wherefore, since, generally speaking, two intersections are given, two different ellipses will be produced.

We substitute in this series for $s$, successively

$$\tfrac{1}{2}\sqrt{\frac{r+r'-\varrho}{a}}, \text{ and } \tfrac{1}{2}\sqrt{\frac{r+r'+\varrho}{a}},$$

and we multiply the results by $a^{\frac{3}{2}}$; and thus obtain respectively, the series,

$$\tfrac{1}{6}(r+r'-\varrho)^{\frac{3}{2}}+\tfrac{1}{80}\frac{1}{a}(r+r'-\varrho)^{\frac{5}{2}}+\tfrac{3}{1792}\frac{1}{aa}(r+r'-\varrho)^{\frac{7}{2}}+$$

$$\tfrac{5}{18432}\frac{1}{a^3}(r+r'-\varrho)^{\frac{9}{2}}+ \text{ etc.}$$

$$\tfrac{1}{6}(r+r'+\varrho)^{\frac{3}{2}}+\tfrac{1}{80}\frac{1}{a}(r+r'+\varrho)^{\frac{5}{2}}+\tfrac{3}{1792}\frac{1}{aa}(r+r'+\varrho)^{\frac{7}{2}}+$$

$$\tfrac{5}{18432}\frac{1}{a^3}(r+r'+\varrho)^{\frac{9}{2}}+ \text{ etc.}$$

the sums of which we will denote by $T, U$. Now it is easily seen, since

$$2\sin\tfrac{1}{2}\delta=\pm\sqrt{\frac{r+r'-\varrho}{a}},$$

the upper or lower sign having effect according as $2f$ is less or more than 180°, that

$$a^{\frac{3}{2}}(\delta-\sin\delta)=\pm T,$$

the sign being similarly determined. In the same manner, if for $\varepsilon$ is taken the smaller value, inferior to 180°, we have

$$a^{\frac{3}{2}}(\varepsilon-\sin\varepsilon)=U;$$

but the other value, which is the complement of the former to 360°, being taken, we evidently have

$$a^{\frac{3}{2}}(\varepsilon-\sin\varepsilon)=a^{\frac{3}{2}}\,360°-U.$$

Hence, therefore, are obtained two values for the time $t$,

$$\frac{U\mp T}{k}, \text{ and } \frac{a^{\frac{3}{2}}\,360°}{k}-\frac{U\pm T}{k}.$$

## 108.

If the parabola is regarded as an ellipse, of which the major axis is infinitely great, the expression for the time, found in the preceding article, passes into

$$\frac{1}{6k}\left((r+r'+\varrho)^{\frac{3}{2}}\mp(r+r'-\varrho)^{\frac{3}{2}}\right):$$

but since this derivation of the formula might perhaps seem open to some doubts, we will give another not depending upon the ellipse.

Putting, for the sake of brevity,

$$\tan \tfrac{1}{2} v = \theta, \ \tan \tfrac{1}{2} v' = \theta', \text{ we have } r = \tfrac{1}{2} p \, (1 + \theta \theta), \ r' = \tfrac{1}{2} p \, (1 + \theta' \theta'),$$

$$\cos v = \frac{1 - \theta \theta}{1 + \theta \theta}, \ \cos v' = \frac{1 - \theta' \theta'}{1 + \theta' \theta'}, \ \sin v = \frac{2 \theta}{1 + \theta \theta}, \ \sin v' = \frac{2 \theta'}{1 + \theta' \theta'}.$$

Hence follow

$$r' \cos v' - r \cos v = \tfrac{1}{2} p \, (\theta \theta - \theta' \theta'), \ r' \sin v' - r \sin v = p \, (\theta' - \theta),$$

and thus

$$\varrho \varrho = \tfrac{1}{4} p p \, (\theta' - \theta)^2 \, (4 + (\theta' + \theta)^2).$$

Now it is readily seen that $\theta' - \theta = \dfrac{\sin f}{\cos \frac{1}{2} v \cos \frac{1}{2} v'}$ is a positive quantity: putting, therefore,

$$\sqrt{(1 + \tfrac{1}{4} (\theta' + \theta)^2)} = \eta, \text{ we have } \varrho = p \, (\theta' - \theta) \, \eta.$$

Moreover,

$$r + r' = \tfrac{1}{2} p \, (2 + \theta \theta + \theta' \theta') = p \, (\eta \eta + \tfrac{1}{4} (\theta' - \theta)^2):$$

wherefore, we have

$$\frac{r + r' + \varrho}{p} = (\eta + \tfrac{1}{2} (\theta' - \theta))^2,$$

$$\frac{r + r' - \varrho}{p} = (\eta - \tfrac{1}{2} (\theta' - \theta))^2.$$

From the former equation is readily deduced,

$$+ \sqrt{\frac{r + r' + \varrho}{p}} = \eta + \tfrac{1}{2} (\theta' - \theta)$$

as $\eta$ and $\theta' - \theta$ are positive quantities; but since $\tfrac{1}{2} (\theta' - \theta)$ is smaller or greater than $\eta$, according as

$$\eta \eta - \tfrac{1}{4} (\theta' - \theta)^2 = 1 + \theta \theta' = \frac{\cos f}{\cos \frac{1}{2} v \cos \frac{1}{2} v'}$$

is positive or negative, we must, evidently, conclude from the latter equation that

$$\pm \sqrt{\frac{r + r' - \varrho}{p}} = \eta - \tfrac{1}{2} (\theta' - \theta),$$

in which the upper or lower sign is to be adopted, according as the angle described about the sun is less than 180°, or more than 180°.

From the equation, which in article 98 follows the second equation, we have, moreover,

$$\frac{2\,k\,t}{p^{\frac{3}{2}}} = (\theta'-\theta)\left((1+\theta\theta'+\tfrac{1}{3}\,(\theta'-\theta)^2\right)=(\theta'-\theta)\left(\eta\eta+\tfrac{1}{12}\,(\theta'-\theta)^2\right)$$

$$= \tfrac{1}{3}\left(\eta+\tfrac{1}{2}\,(\theta'-\theta)\right)^3 - \tfrac{1}{3}\left(\eta-\tfrac{1}{2}\,(\theta'-\theta)\right)^3,$$

whence readily follows,

$$k\,t = \tfrac{1}{6}\left((r+r'+\varrho)^{\frac{3}{2}}\mp(r+r'-\varrho)^{\frac{3}{2}}\right),$$

the upper or lower sign taking effect, as $2f$ is less or more than $180°$.

## 109.

If, in the hyperbola, we take the symbols $\alpha$, $C$, $c$, with the same meaning as in article 99, we have, from equations VIII., IX., article 21,

$$r'\cos v' - r\cos v = -\tfrac{1}{2}\left(c-\tfrac{1}{c}\right)\left(C-\tfrac{1}{C}\right)\alpha$$

$$r'\sin v' - r\sin v = \tfrac{1}{2}\left(c-\tfrac{1}{c}\right)\left(C+\tfrac{1}{C}\right)\alpha\sqrt{(ee-1)};$$

and consequently,

$$\varrho = \tfrac{1}{2}\,\alpha\left(c-\tfrac{1}{c}\right)\sqrt{\left(ee\,(C+\tfrac{1}{C})^2-4\right)}.$$

Let us suppose that $\gamma$ is a quantity determined by the equation

$$\gamma+\tfrac{1}{\gamma}=e\left(C+\tfrac{1}{C}\right):$$

since this is evidently satisfied by *two* values, the reciprocals of each other, we may adopt the one which is greater than 1. In this manner

$$\varrho = \tfrac{1}{2}\,\alpha\left(c-\tfrac{1}{c}\right)\left(\gamma-\tfrac{1}{\gamma}\right).$$

Moreover,

$$r+r' = \tfrac{1}{2}\,\alpha\left(e(c+\tfrac{1}{c})\,(C+\tfrac{1}{C})-4\right)=\tfrac{1}{2}\,\alpha\left((c+\tfrac{1}{c})\,(\gamma+\tfrac{1}{\gamma})-4\right),$$

and thus,

$$r+r'+\varrho = \alpha\left(\sqrt{c\gamma}-\sqrt{\tfrac{1}{c\gamma}}\right)^2$$

$$r+r'-\varrho = \alpha\left(\sqrt{\tfrac{\gamma}{c}}-\sqrt{\tfrac{c}{\gamma}}\right)^2.$$

Putting, therefore,

$$\sqrt{\frac{r+r'+\varrho}{4\,\alpha}}=m, \quad \sqrt{\frac{r+r'-\varrho}{4\,\alpha}}=n,$$

we necessarily have

$$\sqrt{c\,\gamma}-\sqrt{\frac{1}{c\,\gamma}}=2\,m\,;$$

but in order to decide the question whether $\sqrt{\frac{\gamma}{c}}-\sqrt{\frac{c}{\gamma}}$ is equal to $+2n$ or $-2n$, it is necessary to inquire whether $\gamma$ is greater or less than $c$: but it follows readily from equation 8, article 99, that the former case occurs when $2f$ is less than 180°, and the latter, when $2f$ is more than 180°. Lastly, we have, from the same article,

$$\frac{k\,t}{a^{\frac{3}{2}}}=\tfrac{1}{2}\left(\gamma+\tfrac{1}{\gamma}\right)\left(c-\tfrac{1}{c}\right)-2\log c=\tfrac{1}{2}\left(c\,\gamma-\tfrac{1}{c\,\gamma}\right)-\tfrac{1}{2}\left(\tfrac{\gamma}{c}-\tfrac{c}{\gamma}\right)-\log c\,\gamma+\log\tfrac{\gamma}{c}$$

$$=2m\sqrt{(1+mm)}\mp 2n\sqrt{(1+nn)}-2\log\left(\sqrt{(1+mm)}+m\right)$$
$$\pm 2\log\left(\sqrt{(1+nn)}+n\right),$$

the lower signs belonging to the case of $2f>180°$. Now, $\log\left(\sqrt{(1+mm)}+m\right)$ is easily developed into the following series:—

$$m-\tfrac{1}{3}\cdot\tfrac{1}{2}m^3+\tfrac{1}{5}\cdot\frac{1.3}{2.4}m^5-\tfrac{1}{7}\cdot\frac{1.3.5}{2.4.6}m^7+\text{etc.}$$

This is readily obtained from

$$d\log\left(\sqrt{(1+mm)}+m\right)=\frac{d\,m}{\sqrt{(1+mm)}}.$$

There follows, therefore, the formula

$$2m\sqrt{(1+mm)}-2\log\left(\sqrt{(1+mm)}+m\right)=4\left(\tfrac{1}{3}m^3-\tfrac{1}{5}\cdot\tfrac{1}{2}m^5+\tfrac{1}{7}\cdot\frac{1.3}{2.4}m^7-\text{etc.}\right),$$

and, likewise, another precisely similar, if $m$ is changed to $n$. Hence, finally, if we put

$$T=\tfrac{1}{6}(r+r'-\varrho)^{\frac{3}{2}}-\tfrac{1}{80}\cdot\tfrac{1}{\alpha}(r+r'-\varrho)^{\frac{5}{2}}+\tfrac{3}{1792}\cdot\tfrac{1}{\alpha\alpha}(r+r'-\varrho)^{\frac{7}{2}}$$
$$-\tfrac{5}{18432}\cdot\tfrac{1}{\alpha^3}(r+r'-\varrho)^{\frac{9}{2}}+\text{etc.}$$

$$U=\tfrac{1}{6}(r+r'+\varrho)^{\frac{3}{2}}-\tfrac{1}{80}\cdot\tfrac{1}{\alpha}(r+r'+\varrho)^{\frac{5}{2}}+\tfrac{3}{1792}\cdot\tfrac{1}{\alpha\alpha}(r+r'+\varrho)^{\frac{7}{2}}$$
$$-\tfrac{5}{18432}\cdot\tfrac{1}{\alpha^3}(r+r'+\varrho)^{\frac{9}{2}}+\text{etc.}$$

we obtain

$$kt = U \mp T;$$

which expressions entirely coincide with those given in article 107, if $a$ is there changed into $-a$.

Finally, these series, as well for the ellipse as the hyperbola, are eminently suited to practical use, when $a$ or $\alpha$ possesses a very great value, that is, where the conic section resembles very nearly the parabola. In such a case, the methods previously discussed (articles 85–105) might be employed for the solution of the problem: but as, in our judgment, they do not furnish the brevity of the solution given above, we do not dwell upon the further explanation of this method.

# FOURTH SECTION.

## RELATIONS BETWEEN SEVERAL PLACES IN SPACE.

---

## 110.

THE relations to be considered in this section are independent of the nature of the orbit, and will rest upon the single assumption, that all points of the orbit lie in the same plane with the sun. But we have thought proper to touch here upon some of the most simple only, and to reserve others more complicated and special for another book.

The position of the plane of the orbit is fully determined by two places of the heavenly body in space, provided these places do not lie in the same straight line with the sun. Wherefore, since the place of a point in space can be assigned in two ways, especially, two problems present themselves for solution.

We will, in the first place, suppose the two places to be given by means of heliocentric longitudes and latitudes, to be denoted respectively by $\lambda, \lambda', \beta, \beta'$ : the distances from the sun will not enter into the calculation. Then if the longitude of the ascending node is denoted by $\Omega$, the inclination of the orbit to the ecliptic by $i$, we shall have,

$$\tan \beta = \tan i \sin (\lambda - \Omega),$$
$$\tan \beta' = \tan i \sin (\lambda' - \Omega).$$

The determination of the unknown quantities $\Omega$, $\tan i$, in this place, is referred to the problem examined in article 78, II. We have, therefore, according to the first solution,

$$\tan i \sin (\lambda - \Omega) = \tan \beta,$$
$$\tan i \cos (\lambda - \Omega) = \frac{\tan \beta' - \tan \beta \cos (\lambda' - \lambda)}{\sin (\lambda' - \lambda)},$$

(153)

likewise, according to the third solution, we find $\Omega$ by equation

$$\tan \left( \tfrac{1}{2} \lambda + \tfrac{1}{2} \lambda' - \Omega \right) = \frac{\sin \left( \beta' + \beta \right) \tan \tfrac{1}{2} \left( \lambda' - \lambda \right)}{\sin \left( \beta' - \beta \right)},$$

and, somewhat more conveniently, if the angles $\beta, \beta'$, are given immediately, and not by the logarithms of their tangents: but, for determining $i$, recourse must be had to one of the formulas

$$\tan i = \frac{\tan \beta}{\sin \left( \lambda - \Omega \right)} = \frac{\tan \beta'}{\sin \left( \lambda' - \Omega \right)}.$$

Finally, the uncertainty in the determination of the angle

$$\lambda - \Omega, \text{ or } \tfrac{1}{2} \lambda + \tfrac{1}{2} \lambda' - \Omega,$$

by its tangent will be decided so that $\tan i$ may become positive or negative, according as the motion projected on the ecliptic is direct or retrograde: this uncertainty, therefore, can be removed only in the case where it may be apparent in what direction the heavenly body has moved in passing from the first to the second place; if this should be unknown, it would certainly be impossible to distinguish the ascending from the descending node.

After the angles $\Omega, i$, are found, the arguments of the latitude $u, u'$, will be obtained by the formulas,

$$\tan u = \frac{\tan \left( \lambda - \Omega \right)}{\cos i}, \ \tan u' = \frac{\tan \left( \lambda' - \Omega \right)}{\cos i},$$

which are to be taken in the first or second semicircle, according as the corresponding latitudes are north or south. To these formulas we add the following, one or the other of which can, at pleasure, be used for proving the calculation:—

$$\cos u = \cos \beta \cos \left( \lambda - \Omega \right), \ \cos u' = \cos \beta' \cos \left( \lambda' - \Omega \right),$$

$$\sin u = \frac{\sin \beta}{\sin i}, \ \sin u' = \frac{\sin \beta'}{\sin i},$$

$$\sin \left( u' + u \right) = \frac{\sin \left( \lambda + \lambda' - 2 \Omega \right) \cos \beta \cos \beta'}{\cos i}, \ \sin \left( u' - u \right) = \frac{\sin \left( \lambda' - \lambda \right) \cos \beta \cos \beta'}{\cos i}.$$

## 111.

Let us suppose, in the second place, the two places to be given by means of their distances from three planes, cutting each other at right angles in the sun ; let us denote these distances, for the first place, by $x$, $y$, $z$, for the second, by $x'$, $y'$, $z'$, and let us suppose the third plane to be the ecliptic itself, also the positive poles of the first and second planes to be situated in $N$, and $90° + N$. We shall thus have by article 53, the two radii vectores being denoted by $r$, $r'$,

$$x = r \cos u \cos (N - \Omega) + r \sin u \sin (N - \Omega) \cos i,$$
$$y = r \sin u \cos (N - \Omega) \cos i - r \cos u \sin (N - \Omega),$$
$$z = r \sin u \sin i$$
$$x' = r' \cos u' \cos (N - \Omega) + r' \sin u' \sin (N - \Omega) \cos i,$$
$$y' = r' \sin u' \cos (N - \Omega) \cos i - r' \cos u' \sin (N - \Omega),$$
$$z' = r' \sin u' \sin i.$$

Hence it follows that

$$z y' - y z' = r r' \sin (u' - u) \sin (N - \Omega) \sin i,$$
$$x z' - z x' = r r' \sin (u' - u) \cos (N - \Omega) \sin i,$$
$$x y' - y x' = r r' \sin (u' - u) \cos i.$$

From the combination of the first formula with the second will be obtained $N - \Omega$ and $r r' \sin (u' - u) \sin i$, hence and from the third formula, $i$ and $r r' \sin (u' - u)$ will be obtained.

Since the place to which the coördinates $x'$, $y'$, $z'$, correspond, is supposed posterior in time, $u'$ must be greater than $u$: if, moreover, it is known whether the angle between the first and second place described about the sun is less or greater than two right angles, $r r' \sin (u' - u) \sin i$ and $r r' \sin (u' - u)$ must be positive quantities in the first case, negative in the second : then, accordingly, $N - \Omega$ is determined without doubt, and at the same time it is settled by the sign of the quantity $x y' - y x'$, whether the motion is direct or retrograde. On the other hand, if the direction of the motion is known, it will be possible to decide from the sign of the quantity $x y' - y x'$, whether $u' - u$ is to be taken less or greater than 180°. But if the direction of the motion, and the nature of the angle described about the sun are altogether unknown, it is evident that we cannot distinguish between the ascending and descending node.

It is readily perceived that, just as $\cos i$ is the cosine of the inclination of the plane of the orbit to the third plane, so $\sin (N - \Omega) \sin i$, $\cos (N - \Omega) \sin i$, are the cosines of the inclinations of the plane of the orbit to the first and second planes respectively; also that $r\, r' \sin (u' - u)$ expresses the double area of the triangle contained between the two radii vectores, and $zy' - yz'$, $xz' - zx'$, $xy' - yx'$, the double area of the projections of this triangle upon each of the planes.

Lastly, it is evident, that any other plane can be the third plane, provided, only, that all the dimensions defined by their relations to the ecliptic, are referred to the third plane, whatever it may be.

## 112.

Let $x'', y'', z''$, be the coördinates of any third place, and $u''$ its argument of the latitude, $r''$ its radius vector. We will denote the quantities $r'\, r'' \sin (u'' - u')$, $r\, r'' \sin (u'' - u)$, $r\, r' \sin (u' - u)$, which are the double areas of the triangles between the second and third radii vectores, the first and third, the first and second, respectively, by $n, n', n''$. Accordingly, we shall have for $x''$, $y''$, $z''$, expressions similar to those which we have given in the preceding article for $x, y, z$, and $x', y', z'$; whence, with the assistance of lemma I., article 78, are easily derived the following equations : —

$$0 = nx - n'x' + n''x'',$$
$$0 = ny - n'y' + n''y'',$$
$$0 = nz - n'z' + n''z'.$$

Let now the geocentric longitudes of the celestial body corresponding to these three places be $\alpha, \alpha', \alpha''$; the geocentric latitudes, $\beta, \beta', \beta''$; the distances from the earth projected on the ecliptic, $\delta, \delta', \delta''$; the corresponding heliocentric longitudes of the earth, $L, L', L''$; the latitudes, $B, B', B''$, which we do not put equal to 0, in order to take account of the parallax, and, if thought proper, to choose any other plane, instead of the ecliptic; lastly, let $D, D', D''$, be the distances of the earth from the sun projected upon the ecliptic. If, then, $x, y, z$, are expressed by means of $L$, $B$, $D$, $\alpha$, $\beta$, $\delta$, and the coördinates relating to the second and third places in a similar manner, the preceding equations will assume the following form: —

[1]  $0 = n\,(\delta \cos \alpha + D \cos L) - n'\,(\delta' \cos \alpha' + D' \cos L')$
$\qquad\qquad + n''\,(\delta'' \cos \alpha'' + D'' \cos L'')$,

[2]  $0 = n\,(\delta \sin \alpha + D \sin L) - n'\,(\delta' \sin \alpha' + D' \sin L')$
$\qquad\qquad + n''\,(\delta'' \sin \alpha'' + D'' \sin L'')$,

[3]  $0 = n\,(\delta \tan \beta + D \tan B) - n'\,(\delta' \tan \beta' + D' \tan B')$
$\qquad\qquad + n''\,(\delta'' \tan \beta'' + D'' \tan B'')$.

If $\alpha$, $\beta$, $D$, $L$, $B$, and the analogous quantities for the two remaining places, are here regarded as known, and the equations are divided by $n'$, or by $n''$, five unknown quantities remain, of which, therefore, it is possible to eliminate two, or to determine, in terms of any two, the remaining three. In this manner these three equations pave the way to several most important conclusions, of which we will proceed to develop those that are especially important.

## 113.

That we may not be too much oppressed with the length of the formulas, we will use the following abbreviations. In the first place we denote the quantity

$$\tan \beta \sin (\alpha'' - \alpha') + \tan \beta' \sin (\alpha - \alpha'') + \tan \beta'' \sin (\alpha' - \alpha)$$

by $(0.1.2)$: if, in this expression, the longitude and latitude corresponding to any one of the three heliocentric places of the earth are substituted for the longitude and latitude corresponding to any geocentric place, we change the number answering to the latter in the symbol $(0.1.2.)$ for the Roman numeral which corresponds to the former. Thus, for example, the symbol $(0.1.\text{I}.)$ expresses the quantity

$$\tan \beta \sin (L' - \alpha') + \tan \beta' \sin (\alpha - L') + \tan B' \sin (\alpha' - \alpha),$$

also the symbol $(0.0.2)$, the following,

$$\tan \beta \sin (\alpha'' - L) + \tan B \sin (\alpha - \alpha'') + \tan \beta'' \sin (L - \alpha).$$

We change the symbol in the same way, if in the first expression any *two* heliocentric longitudes and latitudes of the earth whatever, are substituted for two geocentric. If two longitudes and latitudes entering into the same expression are only interchanged with each other, the corresponding numbers should also be interchanged; but the value is not changed from this cause, but it only becomes negative from being positive, or positive from negative. Thus, for example, we have

$$(0.\,1.\,2) = -(0.\,2.\,1) = (1.\,2.\,0) = -(1.\,0.\,2) = (2.\,0.\,1) = -(2.\,1.\,0).$$

All the quantities, therefore, originating in this way are reduced to the nineteen following: —

$(0.\,1.\,2)$

$(0.\,1.\,0),\ (0.\,1.\,I.),\ (0.\,1.\,II.),\ (0.\,O.\,2),\ (0.\,I.\,2),\ (0.\,II.\,2),\ (O.\,1.\,2),\ (I.\,1.\,2),\ (II.\,1.\,2),$
$(0.\,O.\,I.),\ (0.\,O.\,II.),\ (0.\,I.\,II.),\ (1.\,O.\,I.),\ (1.\,O.\,II.),\quad (1.\,I.\,II.),\ (2.\,O.\,I.),\ (2.\,O.\,II.),$
$(2.\,I.\,II.),$

to which is to be added the twentieth $(O.\,I.\,II.)$.

Moreover, it is easily shown, that each of these expressions multiplied by the product of the three cosines of the latitudes entering into them, becomes equal to the sextuple volume of a pyramid, the vertex of which is in the sun, and the base of which is the triangle formed between the three points of the celestial sphere which correspond to the places entering into that expression, the radius of the sphere being put equal to unity. When, therefore, these three places lie in the same great circle, the value of the expression should become equal to 0; and as this always occurs in three heliocentric places of the earth, when we do not take account of the parallaxes and the latitudes arising from the perturbations of the earth, that is, when we suppose the earth to be exactly in the plane of the ecliptic, so we shall always have, on this assumption, $(O.\,I.\,II.) = 0$, which is, in fact, an identical equation if the ecliptic is taken for the third plane. And further, when $B, B', B''$, each, $= 0$, all those expressions, except the first, become much more simple; every one from the second to the tenth will be made up of two parts, but from the eleventh to the twentieth they will consist of only one term.

### 114.

By multiplying equation [1] by $\sin \alpha'' \tan B'' - \sin L'' \tan \beta''$, equation [2] by $\cos L'' \tan \beta'' - \cos \alpha'' \tan B''$, equation [3] by $\sin (L'' - \alpha'')$, and adding the products, we get,

[4]　$0 = n\left((0.2.\,\mathrm{II.})\,\delta + (0.2.\,\mathrm{II.})\,D\right) - n'\left((1.2.\,\mathrm{II.})\,\delta' + (\mathrm{I}.2.\,\mathrm{II.})\,D'\right);$

and in the same manner, or more conveniently by an interchange of the places, simply

[5]　$0 = n\left((0.1.\,\mathrm{I.})\,\delta + (0.1.\,\mathrm{I.})\,D\right) + n''\left((2.1.\,\mathrm{I.})\,\delta'' + (\mathrm{II}.1.\,\mathrm{I.})\,D''\right)$

[6]　$0 = n'\left((1.0.\,\mathrm{O.})\,\delta' + (\mathrm{I}.0.\,\mathrm{O.})D'\right) - n''\left((2.0.\,\mathrm{O.})\,\delta'' + (\mathrm{II}.0.\,\mathrm{O.})\,D''\right).$

If, therefore, the ratio of the quantities $n, n'$, is given, with the aid of equation 4, we can determine $\delta'$ from $\delta$, or $\delta$ from $\delta'$; and so likewise of the equations 5, 6. From the combination of the equations 4, 5, 6, arises the following,

[7]　$\dfrac{(0.2.\,\mathrm{II.})\,\delta + (0.2.\,\mathrm{II.})\,D}{(0.1.\,\mathrm{I.})\,\delta + (0.1.\,\mathrm{I.})\,D} \times \dfrac{(1.0.\,\mathrm{O.})\,\delta' + (\mathrm{I}.0.\,\mathrm{O.})\,D'}{(1.2.\,\mathrm{II.})\,\delta' + (\mathrm{I}.2.\,\mathrm{II.})\,D'} \times \dfrac{(2.1.\,\mathrm{I.})\,\delta'' + (\mathrm{II}.1.\,\mathrm{I.})\,D''}{(2.0.\,\mathrm{O.})\,\delta'' + (\mathrm{II}.0.\,\mathrm{O.})\,D''} = -1,$

by means of which, from two distances of a heavenly body from the earth, the third can be determined. But it can be shown that this equation, 7, becomes identical, and therefore unfit for the determination of one distance from the other two, when

$$B = B' = B'' = 0,$$

and

$$\tan \beta' \tan \beta'' \sin (L - \alpha) \sin (L'' - L') + \tan \beta'' \tan \beta \sin (L' - \alpha') \sin (L - L'')$$
$$+ \tan \beta \tan \beta' \sin (L'' - \alpha'') \sin (L' - L) = 0.$$

The following formula, obtained easily from equations 1, 2, 3, is free from this inconvenience : —

[8]　$(0.\,1.\,2.)\,\delta\delta'\delta'' + (0.1.2)\,D\delta'\delta'' + (0.\mathrm{I}.2)\,D'\delta\,\delta'' + (0.1.\,\mathrm{II.})\,D''\delta\delta'$
$+ (0.\mathrm{I}.\mathrm{II.})\,D'D''\delta + (0.1.\,\mathrm{II.})\,D\,D''\delta' + (0.\mathrm{I}.2)\,D\,D'\delta'' + (0.\mathrm{I}.\mathrm{II.})\,D\,D'D'' = 0.$

By multiplying equation 1 by $\sin \alpha' \tan \beta'' - \sin \alpha'' \tan \beta'$, equation 2 by $\cos \alpha'' \tan \beta' - \cos \alpha' \tan \beta''$, equation 3 by $\sin (\alpha'' - \alpha')$, and adding the products, we get

[9]　$0 = n\left((0.1.2)\,\delta + (0.1.2)\,D\right) - n'\,(\mathrm{I}.1.2)\,D' + n''\,(\mathrm{II}.1.2)\,D''$

and in the same manner,

[10]   $0 = n\,(0.\,0.\,2.)\,D - n'\,\big((0.\,1.\,2)\,\delta' + (0.\,\mathrm{I}.\,2)\,D'\big) + n''\,(0.\,\mathrm{II}.\,2)\,D''$,

[11]   $0 = n\,(0.\,1.\,0)\,D - n'\,(0.\,1.\,\mathrm{I}.)\,D' + n''\,\big((0.\,1.\,2)\,\delta'' + (0.\,1.\,\mathrm{II}.)\,D'\big)$.

By means of these equations the distances $\delta, \delta', \delta''$, can be derived from the ratio between the quantities $n, n', n''$, when it is known. But this conclusion only holds in general, and suffers an exception when $(0.\,1.\,2) = 0$. For it can be shown, that in this case nothing follows from the equations 8, 9, 10, except a necessary relation between the quantities $n, n', n''$, and indeed the same relation from each of the three. Analogous restrictions concerning the equations 4, 5, 6, will readily suggest themselves to the reader.

Finally, all the results here developed, are of no utility when the plane of the orbit coincides with the ecliptic. For if $\beta, \beta', \beta'', B, B\ B''$ are all equal to 0, equation 3 is identical, and also, therefore, all those which follow.

# SECOND BOOK.

## INVESTIGATION OF THE ORBITS OF HEAVENLY BODIES FROM GEOCENTRIC OBSERVATIONS.

---

## FIRST SECTION.

### DETERMINATION OF AN ORBIT FROM THREE COMPLETE OBSERVATIONS.

## 115.

SEVEN elements are required for the complete determination of the motion of a heavenly body in its orbit, the number of which, however, may be diminished by one, if the mass of the heavenly body is either known or neglected; neglecting the mass can scarcely be avoided in the determination of an orbit wholly unknown, where all the quantities of the order of the perturbations must be omitted, until the masses on which they depend become otherwise known. Wherefore, in the present inquiry, the mass of the body being neglected, we reduce the number of the elements to six, and, therefore, it is evident, that as many quantities depending on the elements, but independent of each other, are required for the determination of the unknown orbit. These quantities are necessarily the places of the heavenly body observed from the earth; since each one of which furnishes two data, that is, the longitude and latitude, or the right ascension and declination, it will certainly be the most simple to adopt *three geocentric places* which will, in general, be sufficient for determining the six unknown elements. This problem is to be regarded as the most important in this work, and, for this reason, will be treated with the greatest care in this section.

But in the special case, in which the plane of the orbit coincides with the ecliptic, and thus both the heliocentric and geocentric latitudes, from their nature, vanish, the three vanishing geocentric latitudes cannot any longer be considered as three data independent of each other: then, therefore, this problem would remain indeterminate, and the three geocentric places might be satisfied by an infinite number of orbits. Accordingly, in such a case, four geocentric longitudes must, necessarily, be given, in order that the four remaining unknown elements (the inclination of the orbit and the longitude of the node being omitted) may be determined. But although, from an indiscernible principle, it is not to be expected that such a case would ever actually present itself in nature, nevertheless, it is easily imagined that the problem, which, in an orbit exactly coinciding with the plane of the ecliptic, is absolutely indeterminate, must, on account of the limited accuracy of the observations, remain nearly indeterminate in orbits very little inclined to the ecliptic, where the very slightest errors of the observations are sufficient altogether to confound the determination of the unknown quantities. Wherefore, in order to examine this case, it will be necessary to select six data : for which purpose we will show in section second, how to determine an unknown orbit from four observations, of which two are complete, but the other two incomplete, the latitudes or declinations being deficient.

Finally, as all our observations, on account of the imperfection of the instruments and of the senses, are only approximations to the truth, an orbit based only on the six absolutely necessary data may be still liable to considerable errors. In order to diminish these as much as possible, and thus to reach the greatest precision attainable, no other method will be given except to accumulate the greatest number of the most perfect observations, and to adjust the elements, not so as to satisfy this or that set of observations with absolute exactness, but so as to agree with all in the best possible manner. For which purpose, we will show in the third section how, according to the principles of the calculus of probabilities, such an agreement may be obtained, as will be, if in no one place perfect, yet in all the places the strictest possible.

The determination of orbits in this manner, therefore, so far as the heavenly bodies move in them according to the laws of KEPLER, will be carried to the highest degree of perfection that is desired.   Then it will be proper to undertake the final correction, in which the perturbations that the other planets cause in the motion, will be taken account of :  we will indicate briefly in the fourth section, how these may be taken account of, so far at least, as it shall appear consistent with our plan.

## 116.

Before the determination of any orbit from geocentric observations, if the greatest accuracy is desired, certain reductions must be applied to the latter on account of nutation, precession, parallax, and aberration : these small quantities may be neglected in the rougher calculation.

Observations of planets and comets are commonly given in apparent (that is, referred to the apparent position of the equator) right ascensions and declinations.   Now as this position is variable on account of nutation and precession, and, therefore, different for different observations, it will be expedient, first of all, to introduce some fixed plane instead of the variable plane, for which purpose, either the equator in its mean position for some epoch, or the ecliptic might be selected : it is customary for the most part to use the latter plane, but the former is recommended by some peculiar advantages which are not to be despised.

When, therefore, the plane of the equator is selected, the observations are in the first place to be freed from nutation, and after that, the precession being applied, they are to be reduced to some arbitrary epoch : this operation agrees entirely with that by which, from the observed place of a fixed star, its mean place is derived for a given epoch, and consequently does not need explanation here.   But if it is decided to adopt the plane of the ecliptic, there are two courses which may be pursued : namely, either the longitudes and latitudes, by means of the mean obliquity, can be deduced from the right ascensions and declinations corrected for nutation and precession, whence the longitudes referred to the mean equinox will be obtained ; or, the latitudes and longitudes will be computed more conveniently from the apparent right ascensions and declinations, using the apparent obliquity, and will afterwards be freed from nutation and precession.

The places of the earth, corresponding to each of the observations, are com-

puted from the solar tables, but they are evidently to be referred to the same
plane, to which the observations of the heavenly body are referred.  For which
reason the nutation will be neglected in the computation of the longitude of the
sun ; but afterwards this longitude, the precession being applied, will be reduced
to the fixed epoch, and increased by 180 degrees; the opposite sign will be given
to the latitude of the sun, if, indeed, it seems worth while to take account of it :
thus will be obtained the heliocentric place of the earth, which, if the equator is
chosen for the fundamental plane, may be changed into right ascension and declination by making use of the mean obliquity.

## 117.

The position of the earth, computed in this manner from the tables, is the
place of the centre of the earth, but the observed place of the heavenly body
is referred to a point on the surface of the earth : there are three methods of
remedying this discrepancy.   Either the observation can be reduced to the centre
of the earth, that is, freed from parallax ; or the heliocentric place of the earth
may be reduced to the place of observation, which is done by applying the
parallax properly to the place of the sun computed from the tables ; or, finally,
both positions can be transferred to some third point, which is most conveniently
taken in the intersection of the visual ray with the plane of the ecliptic ; the
observation itself then remains unchanged, and we have explained, in article 72,
the reduction of the place of the earth to this point.   The first method cannot be
applied, except the distance of the heavenly body from the earth be approximately, at least, known :  but then it is very convenient, especially when the
observation has been made in the meridian, in which case the declination only is
affected by parallax.   Moreover, it will be better to apply this reduction immediately to the observed place, before the transformations of the preceding article
are undertaken.   But if the distance from the earth is still wholly unknown,
recourse must be had to the second or third method, and the former will be employed when the equator is taken for the fundamental plane, but the third will
have the preference when all the positions are referred to the ecliptic.

### 118.

If the distance of a heavenly body from the earth answering to any observation is already approximately known, it may be freed from the effect of aberration in several ways, depending on the different methods given in article 71. Let $t$ be the true time of observation; $\theta$ the interval of time in which light passes from the heavenly body to the earth, which results from multiplying $493^s$ into the distance; $l$ the observed place, $l'$ the same place reduced to the time $t + \theta$ by means of the diurnal geocentric motion; $l''$ the place $l$ freed from that part of the aberration which is common to the planets and fixed stars; $L$ the true place of the earth corresponding to the time $t$ (that is, the tabular place increased by $20''.25$); lastly, $'L$ the true place of the earth corresponding to the time $t - \theta$. These things being premised, we shall have

    I.   $l$ the true place of the heavenly body seen from $'L$ at the time $t - \theta$.

    II.   $l'$ the true place of the heavenly body seen from $L$ at the time $t$.

    III.   $l''$ the true place of the heavenly body seen from $L$ at the time $t - \theta$.

By method I., therefore, the observed place is preserved unchanged, but the fictitious time $t - \theta$ is substituted for the true, the place of the earth being computed for the former; method II., applies the change to the observation alone, but it requires, together with the distance, the diurnal motion; in method III., the observation undergoes a correction, not depending on the distance; the fictitious time $t - \theta$ is substituted for the true, but the place of the earth corresponding to the true time is retained. Of these methods, the first is much the most convenient, whenever the distance is known well enough to enable us to compute the reduction of the time with sufficient accuracy. But if the distance is wholly unknown, neither of these methods can be immediately applied: in the first, to be sure, the geocentric place of the heavenly body is known, but the time and the position of the earth are wanting, both depending on the unknown distance; in the second, on the other hand, the latter are given, and the former is wanting; finally, in the third, the geocentric place of the heavenly body and the position of the earth are given, but the time to be used with these is wanting.

What, therefore, is to be done with our problem, if, in such a case, a solution exact with respect to aberration is required? The simplest course undoubtedly is, to determine the orbit neglecting at first the aberration, the effect of which can never be important; the distances will thence be obtained with at least such precision that the observations can be freed from aberration by some one of the methods just explained, and the determination of the orbit can be repeated with greater accuracy. Now, in this case the third method will be far preferable to the others: for, in the first method all the computations depending on the position of the earth must be commenced again from the very beginning; in the second (which in fact is never applicable, unless the number of observations is sufficient to obtain from them the diurnal motion), it is necessary to begin anew all the computations depending upon the geocentric place of the heavenly body ; in the third, on the contrary, (if the first calculation had been already based on geocentric places freed from the aberration of the fixed stars) all the preliminary computations depending upon the position of the earth and the geocentric place of the heavenly body, can be retained unchanged in the new computation. But in this way it will even be possible to include the aberration directly in the first calculation, if the method used for the determination of the orbit has been so arranged, that the values of the distances are obtained before it shall have been necessary to introduce into the computation the corrected times. Then the double computation on account of the aberration will not be necessary, as will appear more clearly in the further treatment of our problem.

## 119.

It would not be difficult, from the connection between the data and unknown quantities of our problem, to reduce its statement to six equations, or even to less, since one or another of the unknown quantities might, conveniently enough, be eliminated : but since this connection is most complicated, these equations would become very intractable ; such a separation of the unknown quantities as finally to produce an equation containing only one, can, generally speaking, be regarded as impossible,* and, therefore, still less will it be possible to obtain a complete solution of the problem by direct processes alone.

But our problem may at least be reduced, and that too in various ways, to the solution of *two* equations $X = 0$, $Y = 0$, in which only two unknown quantities $x, y$, remain.  It is by no means necessary that $x, y$, should be two of the elements: they may be quantities connected with the elements in any manner whatever, if, only, the elements can be conveniently deduced from them when found.  Moreover, it is evidently not requisite that $X$, $Y$, be expressed in explicit functions of $x, y$ : it is sufficient if they are connected with them by a system of equations in such manner that we can proceed from given values of $x, y$, to the corresponding values of $X$, $Y$.

## 120.

Since, therefore, the nature of the problem does not allow of a further reduction than to two equations, embracing indiscriminately two unknown quantities, the principal point will consist, first, in the suitable *selection* of these unknown quantities and *arrangement* of the equations, so that both $X$ and $Y$ may depend in the simplest manner upon $x, y$, and that the elements themselves may follow most conveniently from the values of the former when known : and then, it will be a subject for careful consideration, how values of the unknown quantities satisfying the equations may be obtained by processes not too laborious.  If this should be practicable only by blind trials, as it were, very great and indeed almost intolerable labor would be required, such as astronomers who have determined the orbits of comets by what is called the indirect method have, nevertheless, often undertaken : at any rate, the labor in such a case is very greatly lessened, if, in the first trials, rougher calculations suffice until approximate values of the unknown quantities are found.  But as soon as an approximate determination is made, the solution of the problem can be completed by safe and easy methods, which, before we proceed further, it will be well to explain in this place.

---

* When the observations are so near to each other, that the intervals of the times may be treated as infinitely small quantities, a separation of this kind is obtained, and the whole problem is reduced to the solution of an algebraic equation of the seventh or eighth degree.

The equations $X = 0$, $Y = 0$ will be exactly satisfied if for $x$ and $y$ their true values are taken; if, on the contrary, values different from the true ones are substituted for $x$ and $y$, then $X$ and $Y$ will acquire values differing from 0. The more nearly $x$ and $y$ approach their true values, the smaller should be the resulting values of $X$ and $Y$, and when their differences from the true values are very small, it will be admissible to assume that the variations in the values of $X$ and $Y$ are nearly proportional to the variation of $x$, if $y$ is not changed, or to the variation of $y$, if $x$ is not changed. Accordingly, if the true values of $x$ and $y$ are denoted by $\xi$, $\eta$, the values of $X$ and $Y$ corresponding to the assumption that $x = \xi + \lambda$, $y = \eta + \mu$, will be expressed in the form

$$X = \alpha\lambda + \beta\mu, \quad Y = \gamma\lambda + \delta\mu,$$

in which the coefficients $\alpha$, $\beta$, $\gamma$, $\delta$ can be regarded as constant, as long as $\lambda$ and $\mu$ remain very small. Hence we conclude that, if for three systems of values of $x$, $y$, differing but little from the true values, corresponding values of $X$, $Y$ have been determined, it will be possible to obtain from them correct values of $x$, $y$ so far, at least, as the above assumption is admissible. Let us suppose that,

$$\text{for } x = a,\, y = b \text{ we have } X = A,\ Y = B,$$
$$x = a',\, y = b' \qquad\qquad X = A'\ Y = B',$$
$$x = a'',\, y = b'' \qquad\qquad X = A''\ Y = B'',$$

and we shall have

$$A = \alpha\,(a - \xi) + \beta\,(b - \eta),\ B = \gamma\,(a - \xi) + \delta\,(b - \eta),$$
$$A' = \alpha\,(a' - \xi) + \beta\,(b' - \eta),\ B' = \gamma\,(a' - \xi) + \delta\,(b' - \eta),$$
$$A'' = \alpha\,(a'' - \xi) + \beta\,(b'' - \eta),\ B'' = \gamma\,(a'' - \xi) + \delta\,(b'' - \eta).$$

From these we obtain, by eliminating $\alpha$, $\beta$, $\gamma$, $\delta$,

$$\xi = \frac{a\,(A'B'' - A''B') + a'\,(A''B - AB'') + a''\,(AB' - A'B)}{A'B'' - A''B' + A''B - AB'' + AB' - A'B},$$

$$\eta = \frac{b\,(A'B'' - A''B') + b'\,(A''B - AB'') + b''\,(AB' - A'B)}{A'B'' - A''B' + A''B - AB'' + AB' - A'B},$$

or, in a form more convenient for computation,

$$\xi = a + \frac{(a' - a)\,(A''B - AB'') + (a'' - a)\,(AB' - A'B)}{A'B'' - A''B' + A''B - AB'' + AB' - A'B},$$

$$\eta = b + \frac{(b' - b)\,(A''B - AB'') + (b'' - b)\,(AB' - A'B)}{A'B'' - A''B' + A''B - AB'' + AB' - A'B}.$$

It is evidently admissible, also, to interchange in these formulas the quantities $a$, $b$, $A$, $B$, with $a'$, $b'$, $A'$, $B'$, or with $a''$, $b''$, $A''$, $B''$.

The common denominator of all these expressions, which may be put under the form $(A' - A) (B'' - B) - (A'' - A) (B' - B)$, becomes

$$(\alpha \delta - \beta \gamma) \left( (a' - a) (b'' - b) - (a'' - a) (b' - b) \right) :$$

whence it appears that $a$, $a'$, $a''$, $b$, $b'$, $b''$ must be so taken as not to make

$$\frac{a'' - a}{b'' - b} = \frac{a' - a}{b' - b},$$

otherwise, this method would not be applicable, but would furnish, for the values of $\xi$ and $\eta$, fractions of which the numerators and denominators would vanish at the same time. It is evident also that, if it should happen that $\alpha \delta - \beta \gamma = 0$, the same defect wholly destroys the use of the method, in whatever way $a$, $a'$, $a''$, $b$, $b'$, $b''$, may be taken. In such a case it would be necessary to assume for the values of $X$ the form

$$\alpha \lambda + \beta \mu + \varepsilon \lambda \lambda + \zeta \lambda \mu + \theta \mu \mu,$$

and a similar one for the values of $Y$, which being done, analysis would supply methods, analogous to the preceding, of obtaining from values of $X$, $Y$, computed for four systems of values of $x$, $y$, true values of the latter. But the computation in this way would be very troublesome, and, moreover, it can be shown that, in such a case, the determination of the orbit does not, from the nature of the question, admit of the requisite precision: as this disadvantage can only be avoided by the introduction of new and more suitable observations, we do not here dwell upon the subject.

## 121.

When, therefore, the approximate values of the unknown quantities are obtained, the true values can be derived from them, in the manner just now explained, with all the accuracy that is needed. First, that is, the values of $X$, $Y$, corresponding to the approximate values $(a, b)$ will be computed : if they do not vanish for these, the calculation will be repeated with two other values $(a', b')$ differing but little from the former, and afterwards with a third system $(a'', b'')$

unless $X$, $Y$, have vanished for the second.  Then, the true values will be deduced by means of the formulas of the preceding article, so far as the assumption on which these formulas are based, does not differ sensibly from the truth.  In order that we may be better able to judge of which, the calculation of the values of $X$, $Y$, will be repeated with those corrected values; if this calculation shows that the equations $X = 0$, $Y = 0$, are, still, not satisfied, at least much smaller values of $X$, $Y$, will result therefrom, than from the three former hypotheses, and therefore, the elements of the orbit resulting from them, will be much more exact than those which correspond to the first hypotheses.  If we are not satisfied with these, it will be best, omitting that hypothesis which produced the greatest differences, to combine the other two with a fourth, and thus, by the process of the preceding article, to obtain a fifth system of the values of $x$, $y$; in the same manner, if it shall appear worth while, we may proceed to a sixth hypothesis, and so on, until the equations $X = 0$, $Y = 0$, shall be satisfied as exactly as the logarithmic and trigonometrical tables permit.  But it will very rarely be necessary to proceed beyond the fourth system, unless the first hypotheses were very far from the truth.

## 122.

As the values of the unknown quantities to be assumed in the second and third hypotheses are, to a certain extent, arbitrary, provided, only, they do not differ too much from the first hypothesis; and, moreover, as care is to be taken that the ratio $(a'' - a) : (b'' - b)$ does not tend to an equality with $(a' - a) : (b' - b)$, it is customary to put $a' = a, b'' = b$.  A double advantage is derived from this; for, not only do the formulas for $\xi$, $\eta$, become a little more simple, but, also, a part of the first calculation will remain the same in the second hypothesis, and another part in the third.

Nevertheless, there is a case in which other reasons suggest a departure from this custom: for let us suppose $X$ to have the form $X' - x$, and $Y$ the form $Y' - y$, and the functions $X'$, $Y'$, to become such, by the nature of the problem, that they are very little affected by small errors in the values of $x, y$, or that

$$\left(\frac{dX'}{dx}\right), \left(\frac{dX'}{dy}\right), \left(\frac{dY'}{dx}\right), \left(\frac{dY'}{dy}\right)$$

may be very small quantities, and it is evident that the differences between the values of those functions corresponding to the system $x = \xi$, $y = \eta$, and those which result from $x = a$, $y = b$, can be referred to a somewhat higher order than the differences $\xi - a$, $\eta - b$; but the former values are $X' = \xi$, $Y' = \eta$, and the latter $X' = a + A$, $Y' = b + B$, whence it follows, that $a + A$, $b + B$, are much more exact values of $x$, $y$, than $a$, $b$. If the second hypothesis is based upon these, the equations $X = 0$, $Y = 0$, are very frequently so exactly satisfied, that it is not necessary to proceed any further; but if not so, the third hypothesis will be formed in the same manner from the second, by making

$$a'' = a' + A' = a + A + A',\ b'' = b' + B' = b + B + B',$$

whence finally, if it is still not found sufficiently accurate, the fourth will be obtained according to the precept of article 120.

## 123.

We have supposed in what goes before, that the approximate values of the unknown quantities $x, y$, are already had in some way. Where, indeed, the approximate dimensions of the whole orbit are known (deduced perhaps from other observations by means of previous calculations, and now to be corrected by new ones), that condition can be satisfied without difficulty, whatever meaning we may assign to the unknown quantities. On the other hand, it is by no means a matter of indifference, in the determination of an orbit still wholly unknown, (which is by far the most difficult problem,) what unknown quantities we may use; but they should be judiciously selected in such a way, that the approximate values may be derived from the nature of the problem itself. Which can be done most satisfactorily, when the three observations applied to the investigation of an orbit do not embrace too great a heliocentric motion of the heavenly body. Observations of this kind, therefore, are always to be used for the first determination, which may be corrected afterwards, at pleasure, by means of observations more remote from each other. For it is readily perceived that the nearer the observations employed are to each other, the more is the calculation affected by their unavoidable errors. Hence it is inferred, that the observations for the first determination are not to be picked out at random, but care is to be taken, *first*, that they be not too near each other, but *then*, also, that they be not too distant from each other; for in the first case, the calculation of elements satisfying the observations would certainly be most expeditiously performed, but the elements themselves would be entitled to little confidence, and might be so erroneous that they could not even be used as an approximation: in the other case, we should abandon the artifices which are to be made use of for an approximate determination of the unknown quantities, nor could we thence obtain any other determination, except one of the rudest kind, or wholly insufficient, without many more hypotheses, or the most tedious trials. But how to form a correct judgment concerning these limits of the method is better learned by frequent practice than by rules: the examples to be given below will show, that elements possessing great accuracy can be derived from observations of Juno, separated from each other only 22 days, and embracing a heliocentric motion of 7° 35′; and again, that our method can also be applied, with the most perfect success, to observations of Ceres, which are 260 days apart, and include a heliocentric motion of 62° 55′; and can give, with the use of four hypotheses or, rather, successive approximations, elements agreeing excellently well with the observations.

## 124.

We proceed now to the enumeration of the most suitable methods based upon the preceding principles, the chief parts of which have, indeed, already been explained in the first book, and require here only to be adapted to our purpose.

The most simple method appears to be, to take for $x, y$, the distances of the heavenly body from the earth in the two observations, or rather the logarithms of these distances, or the logarithms of the distances projected upon the ecliptic or equator. Hence, by article 64, V., will be derived the heliocentric places and the distances from the sun pertaining to those places; hence, again, by article 110, the position of the plane of the orbit and the heliocentric longitudes in it; and from these, the radii vectores, and the corresponding times, according to the problem treated at length in articles 85–105, all the remaining elements, by which, it is evident, these observations will be exactly represented, whatever values may have been assigned to $x, y$. If, accordingly, the geocentric place for the time of the third observation is computed by means of these elements, its agreement or disagreement with the observed place will determine whether the assumed values are the true ones, or whether they differ from them; whence, as a double comparison will be obtained, one difference (in longitude or right ascension) can be taken for $X$, and the other (in latitude or declination) for $Y$. Unless, therefore, the values of these differences come out at once $= 0$, the true values of $x, y$, may be got by the method given in 120 and the following articles. For the rest, it is in itself arbitrary from which of the three observations we set out: still, it is better, in general, to choose the first and last, the special case of which we shall speak directly, being excepted.

This method is preferable to most of those to be explained hereafter, on this account, that it admits of the most general application. The case must be excepted, in which the two extreme observations embrace a heliocentric motion of 180, or 360, or 540, etc., degrees; for then the position of the plane of the orbit cannot be determined, (article 110). It will be equally inconvenient to apply the method, when the heliocentric motion between the two extreme observations differs very little from 180° or 360°, etc., because an accurate determination of the position of the orbit cannot be obtained in this case, or rather, because the slightest changes in the assumed values of the unknown quantities would cause such great variations in the position of the orbit, and, therefore, in the values of $X, Y$, that the variations of the latter could no longer be regarded as proportional to those of the former. But the proper remedy is at hand; which is, that we should not, in such an event, start from the two extreme observations, but from the first and middle, or from the middle and last, and, therefore, should take for $X, Y$, the differences between calculation and observation in the third or first place. But, if both the second place should be distant from the first, and the third from the second nearly 180 degrees, the disadvantage could not be removed in this way; but it is better not to make use, in the computation of the elements, of observations of this sort, from which, by the nature of the case, it is wholly impossible to obtain an accurate determination of the position of the orbit.

Moreover, this method derives value from the fact, that by it the amount of the variations which the elements experience, if the middle place changes while the extreme places remain fixed, can be estimated without difficulty: in this way, therefore, some judgment may be formed as to the degree of precision to be attributed to the elements found.

## 125.

We shall derive the *second* from the preceding method by applying a slight change. Starting from the distances in two observations, we shall determine all the elements in the same manner as before; we shall not, however, compute from these the geocentric place for the third observation, but will only proceed as far as the heliocentric place in the orbit; on the other hand we will obtain the same heliocentric place, by means of the problem treated in articles 74, 75, from the observed geocentric place and the position of the plane of the orbit; these two determinations, different from each other (unless, perchance, the true values of $x, y$, should be the assumed ones), will furnish us $X$ and $Y$, the difference between the two values of the longitude in orbit being taken for $X$, and the difference between the two values of the radius vector, or rather its logarithm, for $Y$. This method is subject to the same cautions we have touched upon in the preceding article: another is to be added, namely, that the heliocentric place in orbit cannot be deduced from the geocentric place, when the place of the earth happens to be in either of the nodes of the orbit; when that is the case, accordingly, this method cannot be applied. But it will also be proper to avoid the use of this method in the case where the place of the earth is very near either of the nodes, since the assumption that, to small variations of $x, y$, correspond proportional variations of $X, Y$, would be too much in error, for a reason similar to that which we have mentioned in the preceding article. But here, also, may be a remedy sought in the interchange of the mean place with one of the extremes, to which may correspond a place of the earth more remote from the nodes, except, perchance, the earth, in all three of the observations, should be in the vicinity of the nodes.

## 126.

The preceding method prepares the way directly for the *third*. In the same manner as before, by means of the distances of the heavenly body from the earth in the extreme observations, the corresponding longitudes in orbit together with the radii vectores may be determined. With the position of the plane of the orbit, which this calculation will have furnished, the longitude in orbit and the radius vector will be got from the middle observation. The remaining elements may be computed from these three heliocentric places, by the problem treated in articles 82, 83, which process will be independent of the times of the observations. In this way, three mean anomalies and the diurnal motion will be known, whence may be computed the intervals of the times between the first and second, and between the second and third observations. The differences between these and the true intervals will be taken for $X$ and $Y$.

This method is less advantageous when the heliocentric motion includes a small arc only. For in such a case this determination of the orbit (as we have already shown in article 82) depends on quantities of the third order, and does not, therefore, admit of sufficient exactness. The slightest changes in the values of $x, y$, might cause very great changes in the elements and, therefore, in the values of $X, Y$, also, nor would it be allowable to suppose the latter proportional to the former. But when the three places embrace a considerable heliocentric motion, the use of the method will undoubtedly succeed best, unless, indeed, it is thrown into confusion by the exceptions explained in the preceding articles, which are evidently in this method too, to be taken into consideration.

## 127.

After the three heliocentric places have been obtained in the way we have described in the preceding article, we can go forward in the following manner. The remaining elements may be determined by the problem treated in articles 85–105, first, from the first and second places with the corresponding interval of time, and, afterwards, in the same manner, from the second and third places and the corresponding interval of time: thus two values will result for each of the elements, and from their differences any two may be taken at pleasure for $X$ and $Y$. One advantage, not to be rejected, gives great value to this method; it is, that in the first hypotheses the remaining elements, besides the two which are chosen for fixing $X$ and $Y$, can be entirely neglected, and will finally be determined in the last calculation based on the corrected values of $x, y$, either from the first combination alone, or from the second, or, which is generally preferable, from the combination of the first place with the third. The choice of those two elements, which is, commonly speaking, arbitrary, furnishes a great variety of solutions; the logarithm of the semi-parameter, together with the logarithm of the semi-axis major, may be adopted, for example, or the former with the eccentricity, or the latter with the same, or the longitude of the perihelion with any one of these elements: any one of these four elements might also be combined with the eccentric anomaly corresponding to the middle place in either calculation, if an elliptical orbit should result, when the formulas 27–30 of article 96, will supply the most expeditious computation. But in special cases this choice demands some consideration; thus, for example, in orbits resembling the parabola, the semi-axis major or its logarithm would be less suitable, inasmuch as excessive variations of these quantities could not be regarded as proportional to changes of $x, y$: in such a case it would be more advantageous to select $\frac{1}{a}$. But we give less time to these precautions, because the fifth method, to be explained in the following article, is to be preferred, in almost all cases, to the four thus far explained.

## 128.

Let us denote three radii vectores, obtained in the same manner as in articles 125, 126, by $r, r', r''$; the angular heliocentric motion in orbit from the second to the third place by $2f$, from the first to the third by $2f'$, from the first to the second by $2f''$, so that we have

$$f' = f + f'';$$

next, let

$$r'\, r'' \sin 2f = n, \ r\, r'' \sin 2f' = n', \ r\, r' \sin 2f'' = n'';$$

lastly, let the product of the constant quantity $k$ (article 2) into the intervals of the time from the second observation to the third, from the first to the third, and from the first to the second be respectively, $\theta$, $\theta'$ $\theta''$. The double computation of the elements is begun, just as in the preceding article, both from $r r' f''$ and $\theta''$, and from $r' r'', f, \theta$: but neither computation will be continued to the determination of the elements, but will stop as soon as that quantity has been obtained which expresses the ratio of the elliptical sector to the triangle, and which is denoted above (article 91) by $y$ or $-Y$. Let the value of this quantity be, in the first calculation, $\eta''$, in the second, $\eta$. Accordingly, by means of formula 18, article 95, we shall have for the semi-parameter $p$ the two values: —

$$\sqrt{p} = \frac{\eta'' n''}{\theta''}, \text{ and } \sqrt{p} = \frac{\eta n}{\theta}.$$

But we have, besides, by article 82, a third value,

$$p = \frac{4 \, r r' r'' \sin f \sin f' \sin f''}{n - n' + n''},$$

which three values would evidently be identical if true values could have been taken in the beginning for $x$ and $y$. For which reason we should have

$$\frac{\theta''}{\theta} = \frac{\eta'' n''}{\eta n},$$

$$n - n' + n'' = \frac{4 \, \theta \theta'' r r' r'' \sin f \sin f' \sin f''}{\eta \eta'' n n''} = \frac{n' \, \theta \theta''}{2 \, \eta \eta'' r r' r'' \cos f \cos f' \cos f''}.$$

Unless, therefore, these equations are fully satisfied in the first calculation, we can put

$$X = \log \frac{\eta n \theta''}{\eta'' n'' \theta},$$

$$Y = n - n' + n'' - \frac{n' \, \theta \theta''}{2 \, \eta \eta'' r r' r'' \cos f \cos f' \cos f''}.$$

This method admits of an application equally general with the second explained in article 125, but it is a great advantage, that in this fifth method the first hypotheses do not require the determination of the elements themselves, but stop, as it were, half way. It appears, also, that in this process we find that, as it can be foreseen that the new hypothesis will not differ sensibly from the truth, it will be sufficient to determine the elements either from $r, r', f'', \theta''$, alone, or from $r', r'', f, \theta$, or, which is better, from $r, r'' f', \theta'$.

## 129.

The five methods thus far explained lead, at once, to as many others which differ from the former only in this, that the inclination of the orbit and the longitude of the ascending node, instead of the distances from the earth, are taken for $x$ and $y$. The new methods are, then, as follows: —

I. From $x$ and $y$, and the two extreme geocentric places, according to articles 74, 75, the heliocentric longitudes in orbit and the radii vectores are determined, and, from these and the corresponding times, all the remaining elements; from these, finally, the geocentric place for the time of the middle observation, the differences of which from the observed place in longitude and latitude will furnish $X$ and $Y$.

The four remaining methods agree in this, that all three of the heliocentric longitudes in orbit and the corresponding radii vectores are computed from the position of the plane of the orbit and the geocentric places. But afterwards: —

II. The remaining elements are determined from the two extreme places only and the corresponding times; with these elements the longitude in orbit and radius vector are computed for the time of the middle observation, the differences of which quantities from the values before found, that is, deduced from the geocentric place, will produce $X$ and $Y$:

III. Or, the remaining dimensions of the orbit are derived from all three heliocentric places (articles 82, 83,) into which calculation the times do not enter: then the intervals of the times are deduced, which, in an orbit thus found, should have elapsed between the first and second observation, and between this last and the third, and their differences from the true intervals will furnish us with $X$ and $Y$:

IV. The remaining elements are computed in two ways, that is, both by the combination of the first place with the second, and by the combination of the second with the third, the corresponding intervals of the times being used. These two systems of elements being compared with each other, any two of the differences may be taken for $X$ and $Y$:

V. Or lastly, the same double calculation is only continued to the values of the quantity denoted by $y$, in article 91, and then the expressions given in the preceding article for $X$ and $Y$, are adopted.

In order that the last four methods may be safely used, the places of the earth for all three of the observations must not be very near the node of the orbit: on the other hand, the use of the first method only requires, that this condition may exist in the two extreme observations, or rather, (since the middle place may be substituted for either of the extremes,) that, of the three places of the earth, not more than one shall lie in the vicinity of the nodes.

## 130.

The ten methods explained from article 124 forwards, rest upon the assumption that approximate values of the distances of the heavenly body from the earth, or of the position of the plane of the orbit, are already known. When the problem is, to correct, by means of observations more remote from each other, the dimensions of an orbit, the approximate values of which are already, by some means, known, as, for instance, by a previous calculation based on other observations, this assumption will evidently be liable to no difficulty. But it does not as yet appear from this, how the first calculation is to be entered upon when all the dimensions of the orbit are still wholly unknown: this case of our problem is by far the most important and the most difficult, as may be imagined from the analogous problem in the theory of comets, which, as is well known, has perplexed geometers for a long time, and has given rise to many fruitless attempts. In order that our problem may be considered as correctly solved, that is, if the solution be given in accordance with what has been explained in the 119th and subsequent articles, it is evidently requisite to satisfy the following conditions: — *First.* the quantities $x$, $y$, are to be chosen in such a manner, that we can find approximate values of them from the very nature of the problem, at all events, as long as the heliocentric motion of the heavenly body between the observations is not too great. *Secondly*, it is necessary that, for small changes in the quantities $x$, $y$, there be not too great corresponding changes in the quantities to be derived from them, lest the errors accidentally introduced in the assumed values of the former, prevent the latter from being considered as approximate.

*Thirdly* and lastly, we require that the processes by which we pass from the quantities $x, y$, to $X, Y$, successively, be not too complicated.

These conditions will furnish the criterion by which to judge of the excellence of any method: this will show itself more plainly by frequent applications. The method which we are now prepared to explain, and which, in a measure, is to be regarded as the most important part of this work, satisfies these conditions so that it seems to leave nothing further to be desired. Before entering upon the explanation of this in the form most suited to practice, we will premise certain preliminary considerations, and we will illustrate and open, as it were, the way to it, which might, perhaps, otherwise, seem more obscure and less obvious.

## 131.

It is shown in article 114, that if the ratio between the quantities denoted there, and in article 128 by $n, n', n''$, were known, the distances of the heavenly body from the earth could be determined by means of very simple formulas. Now, therefore, if

$$\frac{n}{n'}, \quad \frac{n''}{n'},$$

should be taken for $x, y$,

$$\frac{\theta}{\theta'}, \quad \frac{\theta''}{\theta'},$$

(the symbols $\theta, \theta', \theta''$, being taken in the same signification as in article 128) immediately present themselves as approximate values of these quantities in that case where the heliocentric motion between the observations is not very great: hence, accordingly, seems to flow an obvious solution of our problem, if two distances from the earth are obtained from $x, y$, and after that we proceed agreeably to some one of the five methods of articles 124–128. In fact, the symbols $\eta, \eta''$ being also taken with the meaning of article 128, and, analogously, the quotient arising from the division of the sector contained between the two radii vectores by the area of the triangle between the same being denoted by $\eta'$, we shall have,

$$\frac{n}{n'} = \frac{\theta}{\theta'} \cdot \frac{\eta'}{\eta}, \quad \frac{n''}{n'} = \frac{\theta''}{\theta'} \cdot \frac{\eta'}{\eta''},$$

and it readily appears, that if $n$, $n'$, $n''$, are regarded as small quantities of the first order, $\eta - 1$, $\eta' - 1$, $\eta'' - 1$ are, generally speaking, quantities of the second order, and, therefore,

$$\frac{\theta}{\theta'}, \frac{\theta''}{\theta'},$$

the approximate values of $x, y$, differ from the true ones only by quantities of the second order. Nevertheless, upon a nearer examination of the subject, this method is found to be wholly unsuitable; the reason of this we will explain in a few words. It is readily perceived that the quantity $(0.1.2)$, by which the distances in the formulas 9, 10, 11, of article 114 have been multiplied, is at least of the third order, while, for example, in equation 9 the quantities $(O.1.2)$, $(I.1.2)$, $(II.1.2)$, are, on the contrary, of the first order; hence, it readily follows, that an error of the second order in the values of the quantities $\frac{n}{n'}, \frac{n''}{n'}$ produces an error of the order zero in the values of the distances. Wherefore, according to the common mode of speaking, the distances would be affected by a finite error even when the intervals of the times were infinitely small, and consequently it would not be admissible to consider either these distances or the remaining quantities to be derived from them even as approximate; and the method would be opposed to the second condition of the preceding article.

## 132.

Putting, for the sake of brevity,

$$(0.1.2) = a, \quad (0.I.2) D' = -b, \quad (0.O.2) D = +c, \quad (0.II.2) D'' = +d,$$

so that the equation 10, article 114, may become

$$a\delta' = b + c\frac{n}{n'} + d\frac{n''}{n'},$$

the coefficients $c$ and $d$ will, indeed, be of the first order, but it can be easily shown that the difference $c - d$ is to be referred to the second order. Then it follows, that the value of the quantity

$$\frac{cn + dn''}{n + n''}$$

resulting from the approximate assumption that $n : n'' = \theta : \theta''$ is affected by an error of the fourth order only, and even of the fifth only when the middle is distant from the extreme observations by equal intervals. For this error is

$$\frac{c\,\theta + d\,\theta''}{\theta + \theta''} - \frac{c\,n + d\,n''}{n + n''} = \frac{\theta\,\theta''\,(d - c)\,(\eta'' - \eta)}{(\theta + \theta'')\,(\eta''\theta + \eta\,\theta'')}$$

where the denominator is of the second order, and one factor of the numerator $\theta\,\theta''\,(d - c)$ of the fourth, the other $\eta'' - \eta$ of the second, or, in that special case, of the third order. The former equation, therefore, being exhibited in this form,

$$a\delta' = b + \frac{c\,n + d\,n''}{n + n''} \cdot \frac{n + n''}{n'},$$

it is evident that the defect of the method explained in the preceding article does not arise from the fact that the quantities $n, n''$ have been assumed proportional to $\theta, \theta''$, but that, *in addition to this*, $n'$ was put proportional to $\theta'$. For, indeed, in this way, instead of the factor $\frac{n + n''}{n'}$, the less exact value $\frac{\theta + \theta''}{\theta'} = 1$ is introduced, from which the true value

$$1 + \frac{\theta\,\theta''}{2\,\eta\eta''r r' r'' \cos f \cos f' \cos f''}$$

differs by a quantity of the second order, (article 128).

## 133.

Since the cosines of the angles $f, f', f''$, as also the quantities $\eta, \eta''$ differ from unity by a difference of the second order, it is evident, that if instead of

$$\frac{n + n''}{n'}$$

the approximate value

$$1 + \frac{\theta\,\theta''}{2\,r r' r''}$$

is introduced, an error of the fourth order is committed. If, accordingly, in place of the equation, article 114, the following is introduced,

$$a\delta' = b + \frac{c\,\theta + d\,\theta''}{\theta'}\left(1 + \frac{\theta\,\theta''}{2\,r r' r''}\right),$$

an error of the second order will show itself in the value of the distance $\delta'$ when the extreme observations are equidistant from the middle; or, of the first order in other cases. But this new form of that equation is not suited to the determination of $\delta'$, because it involves the quantities $r$, $r'$, $r''$, still unknown.

Now, generally speaking, the quantities $\frac{r}{r'}$, $\frac{r''}{r'}$, differ from unity by a quantity of the first order, and in the same manner also the product $\frac{rr''}{r'r'}$: it is readily perceived that in the special case frequently mentioned, this product differs from unity by a quantity of the second order only. And even when the orbit of the ellipse is slightly eccentric, so that the eccentricity may be regarded as a quantity of the first order, the difference of $\frac{rr''}{r'r'}$ can be referred to an order one degree higher. It is manifest, therefore, that this error remains of the same order as before if, in our equation, $\frac{\theta\theta''}{2rr'r''}$ is substituted for $\frac{\theta\theta''}{2r'^3}$, whence is obtained the following form,

$$a\delta' = b + \frac{c\theta + d\theta''}{\theta'}\left(1 + \frac{\theta\theta''}{2r'^3}\right).$$

In fact, this equation still contains the unknown quantity $r'$, which, it is evident nevertheless, can be eliminated, since it depends only on $\delta'$ and known quantities. If now the equation should be afterwards properly arranged, it would ascend to the eighth degree.

## 134.

From the preceding it will be understood why, in our method, we are about to take for $x$, $y$, respectively, the quantities

$$\frac{n''}{n} = P, \text{ and } 2\left(\frac{n+n''}{n'} - 1\right)r'^3 = Q.$$

For, *in the first place*, it is evident that if $P$ and $Q$ are regarded as known quantities, $\delta'$ can be determined from them by means of the equation

$$a\delta' = b + \frac{c + dP}{1+P}\left(1 + \frac{Q}{2r'^3}\right),$$

and afterwards $\delta$, $\delta''$, by equations 4, 6, article 114, since we have

$$\frac{n}{n'} = \frac{1}{1+P}\left(1 + \frac{Q}{2r'^3}\right), \quad \frac{n''}{n'} = \frac{P}{1+P}\left(1 + \frac{Q}{2r'^3}\right).$$

*In the second place*, it is manifest that $\frac{\theta''}{\theta}$, $\theta\theta''$ are, in the first hypothesis, the obvious approximate values of the quantities $P$, $Q$, of which the true values are precisely

$$\frac{\theta''}{\theta}\frac{\eta}{\eta''}, \quad \frac{r'r''\theta\theta''}{r\,r''\eta\eta''\cos f\cos f'\cos f''},$$

from which hypothesis will result errors of the first order in the determination of $\delta'$, and therefore of $\delta$, $\delta''$, or of the second order in the special case several times mentioned. Although we may rely with safety upon these conclusions, generally speaking, yet in a particular case they can lose their force, as when the quantity (0. 1. 2), which in general is of the third order, happens to be equal to zero, or so small that it must be referred to a higher order. This occurs when the geocentric path in the celestial sphere has a point of contrary flexure near the middle place. Lastly, it appears to be required, for the use of our method, that the heliocentric motion between the three observations be not too great: but this restriction, by the nature of the very complicated problem, cannot be avoided in any way; neither is it to be regarded as a disadvantage, since it will always be desired to begin at the earliest possible moment the first determination of the unknown orbit of a new heavenly body. Besides, the restriction itself can be taken in a sufficiently broad sense, as the example to be given below will show.

## 135.

The preceding discussions have been introduced, in order that the principles on which our method rests, and its true force, as it were, may be more clearly seen: the practical treatment, however, will present the method in an entirely different form which, after very numerous applications, we can recommend as the most convenient of many tried by us. Since in determining an unknown orbit from three observations the whole subject may always be reduced to certain hypotheses, or rather successive approximations, it will be regarded as a great advantage to have succeeded in so arranging the calculation, as, at the beginning, to separate from these hypotheses as many as possible of the computations which depend, not on $P$ and $Q$, but only on a combination of the known quantities. Then, evidently, these preliminary processes, common to each hypothesis, can be gone through once for all, and the hypotheses themselves are reduced to the fewest possible details.  It will be of equally great importance, if it should not be necessary to proceed in every hypothesis as far as the elements, but if their computation might be reserved for the last hypothesis.  In both these respects, our method, which we are now about to explain, seems to leave nothing to be desired.

## 136.

We are, in the first place, to connect by great circles three heliocentric places of the earth in the celestial sphere, $A, A', A''$ (figure 4), with three geocentric places of the heavenly body, $B, B', B''$, and then to compute the positions of these great circles with respect to the ecliptic (if we adopt the ecliptic as the fundamental plane), and the places of the points $B, B', B''$, in these circles.

Let $\alpha, \alpha', \alpha''$ be three geocentric longitudes of the heavenly body, $\beta, \beta', \beta''$, latitudes; $l, l', l''$, heliocentric longitudes of the earth, the latitudes of which we put equal to zero, (articles 117, 72).  Let, moreover, $\gamma, \gamma', \gamma''$ be the inclinations to the ecliptic of the great circles drawn from $A, A', A''$, to $B, B', B''$, respectively; and, in order to follow a fixed rule in the determination of these inclinations, we shall always measure them from that part of the ecliptic which lies in the direction of the order of the signs from the points $A, A', A''$, so that their magnitudes will be counted from 0 to 360°, or, which amounts to the same thing, from 0 to 180° north, and from 0 to —180° south.  We denote the arcs $AB, A'B', A''B''$, which may always be taken between 0 and 180°, by $\delta, \delta', \delta''$.  Thus we have for the determination of $\gamma$ and $\delta$ the formulas,

[1]  $\tan \gamma = \dfrac{\tan \beta}{\sin (\alpha - l)}$

[2]  $\tan \delta = \dfrac{\tan (\alpha - l)}{\cos \gamma}.$

To which, if desirable for confirming the calculation, can be added the following,

$$\sin \delta = \frac{\sin \beta}{\sin \gamma}, \ \cos \delta = \cos \beta \cos (\alpha - l).$$

We have, evidently, entirely analogous formulas for determining $\gamma', \delta', \gamma'', \delta''$.  Now, if at the same time $\beta = 0.$ $\alpha - l = 0$ or 180°, that is, if the heavenly body should be in opposition or conjunction and in the ecliptic at the same time, $\gamma$ would be indeterminate. But we assume that this is not the case in either of the three observations.

If the equator is adopted as the fundamental plane, instead of the ecliptic, then, for determining the positions of the three great circles with respect to the equator, will be required the right ascensions of their intersections with the equator, besides the inclinations; and it will be necessary to compute, in addition to the distances of the points $B, B', B''$, from these intersections, the distances of the points $A, A', A''$ also from the same intersections. Since these depend on the problem discussed in article 110, we do not stop here to obtain the formulas.

### 137.

The *second* step will be the determination of the positions of these three great circles relatively to each other, which depend on their inclinations and the places of their mutual intersections. If we wish to bring these to depend upon clear and general conceptions, without ambiguity, so as not to be obliged to use special figures for different individual cases, it will be necessary to premise some preliminary explanations. *Firstly,* in every great circle two opposite *directions* are to be distinguished in some way, which will be done if we regard one of them as direct or positive, and the other as retrograde or negative. This being wholly arbitrary in itself, we shall always, for the sake of establishing a uniform rule, consider the directions from $A, A', A''$ towards $B, B', B''$ as positive; thus, for example, if the intersection of the first circle with the second is represented by a positive distance from the point $A$, it will be understood that it is to be taken from $A$ towards $B$ (as $D''$ in our figure); but if it should be negative, then the distance is to be taken on the other side of $A$. And *secondly,* the two hemispheres, into which every great circle divides the whole sphere, are to be distinguished by suitable denominations; accordingly, we shall call that the *superior* hemisphere, which, to one walking on the inner surface of the sphere, in the positive direction along the great circle, is on the right hand; the other, the *inferior*. The superior hemisphere will be analogous to the northern hemisphere in regard to the ecliptic or equator, the inferior to the southern.

These definitions being correctly understood, it will be possible conveniently to distinguish *both* intersections of the two great circles from each other.   In fact, in one the first circle tends from the inferior to the superior hemisphere of the second, or, which is the same thing, the second from the superior to the inferior hemisphere of the first; in the other intersection the opposite takes place.

It is, indeed, wholly arbitrary in itself which intersections we shall select for our problem; but, that we may proceed here also according to an invariable rule, we shall always adopt these ($D, D', D''$, figure 4) where the third circle $A''B''$ passes into the superior hemisphere of the second $A'B'$, the third into that of the first $AB$, and the second into that of the first, respectively.   The places of these intersections will be determined by their distances from the points $A'$ and $A''$, $A$ and $A''$, $A$ and $A'$, which we shall simply denote by $A'D$, $A''D$, $AD'$, $A''D'$, $AD''$, $A'D''$.

Which being premised, the mutual inclinations of the circles will be the angles which are contained, at the points of intersection $D, D', D''$, between those parts of the circles cutting each other that lie in the positive direction; we shall denote these inclinations, taken always between 0 and 180°, by $\varepsilon, \varepsilon', \varepsilon''$.   The determination of these nine unknown quantities from those that are known, evidently rests upon the problem discussed by us in article 55.   We have, consequently, the following equations: —

[3]   $\sin \frac{1}{2}\varepsilon \sin \frac{1}{2}(A'D + A''D) = \sin \frac{1}{2}(l'' - l)\sin \frac{1}{2}(\gamma'' + \gamma')$,

[4]   $\sin \frac{1}{2}\varepsilon \cos \frac{1}{2}(A'D + A''D) = \cos \frac{1}{2}(l'' - l)\sin \frac{1}{2}(\gamma'' - \gamma')$,

[5]   $\cos \frac{1}{2}\varepsilon \sin \frac{1}{2}(A'D - A''D) = \sin \frac{1}{2}(l'' - l)\cos \frac{1}{2}(\gamma'' + \gamma')$,

[6]   $\cos \frac{1}{2}\varepsilon \cos \frac{1}{2}(A'D - A''D) = \cos \frac{1}{2}(l'' - l)\cos \frac{1}{2}(\gamma'' - \gamma')$.

$\frac{1}{2}(A'D + A''D)$ and $\sin \frac{1}{2}\varepsilon$ are made known by equations 3 and 4, $\frac{1}{2}(A'D - A''D)$ and $\cos \frac{1}{2}\varepsilon$ by the remaining two; hence $A'D$, $A''D$ and $\varepsilon$.   The ambiguity in the determination of the arcs $\frac{1}{2}(A'D + A''D)$, $\frac{1}{2}(A'D - A''D)$, by means of the tangents, is removed by the condition that $\sin \frac{1}{2}\varepsilon$, $\cos \frac{1}{2}\varepsilon$, must be positive, and the agreement between $\sin \frac{1}{2}\varepsilon$, $\cos \frac{1}{2}\varepsilon$, will serve to verify the whole calculation.

The determination of the quantities $AD'$, $A''D'$, $\varepsilon'$, $AD''$, $A'D''$, $\varepsilon''$ is effected in precisely the same manner, and it will not be worth while to transcribe here the eight equations used in this calculation, since, in fact, they readily appear if we change

$$\text{for } \begin{array}{c} A'D \\ AD' \\ AD'' \end{array} \quad \begin{array}{c} A''D \\ A''D' \\ A'D'' \end{array} \quad \begin{array}{c} \varepsilon \\ \varepsilon' \\ \varepsilon'' \end{array} \quad \begin{array}{c} l''-l \\ l''-l \\ l-l \end{array} \quad \begin{array}{c} \gamma'' \\ \gamma'' \\ \gamma' \end{array} \quad \begin{array}{c} \gamma' \\ \gamma \\ \gamma \end{array}$$

respectively.

A new verification of the whole calculation thus far can be obtained from the mutual relation between the sides and angles of the spherical triangle formed by joining the three points $D, D', D''$, from which result the equations, true in general, whatever may be the positions of these points,

$$\frac{\sin(AD'-AD'')}{\sin \varepsilon} = \frac{\sin(A'D-A'D'')}{\sin \varepsilon'} = \frac{\sin(A''D-A''D')}{\sin \varepsilon''}.$$

Finally, if the equator is selected for the fundamental plane instead of the ecliptic, the computation undergoes no change, except that it is necessary to substitute for the heliocentric places of the earth $A, A', A''$ those points of the equator where it is cut by the circles $AB, A'B', A''B''$; consequently, the right ascensions of these intersections are to be taken instead of $l, l, l'$, and also instead of $A'D$, the distance of the point $D$ from the second intersection, etc.

## 138.

The *third* step consists in this, that the two extreme geocentric places of the heavenly body, that is, the points $B, B''$, are to be joined by a great circle, and the intersection of this with the great circle $A'B'$ is to be determined. Let $B^*$ be this intersection, and $\delta' - \sigma$ its distance from the point $A'$; let $a^*$ be its longitude, and $\beta^*$ its latitude. We have, consequently, for the reason that $B, B^*, B''$ lie in the same great circle, the well-known equation,

$$0 = \tan \beta \sin(\alpha'' - \alpha^*) - \tan \beta^* \sin(\alpha'' - \alpha) + \tan \beta'' \sin(\alpha^* - \alpha),$$

which, by the substitution of $\tan \gamma' \sin(\alpha^* - l)$ for $\tan \beta^*$, takes the following form: —

$$0 = \cos(\alpha^* - l)\,(\tan \beta \sin(\alpha'' - l) - \tan \beta'' \sin(\alpha - l))$$
$$- \sin(\alpha^* - l)\,(\tan \beta \cos(\alpha'' - l) + \tan \gamma' \sin(\alpha'' - \alpha) - \tan \beta'' \cos(\alpha - l)).$$

Wherefore, since $\tan(\alpha^* - l) = \cos \gamma' \tan(\delta' - \sigma)$ we shall have,

$$\tan(\delta' - \sigma) = \frac{\tan \beta \sin(\alpha'' - l') - \tan \beta'' \sin(\alpha - l')}{\cos \gamma'\,(\tan \beta \cos(\alpha'' - l') - \tan \beta'' \cos(\alpha - l')) + \sin \gamma' \sin(\alpha'' - \alpha)}.$$

Thence are derived the following formulas, better suited to numerical calculations. Putting,

[7]   $\tan \beta \sin (\alpha'' - l') - \tan \beta'' \sin (\alpha - l') = S,$

[8]   $\tan \beta \cos (\alpha'' - l') - \tan \beta'' \cos (\alpha - l') = T \sin t,$

[9]   $\sin (\alpha'' - \alpha) = T \cos t,$

we shall have (article 14, II.)

[10]   $\tan (\delta' - \sigma) = \dfrac{S}{T \sin (t + \gamma')}.$

The uncertainty in the determination of the arc $(\delta' - \sigma)$ by means of the tangent arises from the fact that the great circles $A'B'$, $BB''$, cut each other in *two* points; we shall always adopt for $B^*$ the intersection nearest the point $B'$, so that $\sigma$ may always fall between the limits of $-90°$ and $+90°$, by which means the uncertainty is removed.

For the most part, then, the value of the arc $\sigma$ (which depends upon the *curvature* of the geocentric motion) will be quite a small quantity, and even, generally speaking, of the second order, if the intervals of the times are regarded as of the first order.

It will readily appear, from the remark in the preceding article, what are the modifications to be applied to the computation, if the equator should be chosen as the fundamental plane instead of the ecliptic. It is, moreover, manifest that the place of the point $B^*$ will remain indeterminate, if the circles $BB''$, $A'B''$ should be wholly coincident; this case, in which the four points $A', B, B', B''$ lie in the same great circle, we exclude from our investigation. It is proper in the selection of observations to avoid that case, also, where the locus of these four points differs but little from a great circle; for then the place of the point $B^*$, which is of great importance in the subsequent operations, would be too much affected by the slightest errors of observation, and could not be determined with the requisite precision. In the same manner the point $B^*$, evidently, remains indeterminate when the points $B, B''$ coincide,† in which case the position of the

---

† Or when they are opposite to each other; but we do not speak of this case, because our method is not extended to observations embracing so great an interval.

circle $BB''$ itself would become indeterminate. Wherefore we exclude this case, also, just as, for reasons similar to the preceding, those observations will be avoided in which the first and last geocentric places fall in points of the sphere near to each other.

## 139.

Let $C$, $C'$, $C''$, be three heliocentric places of the heavenly body in the celestial sphere, which will be (article 64, III.) in the great circles $AB$, $A'B'$, $A''B''$, respectively, and, indeed, between $A$ and $B$, $A'$ and $B'$, $A''$ and $B''$; moreover, the points $C$, $C'$, $C''$ will lie in the same great circle, that is, in the circle which the plane of the orbit projects on the celestial sphere.

We will denote by $r, r', r''$, three distances of the heavenly body from the sun; by $\varrho, \varrho', \varrho''$, its distances from the earth; by $R, R', R''$, the distances of the earth from the sun. Moreover, we put the arcs $C'C''$, $CC''$, $CC'$ equal to $2f$, $2f'$, $2f''$, respectively, and

$$r'r'' \sin 2f = n,\ rr'' \sin 2f' = n',\ rr' \sin 2f'' = n''.$$

Consequently we have

$$f' = f + f'',\ AC + CB = \delta,\ A'C' + C'B' = \delta',\ A''C'' + C''B'' = \delta'';$$

also,

$$\frac{\sin \delta}{r} = \frac{\sin AC}{\varrho} = \frac{\sin CB}{R}$$

$$\frac{\sin \delta'}{r'} = \frac{\sin A'C'}{\varrho'} = \frac{\sin C'B'}{R'}$$

$$\frac{\sin \delta''}{r''} = \frac{\sin A''C''}{\varrho''} = \frac{\sin C''B''}{R''}.$$

Hence it is evident, that, as soon as the positions of the points $C$, $C'$, $C''$ are known, the quantities $r, r', r'', \varrho, \varrho', \varrho''$ can be determined. We shall now show how the former may be derived from the quantities

$$\frac{n''}{n} = P,\ 2\left(\frac{n + n''}{n'} - 1\right) r'^3 = Q,$$

from which, as we have before said, our method started.

## 140.

We first remark, that if $N$ were any point whatever of the great circle $CC'C''$, and the distances of the points $C$, $C'$, $C''$ from the point $N$ were counted in the direction from $C$ to $C''$, so that in general

$$NC'' - NC' = 2f, \quad NC'' - NC = 2f', \quad NC' - NC = 2f'',$$

we shall have

I. $\qquad\qquad 0 = \sin 2f \sin NC - \sin 2f' \sin NC' + \sin 2f'' \sin NC''.$

We will now suppose $N$ to be taken in the intersection of the great circles $BB^*B''$, $CC'C''$, as in the ascending node of the former on the latter. Let us denote by $\mathfrak{C}, \mathfrak{C}', \mathfrak{C}'', \mathfrak{D}, \mathfrak{D}', \mathfrak{D}''$, respectively, the distances of the points $C$, $C'$, $C''$, $D$, $D'$, $D''$ from the great circle $BB^*B''$, taken positively on one side, and negatively on the other. Then $\sin \mathfrak{C}$, $\sin \mathfrak{C}'$, $\sin \mathfrak{C}''$, will evidently be proportional to $\sin NC$, $\sin NC'$, $\sin NC''$, whence equation I. is expressed in the following form:—

$$0 = \sin 2f \sin \mathfrak{C} - \sin 2f' \sin \mathfrak{C}' + \sin 2f'' \sin \mathfrak{C}'';$$

or multiplying by $rr'r''$,

II. $\qquad\qquad 0 = nr \sin \mathfrak{C} - n'r' \sin \mathfrak{C}' + n''r'' \sin \mathfrak{C}''.$

It is evident, moreover, that $\sin \mathfrak{C}$ is to $\sin \mathfrak{D}'$, as the sine of the distance of the point $C$ from $B$ is to that of $D'$ from $B$, both distances being measured in the same direction. We have, therefore,

$$- \sin \mathfrak{C} = \frac{\sin \mathfrak{D}' \sin CB}{\sin (AD' - \delta)},$$

in precisely the same way, are obtained,

$$- \sin \mathfrak{C} = \frac{\sin \mathfrak{D}'' \sin CB}{\sin (AD' - \delta)},$$

$$- \sin \mathfrak{C}' = \frac{\sin \mathfrak{D} \sin C'B^*}{(\sin A'D - \delta' + \sigma)} = \frac{\sin \mathfrak{D}'' \sin C'B^*}{\sin (A'D'' - \delta' + \sigma)},$$

$$- \sin \mathfrak{C}'' = \frac{\sin \mathfrak{D} \sin C''B''}{\sin (A''D - \delta'')} = \frac{\sin \mathfrak{D}' \sin C''B''}{\sin (A''D' - \delta'')}.$$

Dividing, therefore, equation II. by $r'' \sin \mathfrak{C}''$, there results,

$$0 = n \cdot \frac{r \sin CB}{r'' \sin C''B''} \cdot \frac{\sin (A''D' - \delta'')}{\sin (AD' - \delta)} - n' \cdot \frac{r' \sin C'B^*}{r'' \sin C''B''} \cdot \frac{\sin (A''D - \delta'')}{\sin (A'D - \delta' + \sigma)} + n''.$$

If now we designate the arc $C'B'$ by $z$, substitute for $r$, $r'$, $r''$ their values in the preceding article, and, for the sake of brevity, put

$$[11] \quad \frac{R \sin \delta \sin (A''D' - \delta'')}{R'' \sin \delta'' \sin (AD' - \delta)} = a,$$

$$[12] \quad \frac{R' \sin \delta' \sin (A''D - \delta'')}{R'' \sin \delta'' \sin (A'D - \delta' + \sigma)} = b,$$

our equation will become

III. $$0 = an - bn' \frac{\sin (z - \sigma)}{\sin z} + n''$$

The coefficient $b$ may be computed by the following formula, which is easily derived from the equations just introduced:—

$$[13] \quad a \times \frac{R' \sin \delta' \sin (AD' - \delta)}{R \sin \delta \sin (A'D'' - \delta' + \sigma)} = b.$$

For verifying the computation, it will be expedient to use both the formulas 12 and 13. When $\sin (A'D'' - \delta' + \sigma)$ is greater than $\sin (A'D - \delta' + \sigma)$, the latter formula is less affected by the unavoidable errors of the tables than the former, and so will be preferred to it, if some small discrepancy to be explained in this way should result in the values of $b$; on the other hand, the former formula is most to be relied upon, when $\sin (A'D'' - \delta' + \sigma)$ is less than $\sin (A'D - \delta' + \sigma)$; a suitable mean between both values will be adopted, if preferred. The following formulas can be made to answer for examining the calculation; their not very difficult derivation we suppress for the sake of brevity.

$$0 = \frac{a \sin (l'' - l')}{R} - \frac{b \sin (l'' - l)}{R'} \cdot \frac{\sin (\delta' - \sigma)}{\sin \delta'} + \frac{\sin (l' - l)}{R''},$$

$$b = \frac{R' \sin \delta'}{R'' \sin \delta''} \cdot \frac{U \cos \beta \cos \beta''}{\sin (AD' - \delta) \sin \varepsilon'},$$

in which (article 138, equation 10,) $U$ expresses the quotient

$$\frac{S}{\sin (\delta' - \sigma)} = \frac{T \sin (t + \gamma)}{\cos (\delta' - \sigma)},$$

## 141.

From $P = \dfrac{n''}{n}$, and equation III. of the preceding article, we have

$$(n + n'') \frac{P + a}{P + 1} = bn' \frac{\sin (z - \sigma)}{\sin z};$$

thence, and from

$$Q = 2\left(\frac{n+n''}{n'} - 1\right)r'^3 \text{ and } r' = \frac{R' \sin \delta'}{\sin z}$$

is obtained,

$$\sin z + \frac{Q \sin z^4}{2 R'^3 \sin \delta'^3} = b \frac{P+1}{P+a} \sin (z - \sigma), \text{ or,}$$

$$\frac{Q \sin^4 z}{2 R'^3 \sin^3 \delta'} = \left(b \frac{P+1}{P+a} - \cos \sigma\right) \sin (z - \sigma) - \sin \sigma \cos (z - \sigma).$$

Putting, therefore, for the sake of brevity,

[14]          $$\frac{1}{2 R'^3 \sin^3 \delta' \sin \sigma} = c,$$

and introducing the auxiliary angle $\omega$ such that

$$\tan \omega = \frac{\sin \sigma}{b \dfrac{P+1}{P+a} - \cos \sigma},$$

we have the equation

IV.          $$c \, Q \sin \omega \sin^4 z = \sin (z - \omega - \sigma),$$

from which we must get the unknown quantity $z$. That the angle $\omega$ may be computed more conveniently, it will be expedient to present the preceding for mula for $\tan \omega$ thus:—

$$\tan \omega = \frac{(P+a) \tan \sigma}{P\left(\dfrac{b}{\cos \sigma} - 1\right) + \left(\dfrac{b}{\cos \sigma} - a\right)}.$$

Whence, putting,

[15]          $$\frac{\dfrac{b}{\cos \sigma} - a}{\dfrac{b}{\cos \sigma} - 1} = d,$$

[16]          $$\frac{\tan \sigma}{\dfrac{b}{\cos \sigma} - 1} = e,$$

we shall have for the determination of $\omega$ the very simple formula,

$$\tan \omega = \frac{e (P+a)}{P+d}.$$

We consider as the fourth step the computation of the quantities $a, b, c, d, e,$

by means of the formulas 11–16, depending on given quantities alone. The quantities $b$, $c$, $e$, will not themselves be required, only their logarithms.

There is a special case in which these precepts require some change. That is, when the great circle $BB''$ coincides with $A''B''$, and thus the points $B$, $B^*$ with $D'$, $D$, respectively, the quantities $a$, $b$ would acquire infinite values. Putting, in this case,

$$\frac{R \sin \delta \sin (A'D'' - \delta' + \sigma)}{R' \sin \delta' \sin (AD'' - \delta)} = \pi,$$

in place of equation III. we shall have

$$0 = \pi n - \frac{n' \sin (z - \sigma)}{\sin z},$$

whence, making

$$\tan \omega = \frac{\pi \sin \sigma}{P + (1 - \pi \cos \sigma)},$$

the same equation IV. is obtained.

In the same manner, in the special case when $\sigma = 0$, $c$ becomes infinite, and $\omega = 0$, on account of which the factor $c \sin \omega$, in equation IV., seems to be indeterminate; nevertheless, it is in reality determinate, and its value is

$$\frac{P + a}{2 R'^3 \sin^3 \delta' \, (b - 1) \, (P + d)},$$

as a little attention will show. In this case, therefore, $\sin z$ becomes

$$R' \sin \delta' \sqrt[3]{\frac{2 (b - 1) (P + d)}{Q (P + a)}}.$$

142.

Equation IV., which being developed rises to the eighth degree, is solved by trial very expeditiously in its unchanged form. But, from the theory of equations, it can be easily shown, (which, for the sake of brevity, we shall dispense with explaining more fully) that this equation admits of two or four solutions by means of real values. In the former case, one value of $\sin z$ will be positive; and the other negative value must be rejected, because, by the nature of the problem, it is impossible for $r'$ to become negative. In the latter case, among the values of $\sin z$ one will be positive, and the remaining three negative, — when, accordingly, it will not be doubtful which must be adopted, — or three positive with one negative; in this case, from among the positive values those, if there are any, are to be rejected which give $z$ greater than $\delta'$, since, by another essential condition of the problem, $\varrho'$ and, therefore, $\sin(\delta' - z)$, must be a positive quantity.

When the observations are distant from each other by moderate intervals of time, the last case will most frequently occur, in which three positive values of $\sin z$ satisfy the equation. Among these solutions, besides that which is true, some one will be found making $z$ differ but little from $\delta'$, either in excess or in defect; this is to be accounted for as follows. The analytical treatment of our problem is based upon the condition, simply, that the three places of the heavenly body in space must fall in right lines, the positions of which are determined by the absolute places of the earth, and the observed places of the body. Now, from the very nature of the case, these places must, in fact, fall in those parts of the right lines whence the light descends to the earth. But the analytical equations do not recognize this restriction, and every system of places, harmonizing of course with the laws of KEPLER, is embraced, whether they lie in these right lines on this side of the earth, or on that, or, in fine, whether they coincide with the earth itself. Now, this last case will undoubtedly satisfy our problem, since the earth moves in accordance with these laws. Thence it is manifest, that the equations must include the solution in which the points $C, C', C'''$ coincide with $A, A', A''$ (so long as we neglect the very small variations in the elliptical places of the earth produced by the perturbations and the parallax). Equation IV., therefore, must always admit the solution $z = \delta'$, if true values answering to the places of the earth are adopted for $P$ and $Q$. So long as values not differing much from these are assigned to those quantities (which is always an admissible supposition, when the intervals of the times are moderate), among the solutions of equation IV., some one will necessarily be found which approaches very nearly to the value $z = \delta'$.

For the most part, indeed, in that case where equation IV. admits of three solutions by means of positive values of $\sin z$, the third of these (besides the true one, and that of which we have just spoken) makes the value of $z$ greater than $\delta'$, and thus is only analytically possible, but physically impossible; so that it cannot then be doubtful which is to be adopted. But yet it certainly can happen, that the equation may admit of two distinct and proper solutions, and thus that our problem may be satisfied by two wholly different orbits. But in such an event, the true orbit is easily distinguished from the false as soon as it is possible to bring to the test other and more remote observations.

### 143.

As soon as the angle $z$ is got, $r'$ is immediately had by means of the equation

$$r' = \frac{R' \sin \delta'}{\sin z}.$$

Further, from the equations $P = \frac{n''}{n}$ and III. we obtain,

$$\frac{n'r'}{n} = \frac{(P + a) R' \sin \delta'}{b \sin (z - \sigma)},$$

$$\frac{n'r'}{n''} = \frac{1}{P} \cdot \frac{n'r'}{n}.$$

Now, in order that we may treat the formulas, according to which the positions of the points $C$, $C''$, are determined from the position of the point $C'$, in such a manner that their general truth in those cases not shown in figure 4 may immediately be apparent, we remark, that the sine of the distance of the point $C'$ from the great circle $CB$ (taken positively in the superior hemisphere, negatively in the inferior) is equal to the product of $\sin \varepsilon''$ into the sine of the distance of the point $C'$ from $D''$, measured in the positive direction, and therefore to

$$- \sin \varepsilon'' \sin C'D'' = - \sin \varepsilon'' \sin (z + A'D'' - \delta');$$

in the same manner, the sine of the distance of the point $C''$ from the same great circle is $- \sin \varepsilon' \sin C''D'$. But, evidently, those sines are as $\sin CC'$ to $\sin CC''$, or as $\frac{n''}{rr'}$ to $\frac{n}{rr''}$, or as $n''r''$ to $n'r'$. Putting, therefore, $C''D' = \zeta''$, we have

V.          $$r'' \sin \zeta'' = \frac{n'r'}{n''} \cdot \frac{\sin \varepsilon''}{\sin \varepsilon'} \sin (z + A'D'' - \delta').$$

Precisely in the same way, putting $CD' = \zeta$, is obtained

VI.          $$r \sin \zeta = \frac{n'r'}{n} \cdot \frac{\sin \varepsilon}{\sin \varepsilon'} \sin (z + A'D - \delta').$$

VII.          $$r \sin (\zeta + AD'' - AD') = r'' P \frac{\sin \varepsilon}{\sin \varepsilon'} \sin (\zeta'' + A''D - A''D').$$

By combining equations V. and VI. with the following taken from article 139,

VIII. $\qquad r'' \sin (\zeta'' - A''D' + \delta'') = R'' \sin \delta''$,

IX. $\qquad r \sin (\zeta - AD' + \delta) = R \sin \delta$,

the quantities $\zeta$, $\zeta''$, $r$, $r''$, will be thence derived by the method of article 78. That this calculation may be more conveniently effected, it will not be unacceptable to produce here the formulas themselves. Let us put

[17] $\quad \dfrac{R \sin \delta}{\sin (AD' - \delta)} = \varkappa$,

[18] $\quad \dfrac{R'' \sin \delta''}{\sin (A''D' - \delta'')} = \varkappa''$,

[19] $\quad \dfrac{\cos (AD' - \delta)}{R \sin \delta} = \lambda$,

[20] $\quad \dfrac{\cos (A''D' - \delta'')}{R'' \sin \delta''} = \lambda''$.

The computation of these, or rather of their logarithms, yet independent of $P$ and $Q$, is to be regarded as the *fifth* and last step in the, as it were, preliminary operations, and is conveniently performed at the same time with the computation of $a$, $b$, themselves, or with the fourth step, where $a$ becomes equal to $\frac{\varkappa}{\varkappa''}$.

Making, then,

$$\frac{n'r'}{n} \cdot \frac{\sin \varepsilon}{\sin \varepsilon'} \sin (z + A'D - \delta') = p,$$

$$\frac{n'r'}{n''} \cdot \frac{\sin \varepsilon''}{\sin \varepsilon'} \sin (z + A'D'' - \delta') = p'',$$

$$\varkappa (\lambda p - 1) = q,$$

$$\varkappa'' (\lambda'' p'' - 1) = q'',$$

we derive $\zeta$ and $r$ from $r \sin \zeta = p$, $r \cos \zeta = q$; also, $\zeta''$ and $r''$ from $r'' \sin \zeta'' = p''$, and $r'' \cos \zeta'' = q''$. No ambiguity can occur in determining $\zeta$ and $\zeta''$, because $r$ and $r''$ must, necessarily, be positive quantities. The complete computation can, if desired, be verified by equation VII.

There are two cases, nevertheless, where another course must be pursued. That is, when the point $D'$ coincides with $B$, or is opposite to it in the sphere, or when $AD' - \delta = 0$ or $180°$, equations VI. and IX. must necessarily be identical, and we should have $\varkappa = \infty$, $\lambda p - 1 = 0$, and $q$, therefore, indeterminate. In this case, $\zeta''$ and $r''$ will be determined, in the manner we have shown, but then $\zeta$ and $r$ must be obtained by the combination of equation VII. with VI. or IX. We dispense with transcribing here the formulas themselves, to be found in article 78; we observe, merely, that in the case where $AD' - \delta$ is in fact neither $= 0$ nor $= 180°$, but is, nevertheless, a very small arc, it is preferable to follow the same method, since the former method does not then admit of the requisite precision. And, in fact, the combination of equation VII. with VI. or IX. will be chosen according as $\sin(AD'' - AD')$ is greater or less than $\sin(AD' - \delta)$.

In the same manner, in the case in which the point $D'$, or the one opposite to it, either coincides with $B''$ or is little removed from it, the determination of $\zeta''$ and $r''$ by the preceding method would be either impossible or unsafe. In this case, accordingly, $\zeta$ and $r$ will be determined by that method, but $\zeta''$ and $r''$ by the combination of equation VII. either with V. or with VIII., according as $\sin(A''D - A''D')$ is greater or less than $\sin(A''D' - \delta'')$.

There is no reason to fear that $D'$ will coincide *at the same time* with the points $B$, $B''$, or with the opposite points, or be very near them; for the case in which $B$ coincides with $B''$, or is but little remote from it, we excluded above, in article 138, from our discussion.

## 144.

The arcs $\zeta$ and $\zeta''$ being found, the positions of the points $C$, $C''$, will be given, and it will be possible to determine the distance $CC'' = 2f'$ from $\zeta$, $\zeta''$ and $\varepsilon'$. Let $u$, $u''$, be the inclinations of the great circles $AB$, $A''B''$ to the great circle $CC''$ (which in figure 4 will be the angles $C''CD'$ and $180° - CC''D'$, respectively), and we shall have the following equations, entirely analogous to the equations 3–6, article 137 : —

$$\sin f' \sin \tfrac{1}{2}(u'' + u) = \sin \tfrac{1}{2} \varepsilon' \sin \tfrac{1}{2}(\zeta + \zeta''),$$
$$\sin f' \cos \tfrac{1}{2}(u'' + u) = \cos \tfrac{1}{2} \varepsilon' \sin \tfrac{1}{2}(\zeta - \zeta''),$$
$$\cos f' \sin \tfrac{1}{2}(u'' - u) = \sin \tfrac{1}{2} \varepsilon' \cos \tfrac{1}{2}(\zeta + \zeta''),$$
$$\cos f' \cos \tfrac{1}{2}(u'' - u) = \cos \tfrac{1}{2} \varepsilon' \cos \tfrac{1}{2}(\zeta - \zeta'').$$

The two former will give $\frac{1}{2}(u''+u)$ and $\sin f'$, the two latter $\frac{1}{2}(u''-u)$ and $\cos f'$; from $\sin f'$ and $\cos f'$ we shall have $f'$. It will be proper to neglect in the first hypotheses the angles $\frac{1}{2}(u''+u)$ and $\frac{1}{2}(u''-u)$, which will be used in the last hypothesis only for determining the position of the plane of the orbit.

In the same way, exactly, $f$ can be derived from $\varepsilon$, $C'D$ and $C''D$; also $f''$ from $\varepsilon''$, $CD''$ and $C'D''$; but the following formulas are used much more conveniently for this purpose:—

$$\sin 2f = r \sin 2f' \cdot \frac{n}{n'r'},$$

$$\sin 2f'' = r'' \sin 2f' \cdot \frac{n''}{n'r'},$$

in which the logarithms of the quantities $\frac{n}{n'r'}$, $\frac{n''}{n'r'}$ are already given by the preceding calculations. Finally, the whole calculation finds a new verification in this, that we must have

$$2f + 2f'' = 2f';$$

if by chance any difference shows itself, it will not certainly be of any importance, if all the processes have been performed as accurately as possible. Nevertheless, occasionally, the calculation being conducted throughout with seven places of decimals, it may amount to some tenths of a second, which, if it appear worth while, we may with the utmost facility so distribute between $2f$ and $2f''$ that the logarithms of the sines may be equally either increased or diminished, by which means the equation

$$P = \frac{r \sin 2f''}{r'' \sin 2f} = \frac{n''}{n}$$

will be satisfied with all the precision that the tables admit. When $f$ and $f''$ differ a little, it will be sufficient to distribute that difference equally between $2f$ and $2f''$.

## 145.

After the positions of the heavenly body in the orbit have been determined in this manner, the double calculation of the elements will be commenced, both by the combination of the second place with the third, and the combination of the first with the second, together with the corresponding intervals of the times.

Before this is undertaken, of course, the intervals of the times themselves require some correction, if it is decided to take account of the aberration agreeably to the third method of article 118. In this case, evidently, for the true times are to be substituted fictitious ones anterior to the former, respectively, by $493\varrho$, $493\varrho'$, $493\varrho''$ seconds. For computing the distances $\varrho, \varrho', \varrho''$, we have the formulas: —

$$\varrho = \frac{R \sin (A D' - \zeta)}{\sin (\zeta - A D' + \delta)} = \frac{r \sin (A D' - \zeta)}{\sin \delta},$$

$$\varrho' = \frac{R' \sin (\delta' - z)}{\sin z} = \frac{r' \sin (\delta' - z)}{\sin \delta'},$$

$$\varrho'' = \frac{R'' \sin (A'' D' - \zeta'')}{\sin (\zeta'' - A'' D' + \delta'')} = \frac{r'' \sin (A'' D' - \zeta'')}{\sin \delta''}.$$

But, if the observations should at the beginning have been freed from aberration by the first or second method of article 118, this calculation may be omitted; so that it will not be necessary to deduce the values of the distances $\varrho$, $\varrho', \varrho''$, unless, perhaps, for the sake of proving that those values, upon which the computation of the aberration was based, were sufficiently exact. Finally, it is apparent that all this calculation is also to be omitted whenever it is thought preferable to neglect the aberration altogether.

## 146.

The calculation of the elements — on the one hand from $r', r'', 2f$ and the corrected interval of the time between the second and third observations, the product of which multiplied by the quantity $k$, (article 1,) we denote by $\theta$, and on the other hand from $r, r', 2f''$ and the interval of time between the first and second observations, the product of which by $k$ will be equal to $\theta''$ — is to be carried, agreeably to the method explained in articles 88–105, only as far as the quantity there denoted by $y$, the value of which in the first of these combinations we shall call $\eta$, in the latter $\eta''$. Let then

$$\frac{\theta'' \eta}{\theta \eta''} = P', \qquad \frac{r'r'\theta \theta''}{r\, r'' \eta \eta'' \cos f \cos f' \cos f''} = Q',$$

and it is evident, that if the values of the quantities $P$, $Q$, upon which the whole calculation hitherto is based, were true, we should have in the result $P' = P$,

$Q' = Q$. And conversely it is readily perceived, that if in the result $P' = P$, $Q' = Q$, the double calculation of the elements from both combinations would, if completed, furnish numbers entirely equal, by which, therefore, all three observations will be exactly represented, and thus the problem wholly satisfied. But when the result is not $P' = P$, $Q' = Q$, let $P' - P$, $Q' - Q$ be taken for $X$ and $Y$, if, indeed, $P$ and $Q$ were taken for $x$ and $y$; it will be still more convenient to put

$$\log P = x, \log Q = y, \log P' - \log P = X, \log Q' - \log Q = Y.$$

Then the calculation must be repeated with other values of $x, y$.

## 147.

Properly, indeed, here also, as in the ten methods before given, it would be arbitrary what new values we assume for $x$ and $y$ in the second hypothesis, if only they are not inconsistent with the general conditions developed above; but yet, since it manifestly is to be considered a great advantage to be able to set out from more accurate values, in this method we should act with but little prudence if we were to adopt the second values rashly, as it were, since it may easily be perceived, from the very nature of the subject, that if the first values of $P$ and $Q$ were affected with slight errors, $P'$ and $Q'$ themselves would represent much more exact values, supposing the heliocentric motion to be moderate. Wherefore, we shall always adopt $P'$ and $Q'$ themselves for the second values of $P$ and $Q$, or $\log P'$, $\log Q'$ for the second values of $x$ and $y$, if $\log P$, $\log Q$ are supposed to denote the first values.

Now, in this second hypothesis, where all the preliminary work exhibited in the formulas 1–20 is to be retained without alteration, the calculation will be undertaken anew in precisely the same manner. That is, first, the angle $\omega$ will be determined; after that $z, r', \frac{n'r'}{n}, \frac{n'r'}{n''}, \zeta, r, \zeta'', r'', f', f, f''$. From the difference, more or less considerable, between the new values of these quantities and the first, a judgment will easily be formed whether or not it is worth while to compute anew the correction of the times on account of aberration; in the latter case, the intervals of the times, and therefore the quantities $\theta$ and $\theta''$, will remain the same as before. Finally, $\eta, \eta''$ are derived from $f, r', r'', f'', r, r'$ and the intervals of the times; and hence new values of $P'$ and $Q'$, which commonly differ much less from those furnished by the first hypothesis, than the latter from the original values themselves of $P$ and $Q$. The second values of $X$ and $Y$ will, therefore, be much smaller than the first, and the second values of $P'$, $Q'$, will be adopted as the third values of $P$, $Q$, and with these the computation will be resumed anew. In this manner, then, as from the second hypothesis more exact numbers had resulted than from the first, so from the third more exact numbers will again result than from the second, and the third values of $P'$, $Q'$ can be taken as the fourth of $P$, $Q$, and thus the calculation be repeated until an hypothesis is arrived at in which $X$ and $Y$ may be regarded as vanishing; but when the third hypothesis appears to be insufficient, it will be preferable to deduce the values of $P$, $Q$, assumed in the fourth hypothesis from the first three, in accordance with the method explained in articles 120, 121, by which means a more rapid approximation will be obtained, and it will rarely be requisite to go forward to the fifth hypothesis.

## 148.

When the elements to be derived from the three observations are as yet wholly unknown (to which case our method is especially adapted), in the first hypothesis, as we have already observed, $\frac{\theta''}{\theta}$, $\theta\,\theta''$, are to be taken for approximate values of $P$ and $Q$, where $\theta$ and $\theta''$ are derived for the present from the intervals of the times not corrected. If the ratio of these to the corrected intervals is expressed by $\mu : 1$ and $\mu'' : 1$, respectively, we shall have in the first hypothesis,

$$X = \log \mu - \log \mu'' + \log \eta - \log \eta'',$$
$$Y = \log \mu + \log \mu'' - \log \eta - \log \eta'' + \text{Comp.} \log \cos f + \text{Comp.} \log \cos f'$$
$$+ \text{Comp.} \log \cos f'' + 2 \log r' - \log r - \log r''.$$

The logarithms of the quantities $\mu$, $\mu''$, are of no importance in respect to the remaining terms; $\log \eta$ and $\log \eta''$, which are both positive, in $X$ cancel each other in some measure, whence $X$ possesses a small value, sometimes positive, sometimes negative; on the other hand, in $Y$ some compensation of the positive terms Comp. log cos $f$, Comp. log cos $f'$, Comp. log cos $f''$ arises also from the negative terms $\log \eta$, $\log \eta''$, but less complete, for the former greatly exceed the latter. In general, it is not possible to determine any thing concerning the sign of $\log \frac{r'r'}{r\,r''}$.

Now, as often as the heliocentric motion between the observations is small, it will rarely be necessary to proceed to the fourth hypothesis; most frequently the third, often the second, will afford sufficient precision, and we may sometimes be satisfied with the numbers resulting from even the first hypothesis. It will be advantageous always to have a regard to the greater or less degree of precision belonging to the observations; it would be an ungrateful task to aim at a precision in the calculation a hundred or a thousand times greater than that which the observations themselves allow. In these matters, however, the judgment is sharpened more by frequent practical exercise than by rules, and the skilful readily acquire a certain faculty of deciding where it is expedient to stop.

## 149.

Lastly, the elements themselves will be computed in the final hypothesis, either from $f$, $r'$, $r''$, or from $f''$, $r$, $r'$, carrying one or the other of the calculations through to the end, which in the previous hypotheses it had only been requisite to continue as far as $\eta$, $\eta''$; if it should be thought proper to finish both, the agreement of the resulting numbers will furnish a new verification of the whole work. It is best, nevertheless, as soon as $f, f', f''$, are got, to obtain the elements from the single combination of the first place with the third, that is, from $f',r,r''$, and the interval of the time, and finally, for the better confirmation of the computation, to determine the middle place in the orbit by means of the elements found.

In this way, therefore, the dimensions of the conic section are made known, that is, the eccentricity, the semi-axis major or the semi-parameter, the place of the perihelion with respect to the heliocentric places $C$, $C'$, $C''$, the mean motion, and the mean anomaly for the arbitrary epoch if the orbit is elliptical, or the time of perihelion passage if the orbit is hyperbolic or parabolic. It only remains, therefore, to determine the positions of the heliocentric places in the orbit with respect to the ascending node, the position of this node with reference to the equinoctial point, and the inclination of the orbit to the ecliptic (or the equator). All this may be effected by the solution of a single spherical triangle. Let $\Omega$ be the longitude of the ascending node; $i$ the inclination of the orbit; $g$ and $g''$ the arguments of the latitude in the first and third observations; lastly, let $l - \Omega = h$, $l'' - \Omega = h''$. Calling, in figure 4, $\Omega$ the ascending node, the sides of the triangle $\Omega AC$ will be $AD' - \zeta$, $g$, $h$, and the angles opposite to them, respectively, $i$, $180° - \gamma$, $u$. We shall have, then,

$$\sin \tfrac{1}{2} i \sin \tfrac{1}{2} (g + h) = \sin \tfrac{1}{2} (AD' - \zeta) \sin \tfrac{1}{2} (\gamma + u)$$
$$\sin \tfrac{1}{2} i \cos \tfrac{1}{2} (g + h) = \cos \tfrac{1}{2} (AD' - \zeta) \sin \tfrac{1}{2} (\gamma - u)$$
$$\cos \tfrac{1}{2} i \sin \tfrac{1}{2} (g - h) = \sin \tfrac{1}{2} (AD' - \zeta) \cos \tfrac{1}{2} (\gamma + u)$$
$$\cos \tfrac{1}{2} i \cos \tfrac{1}{2} (g - h) = \cos \tfrac{1}{2} (AD' - \zeta) \cos \tfrac{1}{2} (\gamma - u).$$

The two first equations will give $\tfrac{1}{2} (g + h)$ and $\sin \tfrac{1}{2} i$, the remaining two $\tfrac{1}{2} (g - h)$ and $\cos \tfrac{1}{2} i$; from $g$ will be known the place of the perihelion with regard to the ascending node, from $h$ the place of the node in the ecliptic; finally, $i$ will become known, the sine and the cosine mutually verifying each other. We can arrive at the same object by the help of the triangle $\Omega A'' C'$, in which it is only necessary to change in the preceding formulas the symbols $g$, $h$, $A$, $\zeta$, $\gamma$, $u$ into $g''$, $h''$, $A''$, $\zeta''$, $\gamma''$, $u''$. That still another verification may be provided for the whole work, it will not be unserviceable to perform the calculation in both ways; when, if any very slight discrepancies should show themselves between the values of $i$, $\Omega$, and the longitude of the perihelion in the orbit, it will be proper to take mean values. These differences rarely amount to $0^s.1$ or $0^s.2$, provided all the computations have been carefully made with seven places of decimals.

When the equator is taken as the fundamental plane instead of the ecliptic, it will make no difference in the computation, except that in place of the points $A$, $A''$ the intersections of the equator with the great circles $AB$, $A''B''$ are to be adopted.

## 150.

We proceed now to the illustration of this method by some examples fully explained, which will show, in the plainest manner, how generally it applies, and how conveniently and expeditiously it leads to the desired result.*

The new planet Juno will furnish us the *first* example, for which purpose we select the following observations made at Greenwich and communicated to us by the distinguished Maskelyne.

| Mean Time, Greenwich. | App. Right Ascension. | App. Declination S. |
|---|---|---|
| 1804, Oct.  5   $10^h$ $51^m$  $6^s$ | 357° 10′ 22″.35 | 6° 40′  8″ |
|       17    9  58  10 | 355  43  45 .30 | 8  47  25 |
|       27    9  16  41 | 355  11  10 .95 | 10   2  28 |

From the solar tables for the same times is found

| | Longitude of the Sun from App. Equin. | Nutation. | Distance from the Earth. | Latitude of the Sun. | Appar. Obliquity of the Ecliptic. |
|---|---|---|---|---|---|
| Oct.  5 | 192° 28′ 53″.72 | + 15″.43 | 0.9988839 | − 0″.49 | 23° 27′ 59″.48 |
|       17 | 204  20  21 .54 | + 15 .51 | 0.9953968 | + 0 .79 | 59 .26 |
|       27 | 214  16  52 .21 | + 15 .60 | 0.9928340 | − 0 .15 | 59 .06 |

We will conduct the calculation as if the orbit were wholly unknown: for which reason, it will not be permitted to free the places of Juno from parallax, but it will be necessary to transfer the latter to the places of the earth.  Accordingly we first reduce the observed places from the equator to the ecliptic, the apparent obliquity being employed, whence results,

---

* It is incorrect to call one method more or less exact than another.  That method alone can be considered to have solved the problem, by which any degree of precision whatever is, at least, attainable. Wherefore, one method excels another in this respect only, that the same degree of precision may be reached by one more quickly, and with less labor, than by the other.

|  | App. Longitude of Juno. | App. Latitude of Juno. |
|---|---|---|
| Oct.  5 | 354° 44′ 54″.27 | — 4° 59′ 31″.59 |
| 17 | 352  34  44 .51 | — 6  21  56 .25 |
| 27 | 351  34  51 .57 | — 7  17  52 .70 |

We join directly to this calculation the determination of the longitude and latitude of the zenith of the place of observation in the three observations: the right ascension, in fact, agrees with the right ascension of Juno (because the observations have been made in the meridian) but the declination is equal to the altitude of the pole, 51° 28′ 39″.  Thus we get

|  | Long. of the Zenith. | Lat. of the Zenith. |
|---|---|---|
| Oct.  5 | 24° 29′ | 46° 53′ |
| 17 | 23  25 | 47  24 |
| 27 | 23   1 | 47  36 |

Now the fictitious places of the earth in the plane of the ecliptic, from which the heavenly body would appear in the same manner as from the true places of the observations, will be determined according to the precepts given in article 72. In this way, putting the mean parallax of the sun equal to 8″.6, there results,

|  | Reduction of Longitude. | Reduction of Distance. | Reduction of Time. |
|---|---|---|---|
| Oct.  5 | — 22″ .39 | + 0.0003856 | — 0ˢ .19 |
| 17 | — 27 .21 | + 0.0002329 | — 0 .12 |
| 27 | — 35 .82 | + 0.0002085 | — 0 .12 |

The reduction of the time is added, only that it may be seen that it is wholly insensible.

After this, all the longitudes, both of the planet and of the earth, are to be reduced to the mean vernal equinox for some epoch, for which we shall adopt the beginning of the year 1805; the nutation being subtracted the precession is to be added, which, for the three observations, is respectively 11″.87, 10″.23, 8″.86, so that — 3″.56 is to be added for the first observation, — 5″.28 for the second, — 6″.74 for the third.

Lastly the longitudes and latitudes of Juno are to be freed from the aberration of the fixed stars; thus it is found by well-known rules, that we must subtract from the longitudes respectively 19″.12, 17″.11, 14″.82, but add to the latitudes 0″.53, 1″.18, 1″.75, by which addition the absolute values are diminished, since south latitudes are considered as negative.

## 151.

All these reductions being properly applied, we have the correct data of the problem as follows: —

| Times of the observations reduced to the meridian of Paris . | Oct. 5.458644 | 17.421885 | 27.393077 |
|---|---|---|---|
| Longitudes of Juno, $\alpha$, $\alpha'$, $\alpha''$ . | 354° 44′ 31″.60 | 352° 34′ 22″.12 | 351° 34′ 30″.01 |
| Latitudes, $\beta$, $\beta'$, $\beta''$ . . . . . | —4 59 31 .06 | —6 21 55 .07 | —7 17 50 .95 |
| Longitudes of the earth, $l$, $l'$, $l''$ | 12 28 27 .76 | 24 19 49 .05 | 34 16 9 .65 |
| Logs. of the distances, $R$, $R'$, $R''$ | 9.9996826 | 9.9980979 | 9.9969678 |

Hence the calculations of articles 136, 137, produce the following numbers,

| $\gamma$, $\gamma'$, $\gamma''$ . . . . . . . . | 196° 0′ 8″.36 | 191° 58′ 0″.33 | 190° 41′ 40″.17 |
|---|---|---|---|
| $\delta$, $\delta'$, $\delta''$ . . . . . . . . | 18 23 59 .20 | 32 19 24 .93 | 43 11 42 .05 |
| logarithms of the sines . . . | 9.4991995 | 9.7281105 | 9.8353631 |
| $A'D$, $AD'$, $AD''$ . . . . . | 232 6 26 .44 | 213 12 29 .82 | 209 43 7 .47 |
| $A''D$, $A''D'$, $A'D''$ . . . . . | 241 51 15 .22 | 234 27 0 .90 | 221 13 57 .87 |
| $\varepsilon$, $\varepsilon'$, $\varepsilon''$, . . . . . . . . | 2 19 34 .00 | 7 13 37 .70 | 4 55 46 .19 |
| logarithms of the sines . . . | 8.6083885 | 9.0996915 | 8.9341440 |
| log sin $\frac{1}{2}\varepsilon'$ . . . . . . . | | 8.7995259 | |
| log cos $\frac{1}{2}\varepsilon'$ . . . . . . . | | 9.9991357 | |

Moreover, according to article 138, we have

| | | | |
|---|---|---|---|
| log tan $\beta$ . . . . | 8.9412494 $n$ | log tan $\beta''$ . . . . | 9.1074080 $n$ |
| log sin $(\alpha'' - l')$ . | 9.7332391 $n$ | log sin $(\alpha - l')$ . . | 9.6935181 $n$ |
| log cos $(\alpha'' - l')$ . | 9.9247904 | log cos $(\alpha - l')$ . . | 9.9393180 |

Hence

$\log \left(\tan \beta \cos (\alpha'' - l') - \tan \beta'' \cos (\alpha - l')\right) = \log T \sin t$     8.5786513

$\log \sin (\alpha'' - \alpha) = \log T \cos t$ . . . . . . . . . .     8.7423191 $n$

Hence $t = 145° 32' 57''.78$     $\log T$ . . . . . . . . .     8.8260683

$t + \gamma' = 337 \ 30 \ 58 \ .11$     $\log \sin (t + \gamma')$ . . . .     9.5825441 $n$

Lastly

$\log \left(\tan \beta \sin (\alpha'' - l) - \tan \beta'' \sin (\alpha - l)\right) = \log S$ . .     8.2033319 $n$

$\log T \sin (t + \gamma')$ . . . . . . . . . . . . .     8.4086124 $n$

whence $\log \tan (\delta' - \sigma)$ . . . . . . . . . . . .     9.7947195

$\delta' - \sigma = 31° 56' 11''.81$, and therefore $\sigma = 0° 23' 13''.12$.

According to article 140 we have

| | | | |
|---|---|---|---|
| $A''D - \delta''$ | $= 191° 15' 18''.85$ | log sin 9.2904352 $n$ | log cos 9.9915661 $n$ |
| $A D' - \delta$ | $= 194 \ 48 \ 30 \ .62$ | " " 9.4075427 $n$ | " " 9.9853301 $n$ |
| $A''D - \delta''$ | $= 198 \ 39 \ 33 \ .17$ | " " 9.5050667 $n$ | |
| $A'D - \delta' + \sigma = 200 \ 10 \ 14 \ .63$ | | " " 9.5375909 $n$ | |
| $A D'' - \delta$ | $= 191 \ 19 \ 8 \ .27$ | " " 9.2928554 $n$ | |
| $A'D'' - \delta' + \sigma = 189 \ 17 \ 46 \ .06$ | | " " 9.2082723 $n$ | |

Hence follow,

$\log a$ . . . 9.5494437,     $a = + 0.3543592$

$\log b$ . . . 9.8613533.

Formula 13 would give $\log b = 9.8613531$, but we have preferred the former value, because $\sin (A'D - \delta' + \sigma)$ is greater than $\sin (A'D'' - \delta' + \sigma)$.

Again, by article 141 we have,

$3 \log R' \sin \delta'$ . . . 9.1786252

$\log 2$ . . . . . . 0.3010300

$\log \sin \sigma$ . . . . . 7.8295601

7.3092153 and therefore $\log c = 2.6907847$

$\log b$ . . . . . . 9.8613533

$\log \cos \sigma$ . . . . . 9.9999901

9.8613632

whence $\dfrac{b}{\cos \sigma} = 0.7267135.$   Hence are derived

$$d = - 1.3625052, \ \log e = 8.3929518\,n$$

Finally, by means of formulas, article 143, are obtained,

$$\log \varkappa \ \ . \ \ . \ \ . \ \ . \ \ 0.0913394\,n$$
$$\log \varkappa'' \ . \ \ . \ \ . \ \ . \ \ 0.5418957\,n$$
$$\log \lambda \ \ . \ \ . \ \ . \ \ . \ \ 0.4864480\,n$$
$$\log \lambda'' \ . \ \ . \ \ . \ \ . \ \ 0.1592352\,n$$

## 152.

The preliminary calculations being despatched in this way, we pass to the first hypothesis. The interval of time (not corrected) between the second and third observations is 9.971192 days, between the first and second is 11.963241. The logarithms of these numbers are 0.9987471, and 1.0778489, whence

$$\log \theta = 9.2343285, \ \log \theta'' = 9.3134303.$$

We will put, therefore, for the *first hypothesis,*

$$x = \log P = 0.0791018$$
$$y = \log Q = 8.5477588$$

Hence we have $P = 1.1997804, \ P + a = 1.5541396, \ P + d = - 0.1627248;$

$$\log e \ \ . \ \ . \ \ . \ \ \ 8.3929518\,n$$
$$\log (P + a) \ . \ \ \ 0.1914900$$
$$\text{C.}\log (P + d) \ \ 0.7885463\,n$$

$$\overline{\log \tan \omega \ . \ \ . \ \ \ 9.3729881,} \ \text{whence} \ \omega = + \ 13°16'51''.89, \ \omega + \sigma = + \ 13°40' \ 5''.01.$$

$$\log Q \ \ . \ \ . \ \ . \ \ \ 8.5477588$$
$$\log c \ \ . \ \ . \ \ . \ \ \ 2.6907847$$
$$\log \sin \omega \ . \ \ . \ \ \ 9.3612147$$

$$\overline{\log Q\,c \sin \omega \ . \ \ \ 0.5997582}$$

The equation

$$Q\,c \sin \omega \sin^4 z = \sin (z - 13°40' \ 5''.01)$$

is found after a few trials to be satisfied by the value $z = 14° 35' \ 4''.90$, whence we have $\log \sin z = 9.4010744, \ \log r' = 0.3251340.$ That equation admits of three other solutions besides this, namely,

$$z = \quad 32° \quad 2'\ 28''$$
$$z = 137 \quad 27 \quad 59$$
$$z = 193 \quad 4 \quad 18$$

The third must be rejected because $\sin z$ is negative; the second because $z$ is greater than $\delta'$; the first answers to an approximation to the orbit of the earth of which we have spoken in article 142.

Further, we have, according to article 143,

$$\log \frac{R' \sin \delta'}{b} \quad . \quad . \quad . \quad . \quad . \quad 9.8648551$$
$$\log (P + a) \quad . \quad . \quad . \quad . \quad 0.1914900$$
$$\text{C.} \log \sin (z - \sigma) . \quad . \quad . \quad . \quad 0.6103578$$

$$\log \frac{n' r'}{n} \quad . \quad . \quad . \quad . \quad . \quad . \quad 0.6667029$$
$$\log P . \quad . \quad . \quad . \quad . \quad . \quad . \quad 0.0791018$$

$$\log \frac{n' r'}{n''} \quad . \quad . \quad . \quad . \quad . \quad . \quad 0.5876011$$

$z + A'D - \delta' = z + 199° 47'\ 1''.51 = 214° 22'\ 6''.41$; $\log \sin = 9.7516736\, n$

$z + A'D'' - \delta' = z + 188\ 54\ 32\ .94 = 203\ 29\ 37\ .84$; $\log \sin = 9.6005923\, n$

Hence we have $\log p = 9.9270735\, n$, $\log p'' = 0.0226459\, n$, and then

$$\log q = 0.2930977\, n, \quad \log q'' = 0.2580086\, n,$$

whence result

$$\zeta = 203° 17' 31''.22 \qquad \log r = 0.3300178$$
$$\zeta'' = 110 \quad 10 \quad 58\ .88 \qquad \log r'' = 0.3212819$$

Lastly, by means of article 144, we obtain

$$\tfrac{1}{2} (u'' + u) = 205° 18' 10''.53$$
$$\tfrac{1}{2} (u'' - u) = -3 \quad 14 \quad 2\ .02$$
$$f' = \quad 3 \quad 48 \quad 14\ .66$$

| | | | | | |
|---|---|---|---|---|---|
| $\log \sin 2f'$ | . . . | 9.1218791 | $\log \sin 2f'$ | . . . | 9.1218791 |
| $\log r$ | . . . . . | 0.3300178 | $\log r''$ | . . . . . | 0.3212819 |
| $\text{C.} \log \dfrac{n' r'}{n}$ | . . . . | 9.3332971 | $\text{C.} \log \dfrac{n' r'}{n''}$ | . . . . | 9.4123989 |
| $\log \sin 2f$ | . . . | 8.7851940 | $\log \sin 2f''$ | . . . | 8.8555599 |
| $2f =$ | | $3° 29'' 46'.03$ | $2f'' =$ | | $4° 6' 43''.28$ |

The sum $2f + 2f''$ differs in this case from $2f'$ only by $0''.01$.

Now, in order that the times may be corrected for aberration, it is necessary to compute the distances $\varrho$, $\varrho'$, $\varrho''$ by the formulas of article 145, and afterwards to multiply them by the time $493^s$, or $0^d.005706$. The following is the calculation,

| | | | | | | | | |
|---|---|---|---|---|---|---|---|---|
| $\log r$ | . . . . | 0.33002 | $\log r'$ | . . . | 0.32513 | $\log r''$ | . . . . | 0.32128 |
| $\log \sin (AD' - \zeta)$ | | 9.23606 | $\log \sin (\delta' - z)$ | | 9.48384 | $\log \sin (A''D' - \zeta'')$ | | 9.61384 |
| C.$\log \sin \delta$ | . . | 0.50080 | C.$\log \sin \delta'$ | . | 0.27189 | C.$\log \sin \delta''$ | . . | 0.16464 |
| $\log \varrho$ | . . . | 0.06688 | $\log \varrho'$ | . . . | 0.08086 | $\log \varrho''$ | . . . . | 0.09976 |
| $\log$ const. | . . | 7.75633 | | | 7.75633 | | | 7.75633 |
| $\log$ of reduction | | 7.82321 | | | 7.83719 | | | 7.85609 |
| reduction = | | 0.006656 | | | 0.006874 | | | 0.007179 |

| Observations. | Corrected times. | Intervals. | Logarithms. |
|---|---|---|---|
| I. | Oct. 5.451988 | | |
| II. | 17.415011 | $11^d.963023$ | 1.0778409 |
| III. | 27.385898 | 9 .970887 | 0.9987339 |

The corrected logarithms of the quantities $\theta$, $\theta''$, are consequently 9.2343153 and 9.3134223. By commencing now the determination of the elements from $f, r'$, $r''$, $\theta$ we obtain $\log \eta = 0.0002285$, and in the same manner from $f'', r, r', \theta''$ we get $\log \eta'' = 0.0003191$. We need not add here this calculation explained at length in section III. of the first book.

Finally we have, by article 146,

| | | | | | |
|---|---|---|---|---|---|
| $\log \theta''$ | . . . . | 9.3134223 | $2 \cdot \log r'$ | . . . . | 0.6502680 |
| C.$\log \theta$ | . . . . | 0.7656847 | C.$\log r r''$ | . . . | 9.3487003 |
| $\log \eta$ | . . . . | 0.0002285 | $\log \theta \theta''$ | . . . . | 8.5477376 |
| C.$\log \eta''$ | . . . | 9.9996809 | C.$\log \eta \eta''$ | . . . | 9.9994524 |
| $\log P'$ | . . . . | 0.0790164 | C.$\log \cos f$ | . . . | 0.0002022 |
| | | | C.$\log \cos f'$ | . . . | 0.0009579 |
| | | | C.$\log \cos f''$ | . . | 0.0002797 |
| | | | $\log Q'$ | . . . . . | 8.5475981 |

The first hypothesis, therefore, results in $X = -0.0000854$, $Y = -0.0001607$.

## 153.

In the *second hypothesis* we shall assign to $P$, $Q$, the very values, which in the first we have found for $P'$, $Q'$. We shall put, therefore,

$$x = \log P = 0.0790164$$
$$y = \log Q = 8.5475981$$

Since the calculation is to be conducted in precisely the same manner as in the first hypothesis, it will be sufficient to set down here its principal results: —

| | | | |
|---|---|---|---|
| $\omega$ . . . . . . | $13° 15' 38''.13$ | $\zeta''$ . . . . . | $210° 8' 24''.98$ |
| $\omega + \sigma$ . . . . | $13\ 38\ 51\ .25$ | $\log r$ . . . . . | $0.3307676$ |
| $\log Qc \sin \omega$ . . | $0.5989389$ | $\log r''$ . . . . | $0.3222280$ |
| $z$ . . . . . . | $14\ 33\ 19\ .00$ | $\tfrac{1}{2}(u'' + u)$ . . . | $205\ 22\ 15\ .58$ |
| $\log r'$ . . . . . | $0.3259918$ | $\tfrac{1}{2}(u'' - u)$ . . . | $-3\ 14\ 4\ .79$ |
| $\log \dfrac{n' r'}{n}$ . . . . | $0.6675193$ | $2 f'$ . . . . . | $7\ 34\ 53\ .32$ |
| $\log \dfrac{n' r'}{n''}$ . . . . | $0.5885029$ | $2 f$ . . . . . | $3\ 29\ 0\ .18$ |
| $\zeta$ . . . . . . | $203\ 16\ 38\ .16$ | $2 f''$ . . . . . | $4\ 5\ 53\ .12$ |

It would hardly be worth while to compute anew the reductions of the times on account of aberration, for they scarcely differ $1^s$ from those which we have got in the first hypothesis.

The further calculations furnish $\log \eta = 0.0002270$, $\log \eta'' = 0.0003173$, whence are derived

$$\log P' = 0.0790167 \qquad X = + 0.0000003$$
$$\log Q' = 8.5476110 \qquad Y = + 0.0000129$$

From this it appears how much more exact the second hypothesis is than the first.

## 154.

In order to leave nothing to be desired, we will still construct the *third hypothesis*, in which we shall again choose the values of $P'$, $Q'$, obtained in the second hypothesis, as the values of $P$, $Q$. Putting, therefore,

$$x = \log P = 0.0790167$$
$$y = \log Q = 8.5476110$$

the following are found to be the principal results of the calculation : —

| | | |
|---|---|---|
| $\omega$ . . . . . . . | $13° 15' 38''.39$ | $\zeta''$ . . . . . $210° \ 8' 25''.65$ |
| $\omega + \sigma$ . . . . | $13 \ 38 \ 51 \ .51$ | $\log r$ . . . . . $\quad 0.3307640$ |
| $\log Qc \sin \omega$ . . | $0.5989542$ | $\log r''$ . . . . $\quad 0.3222239$ |
| $z$ . . . . . . . | $14 \ 33 \ 19 \ .50$ | $\frac{1}{2}(u'' + u)$ . . . $205 \ 22 \ 14 \ .57$ |
| $\log r'$ . . . . | $0.3259878$ | $\frac{1}{2}(u'' - u)$ . . . $-3 \ 14 \ 4 \ .78$ |
| $\log \frac{n'r'}{n}$ . . . . | $0.6675154$ | $2f'$ . . . . . $\quad 7 \ 34 \ 53 \ .73$ |
| $\log \frac{n'r'}{n''}$ . . . . | $0.5884987$ | $2f$ . . . . . $\quad 3 \ 29 \ 0 \ .39$ |
| $\zeta$ . . . . . . $203 \ 16 \ 38 \ .41$ | | $2f''$ . . . . . $\quad 4 \ 5 \ 53 \ .34$ |

All these numbers differ so little from those which the second hypothesis furnished, that we may safely conclude that the third hypothesis requires no further correction.* We may, therefore, proceed to the determination of the elements from $2f'$, $r$, $r''$, $\theta'$, which we dispense with transcribing here, since it has already been given in detail in the example of article 97. Nothing, therefore, remains but to compute the position of the plane of the orbit by the method of article 149, and to transfer the epoch to the beginning of the year 1805. This computation is to be based upon the following numbers : —

$$AD' - \zeta = \quad 9° 55' 51''.41$$
$$\tfrac{1}{2}(\gamma + u) = 202 \ 18 \ 13 \ .855$$
$$\tfrac{1}{2}(\gamma - u) = -6 \ 18 \ 5 \ .495$$

whence we obtain

$$\tfrac{1}{2}(g + h) = 196° 43' 14''.62$$
$$\tfrac{1}{2}(g - h) = -4 \ 37 \ 24 \ .41$$
$$\tfrac{1}{2}i \quad = \quad 6 \ 33 \ 22 \ .05$$

---

* If the calculation should be carried through in the same manner as in the preceding hypotheses, we should obtain $X = 0$, and $Y = + 0.0000003$, which value must be regarded as vanishing, and, in fact, it hardly exceeds the uncertainty always remaining in the last decimal place.

We have, therefore, $h = 201° 20' 39''.03$, and so $\Omega = l - h = 171° 7' 48''.73$; further, $g = 192° 5' 50''.21$, and hence, since the true anomaly for the first observation is found, in article 97, to be $310°55'29''.64$, the distance of perihelion from the ascending node in the orbit, $241° 10' 20''.57$, the longitude of the perihelion $52° 18' 9''.30$; lastly, the inclination of the orbit, $13° 6' 44''.10$. If we prefer to proceed to the same calculation from the third place, we have,

$$A''D' - \zeta'' = \quad 24° 18' 35''.25$$
$$\tfrac{1}{2}(\gamma''+u'') = 196 \ 24 \ 54 \ .98$$
$$\tfrac{1}{2}(\gamma''-u'') = -5 \ 43 \ 14 \ .81$$

Thence **are** derived

$$\tfrac{1}{2}(g'' + h'') = \quad 211° 24' 32''.45$$
$$\tfrac{1}{2}(g'' - h'') = -11 \ 43 \ 48 \ .48$$
$$\tfrac{1}{2}i \qquad = \quad 6 \ 33 \ 22 \ .05$$

and hence the longitude of the ascending node, $l'' - h'' = 171° 7' 48''.72$, the longitude of the perihelion $52° 18' 9''.30$, the inclination of the orbit $13° 6' 44''.10$, just the same as before.

The interval of time from the last observation to the beginning of the year 1805 is 64.614102 days; the mean heliocentric motion corresponding to which is $53293''.66 = 14° 48' 13''.66$; hence the epoch of the mean anomaly at the beginning of the year 1805 for the meridian of Paris is $349° 34' 12''.38$, and the epoch of the mean longitude, $41° 52' 21''.68$.

## 155.

That it may be more clearly manifest what is the accuracy of the elements just found, we will compute from them the middle place. For October 17.415011 the mean anomaly is found to be $332° 28' 54''.77$, hence the true is $315° 1' 23''.02$ and $\log r''$, 0.3259877, (see the examples of articles 13, 14); this true anomaly ought to be equal to the true anomaly in the first observation increased by the angle $2 f''$, or to the true anomaly in the third observation diminished by the angle $2 f$, that is, equal to $315° 1' 22''.98$; and the logarithm of the radius vector should be 0.3259878: the differences are of no consequence. If the calculation

for the middle observation is continued to the geocentric place, the results differ from observation only by a few hundredths of a second, (article 63;) these
differences are absorbed, as it were, in the unavoidable errors arising from the
want of strict accuracy in the tables.

We have worked out the preceding example with the utmost precision, to
show how easily the most exact solution possible can be obtained by our method.
In actual practice it will rarely be necessary to adhere scrupulously to this
type. It will generally be sufficient to use six places of decimals throughout;
and in our example the second hypothesis would have given results not less accurate than the third, and even the first would have been entirely satisfactory. We
imagine that it will not be unacceptable to our readers to have a comparison of
the elements derived from the third hypothesis with those which would result
from the use of the second or first hypothesis for the same object. We exhibit
the three systems of elements in the following table: —

|  | From hypothesis III. | From hypothesis II. | From hypothesis I. |
|---|---|---|---|
| Epoch of mean long. 1805 | 41° 52′ 21″.68 | 41° 52′ 18″.40 | 42° 12′ 37″.83 |
| Mean daily motion . . | 824″.7989 | 824″.7983 | 823″.5025 |
| Perihelion . . . . . | 52 18  9 .30 | 52 18  6 .66 | 52 41  9 .81 |
| φ . . . . . . . . | 14 12  1 .87 | 14 11 59 .94 | 14 24 27 .49 |
| Log of semi-axis major . | 0.4224389 | 0.4224392 | 0.4228944 |
| Ascending node . . . | 171  7 48 .73 | 171  7 49 .15 | 171  5 48 .86 |
| Inclination of the orbit . | 13  6 44 .10 | 13  6 45 .12 | 13  2 37 .50 |

By computing the heliocentric place in orbit for the middle observation from
the second system of elements, the error of the logarithm of the radius vector is
found equal to zero, the error of the longitude in orbit, 0″.03; and in computing the same place by the system derived from the first hypothesis, the error of
the logarithm of the radius vector is 0.0000002, the error of the longitude in
orbit, 1″.31. And by continuing the calculation to the geocentric place we have,

| | From hypothesis II. | From hypothesis I. |
|---|---|---|
| Geocentric longitude | 352° 34′ 22″.26 | 352° 34′ 19″.97 |
| Error . . . . . | 0 .14 | 2 .15 |
| Geocentric latitude . | 6 21 55 .06 | 6 21 54 .47 |
| Error . . . . . | 0 .01 | 0 .60 |

## 156.

We shall take the *second* example from Pallas, the following observations of which, made at Milan, we take from VON ZACH'S *Monatliche Correspondenz*, Vol. XIV., p. 90.

| Mean Time, Milan. | App. Right Ascension. | App. Declination S. |
|---|---|---|
| 1805, Nov. 5$^d$14$^h$ 14$^m$ 4$^s$ | 78° 20′ 37″.8 | 27° 16′ 56″.7 |
| Dec. 6 11 51 27 | 73 8 48 .8 | 32 52 44 .3 |
| 1806, Jan. 15 8 50 36 | 67 14 11 .1 | 28 38 8 .1 |

We will here take the equator as the fundamental plane instead of the ecliptic, and we will make the computation as if the orbit were still wholly unknown. In the first place we take from the tables of the sun the following data for the given dates: —

| | Longitude of the Sun from mean Equinox. | Distance from the Earth. | Latitude of the Sun. |
|---|---|---|---|
| Nov. 5 | 223° 14′ 7″.61 | 0.9804311 | + 0″.59 |
| Dec. 6 | 254 28 42 .59 | 0.9846753 | + 0 .12 |
| Jan. 15 | 295 5 47 .62 | 0.9838153 | — 0 .19 |

We reduce the longitudes of the sun, the precessions $+7″.59, +3″.36, -2″.11$, being added, to the beginning of the year 1806, and thence we afterwards derive the right ascensions and declinations, using the mean obliquity 23° 27′ 53″.53 and taking account of the latitudes. In this way we find

|  | Right ascension of the Sun. | Decl. of the Sun S. |
|---|---|---|
| Nov. 5 | 220° 46' 44".65 | 15° 49' 43".94 |
| Dec. 6 | 253 9 23 .26 | 22 33 39 .45 |
| Jan. 15 | 297 2 51 .11 | 21 8 12 .98 |

These places are referred to the centre of the earth, and are, therefore, to be reduced by applying the parallax to the place of observation, since the places of the planet cannot be freed from parallax. The right ascensions of the zenith to be used in this calculation agree with the right ascensions of the planet (because the observations have been made in the meridian), and the declination will be throughout the altitude of the pole, 45° 28'. Hence are derived the following numbers: —

|  | Right asc. of the Earth. | Decl. of the Earth N. | Log of dist. from the Sun. |
|---|---|---|---|
| Nov. 5 | 40° 46' 48".51 | 15° 49' 48".59 | 9.9958575 |
| Dec. 6 | 73 9 23 .26 | 22 33 42 .83 | 9.9933099 |
| Jan. 15 | 117 2 46 .09 | 21 8 17 .29 | 9.9929259 |

The observed places of Pallas are to be freed from nutation and the aberration of the fixed stars, and afterwards to be reduced, by applying the precession, to the beginning of the year 1806. On these accounts it will be necessary to apply the following corrections to the observed places: —

|  | Observation I. | | Observation II. | | Observation III. | |
|---|---|---|---|---|---|---|
|  | Right asc. | Declination. | Right asc. | Declination. | Right asc. | Declination. |
| Nutation | — 12".86 | — 3".08 | — 13".68 | — 3".42 | — 13".06 | — 3".75 |
| Aberration | — 18 .13 | — 9 .89 | — 21 .51 | — 1 .63 | — 15 .60 | + 9˙.76 |
| Precession | + 5 .43 | + 0 .62 | + 2 .55 | + 0 .39 | — 1 .51 | — 0 .33 |
| Sum | — 25 .56 | — 12 .35 | — 32 .64 | — 4 .66 | — 30 .17 | + 5 .68 |

Hence we have the following places of Pallas, for the basis of the computation: —

| Mean Time, Paris. | Right Ascension. | Declination. |
|---|---|---|
| Nov. 5.574074 | 78° 20′ 12″.24 | — 27° 17′ 9″.05 |
| 36.475035 | 73 8 16 .16 | — 32 52 48 .96 |
| 76.349444 | 67 13 40 .93 | — 28 38 2 .42 |

## 157.

Now in the first place we will determine the positions of the great circles drawn from the heliocentric places of the earth to the geocentric places of the planet. We take the symbols $\mathfrak{A}$, $\mathfrak{A}'$, $\mathfrak{A}''$, for the intersections of these circles with the equator, or, if you please, for their ascending nodes, and we denote the distances of the points $B$, $B'$, $B''$ from the former points by $\varDelta$, $\varDelta'$, $\varDelta''$. In the greater part of the work it will be necessary to substitute the symbols $\mathfrak{A}$, $\mathfrak{A}'$, $\mathfrak{A}''$, for $A$, $A'$, $A''$, and also $\varDelta$, $\varDelta'$, $\varDelta''$ for $\delta$, $\delta'$, $\delta''$; but the careful reader will readily understand when it is necessary to retain $A$, $A'$, $A''$, $\delta$, $\delta'$, $\delta''$, even if we fail to advise him.

The calculation being made, we find

| Right ascensions of the | | | |
|---|---|---|---|
| points $\mathfrak{A}$, $\mathfrak{A}'$, $\mathfrak{A}''$ . . . | 233° 54′ 57″.10 | 253° 8′ 57″.01 | 276° 40′ 25″.87 |
| $\gamma$, $\gamma'$, $\gamma''$ . . . . . | 51 17 15 .74 | 90 1 3 .19 | 131 59 58 .03 |
| $\varDelta$, $\varDelta'$, $\varDelta''$ . . . . . | 215 58 49 .27 | 212 52 48 .96 | 220 9 12 .96 |
| $\delta$, $\delta'$, $\delta''$ . . . . . . | 56 26 34 .19 | 55 26 31 .79 | 69 10 57 .84 |
| $\mathfrak{A}D$, $\mathfrak{A}D'$, $\mathfrak{A}D''$ . . . | 23 54 52 .13 | 30 18 3 .25 | 29 8 43 .32 |
| $\mathfrak{A}''D$, $\mathfrak{A}''D'$, $\mathfrak{A}''D''$ . . | 33 3 26 .35 | 31 59 21 .14 | 22 20 6 .91 |
| $\varepsilon$, $\varepsilon'$, $\varepsilon''$ . . . . . . | 47 1 54 .69 | 89 34 57 .17 | 42 33 41 .17 |
| logarithms of the sines | 9.8643525 | 9.9999885 | 9.8301910 |
| log sin ½ $\varepsilon'$ . . . . . | | 9.8478971 | |
| log cos ½ $\varepsilon'$ . . . . | | 9.8510614 | |

The right ascension of the point $\mathfrak{A}'$ is used in the calculation of article 138 instead of $l'$.   In this manner are found

$$\log T \sin t \quad . \quad . \quad . \quad . \quad . \quad 8.4868236\,n$$
$$\log T \cos t \quad . \quad . \quad . \quad . \quad . \quad 9.2848162\,n$$

Hence $t = 189°\ 2'48''.83$, $\log T = 9.2902527$; moreover, $t + \gamma' = 279°\ 3'52''.02$,

$$\log S \quad . \quad . \quad . \quad . \quad . \quad . \quad . \quad 9.0110566\,n$$
$$\log T \sin (t + \gamma') \quad . \quad . \quad . \quad 9.2847950\,n$$

whence $\varDelta' - \sigma = 208°\ 1'55''.64$, and $\sigma = 4°\ 50'53''.32$.

In the formulas of article 140 $\sin \delta$, $\sin \delta'$, $\sin \delta''$ must be retained instead of $a$, $b$ and $\dfrac{b}{a}$, and also in the formulas of article 142.   For these calculations we have

| | | log sin | log cos |
|---|---|---|---|
| $\mathfrak{A}''D' - \varDelta''$ | $= 171°\ 50'\ 8''.18$ | 9.1523306 | 9.9955759 $n$ |
| $\mathfrak{A}\ D' - \varDelta$ | $= 174\ 19\ 13\ .98$ | " " 8.9954722 | " " 9.9978629 $n$ |
| $\mathfrak{A}''D - \varDelta''$ | $= 172\ 54\ 13\ .39$ | " " 9.0917972 | |
| $\mathfrak{A}'D - \varDelta' + \sigma$ | $= 175\ 52\ 56\ .49$ | " " 8.8561520 | |
| $\mathfrak{A}\ D'' - \varDelta$ | $= 173\ \ 9\ 54\ .05$ | " " 9.0755844 | |
| $\mathfrak{A}'D'' - \varDelta' + \sigma$ | $= 174\ 18\ 11\ .27$ | " " 8.9967978 | |

Hence we deduce

$$\log \varkappa = 0.9211850, \qquad \log \lambda = 0.0812057\,n$$
$$\log \varkappa'' = 0.8112762, \qquad \log \lambda'' = 0.0319691\,n$$
$$\log a = 0.1099088, \qquad a = +\ 1.2879790$$
$$\log b = 0.1810404,$$
$$\log \frac{b}{a} = 0.0711314,$$

whence we have $\log b = 0.1810402$.   We shall adopt $\log b = 0.1810403$ the mean between these two nearly equal values.   Lastly we have

$$\log c = 1.0450295$$
$$d = +\ 0.4489906$$
$$\log e = 9.2102894$$

with which the preliminary calculations are completed.

The interval of time between the second and third observations is 39.874409 days, between the first and second 30.900961: hence we have

$$\log \theta = 9.8362757, \ \log \theta'' = 9.7255533.$$

We put, therefore, for the *first hypothesis*,

$$x = \log P = 9.8892776$$
$$y = \log Q = 9.5618290$$

The chief results of the calculation are as follows:—

$$\omega + \sigma = 20°\ 8'\ 46''.72$$
$$\log Q c \sin \omega = 0.0282028$$

Thence the true value of $z$ is $21°\ 11'\ 24''.30$, and of $\log r'$, $0.3509379$. The three remaining values of $z$ satisfying equation IV., article 141, are, in this instance,

$$z = \quad 63°\ 41'\ 12''$$
$$z = 101\ \ 12\ \ 58$$
$$z = 199\ \ 24\ \ \ 7$$

the first of which is to be regarded as an approximation to the orbit of the earth, the deviation of which, however, is here much greater than in the preceding example, on account of the too great interval of time. The following numbers result from the subsequent calculation:—

| | |
|---|---|
| $\zeta$ . . . . . . | $195°\ 12'\ \ 2''.48$ |
| $\zeta''$ . . . . . | $196\ \ 57\ \ 50\ .78$ |
| $\log r$ . . . . . | $0.3647022$ |
| $\log r''$ . . . . | $0.3355758$ |
| $\frac{1}{2}(u'' + u)$ . . . | $266\ \ 47\ \ 50\ .47$ |
| $\frac{1}{2}(u'' - u)$ . . . | $-43\ \ 39\ \ \ 5\ .33$ |
| $2f'$ . . . . . | $22\ \ 32\ \ 40\ .86$ |
| $2f$ . . . . . | $13\ \ \ 5\ \ 41\ .17$ |
| $2f''$ . . . . . | $9\ \ 27\ \ \ 0\ .05$ |

We shall distribute the difference between $2f'$ and $2f + 2f''$, which in this case is $0''.36$, between $2f$ and $2f''$ in such a manner as to make $2f = 13°\ 5'\ 40''.96$, and $2f'' = 9°\ 26'\ 59''.90$.

The times are now to be corrected for aberration, for which purpose we are to put in the formulas of article 145,

$$AD' - \zeta = \mathfrak{A}D' - A + \delta - \zeta, \quad A''D' - \zeta'' = \mathfrak{A}''D' - A'' + \delta'' - \zeta''.$$

We have, therefore,

| | | | | | | |
|---|---|---|---|---|---|
| $\log r$ . . . . | 0.36470 | $\log r'$ . . . | 0.35094 | $\log r''$ . . . . | 0.33557 |
| $\log \sin(AD' - \zeta)$ | 9.76462 | $\log \sin(\delta' - z)$ | 9.75038 | $\log \sin(A''D' - \zeta'')$ | 9.84220 |
| C. $\log \sin \delta$ . . | 0.07918 | C. $\log \sin \delta'$ . | 0.08431 | C. $\log \sin \delta''$ . . | 0.02932 |
| $\log$ const. . . | 7.75633 | $\log$ const. . . | 7.75633 | $\log$ const. . . | 7.75633 |
| | 7.96483 | | 7.94196 | | 7.96342 |
| reduction of $\}$ the time $\}$ | 0.009222 | | 0.008749 | | 0.009192 |

Hence follow,

| Observations. | Corrected times. | Intervals. | Logarithms. |
|---|---|---|---|
| I. | Nov. 5.564852 | | |
| II. | 36.466286 | $30^d.901434$ | 1.4899785 |
| III. | 76.340252 | 39 .873966 | 1.6006894 |

whence are derived the corrected logarithms of the quantities $\theta$, $\theta''$ respectively 9.8362708 and 9.7255599. Beginning, then, the calculation of the elements from $r'$, $r''$, $2f$, $\theta$, we get $\log \eta = 0.0031921$, just as from $r$, $r'$, $2f''$, $\theta''$ we obtain $\log \eta'' = 0.0017300$. Hence is obtained

$$\log P' = 9.8907512 \qquad \log Q' = 9.5712864,$$

and, therefore,

$$X = +0.0014736 \qquad Y = +0.0094574$$

The chief results of the *second hypothesis,* in which we put

$$x = \log P = 9.8907512$$
$$y = \log Q = 9.5712864$$

are the following:—

| | | | | |
|---|---|---|---|---|
| $\omega + \sigma$ . . . . | 20° 8′ 0″.87 | $\zeta$ . . . . . . | 195° 16′ 59″.90 |
| $\log Q c \sin \omega$ . . | 0.0373071 | $\zeta''$ . . . . . | 196 52 40 .63 |
| $z$ . . . . . . | 21 12 6 .09 | $\log r$ . . . . | 0.3630642 |
| $\log r'$ . . . . | 0.3507110 | $\log r''$ . . . . | 0.3369708 |

| | | | |
|---|---|---|---|
| $\frac{1}{2}(u'' + u)$ . . . | 267° 6′ 10″.75 | $2f'$ . . . . . | 22° 32′ 8″.69 |
| $\frac{1}{2}(u'' - u)$ . . . | −43 39 4 .00 | $2f$ . . . . . | 13 1 54 .65 |
| | | $2f''$ . . . . . | 9 30 14 .38 |

The difference 0.″34, between $2f'$ and $2f + 2f''$ is to be so distributed, as to make $2f = 13° 1′ 54″.45$, $2f'' = 9° 30′ 14″.24$.

If it is thought worth while to recompute here the corrections of the times, there will be found for the first observation, 0.009169, for the second, 0.008742, for the third, 0.009236, and thus the corrected times, November 5.564905, November 36.466293, November 76.340280. Hence we have

| | | | |
|---|---|---|---|
| $\log \theta$ . . . . . . | 9.8362703 | $\log \eta''$ . . . . . . | 0.0017413 |
| $\log \theta''$ . . . . . . | 9.7255594 | $\log P'$ . . . . . . | 9.8907268 |
| $\log \eta$ . . . . . . | 0.0031790 | $\log Q'$ . . . . . . | 9.5710593 |

Accordingly, the results from the second hypothesis are

$$X = -0.0000244, \quad Y = -0.0002271.$$

Finally, in the *third hypothesis*, in which we put

$$x = \log P = 9.8907268$$
$$y = \log Q = 9.5710593$$

the chief results of the calculation are as follows: —

| | | | |
|---|---|---|---|
| $\omega + \sigma$ . . . . | 20° 8′ 1″.62 | $\log r''$ . . . . | 0.3369536 |
| $\log Qc \sin \omega$ . . | 0.0370857 | $\frac{1}{2}(u'' + u)$ . . . | 267 5 53 .09 |
| $z$ . . . . . . | 21 12 4 .60 | $\frac{1}{2}(u'' - u)$ . . . | −43 39 4 .19 |
| $\log r'$ . . . . . | 0.3507191 | $2f'$ . . . . . | 22 32 7 .67 |
| $\zeta$ . . . . . | 195 16 54 .08 | $2f$ . . . . . | 13 1 57 .42 |
| $\zeta''$ . . . . . | 196 52 44 .45 | $2f''$ . . . . | 9 30 10 .63 |
| $\log r$ . . . . . | 0.3630960 | | |

The difference 0″.38 will be here distributed in such a manner as to make $2f = 13° 1′ 57″.20$, $2f'' = 9° 30′ 10″.47$.*

---

* This somewhat increased difference, nearly equal in all the hypotheses, has arisen chiefly from this, that $\sigma$ had been got too little by almost two hundredths of a second, and the logarithm of $b$ too great by several units.

Since the differences of all these numbers from those which the second hypothesis furnished are very small, it may be safely concluded that the third hypothesis requires no further correction, and, therefore, that a new hypothesis would be superfluous. Wherefore, it will now be proper to proceed to the calculation of the elements from $2f'$, $\theta'$, $r$, $r''$: and since the processes comprised in this calculation have been most fully explained above, it will be sufficient to add here the resulting elements, for the benefit of those who may wish to perform the computation themselves: —

Right ascension of the ascending node on the equator . . . . . 158° 40′ 38″.93
Inclination of the orbit to the equator . . . . . . . . . . 11 42 49 .13
Distance of the perihelion from the ascending node . . . . . 323 14 56 .92
Mean anomaly for the epoch 1806 . . . . . . . . . . . . 335  4 13 .05
Mean daily (sidereal) motion . . . . . . . . . . . . . . . 770″.2662
Angle of eccentricity, $\varphi$ . . . . . . . . . . . . . . . . 14  9  3 .91
Logarithm of the semi-axis major . . . . . . . . . . . . . 0.4422438

## 158.

The two preceding examples have not yet furnished occasion for using the method of article 120: for the successive hypotheses converged so rapidly that we might have stopped at the second, and the third scarcely differed by a sensible amount from the truth. We shall always enjoy this advantage, and be able to do without the fourth hypothesis, when the heliocentric motion is not great and the three radii vectores are not too unequal, particularly if, in addition to this, the intervals of the times differ from each other but little. But the further the conditions of the problem depart from these, the more will the first assumed values of $P$ and $Q$ differ from the correct ones, and the less rapidly will the subsequent values converge to the truth. In such a case the first three hypotheses are to be completed in the manner shown in the two preceding examples, (with this difference only, that the elements themselves are not to be computed in the third hypothesis, but, exactly as in the first and second hypotheses, the quantities $\eta$, $\eta''$, $P'$, $Q'$, $X$, $Y$); but then, the last values of $P'$, $Q'$ are no longer to be taken as the new values of the quantities $P$, $Q$ in the new hypothesis, but these are to be derived from the combination of the first three hypotheses, agreeably to the method of article 120. It will then very rarely be requisite to proceed to the fifth hypothesis, according to the precepts of article 121. We will now explain these calculations further by an example, from which it will appear how far our method extends.

### 159.

For the *third* example we select the following observations of Ceres, the first of which has been made by OLBERS, at Bremen, the second by HARDING, at Gottingen, and the third by BESSEL, at Lilienthal.

| Mean time of place of observation. | Right Ascension. | North declination. |
|---|---|---|
| 1805, Sept. $5^d 13^h$ $8^m 54^s$ | 95° 59′ 25″ | 22° 21′ 25″ |
| 1806, Jan. 17 10 58 51 | 101 18 40 .6 | 30 21 22 .3 |
| 1806, May 23 10 23 53 | 121 56 7 | 28 2 45 |

As the methods by which the parallax and aberration are taken account of, when the distances from the earth are regarded as wholly unknown, have already been sufficiently explained in the two preceding examples, we shall dispense with this unnecessary increase of labor in this third example, and with that object will take the approximate distances from VON ZACH's *Monatliche Correspondenz*, Vol. XI., p. 284, in order to free the observations from the effects of parallax and aberration. The following table shows these distances, together with the reductions derived from them: —

| | | | |
|---|---|---|---|
| Distance of Ceres from the earth . . . | 2.899 | 1.638 | 2.964 |
| Time in which the light reaches the earth | $23^m 49^s$ | $13^m 28^s$ | $24^m 21^s$ |
| Reduced time of observation . . . . . | $12^h 45^m$ $5^s$ | $10^h 45^m 23^s$ | $9^h 59^m 32^s$ |
| Sidereal time in degrees . . . . . . | 355° 55′ | 97° 59′ | 210° 41′ |
| Parallax in right ascension . . . . . | $+1''.90$ | $+0''.22$ | $-1''.97$ |
| Parallax in declination . . . . . . . | $-2.08$ | $-1.90$ | $-2.04$ |

Accordingly, the data of the problem, after being freed from parallax and aberration, and after the times have been reduced to the meridian of Paris, are as follows: —

| Times of the observations. | Right Ascension. | Declination. |
|---|---|---|
| 1805, Sept. 5, 12$^h$ 19$^m$ 14$^s$ | 95° 59′ 23″.10 | 22° 21′ 27″.08 |
| 1806, Jan. 17, 10 15 2 | 101 18 40 .38 | 30 21 24 .20 |
| 1806, May 23, 9 33 18 | 121 56 8 .97 | 28 2 47 .04 |

From these right ascensions and declinations have been deduced the longitudes and latitudes, using for the obliquity of the ecliptic 23° 27′ 55″.90, 23° 27′ 54″.59, 23° 27′ 53″.27; the longitudes have been afterwards freed from nutation, which was for the respective times $+ 17″.31$, $+ 17″.88$, $+ 18″.00$, and next reduced to the beginning of the year 1806, by applying the precession $+ 15″.98$, $- 2″.39$, $- 19″.68$. Lastly, the places of the sun for the reduced times have been taken from the tables, in which the nutation has been omitted in the longitudes, but the precession has been added in the same way as to the longitudes of Ceres. The latitude of the sun has been wholly neglected. In this manner have resulted the following numbers to be used in the calculation: —

| Times, 1805, September | 5.51336 | 139.42711 | 265.39813 |
|---|---|---|---|
| $\alpha, \alpha', \alpha''$ . . . . . . | 95° 32′ 18″.56 | 99° 49′ 5″.87 | 118° 5′ 28″.85 |
| $\beta, \beta', \beta''$ . . . . . . | $- 0$ 59 34 .06 | $+ 7$ 16 36 .80 | $+ 7$ 38 49 .39 |
| $l, l', l''$ . . . . . . | 342 54 56 .00 | 117 12 43 .25 | 241 58 50 .71 |
| $\log R, \log R', \log R''$ . | 0.0031514 | 9.9929861 | 0.0056974 |

The preliminary computations explained in articles 136–140 furnish the following: —

| $\gamma, \gamma', \gamma''$ . . . . . . | 358° 55′ 28″.09 | 156° 52′ 11″.49 | 170° 48′ 44″.79 |
|---|---|---|---|
| $\delta, \delta', \delta''$ . . . . . . | 112 37 9 .66 | 18 48 39 .81 | 123 32 52 .13 |
| $A'D, AD', AD''$ . . . | 15 32 41 .40 | 252 42 19 .14 | 136 2 22 .38 |
| $A''D, A''D', A'D''$ . . . | 138 45 4 .60 | 6 26 41 .10 | 358 5 57 .00 |
| $\varepsilon, \varepsilon', \varepsilon''$ . . . . . . | 29 18 8 .21 | 170 32 59 .08 | 156 6 25 .25 |

$$\sigma = 8°\ 52'\ 4''.05$$
$$\log a = 0.1840193\,n,\ a = -1.5276340$$
$$\log b = 0.0040987$$
$$\log c = 2.0066735$$
$$d = 117.50873$$

$$\log e = 0.8568244$$
$$\log \varkappa = 0.1611012$$
$$\log \varkappa'' = 9.9770819\,n$$
$$\log \lambda = 9.9164090\,n$$
$$\log \lambda'' = 9.7320127\,n$$

The interval of time between the first and second observations is 133.91375 days, between the second and third, 125.97102: hence

$$\log \theta = 0.3358520,\ \log \theta'' = 0.3624066,\ \log \frac{\theta''}{\theta} = 0.0265546,\ \log \theta\theta'' = 0.6982586.$$

We now exhibit in the following table the principal results of the first three hypotheses: —

|  | I. | II. | III. |
|---|---|---|---|
| $\log P = x$ | 0.0265546 | 0.0256968 | 0.0256275 |
| $\log Q = y$ | 0.6982586 | 0.7390190 | 0.7481055 |
| $\omega + \sigma$ | 7° 15' 13''.523 | 7° 14' 47''.139 | 7° 14' 45''.071 |
| $\log Qc \sin \omega$ | 1.1546650 $n$ | 1.1973925 $n$ | 1.2066327 $n$ |
| $z$ | 7  3 59 .018 | 7  2 32 .870 | 7  2 16 .900 |
| $\log r'$ | 0.4114726 | 0.4129371 | 0.4132107 |
| $\zeta$ | 160 10 46 .74 | 160 20  7 .82 | 160 22  9 .42 |
| $\zeta''$ | 262  6  1 .03 | 262 12 18 .26 | 262 14 19 .49 |
| $\log r$ | 0.4323934 | 0.4291773 | 0.4284841 |
| $\log r''$ | 0.4094712 | 0.4071975 | 0.4064697 |
| $\frac{1}{2}(u'' + u)$ | 262 55 23 .22 | 262 57  6 .83 | 262 57 31 .17 |
| $\frac{1}{2}(u'' - u)$ | 273 28 50 .95 | 273 29 15 .06 | 273 29 19 .56 |
| $2f'$ | 62 34 28 .40 | 62 49 56 .50 | 62 53 57 .06 |
| $2f$ | 31  8 30 .03 | 31 15 59 .09 | 31 18 13 .83 |
| $2f''$ | 31 25 58 .43 | 31 33 57 .32 | 31 35 43 .32 |
| $\log \eta$ | 0.0202496 | 0.0203158 | 0.0203494 |
| $\log \eta''$ | 0.0211074 | 0.0212429 | 0.0212751 |
| $\log P'$ | 0.0256968 | 0.0256275 | 0.0256289 |
| $\log Q'$ | 0.7390190 | 0.7481055 | 0.7502337 |
| $X$ | − 0.0008578 | − 0.0000693 | + 0.0000014 |
| $Y$ | + 0.0407604 | + 0.0090865 | + 0.0021282 |

If we designate the three values of $X$ by $A$, $A'$, $A''$; the three values of $Y$ by $B$, $B'$, $B''$; the quotients arising from the division of the quantities $A'B'' - A''B'$, $A''B - AB''$, $AB' - A'B$, by the sum of these quantities, by $k$, $k'$, $k''$, respectively, so that we have $k + k' + k'' = 1$; and, finally, the values of $\log P'$ and $\log Q'$ in the third hypothesis, by $M$ and $N$, (which would become new values of $x$ and $y$ if it should be expedient to derive the fourth hypothesis from the third, as the third had been derived from the second): it is easily ascertained from the formulas of article 120, that the corrected value of $x$ is $M - k(A' + A'') - k'A''$, and the corrected value of $y$, $N - k(B' + B'') - k'B''$. The calculation being made, the former becomes 0.0256331, the latter, 0.7509143. Upon these corrected values we construct the *fourth hypothesis*, the chief results of which are the following: —

| | | | | |
|---|---|---|---|---|
| $\omega + \sigma$ . . . . | $7° 14' 45''.247$ | $\log r''$ . . . . | 0.4062033 |
| $\log Qc \sin \omega$ . . | $1.2094284 n$ | $\frac{1}{2}(u'' + u)$ . . . | $262° 57' 38''.78$ |
| $z$ . . . . . . . | $7 \ 2 \ 12 \ .736$ | $\frac{1}{2}(u'' - u)$ . . . | $273 \ 29 \ 20 \ .73$ |
| $\log r'$ . . . . . | 0.4132817 | $2f'$ . . . . . | $62 \ 55 \ 16 \ .64$ |
| $\zeta$ . . . . . . | $160 \ 22 \ 45 \ .38$ | $2f$ . . . . . | $31 \ 19 \ 1 \ .49$ |
| $\zeta''$ . . . . . . | $262 \ 15 \ 3 \ .90$ | $2f''$ . . . . . | $31 \ 36 \ 15 \ .20$ |
| $\log r$ . . . . . | 0.4282792 | | |

The difference between $2f'$ and $2f + 2f''$ proves to be $0''.05$, which we shall distribute in such a manner as to make $2f = 31° 19' 1''.47$, $2f'' = 31° 36' 15''.17$. If now the elements are determined from the two extreme places, the following values result: —

| | |
|---|---|
| True anomaly for the first place . . . . . . . . | $289° \ 7' \ 39''.75$ |
| True anomaly for the third place . . . . . . . . | $352 \ 2 \ 56 \ .39$ |
| Mean anomaly for the first place . . . . . . . | $297 \ 41 \ 35 \ .65$ |
| Mean anomaly for the third place . . . . . . . | $353 \ 15 \ 22 \ .49$ |
| Mean daily sidereal motion . . . . . . . . . | $769''.6755$ |
| Mean anomaly for the beginning of the year 1806 . . | $322 \ 35 \ 52 \ .51$ |
| Angle of eccentricity, $\varphi$ . . . . . . . . . . | $4 \ 37 \ 57 \ .78$ |
| Logarithm of the semi-axis major . . . . . . . | 0.4424661 |

By computing from these elements the heliocentric place for the time of the middle observation, the mean anomaly is found to be $326° 19' 25''.72$, the logarithm of the radius vector, $0.4132825$, the true anomaly, $320° 43' 54''.87$: this last should differ from the true anomaly for the first place by the quantity $2f''$, or from the true anomaly for the third place by the quantity $2f$, and should, therefore, be $320° 43' 54''.92$, as also the logarithm of the radius vector, $0.4132817$: the difference $0''.05$ in the true anomaly, and of eight units in the logarithm, is to be considered as of no consequence.

If the fourth hypothesis should be conducted to the end in the same way as the three preceding, we would have $X = 0$, $Y = 0.0000168$, whence the following corrected values of $x$ and $y$ would be obtained,

$$x = \log P = 0.0256331, \text{ (the same as in the fourth hypothesis,)}$$
$$y = \log Q = 0.7508917.$$

If the fifth hypothesis should be constructed on these values, the solution would reach the utmost precision the tables allow: but the resulting elements would not differ sensibly from those which the fourth hypothesis has furnished.

Nothing remains now, to obtain the complete elements, except that the position of the plane of the orbit should be computed. By the precepts of article 149 we have

| | From the first place. | | From the third place. |
|---|---|---|---|
| $g$ . . . . . . . . . | $354° 9' 44''.22$ | $g''$ . . . . | $57° 5' 0''.91$ |
| $h$ . . . . . . . . . | $261\ 56\ 6\ .94$ | $h''$ . . . . | $161\ 0\ 1\ .61$ |
| $i$ . . . . . . . . . | $10\ 37\ 33\ .02$ | | $10\ 37\ 33\ .00$ |
| ☊ . . . . . . . . | $80\ 58\ 49\ .06$ | | $80\ 58\ 49\ .10$ |
| Distance of the perihelion from the ascending node } | $65\ 2\ 4\ .47$ | | $65\ 2\ 4\ .52$ |
| Longitude of the perihelion | $146\ 0\ 53\ .53$ | | $146\ 0\ 53\ .62$ |

The mean being taken, we shall put $i = 10° 37' 33''.01$, ☊ $= 80° 58' 49''.08$, the longitude of the perihelion $= 146° 0' 53''.57$. Lastly, the mean longitude for the beginning of the year 1806 will be $108° 36' 46''.08$.

## 160.

In the exposition of the method to which the preceding investigations have been devoted, we have come upon certain special cases to which it did not apply, at least not in the form in which it has been exhibited by us. We have seen that this defect occurs *first*, when any one of the three geocentric places coincides either with the corresponding heliocentric place of the earth, or with the opposite point (the last case can evidently only happen when the heavenly body passes between the sun and earth): *second*, when the first geocentric place of the heavenly body coincides with the third; *third*, when all three of the geocentric places together with the second heliocentric place of the earth are situated in the same great circle.

In the first case the position of one of the great circles $AB$, $A'B'$, $A''B''$, and in the second and third the place of the point $B^*$, will remain indeterminate. In these cases, therefore, the methods before explained, by means of which we have shown how to determine the heliocentric from the geocentric places, if the quantities $P$, $Q$, are regarded as known, lose their efficacy: but an essential distinction is here to be noted, which is, that in the first case the defect will be attributable to the method alone, but in the second and third cases to the nature of the problem; in the first case, accordingly, that determination can undoubtedly be effected if the method is suitably altered, but in the second and third it will be absolutely impossible, and the heliocentric places will remain indeterminate. It will not be uninteresting to develop these relations in a few words: but it would be out of place to go through all that belongs to this subject, the more so, because in all these special cases the exact determination of the orbit is impossible where it would be greatly affected by the smallest errors of observation. The same defect will also exist when the observations resemble, not exactly indeed, but nearly, any one of these cases; for which reason, in selecting observations this is to be recollected, and properly guarded against, that no place be chosen where the heavenly body is at the same time in the vicinity of the node and of opposition or conjunction, nor such observations as where the heavenly body has nearly returned in the last to the geocentric place of the first observation, nor, finally, such as where the great circle drawn from the middle heliocentric place of the earth to the middle geocentric place of the heavenly body makes a very acute angle with the direction of the geocentric motion, and nearly passes through the first and third places.

## 161.

We will make three subdivisions of the *first case*.

I. If the point $B$ coincides with $A$ or with the opposite point, $\delta$ will be equal to zero, or to 180°; $\gamma$, $\varepsilon'$, $\varepsilon''$ and the points $D'$, $D''$, will be indeterminate; on the other hand, $\gamma'$, $\gamma''$, $\varepsilon$ and the points $D$, $B^*$, will be determinate; the point $C$ will necessarily coincide with $A$. By a course of reasoning similar to that pursued in article 140, the following equation will be easily obtained:—

$$0 = n' \frac{\sin (z - \sigma) \, R' \sin \delta' \sin (A''D - \delta'')}{\sin z \, R'' \sin \delta'' \sin (A'D - \delta' + \sigma)} - n''.$$

It will be proper, therefore, to apply in this place all which has been explained in articles 141, 142, if, only, we put $a = 0$, and $b$ is determined by equation 12, article 140, and the quantities $z$, $r'$, $\frac{n'r'}{n}$, $\frac{n'r'}{n''}$, will be computed in the same manner as before. Now as soon as $z$ and the position of the point $C'$ have become known, it will be possible to assign the position of the great circle $CC'$, its intersection with the great circle $A''B''$, that is the point $C'''$, and hence the arcs $CC'$, $CC''$, $C'C''$, or $2f''$, $2f'$, $2f$. Lastly, from these will be had

$$r = \frac{n'r' \sin 2f}{n \sin 2f'}, \quad r'' = \frac{n'r' \sin 2f''}{n'' \sin 2f'}.$$

II. Every thing we have just said can be applied to that case in which $B''$ coincides with $A''$ or with the opposite point, if, only, all that refers to the first place is exchanged with what relates to the third place.

III. But it is necessary to treat a little differently the case in which $B'$ coincides with $A'$ or with the opposite point. There the point $C'$ will coincide with $A'$; $\gamma'$, $\varepsilon$, $\varepsilon''$ and the points $D$, $D''$, $B^*$, will be indeterminate: on the other hand, the intersection of the great circle $BB''$ with the ecliptic,† the longitude of which

---

† More generally, with the great circle $AA''$: but for the sake of brevity we are now considering that case only where the ecliptic is taken as the fundamental plane.

may be put equal to $l' + \pi$, may be determined. By reasonings analogous to those which have been developed in article 140, will be obtained the equation

$$0 = n \frac{R \sin \delta \sin (A''D' - \delta'')}{R'' \sin \delta'' \sin (AD' - \delta)} + n'r' \frac{\sin \pi}{R'' \sin (l'' - l' - \pi)} + n''.$$

Let us designate the coefficient of $n$, which agrees with $a$, article 140, by the same symbol $a$, and the coefficient of $n'r'$ by $\beta$: $a$ may be here also determined by the formula

$$a = - \frac{R \sin (l' + \pi - l)}{R'' \sin (l'' - l' - \pi)}.$$

We have, therefore,

$$0 = an + \beta n'r' + n'',$$

which equation combined with these,

$$P = \frac{n''}{n}, \quad Q = 2 \left( \frac{n + n''}{n'} - 1 \right) r'^3,$$

produces

$$\frac{\beta (P+1)}{P+a} r'^4 + r'^3 + \tfrac{1}{2} Q = 0,$$

whence we shall be able to get $r'$, unless, indeed, we should have $\beta = 0$, in which case nothing else would follow from it except $P = -a$. Further, although we might not have $\beta = 0$ (when we should have the third case to be considered in the following article), still $\beta$ will always be a very small quantity, and therefore $P$ will necessarily differ but little from $-a$: hence it is evident that the determination of the coefficient

$$\frac{\beta (P+1)}{P+a}$$

is very uncertain, and that $r'$, therefore, is not determinable with any accuracy.

Moreover, we shall have

$$\frac{n'r'}{n} = - \frac{P+a}{\beta}, \quad \frac{n'r'}{n''} = - \frac{P+a}{\beta P}:$$

after this, the following equations will be easily developed in the same manner as in article 143,

$$r \sin \zeta = \frac{n'r' \sin \gamma''}{n \sin \varepsilon'} \sin (l'' - l'),$$

$$r'' \sin \zeta'' = -\frac{n' r' \sin \gamma}{n'' \sin \varepsilon'} \sin (l' - l),$$

$$r \sin (\zeta - AD') = r'' P \frac{\sin \gamma''}{\sin \gamma} \sin (\zeta'' - A''D'),$$

from the combination of which with equations VIII. and IX. of article 143, the quantities $r$, $\zeta$, $r''$, $\zeta''$ can be determined. The remaining processes of the calculation will agree with those previously described.

## 162.

In the *second* case, where $B''$ coincides with $B$, $D'$ will also coincide with them or with the opposite point. Accordingly, we shall have $AD' - \delta$ and $A''D' - \delta''$ either equal to 0 or 180°: whence, from the equations of article 143, we obtain

$$\frac{n' r'}{n} = \pm \frac{\sin \varepsilon' R \sin \delta}{\sin \varepsilon \sin (z + A'D - \delta')},$$

$$\frac{n' r'}{n''} = \pm \frac{\sin \varepsilon' R'' \sin \delta''}{\sin \varepsilon'' \sin (z + A'D'' - \delta')}.$$

$$R \sin \delta \sin \varepsilon'' \sin (z + A'D'' - \delta') = PR'' \sin \delta'' \sin \varepsilon \sin (z + A'D - \delta').$$

Hence it is evident that $z$ is determinable by $P$ alone, independently of $Q$, (unless it should happen that $A'D'' = A'D$, or $= A'D \pm 180°$, when we should have the third case): $z$ being found, $r'$ will also be known, and hence, by means of the values of the quantities

$$\frac{n' r'}{n}, \frac{n' r'}{n''}, \text{ also } \frac{n}{n'} \text{ and } \frac{n''}{n'};$$

and, lastly, from this also

$$Q = 2\left(\frac{n}{n'} + \frac{n''}{n'} - 1\right) r'^3.$$

Evidently, therefore, $P$ and $Q$ cannot be considered as data independent of each other, but they will either supply a single datum only, or inconsistent data. The positions of the points $C$, $C''$ will in this case remain arbitrary, if they are only taken in the same great circle as $C'$.

In the *third* case, where $A'$, $B$, $B'$, $B''$, lie in the same great circle, $D$ and $D''$ will coincide with the points $B''$, $B$, respectively, or with the opposite points: hence is obtained from the combination of equations VII., VIII., IX., article 143,

$$P = \frac{R \sin \delta \sin \varepsilon''}{R'' \sin \delta'' \sin \varepsilon} = \frac{R \sin (l'-l)}{R'' \sin (l''-l')}.$$

In this case, therefore, the value of $P$ is had from the data of the problem, and, therefore, the positions of the points $C$, $C'$, $C''$, will remain indeterminate.

## 163.

The method which we have fully explained from article 136 forwards, is principally suited to the first determination of a wholly unknown orbit: still it is employed with equally great success, where the object is the correction of an orbit already approximately known by means of three observations however distant from each other.    But in such a case it will be convenient to change some things. When, for example, the observations embrace a very great heliocentric motion, it will no longer be admissible to consider $\frac{\theta''}{\theta}$ and $\theta \theta''$ as approximate values of the quantities $P$, $Q$: but much more exact values will be obtained from the very nearly known elements.    Accordingly, the heliocentric places in orbit for the three times of observation will be computed roughly by means of these elements, whence, denoting the true anomalies by $v$, $v'$, $v''$, the radii vectores by $r$, $r'$, $r''$, the semi-parameter by $p$, the following approximate values will result:—

$$P = \frac{r \sin (v'-v)}{r'' \sin (v''-v')}, \quad Q = \frac{4\,r'^4 \sin \frac{1}{2}(v'-v) \sin \frac{1}{2}(v''-v')}{p \cos \frac{1}{2}(v''-v)}.$$

With these, therefore, the first hypothesis will be constructed, and with them, a little changed at pleasure, the second and third: it would be of no advantage to adopt $P'$ and $Q'$ for the new values, since we are no longer at liberty to suppose that these values come out more exact.    For this reason all three of the hypotheses can be most conveniently despatched *at the same time:* the fourth will then be formed according to the precepts of article 120.    Finally, we shall not object, if any person thinks that some one of the ten methods explained in articles 124–129 is, if not more, at least almost equally expeditious, and prefers to use it.

# SECOND SECTION.

## DETERMINATION OF AN ORBIT FROM FOUR OBSERVATIONS, OF WHICH TWO ONLY ARE COMPLETE.

---

## 164.

WE have already, in the beginning of the second book (article 115), stated that the use of the problem treated at length in the preceding section is limited to those orbits of which the inclination is neither nothing, nor very small, and that the determination of orbits slightly inclined must necessarily be based on four observations. But four complete observations, since they are equivalent to eight equations, and the number of the unknown quantities amounts only to six, would render the problem more than determinate: on which account it will be necessary to set aside from two observations the latitudes (or declinations), that the remaining data may be exactly satisfied. Thus a problem arises to which this section will be devoted: but the solution we shall here give will extend not only to orbits slightly inclined, but can be applied also with equal success to orbits, of any inclination however great. Here also, as in the problem of the preceding section, it is necessary to separate the case, in which the approximate dimensions of the orbit are already known, from the first determination of a wholly unknown orbit: we will begin with the former.

## 165.

The simplest method of adjusting a known orbit to satisfy four observations appears to be this. Let $x, y$, be the approximate distances of the heavenly body from the earth in two complete observations: by means of these the corresponding heliocentric places may be computed, and hence the elements; after this,

(234)

from these elements the geocentric longitudes or right ascensions for the two remaining observations may be computed. If these happen to agree with the observations, the elements will require no further correction: but if not, the differences $X$, $Y$, will be noted, and the same calculation will be repeated twice, the values of $x$, $y$ being a little changed. Thus will be obtained three systems of values of the quantities $x, y$, and of the differences $X$, $Y$, whence, according to the precepts of article 120, will be obtained the corrected values of the quantities $x$, $y$, to which will correspond the values $X = 0$, $Y = 0$. From a similar calculation based on this fourth system elements will be found, by which all four observations will be correctly represented.

If it is in your power to choose, it will be best to retain those observations complete from which the situation of the orbit can be determined with the greatest precision, therefore the two extreme observations, when they embrace a heliocentric motion of 90° or less. But if they do not possess equal accuracy, you will set aside the latitudes or declinations of those you may suspect to be the less accurate.

## 166.

Such places will necessarily be used for the first determination of an entirely unknown orbit from four observations, as include a heliocentric motion not too great; for otherwise we should be without the aids for forming conveniently the first approximation. The method which we shall give directly admits of such extensive application, that observations comprehending a heliocentric motion of 30° or 40° may be used without hesitation, provided, only, the distances from the sun are not too unequal: where there is a choice, it will be best to take the intervals of the times between the first and second, the second and third, the third and fourth but little removed from equality. But it will not be necessary to be very particular in regard to this, as the annexed example will show, in which the intervals of the times are 48, 55, and 59 days, and the heliocentric motion more than 50°.

Moreover, our solution requires that the second and third observations be complete, and, therefore, the latitudes or declinations in the extreme observations are neglected. We have, indeed, shown above that, for the sake of accuracy, it is generally better that the elements be adapted to two extreme complete observations, and to the longitudes or right ascensions of the intermediate ones; nevertheless, we shall not regret having lost this advantage in the first determination of the orbit, because the most rapid approximation is by far the most important, and the loss, which affects chiefly the longitude of the node and the inclination of the orbit, and hardly, in a sensible degree, the other elements, can afterwards easily be remedied.

We will, for the sake of brevity, so arrange the explanation of the method, as to refer all the places to the ecliptic, and, therefore, we will suppose four longitudes and two latitudes to be given: but yet, as we take into account the latitude of the earth in our formulas, they can easily be transferred to the case in which the equator is taken as the fundamental plane, provided that right ascensions and declinations are substituted in the place of longitudes and latitudes.

Finally, all that we have stated in the preceding section with respect to nutation, precession, and parallax, and also aberration, applies as well here: unless, therefore, the approximate distances from the earth are otherwise known, so that method I., article 118, can be employed, the observed places will in the beginning be freed from the aberration of the fixed stars only, and the times will be corrected as soon as the approximate determination of the distances is obtained in the course of the calculation, as will appear more clearly in the sequel.

## 167.

We preface the explanation of the solution with a list of the principal symbols. We will make

$t, t', t'', t'''$, the times of the four observations,
$\alpha, \alpha', \alpha'', \alpha'''$, the geocentric longitudes of the heavenly body,
$\beta, \beta', \beta'', \beta'''$, their latitudes,
$r, r', r'', r'''$, the distances from the sun,
$\varrho, \varrho', \varrho'', \varrho'''$, the distances from the earth,
$l, l', l'', l'''$, the heliocentric longitudes of the earth,

$B, B', B'', B'''$, the heliocentric latitudes of the earth,

$R, R', R'', R'''$, the distances of the earth from the sun,

$(n\,01), (n\,12), (n\,23), (n\,02), (n\,13)$, the duplicate areas of the triangles which are contained between the sun and the first and second places of the heavenly body, the second and third, the third and fourth, the first and third, the second and fourth respectively; $(\eta\,01), (\eta\,12), (\eta\,23)$ the quotients arising from the division of the areas $\frac{1}{2}(n\,01), \frac{1}{2}(n\,12), \frac{1}{2}(n\,23)$, by the areas of the corresponding sectors;

$$P' = \frac{(n\,12)}{(n\,01)}, \ P'' = \frac{(n\,12)}{(n\,23)},$$

$$Q' = \left(\frac{(n\,01)+(n\,12)}{(n\,02)} - 1\right) r'^3, \ Q'' = \left(\frac{(n\,12)+(n\,23)}{(n\,13)} - 1\right) r''^3,$$

$v, v', v'', v'''$, the longitudes of the heavenly body in orbit reckoned from an arbitrary point. Lastly, for the second and third observations, we will denote the heliocentric places of the earth in the celestial sphere by $A', A''$, the geocentric places of the heavenly body by $B', B''$, and its heliocentric places by $C', C''$.

These things being understood, the first step will consist, exactly as in the problem of the preceding section (article 136), in the determination of the positions of the great circles $A'C'B', A''C''B''$, the inclinations of which to the ecliptic we denote by $\gamma', \gamma''$: the determination of the arcs $A'B' = \delta', A''B'' = \delta''$ will be connected at the same time with this calculation. Hence we shall evidently have

$$r' = \sqrt{(\varrho'\varrho' + 2\,\varrho'R'\cos\delta' + R'R')}$$
$$r'' = \sqrt{(\varrho''\varrho'' + 2\,\varrho''R''\cos\delta'' + R''R'')},$$

or by putting $\varrho' + R'\cos\delta' = x', \varrho'' + R''\cos\delta'' = x'', R'\sin\delta' = a', R''\sin\delta'' = a''$,

$$r' = \sqrt{(x'x' + a'a')}$$
$$r'' = \sqrt{(x''x'' + a''a'')}.$$

## 168.

By combining equations 1 and 2, article 112, the following equations in symbols of the present discussion are produced: —

$$0 = (n\,12)\,R\cos B\sin(l-\alpha) - (n\,02)\,(\varrho'\cos\beta'\sin(\alpha'-\alpha) + R'\cos B'\sin(l'-\alpha))$$
$$+ (n\,01)\,(\varrho''\cos\beta''\sin(\alpha''-\alpha) + R''\cos B''\sin(l''-\alpha)),$$

$l$

$$0 = (n\,23)\left(\varrho'\cos\beta'\sin(\alpha'''-\alpha')+R'\cos B'\sin(\alpha'''-l')\right)$$
$$-(n\,13)\left(\varrho''\cos\beta''\sin(\alpha'''-\alpha'')+R''\cos B''\sin(\alpha'''-l'')\right)$$
$$+(n\,12)\,R'''\cos B'''\sin(\alpha'''-l''').$$

These equations, by putting

$$\frac{R'\cos B'\sin(l'-\alpha)}{\cos\beta'\sin(\alpha'-\alpha)}-R'\cos\delta'=b',$$

$$\frac{R''\cos B''\sin(\alpha'''-l'')}{\cos\beta''\sin(\alpha'''-\alpha'')}-R''\cos\delta''=b'',$$

$$\frac{R'\cos B'\sin(\alpha'''-l')}{\cos\beta'\sin(\alpha'''-\alpha')}-R'\cos\delta'=\varkappa',$$

$$\frac{R''\cos B''\sin(l''-\alpha)}{\cos\beta''\sin(\alpha''-\alpha)}-R''\cos\delta''=\varkappa'',$$

$$\frac{R\cos B\sin(l-\alpha)}{\cos\beta''\sin(\alpha''-\alpha)}=\lambda,$$

$$\frac{R'''\cos B'''\sin(\alpha'''-l''')}{\cos\beta'\sin(\alpha'''-\alpha')}=\lambda''',$$

$$\frac{\cos\beta'\sin(\alpha'-\alpha)}{\cos\beta''\sin(\alpha''-\alpha)}=\mu',$$

$$\frac{\cos\beta''\sin(\alpha'''-\alpha'')}{\cos\beta'\sin(\alpha'''-\alpha')}=\mu'',$$

and all the reductions being properly made, are transformed into the following:—

$$\frac{\mu'(1+P')(\varkappa'+b')}{1+\dfrac{Q'}{(\varkappa'\varkappa'+a'a')^{\frac{3}{2}}}}=\varkappa''+\varkappa''+\lambda P',$$

$$\frac{\mu''(1+P'')(\varkappa''+b'')}{1+\dfrac{Q''}{(\varkappa''\varkappa''+a''a'')^{\frac{3}{2}}}}=\varkappa'+\varkappa'+\lambda'''P'';$$

or, by putting besides,

$$-\varkappa''-\lambda P'=c',\ \mu'(1+P')=d',$$
$$-\varkappa'-\lambda'''P''=c'',\ \mu''(1+P'')=d'',$$

into these,

I.
$$\varkappa''=c'+\frac{d'(\varkappa'+b')}{1+\dfrac{Q'}{(\varkappa'\varkappa'+a'a')^{\frac{3}{2}}}},$$

II.
$$x' = c'' + \frac{d'' (x'' + b'')}{1 + \dfrac{Q''}{(x''x'' + a''a'')^{\frac{3}{2}}}}.$$

With the aid of these two equations $x'$ and $x''$ can be determined from $a'$, $b'$, $c'$, $d'$, $Q'$. $a''$, $b''$, $c''$, $d''$, $Q''$. If, indeed, $x'$ or $x''$ should be eliminated from them, we should obtain an equation of a very high order: but still the values of the unknown quantities $x'$, $x''$, will be deduced quickly enough from these equations by indirect methods without any change of form. Generally approximate values of the unknown quantities result if, at first, $Q'$ and $Q''$ are neglected; thus:—

$$x' = \frac{c'' + d'' (b'' + c') + d'd''b'}{1 - d'd''},$$

$$x'' = \frac{c' + d' (b' + c'') + d'd''b''}{1 - d'd''}.$$

But as soon as the approximate value of either unknown quantity is obtained, values exactly satisfying the equations will be very easily found. Let, for example, $\xi'$ be an approximate value of $x'$, which being substituted in equation I., there results $x'' = \xi''$; in the same manner from $x'' = \xi''$ being substituted in equation II., we may have $x' = X'$; the same processes may be repeated by substituting for $x'$ in I., another value $\xi' + \nu'$, which may give $x'' = \xi'' + \nu''$; this value being substituted in II., may give $x' = X' + N'$. Thereupon the corrected value of $x'$ will be

$$\xi' + \frac{(\xi' - X')\nu'}{N' - \nu'} = \frac{\xi'N' - X'\nu'}{N' - \nu'},$$

and the corrected value of $x''$,

$$\xi'' + \frac{(\xi' - X')\nu''}{N' - \nu'}.$$

If it is thought worth while, the same processes will be repeated with the corrected value of $x'$ and another one slightly changed, until values of $x'$, $x''$ satisfying the equations I., II. exactly, shall have been found. Besides, means will not be wanting even to the moderately versed analyst of abridging the calculation.

In these operations the irrational quantities $(x'x' + a'a')^{\frac{3}{2}}$, $(x''x'' + a''a'')^{\frac{3}{2}}$, are conveniently calculated by introducing the arcs $z'$, $z''$, of which the tangents are respectively $\frac{d'}{x'}$, $\frac{d''}{x''}$, whence come

$$\sqrt{(x'x' + d'd')} = r' = \frac{d'}{\sin z'} = \frac{x'}{\cos z'},$$

$$\sqrt{(x''x'' + d''d'')} = r'' = \frac{d''}{\sin z''} = \frac{x''}{\cos z''}.$$

These auxiliary arcs, which must be taken between 0° and 180°, in order that $r'$, $r''$, may come out positive will, manifestly, be identical with the arcs $C'B'$, $C''B''$, whence it is evident that in this way not only $r'$ and $r''$, but also the situation of the points $C'$, $C''$, are known.

This determination of the quantities $x'$, $x''$ requires $d'$, $d''$, $b'$, $b''$, $c'$, $c''$, $d'$, $d''$, $Q'$, $Q''$ to be known, the first four of which quantities are, in fact, had from the data of the problem, but the four following depend on $P'$, $P''$. Now the quantities $P'$, $P''$, $Q'$, $Q''$, cannot yet be exactly determined; but yet, since

III.  $P' = \dfrac{t''-t}{t'-t}\dfrac{(\eta\,01)}{(\eta\,12)},$

IV.  $P'' = \dfrac{t'-t}{t'''-t''}\dfrac{(\eta\,23)}{(\eta\,12)},$

V.  $Q' = \frac{1}{2}kk\,(t'-t)\,(t''-t')\dfrac{r'r'}{r\,r''}\dfrac{1}{(\eta\,01)\,(\eta\,12)\cos\frac{1}{2}(v'-v)\cos\frac{1}{2}(v''-v)\cos\frac{1}{2}(v''-v')},$

VI.  $Q'' = \frac{1}{2}kk\,(t''-t')\,(t'''-t'')\dfrac{r''\,r''}{r'\,r'''}\dfrac{1}{(\eta\,12)\,(\eta\,23)\cos\frac{1}{2}(v''-v')\cos\frac{1}{2}(v'''-v')\cos\frac{1}{2}(v'''-v'')},$

the approximate values are immediately at hand,

$$P' = \frac{t''-t'}{t'-t},\quad P'' = \frac{t''-t'}{t'''-t''},$$

$$Q' = \tfrac{1}{2}kk\,(t'-t)\,(t''-t'),\quad Q'' = \tfrac{1}{2}kk\,(t''-t')\,(t'''-t''),$$

on which the first calculation will be based.

## 169.

The calculation of the preceding article being completed, it will be necessary first to determine the arc $C'C''$. Which may be most conveniently done, if, as in article 137, the intersection $D$ of the great circles $A'C'B'$, $A''C''B''$, and their mutual inclination $\varepsilon$ shall have been previously determined: after this, will be found from $\varepsilon$, $C'D = z' + B'D$, and $C''D = z'' + B''D$, by the same formulas which we have given in article 144, not only $C'C'' = v'' - v'$, but also the angles $(u', u'',)$ at which the great circles $A'B'$, $A''B''$, cut the great circle $C'C''$.

After the arc $v'' - v'$ has been found, $v' - v$, and $r$ will be obtained from a combination of the equations

$$r \sin (v' - v) = \frac{r'' \sin (v'' - v')}{P'},$$

$$r \sin (v' - v + v'' - v') = \frac{1 + P'}{P'} \frac{r' \sin (v'' - v')}{1 + \frac{Q'}{r'^3}},$$

and in the same manner, $r'''$ and $v''' - v''$ from a combination of these:—

$$r''' \sin (v''' - v'') = \frac{r' \sin (v'' - v')}{P''},$$

$$r''' \sin (v''' - v'' + v'' - v') = \frac{1 + P''}{P''} \frac{r'' \sin (v'' - v')}{1 + \frac{Q''}{r''^3}}.$$

All the numbers found in this manner would be accurate if we could set out in the beginning from true values of $P'$, $Q'$, $P''$, $Q''$: and then the position of the plane of the orbit might be determined in the same manner as in article 149, either from $A'C$, $u'$ and $\gamma'$, or from $A''C''$, $u''$ and $\gamma''$; and the dimensions of the orbit either from $r'$, $r''$, $t'$, $t''$, and $v'' - v'$, or, which is more exact, from $r$, $r'''$, $t$, $t'''$, $v''' - v$. But in the first calculation we will pass by all these things, and will direct our attention chiefly to obtaining the most approximate values of $P'$, $P''$, $Q'$, $Q''$. We shall reach this end, if by the method explained in 88 and the following articles,

from $r$, $r'$, $v' - v$, $t' - t$ we obtain $(\eta\ 01)$
" 　$r'$, $r''$, $v'' - v'$, $t'' - t'$ 　" 　　$(\eta\ 12)$
" 　$r''$, $r'''$, $v''' - v''$, $t''' - t''$ 　" 　$(\eta\ 23)$.

We shall substitute these quantities, and also the values of $r$, $r'$, $r''$, $r'''$, $\cos \frac{1}{2} (v' - v)$, etc., in formulas III.–VI., whence the values of $P'$, $Q'$, $P''$, $Q''$ will result much more exact than those on which the first hypothesis had been constructed. With these, accordingly, the second hypothesis will be formed, which, if it is carried to a conclusion exactly in the same manner as the first, will furnish much more exact values of $P'$, $Q'$, $P''$, $Q''$, and thus lead to the third hypothesis. These processes will continue to be repeated, until the values of $P'$, $Q'$, $P''$, $Q''$ seem to require no further correction, how to judge correctly of which, frequent practice will in time show. When the heliocentric motion is small, the first hypothesis generally supplies those values with sufficient accuracy: but if the motion includes a greater arc, if, moreover, the intervals of the times are very unequal, hypotheses several times repeated will be wanted; but in such a case the first hypotheses do not demand great preciseness of calculation. Finally, in the last hypothesis, the elements themselves will be determined as we have just indicated.

## 170.

It will be necessary in the first hypothesis to make use of the times $t, t', t'', t'''$, uncorrected, because the distances from the earth cannot yet be computed: as soon, however, as the approximate values of the quantities $x', x''$ have become known, we shall be able to determine also those distances approximately. But yet, since the formulas for $\varrho$ and $\varrho'''$ come out here a little more complicated, it will be well to put off the computation of the correction of the times until the values of the distances have become correct enough to render a repetition of the work unnecessary. On which account it will be expedient to base this operation on those values of the quantities $x', x''$, to which the last hypothesis but one leads, so that the last hypothesis may start with corrected values of the times and of the quantities $P', P'', Q', Q''$. The following are the formulas to be employed for this purpose:—

VII.  $\varrho' = x' - R' \cos \delta'$,

VIII.  $\varrho'' = x'' - R'' \cos \delta''$,

IX.  $\varrho \cos \beta = - R \cos B \cos (\alpha - l)$

$$+ \frac{1+P'}{P'\left(1+\frac{Q'}{r'^3}\right)} \Big( \varrho' \cos \beta' \cos (\alpha' - \alpha) + R' \cos B' \cos (l' - \alpha) \Big)$$

$$- \frac{1}{P'} \Big( \varrho'' \cos \beta'' \cos (\alpha'' - \alpha) + R'' \cos B'' \cos (l'' - \alpha) \Big),$$

X.  $\varrho \sin \beta = - R \sin B + \frac{1+P'}{P'\left(1+\frac{Q'}{r'^3,}\right)} (\varrho' \sin \beta' + R' \sin B')$

$$- \frac{1}{P'} (\varrho'' \sin \beta'' + R'' \sin B''),$$

XI. $\varrho''' \cos \beta''' = - R''' \cos B''' \cos (\alpha''' - l''')$

$$+ \frac{1 + P''}{P''(1 + \frac{Q''}{r''^3})} \Big( \varrho'' \cos \beta'' \cos (\alpha''' - \alpha'') + R'' \cos B'' \cos (\alpha''' - l'') \Big)$$

$$- \frac{1}{P''} \Big( \varrho' \cos \beta' \cos (\alpha''' - \alpha') + R' \cos B' \cos (\alpha''' - l') \Big),$$

XII. $\varrho''' \sin \beta''' = - R''' \sin B''' + \frac{1 + P''}{P''(1 + \frac{Q''}{r''^3})} (\varrho'' \sin \beta'' + R'' \sin B'')$

$$- \frac{1}{P''} (\varrho' \sin \beta' + R' \sin B').$$

The formulas IX.–XII. are derived without difficulty from equations 1, 2, 3, article 112, if, merely, the symbols there used are properly converted into those we here employ. The formulas will evidently come out much more simple if $B$, $B'$, $B''$ vanish. Not only $\varrho$, but also $\beta$ will follow from the combination of the formulas IX. and X., and, in the same manner, besides $r'''$, also $\beta'''$ from XI. and XII.: the values of these, compared with the observed latitudes (not entering into the calculation), if they have been given, will show with what degree of accuracy the extreme latitudes may be represented by elements adapted to the six remaining data.

## 171.

A suitable example for the illustration of this investigation is taken from *Vesta*, which, of all the most recently discovered planets, has the least inclination to the ecliptic.* We select the following observations made at Bremen, Paris, Lilienthal, and Milan, by the illustrious astronomers OLBERS, BOUVARD, BESSEL, and ORIANI : —

---

* Nevertheless this inclination is still great enough to admit of a sufficiently safe and accurate determination of the orbit based upon *three* observations: in fact the first elements which had been derived in this way from observations only 19 days distant from each other (see VON ZACH's *Monatliche Correspondenz*, Vol. XV. p. 595), approach nearly to those which were here deduced from four observations, removed from each other 162 days.

| Mean time of place of observation. | Right Ascension. | Declination. |
|---|---|---|
| 1807, March 30, $12^h$ $33^m$ $17^s$ | 183° 52′ 40″.8 | 11° 54′ 27″.0 N. |
| May  17,  8  16   5 | 178  36  42 .3 | 11  39  46 .8 |
| July  11, 10  30  19 | 189  49   7 .7 | 3   9  10 .1 N. |
| Sept.   8,  7  22  16 | 212  50   3 .4 | 8  38  17 .0 S. |

We find for the same times from the tables of the sun,

| | Longitude of the Sun from app. Equinox. | Nutation. | Distance from the Earth. | Latitude of the Sun. | Apparent obliquity of the Ecliptic. |
|---|---|---|---|---|---|
| March 30 | 9° 21′ 59″.5 | $+16.8$ | 0.9996448 | $+0''.23$ | 23° 27′ 50″.82 |
| May   17 | 55  56  20 .0 | $+16.2$ | 1.0119789 | $-0 .63$ | 49 .83 |
| July   11 | 108  34  53 .3 | $+17.3$ | 1.0165795 | $-0 .46$ | 49 .19 |
| Sept.   8 | 165   8  57 .1 | $+16.7$ | 1.0067421 | $+0 .29$ | 23  27  49 .26 |

The observed places of the planets have, the apparent obliquity of the ecliptic being used, been converted into longitudes and latitudes, been freed from nutation and aberration of the fixed stars, and, lastly, reduced, the precession being subtracted, to the beginning of the year 1807; the fictitious places of the earth have then been derived from the places of the sun by the precepts of article 72 (in order to take account of the parallax), and the longitudes transferred to the same epoch by subtracting the nutation and precession; finally, the times have been counted from the beginning of the year and reduced to the meridian of Paris.   In this manner have been obtained the following numbers: —

| $t, t', t'', t'''$ . . | 89.505162 | 137.344502 | 192.419502 | 251.288102 |
|---|---|---|---|---|
| $\alpha, \alpha', \alpha'', \alpha'''$ . . | 178° 43′ 38″.87 | 174° 1′ 30″.08 | 187° 45′ 42″.23 | 213° 34′ 15″.63 |
| $\beta, \beta', \beta'', \beta'''$ . . | 12  27   6 .16 | 10   8   7 .80 | 6  47  25 .51 | 4  20  21 .63 |
| $l, l', l'', l'''$ . . | 189  21  33 .71 | 235  56   0 .63 | 288  35  20 .32 | 345   9  18 .69 |
| $\log R, R', R'', R'''$ | 9.9997990 | 0.0051376 | 0.0071739 | 0.0030625 |

Hence we deduce

$$\gamma' = 168° 32′ 41''.34, \qquad \delta' = 62° 23′ 4''.88, \qquad \log a' = 9.9526104,$$
$$\gamma'' = 173 \quad 5 \quad 15 .68, \qquad \delta'' = 100 \quad 45 \quad 1 .40, \qquad \log a'' = 9.9994839,$$

$b' = - 11.009449,$   $\varkappa' = -1.083306,$   $\log \lambda = 0.0728800,$   $\log \mu' = 9.7139702\,n$

$b'' = - 2.082036,$   $\varkappa'' = + 6.322006,$   $\log \lambda''' = 0.0798512\,n$   $\log \mu'' = 9.8387061$

$A'D = 37° 17' 51''.50,$      $A''D = 89° 24' 11''.84,$      $\varepsilon = 9° 5' 5''.48$

$B'D = - 25\ \ 5\ 13\ .38,$      $B''D = - 11\ 20\ 49\ .56.$

These preliminary calculations completed, we enter upon the *first hypothesis*. From the intervals of the times we obtain

$$\log k\,(t' - t) = 9.9153666$$
$$\log k\,(t'' - t') = 9.9765359$$
$$\log k\,(t''' - t'') = 0.0054651,$$

and hence the first approximate values

$\log P' = 0.06117,$     $\log(1 + P') = 0.33269,$     $\log Q' = 9.59087$

$\log P'' = 9.97107,$     $\log(1 + P'') = 0.28681,$     $\log Q'' = 9.67997,$

hence, further,

$$c' = - 7.68361,\qquad \log d' = 0.04666\,n$$
$$c'' = + 2.20771,\qquad \log d'' = 0.12552.$$

With these values the following solution of equations I., II., is obtained, after a few trials:—

$x' = 2.04856,$     $z' = 23° 38' 17'',$     $\log r' = 0.34951$

$x'' = 1.95745,$     $z'' = 27\ \ 2\ \ 0,$     $\log r'' = 0.34194.$

From $z'$, $z''$ and $\varepsilon$, we get

$$C'\,C'' = v'' - v' = 17° 7' 5'':$$

hence $v' - v,\ r,\ v''' - v'',\ r'''$, will be determinable by the following equations:—

$\log r \sin(v' - v) = 9.74942,$     $\log r \sin(v' - v + 17° 7' 5'') = 0.07500$

$\log r''' \sin(v''' - v'') = 9.84729,$     $\log r''' \sin(v''' - v'' + 17\ \ 7\ \ 5'') = 0.10733$

whence we derive

$v' - v = 14° 14' 32'',$     $\log r = 0.35865$

$v''' - v'' = 18\ 48\ 33,$     $\log r''' = 0.33887.$

Lastly, is found

$$\log(n\ 01) = 0.00426,\quad \log(n\ 12) = 0.00599,\quad \log(n\ 23) = 0.00711,$$

and hence the corrected values of $P'$, $P''$, $Q'$, $Q''$,

$$\log P' = 0.05944, \qquad \log Q' = 9.60374,$$
$$\log P'' = 9.97219, \qquad \log Q'' = 9.69581,$$

upon which the *second hypothesis* will be constructed. The principal results of this are as follows: —

$c' = -7.67820, \ \log d' = 0.045736\,n$

$c'' = +2.21061, \ \log d'' = 0.126054$

$x' = 2.03308, \ z' = 23° \ 47' \ 54'', \ \log r' = 0.346747,$

$x'' = 1.94290, \ z'' = 27 \ 12 \ 25, \ \log r'' = 0.339373$

$C' C'' = v'' - v' = 17° \ 8' \ 0''$

$v' - v = 14° \ 21' \ 36'', \ \log r = 0.354687$

$v''' - v'' = 18 \ 50 \ 43, \ \log r''' = 0.334564$

$\log (n\,01) = 0.004359, \quad \log (n\,12) = 0.006102, \log (n\,23) = 0.007280.$

Hence result newly corrected values of $P'$, $P''$, $Q'$, $Q''$,

$$\log P' = 0.059426, \qquad \log Q' = 9.604749$$
$$\log P'' = 9.972249, \qquad \log Q'' = 9.697564,$$

from which, if we proceed to the *third hypothesis*, the following numbers result: —

$c' = -7.67815, \ \log d' = 0.045729\,n$

$c'' = +2.21076, \ \log d'' = 0.126082$

$x' = 2.03255, \ z' = 23° \ 48' \ 14'', \ \log r' = 0.346653$

$x'' = 1.94235, \ z'' = 27 \ 12 \ 49, \ \log r'' = 0.339276$

$C' C'' = v'' - v' = 17° \ 8' \ 4''$

$v' - v = 14° \ 21' \ 49'', \ \log r = 0.354522$

$v''' - v'' = 18 \ 51 \ 7, \ \log r''' = 0.334290$

$\log (n\,01) = 0.004363, \ \log (n\,12) = 0.006106, \ \log (n\,23) = 0.007290.$

If now the distances from the earth are computed according to the precepts of the preceding article, there appears: —

$\varrho' = 1.5635, \qquad\qquad\qquad \varrho'' = 2.1319$

$\log \varrho \cos \beta = 0.09876 \qquad\quad \log \varrho''' \cos \beta''' = 0.42842$

$\log \varrho \sin \beta = 9.44252 \qquad\quad \log \varrho''' \sin \beta''' = 9.30905$

$\beta = 12° \ 26' \ 40'' \qquad\qquad\quad \beta''' = 4° \ 20' \ 39''$

$\log \varrho = 0.10909 \qquad\qquad\quad \log \varrho''' = 0.42967.$

Hence are found

|      | Corrections of the Times. | Corrected Times. |
| :---: | :---: | :---: |
| I.   | 0.007335 | 89.497827 |
| II.  | 0.008921 | 135.335581 |
| III. | 0.012165 | 192.407337 |
| IV.  | 0.015346 | 251.272756 |

whence will result newly corrected values of the quantities $P'$, $P''$, $Q'$, $Q''$,

$$\log P' = 0.059415, \qquad \log Q' = 9.604782,$$
$$\log P'' = 9.972253, \qquad \log Q'' = 9.697687.$$

Finally, if the *fourth hypothesis* is formed with these new values, the following numbers are obtained: —

$$c' = -7.678116, \quad \log d' = 0.045723$$
$$c'' = +2.210773, \quad \log d'' = 0.126084$$
$$x' = 2.032473, \quad z' = 23°\ 48'\ 16''.7, \quad \log r' = 0.346638$$
$$x'' = 1.942281, \quad z'' = 27\ 12\ 51\ .7, \quad \log r'' = 0.339263$$
$$v'' - v' = 17°\ 8'\ 5''.1, \quad \tfrac{1}{2}(u'' + u') = 176°\ 7'\ 50''.5, \quad \tfrac{1}{2}(u'' - u') = 4°\ 33'\ 23''.6$$
$$v' - v = 14\ 21\ 51\ .9, \quad \log r = 0.354503$$
$$v''' - v'' = 18\ 51\ 9\ .5, \quad \log r''' = 0.334263$$

These numbers differ so little from those which the third hypothesis furnished, that we may now safely proceed to the determination of the elements. In the first place we get out the position of the plane of the orbit. The inclination of the orbit $7°\ 8'\ 14''.8$ is found by the precepts of article 149 from $\gamma'$, $u'$, and $A'C' = \delta' - z'$, also the longitude of the ascending node $103°\ 16'\ 37''.2$, the argument of the latitude in the second observation $94°\ 36'\ 4''.9$, and, therefore, the longitude in orbit $197°\ 52'\ 42''.1$; in the same manner, from $\gamma''$, $u''$, and $A''C'' = \delta'' - z''$, are derived the inclination of the orbit $= 7°\ 8'\ 14''.8$, the longitude of the ascending node $103°\ 16'\ 37''.5$, the argument of the latitude in the third observation $111°\ 44'\ 9''.7$, and therefore the longitude in orbit $215°\ 0'\ 47''.2$. Hence the longitude in orbit for the first observation will be $183°\ 30'\ 50''.2$, for the fourth $233°\ 51'\ 56''.7$. If now the dimensions of the orbit are determined from $t''' - t$, $r$, $r'''$, and $v''' - v = 50°\ 21'\ 6''.5$, we shall have,

| | |
|---|---|
| True anomaly for the first place . . . . . . . | 293° 33′ 43″.7 |
| True anomaly for the fourth place . . . . . . | 343 54 50 .2 |
| Hence the longitude of the perihelion . . . . . | 249 57 6 .5 |
| Mean anomaly for the first place . . . . . . . | 302 33 32 .6 |
| Mean anomaly for the fourth place . . . . . . | 346 32 25 .2 |
| Mean daily sidereal motion . . . . . . . . . | 978″.7216 |
| Mean anomaly for the beginning of the year 1807 . | 278 13 39 .1 |
| Mean longitude for the same epoch . . . . . . | 168 10 45 .6 |
| Angle of eccentricity $\varphi$ . . . . . . . . . . | 5 2 58 .1 |
| Logarithm of the semi-axis major . . . . . . | 0.372898 |

If the geocentric places of the planet are computed from these elements for the corrected times $t$, $t'$, $t''$, $t'''$, the four longitudes agree with $\alpha$, $\alpha'$, $\alpha''$, $\alpha'''$, and the two intermediate latitudes with $\beta'$, $\beta''$, to the tenth of a second; but the extreme latitudes come out 12° 26′ 43″.7 and 4° 20′ 40″.1. The former in error 22″.4 in defect, the latter 18″.5 in excess. But yet, if the inclination of the orbit is only increased 6″, and the longitude of the node is diminished 4′ 40″, the other elements remaining the same, the errors distributed among all the latitudes will be reduced to a few seconds, and the longitudes will only be affected by the smallest errors, which will themselves be almost reduced to nothing, if, in addition, 2″ is taken from the epoch of the longitude.

# THIRD SECTION.

------

## 172.

IF the astronomical observations and other quantities, on which the computation of orbits is based, were absolutely correct, the elements also, whether deduced from three or four observations, would be strictly accurate (so far indeed as the motion is supposed to take place exactly according to the laws of KEPLER), and, therefore, if other observations were used, they might be confirmed, but not corrected. But since all our measurements and observations are nothing more than approximations to the truth, the same must be true of all calculations resting upon them, and the highest aim of all computations made concerning concrete phenomena must be to approximate, as nearly as practicable, to the truth. But this can be accomplished in no other way than by a suitable combination of more observations than the number absolutely requisite for the determination of the unknown quantities. This problem can only be properly undertaken when an approximate knowledge of the orbit has been already attained, which is afterwards to be corrected so as to satisfy all the observations in the most accurate manner possible.

It then can only be worth while to aim at the highest accuracy, when the final correction is to be given to the orbit to be determined. But as long as it appears probable that new observations will give rise to new corrections, it will be convenient to relax more or less, as the case may be, from extreme precision, if in this way the length of the computations can be considerably diminished We will endeavor to meet both cases.

## 173.

In the first place, it is of the greatest importance, that the several positions of the heavenly body on which it is proposed to base the orbit, should not be taken from single observations, but, if possible, from several so combined that the accidental errors might, as far as may be, mutually destroy each other. Observations, for example, such as are distant from each other by an interval of a few days, — or by so much, in some cases, as an interval of fifteen or twenty days, — are not to be used in the calculation as so many different positions, but it would be better to derive from them a single place, which would be, as it were, a mean among all, admitting, therefore, much greater accuracy than single observations considered separately. This process is based on the following principles.

The geocentric places of a heavenly body computed from approximate elements ought to differ very little from the true places, and the differences between the former and latter should change very slowly, so that for an interval of a few days they can be regarded as nearly constant, or, at least, the changes may be regarded as proportional to the times. If, accordingly, the observations should be regarded as free from all error, the differences between the observed places corresponding to the times $t$, $t'$, $t''$, $t'''$, and those which have been computed from the elements, that is, the differences between the observed and the computed longitudes and latitudes, or right ascensions and declinations, would be quantities either sensibly equal, or, at least, uniformly and very slowly increasing or decreasing. Let, for example, the observed right ascensions $\alpha$, $\alpha'$, $\alpha''$, $\alpha'''$, etc., correspond to those times, and let $\alpha + \delta$, $\alpha' + \delta'$, $\alpha'' + \delta''$, $\alpha''' + \delta'''$, etc., be the computed ones; then the differences $\delta$, $\delta'$, $\delta''$, $\delta'''$, etc. will differ from the true deviations of the elements so far only as the observations themselves are erroneous: if, therefore, these deviations can be regarded as constant for all these observations, the quantities $\delta$, $\delta'$, $\delta''$, $\delta'''$, etc. will furnish as many different determinations of the same quantity, for the correct value of which it will be proper to take the arithmetical mean between those determinations, so far, of course, as there is no reason for preferring one to the other. But if it seems that the same degree of accuracy cannot be attributed to the several observations, let us assume that the degree of accuracy in each may be considered proportional to the numbers $e$, $e'$, $e''$, $e'''$, etc. respectively, that is, that errors reciprocally proportional to these numbers could have been made in the observations with equal facility; then, according to the principles to be propounded below, the most probable mean value will no longer be the simple arithmetical mean, but

$$\frac{ee\,\delta + e'e'\delta' + e''e''\delta'' + e'''e'''\delta''' + \text{etc.}}{ee + e'e' + e''e'' + e'''e''' + \text{etc.}}.$$

Putting now this mean value equal to $\varDelta$, we can assume for the true right ascensions, $\alpha + \delta - \varDelta$, $\alpha' + \delta' - \varDelta$, $\alpha'' + \delta'' - \varDelta$, $\alpha''' + \delta''' - \varDelta$, respectively, and then it will be arbitrary, which we use in the calculation. But if either the observations are distant from each other by too great an interval of time, or if sufficiently approximate elements of the orbit are not yet known, so that it would not be admissible to regard their deviations as constant for all the observations, it will readily be perceived, that no other difference arises from this except that the mean deviation thus found cannot be regarded as common to all the observations, but is to be referred to some intermediate time, which must be derived from the individual times in the same manner as $\varDelta$ from the corresponding deviations, and therefore generally to the time

$$\frac{ee\,t + e'e't' + e''e''t'' + e'''e'''t''' + \text{etc.}}{ee + e'e' + e''e'' + e'''e''' + \text{etc.}}.$$

Consequently, if we desire the greatest accuracy, it will be necessary to compute the geocentric place from the elements for the same time, and afterwards to free it from the mean error $\varDelta$, in order that the most accurate position may be obtained. But it will in general be abundantly sufficient if the mean error is referred to the observation nearest to the mean time. What we have said here of right ascensions, applies equally to declinations, or, if it is desired, to longitudes and latitudes: however, it will always be better to compare the right ascensions and declinations computed from the elements immediately with those observed; for thus we not only gain a much more expeditious calculation, especially if we make use of the methods explained in articles 53–60, but this method has the additional advantage, that the incomplete observations can also be made use of; and besides, if every thing should be referred to longitudes and latitudes, there would be cause to fear lest an observation made correctly in right ascension, but badly in declination (or the opposite), should be vitiated in respect to both longitude and latitude, and thus become wholly useless. The degree of precision to be assigned to the mean found as above will be, according to the principles to be explained hereafter,

$$\sqrt{(ee + e'e' + e''e'' + e'''e''' + \text{etc.})};$$

so that four or nine equally exact observations are required, if the mean is to possess a double or triple accuracy.

## 174.

If the orbit of a heavenly body has been determined according to the methods given in the preceding sections from three or four geocentric positions, each one of which has been derived, according to the precepts of the preceding article, from a great many observations, that orbit will hold a mean, as it were, among all these observations; and in the differences between the observed and computed places there will remain no trace of any law, which it would be possible to remove or sensibly diminish by a correction of the elements. Now, when the whole number of observations does not embrace too great an interval of time, the best agreement of the elements with all the observations can be obtained, if only three or four normal positions are judiciously selected. How much advantage we shall derive from this method in determining the orbits of new planets or comets, the observations of which do not yet embrace a period of more than one year, will depend on the nature of the case. When, accordingly, the orbit to be determined is inclined at a considerable angle to the ecliptic, it will be in general based upon three observations, which we shall take as remote from each other as possible: but if in this way we should meet with any one of the cases excluded above (articles 160–162), or if the inclination of the orbit should seem too small, we shall prefer the determination from four positions, which, also, we shall take as remote as possible from each other.

But when we have a longer series of observations, embracing several years, more normal positions can be derived from them; on which account, we should not insure the greatest accuracy, if we were to select three or four positions only for the determination of the orbit, and neglect all the rest. But in such a case, if it is proposed to aim at the greatest precision, we shall take care to collect and employ the greatest possible number of accurate places. Then, of course, more data will exist than are required for the determination of the unknown quantities: but all these data will be liable to errors, however small, so that it will generally be impossible to satisfy all perfectly. Now as no reason exists, why, from among those data, we should consider any six as absolutely exact, but since we must assume, rather, upon the principles of probability, that greater or less errors are equally possible in all, promiscuously; since, moreover, generally speaking, small errors oftener occur than large ones; it is evident, that an orbit which, while it satisfies precisely the six data, deviates more or less from the others, must be regarded as less consistent with the principles of the calculus of probabilities, than one which, at the same time that it differs a little from those six data, presents so much the better an agreement with the rest. The investigation of an orbit having, strictly speaking, the *maximum* probability, will depend upon a knowledge of the law according to which the probability of errors decreases as the errors increase in magnitude: but that depends upon so many vague and doubtful considerations — physiological included — which cannot be subjected to calculation, that it is scarcely, and indeed less·than scarcely, possible to assign properly a law of this kind in any case of practical astronomy. Nevertheless, an investigation of the connection between this law and the most probable orbit, which we will undertake in its utmost generality, is not to be regarded as by any means a barren speculation.

## 175.

To this end let us leave our special problem, and enter upon a very general discussion and one of the most fruitful in every application of the calculus to natural philosophy. Let $V, V', V''$, etc. be functions of the unknown quantities $p, q, r, s$, etc., $\mu$ the number of those functions, $\nu$ the number of the unknown quantities; and let us suppose that the values of the functions found by direct observation are $V = M, \; V' = M', \; V'' = M''$, etc. Generally speaking, the determination of the unknown quantities will constitute a problem, indeterminate, determinate, or more than determinate, according as $\mu < \nu$, $\mu = \nu$, or $\mu > \nu$.* We shall confine ourselves here to the last case, in which, evidently, an exact representation of all the observations would only be possible when they were all absolutely free from error. And since this cannot, in the nature of things, happen, every system of values of the unknown quantities $p$, $q$, $r$, $s$, etc., must be regarded as possible, which gives the values of the functions $V - M$, $V' - M'$, $V'' - M''$, etc., within the limits of the possible errors of observation; this, however, is not to be understood to imply that each one of these systems would possess an equal degree of probability.

Let us suppose, in the first place, the state of things in all the observations to have been such, that there is no reason why we should suspect one to be less exact than another, or that we are bound to regard errors of the same magnitude as equally probable in all. Accordingly, the probability to be assigned to each error $\varDelta$ will be expressed by a function of $\varDelta$ which we shall denote by $\varphi \varDelta$. Now although we cannot precisely assign the form of this function, we can at least affirm that its value should be a maximum for $\varDelta = 0$, equal, generally, for equal opposite values of $\varDelta$, and should vanish, if, for $\varDelta$ is taken the greatest error, or a value greater than the greatest error: $\varphi \varDelta$, therefore, would appropriately be referred to the class of discontinuous functions, and if we undertake to substitute any analytical function in the place of it for practical purposes, this must be of such a form that it may converge to zero on both sides, asymptotically, as it were, from $\varDelta = 0$, so that beyond this limit it can be regarded as actually vanishing. Moreover, the probability that an error lies between the limits $\varDelta$ and $\varDelta + \mathrm{d}\,\varDelta$ differing from each other by the infinitely small difference $\mathrm{d}\,\varDelta$, will be expressed by $\varphi \varDelta \, \mathrm{d}\varDelta$; hence the probability generally, that the error lies between $D$ and

---

* If, in the third case, the functions $V$, $V'$, $V''$ should be of such a nature that $\mu + 1 - \nu$ of them, or more, might be regarded as functions of the remainder, the problem would still be more than determinate with respect to these functions, but indeterminate with respect to the quantities $p$, $q$, $r$, $s$, etc.; that is to say, it would be impossible to determine the values of the latter, even if the values of the functions $V$, $V'$, $V''$, etc. should be given with absolute exactness: but we shall exclude this case from our discussion.

$D'$, will be given by the integral $\int \varphi \varDelta . \mathrm{d} \varDelta$ extended from $\varDelta = D$ to $\varDelta = D'$. This integral taken from the greatest negative value of $\varDelta$ to the greatest positive value, or more generally from $\varDelta = -\infty$ to $\varDelta = +\infty$ must necessarily be equal to unity. Supposing, therefore, any determinate system of the values of the quantities $p$, $q$, $r$, $s$, etc., the probability that observation would give for $V$ the value $M$, will be expressed by $\varphi(M - V)$, substituting in $V$ for $p$, $q$, $r$, $s$, etc., their values; in the same manner $\varphi(M' - V)$, $\varphi(M'' - V'')$, etc. will express the probabilities that observation would give the values $M'$, $M''$, etc. of the functions $V'$, $V''$, etc. Wherefore, since we are authorized to regard all the observations as events independent of each other, the product

$$\varphi(M - V) \; \varphi(M' - V') \; \varphi(M'' - V'') \text{ etc.,} = \Omega$$

will express the expectation or probability that all those values will result together from observation.

## 176.

Now in the same manner as, when any determinate values whatever of the unknown quantities being taken, a determinate probability corresponds, previous to observation, to any system of values of the functions $V$, $V'$, $V''$, etc.; so, inversely, after determinate values of the functions have resulted from observation, a determinate probability will belong to every system of values of the unknown quantities, from which the values of the functions could possibly have resulted: for, evidently, those systems will be regarded as the more probable in which the greater expectation had existed of the event which actually occurred. The estimation of this probability rests upon the following theorem : —

*If, any hypothesis* H *being made, the probability of any determinate event* E *is* h, *and if, another hypothesis* H' *being made excluding the former and equally probable in itself, the probability of the same event is* h' : *then I say, when the event* E *has actually occurred, that the probability that* H *was the true hypothesis, is to the probability that* H' *was the true hypothesis, as* h *to* h'.

For demonstrating which let us suppose that, by a classification of all the circumstances on which it depends whether, with $H$ or $H'$ or some other hypothesis, the event $E$ or some other event, should occur, a system of the different cases is formed, each one of which cases is to be considered as equally probable in itself (that is, as long as it is uncertain whether the event $E$, or some other, will occur), and that these cases be so distributed,

| that among them may be found | in which should be assumed the hypothesis | in such a mode as would give occasion to the event. |
|---|---|---|
| $m$ | $H$ | $E$ |
| $n$ | $H$ | different from $E$ |
| $m'$ | $H'$ | $E$ |
| $n'$ | $H'$ | different from $E$ |
| $m''$ | different from $H$ and $H'$ | $E$ |
| $n''$ | different from $H$ and $H'$ | different from $E$ |

Then we shall have

$$h = \frac{m}{m+n}, \quad h' = \frac{m'}{m'+n'};$$

moreover, before the event was known the probability of the hypothesis $H$ was

$$\frac{m+n}{m+n+m'+n'+m''+n''};$$

but after the event is known, when the cases $n$, $n'$, $n''$ disappear from the number of the possible cases, the probability of the same hypothesis will be

$$\frac{m}{m+m'+m''};$$

in the same way the probability of the hypothesis $H'$ before and after the event, respectively, will be expressed by

$$\frac{m'+n'}{m+n+m'+n'+m''+n''} \text{ and } \frac{m'}{m+m'+m''}:$$

since, therefore, the same probability is assumed for the hypotheses $H$ and $H'$ before the event is known, we shall have

$$m+n = m'+n',$$

whence the truth of the theorem is readily inferred.

Now, so far as we suppose that no other data exist for the determination of the unknown quantities besides the observations $V = M$, $V' = M'$, $V'' = M''$, etc., and, therefore, that all systems of values of these unknown quantities were equally probable previous to the observations, the probability, evidently, of any determinate system subsequent to the observations will be proportional to $\Omega$. This is to be understood to mean that the probability that the values of the unknown quantities lie between the infinitely near limits $p$ and $p+\mathrm{d}p$, $q$ and $q+\mathrm{d}q$, $r$ and $r+\mathrm{d}r$, $s$ and $s+\mathrm{d}s$, etc. respectively, is expressed by

$$\lambda \Omega \,\mathrm{d}p\,\mathrm{d}q\,\mathrm{d}r\,\mathrm{d}s\ldots\ldots, \text{ etc.,}$$

where the quantity $\lambda$ will be a constant quantity independent of $p, q, r, s$, etc.: and, indeed, $\frac{1}{\lambda}$ will, evidently, be the value of the integral of the order $\nu$,

$$\int^{\nu} \Omega \,\mathrm{d}p\,\mathrm{d}q\,\mathrm{d}r\,\mathrm{d}s\ldots\ldots, \text{ etc.,}$$

for each of the variables $p, q, r, s$, etc., extended from the value $-\infty$ to the value $+\infty$.

## 177.

Now it readily follows from this, that the most probable system of values of the quantities $p, q, r, s$, etc. is that in which $\Omega$ acquires the maximum value, and, therefore, is to be derived from the $\nu$ equations

$$\frac{\mathrm{d}\Omega}{\mathrm{d}p}=0, \ \frac{\mathrm{d}\Omega}{\mathrm{d}q}=0, \ \frac{\mathrm{d}\Omega}{\mathrm{d}r}=0, \ \frac{\mathrm{d}\Omega}{\mathrm{d}s}=0, \text{ etc.}$$

These equations, by putting

$$V-M=v, \ V'-M'=v', \ V''-M''=v'', \text{ etc., and } \frac{\mathrm{d}\varphi\varDelta}{\varphi\varDelta\,\mathrm{d}\varDelta}=\varphi'\varDelta,$$

assume the following form:—

$$\frac{\mathrm{d}v}{\mathrm{d}p}\varphi'v + \frac{\mathrm{d}v'}{\mathrm{d}p}\varphi'v' + \frac{\mathrm{d}v''}{\mathrm{d}p}\varphi'v'' + \text{etc.}=0,$$

$$\frac{\mathrm{d}v}{\mathrm{d}q}\varphi'v + \frac{\mathrm{d}v'}{\mathrm{d}q}\varphi'v' + \frac{\mathrm{d}v''}{\mathrm{d}q}\varphi'v'' + \text{etc.}=0,$$

$$\frac{\mathrm{d}v}{\mathrm{d}r}\varphi'v + \frac{\mathrm{d}v'}{\mathrm{d}r}\varphi'v' + \frac{\mathrm{d}v''}{\mathrm{d}r}\varphi'v'' + \text{etc.}=0,$$

$$\frac{\mathrm{d}v}{\mathrm{d}s}\varphi'v + \frac{\mathrm{d}v'}{\mathrm{d}s}\varphi'v' + \frac{\mathrm{d}v''}{\mathrm{d}s}\varphi'v'' + \text{etc.}=0.$$

Hence, accordingly, a completely determinate solution of the problem can be obtained by elimination, as soon as the nature of the function $\varphi'$ is known.   Since this cannot be defined *a priori*, we will, approaching the subject from another point of view, inquire upon what function, tacitly, as it were, assumed as a base, the common principle, the excellence of which is generally acknowledged, depends. It has been customary certainly to regard as an axiom the hypothesis that if any quantity has been determined by several direct observations, made under the same circumstances and with equal care, the arithmetical mean of the observed values affords the most probable value, if not rigorously, yet very nearly at least, so that it is always most safe to adhere to it. By putting, therefore,

$$V = V' = V'' \text{ etc.} = p,$$

we ought to have in general,

$$\varphi'(M - p) + \varphi'(M' - p) + \varphi'(M'' - p) + \text{etc.} = 0,$$

if instead of $p$ is substituted the value

$$\frac{1}{\mu}(M + M' + M'' + \text{etc.}),$$

whatever positive integer $\mu$ expresses. By supposing, therefore,

$$M' = M'' = \text{etc.} = M - \mu N,$$

we shall have in general, that is, for any positive integral value of $\mu$,

$$\varphi'(\mu - 1) N = (1 - \mu) \varphi'(-N),$$

whence it is readily inferred that $\frac{\varphi' \Delta}{\Delta}$ must be a constant quantity, which we will denote by $k$. Hence we have

$$\log \varphi \Delta = \tfrac{1}{2} k \Delta \Delta + \text{Constant},$$

$$\varphi \Delta = \varkappa e^{\frac{1}{2}k \Delta \Delta}.$$

denoting the base of the hyperbolic logarithms by $e$ and assuming

$$\text{Constant} = \log \varkappa.$$

Moreover, it is readily perceived that $k$ must be negative, in order that $\Omega$ may really become a maximum, for which reason we shall put

$$\tfrac{1}{2} k = - h h;$$

and since, by the elegant theorem first discovered by Laplace, the integral

$$\int e^{-h h \Delta \Delta} \, d\Delta$$

from $\varDelta = -\infty$ to $\varDelta = +\infty$ is $\frac{\sqrt{\pi}}{h}$, (denoting by $\pi$ the semicircumference of the circle the radius of which is unity), our function becomes

$$\varphi \varDelta = \frac{h}{\sqrt{\pi}} e^{-hh \varDelta \varDelta}.$$

## 178.

The function just found cannot, it is true, express rigorously the probabilities of the errors: for since the possible errors are in all cases confined within certain limits, the probability of errors exceeding those limits ought always to be zero. while our formula always gives some value. However, this defect, which every analytical function must, from its nature, labor under, is of no importance in practice, because the value of our function decreases so rapidly, when $h \varDelta$ has acquired a considerable magnitude, that it can safely be considered as vanishing. Besides, the nature of the subject never admits of assigning with absolute rigor the limits of error.

Finally, the constant $h$ can be considered as the measure of precision of the observations. For if the probability of the error $\varDelta$ is supposed to be expressed in any one system of observations by

$$\frac{h}{\sqrt{\pi}} e^{-hh \varDelta \varDelta},$$

and in another system of observations more or less exact by

$$\frac{h'}{\sqrt{\pi}} e^{-h'h' \varDelta \varDelta},$$

the expectation, that the error of any observation in the former system is contained between the limits $-\delta$ and $+\delta$ will be expressed by the integral

$$\int \frac{h}{\sqrt{\pi}} e^{-hh \varDelta \varDelta} d\varDelta$$

taken from $\varDelta = -\delta$ to $\varDelta = +\delta$; and in the same manner the expectation, that the error of any observation in the latter system does not exceed the limits $-\delta'$ and $+\delta'$ will be expressed by the integral

$$\int \frac{h'}{\sqrt{\pi}} e^{-h'h' \varDelta \varDelta} d\varDelta$$

extended from $\varDelta = -\delta'$ to $\varDelta = +\delta'$: but both integrals manifestly become equal when we have $h\,\delta = h'\delta'$. Now, therefore, if for example $h' = 2\,h$, a double error can be committed in the former system with the same facility as a single error in the latter, in which case, according to the common way of speaking, a double degree of precision is attributed to the latter observations.

## 179.

We will now develop the conclusions which follow from this law. It is evident, in order that the product

$$\Omega = h^\mu \pi^{-\frac{1}{2}\mu} e^{-hh(vv + v'v' + v''v'' + \,\cdots\,)}$$

may become a maximum, that the sum

$$v\,v + v'v' + v''v'' + \text{etc.,}$$

must become a minimum. *Therefore, that will be the most probable system of values of the unknown quantities* p, q, r, s, *etc., in which the sum of the squares of the differences between the observed and computed values of the functions* V, V', V'', *etc. is a minimum,* if the same degree of accuracy is to be presumed in all the observations. This principle, which promises to be of most frequent use in all applications of the mathematics to natural philosophy, must, everywhere, be considered an axiom with the same propriety as the arithmetical mean of several observed values of the same quantity is adopted as the most probable value.

This principle can be extended without difficulty to observations of *unequal* accuracy. If, for example, the measures of precision of the observations by means of which $V = M$, $V' = M'$, $V'' = M''$, etc. have been found, are expressed, respectively, by $h$, $h'$, $h''$, etc., that is, if it is assumed that errors reciprocally proportional to these quantities might have been made with equal facility in those observations, this, evidently, will be the same as if, by means of observations of equal precision (the measure of which is equal to unity), the values of the functions $hV$, $h'V'$, $h''V''$, etc., had been directly found to be $hM$, $h'M'$, $h''M''$, etc.: wherefore, the most probable system of values of the quantities $p$, $q$, $r$, $s$, etc., will be that in which the sum of $hhvv + h'h'v'v' + h''h''v''v'' + $ etc., that is, *in which the sum of the squares of the differences between the actually observed and computed values multiplied by numbers that measure the degree of precision, is a minimum.* In this way it is not even necessary that the functions $V$, $V'$, $V''$, etc. relate to homogeneous quantities, but they may represent heterogeneous quantities also, (for example, seconds of arc and time), provided only that the ratio of the errors, which might have been committed with equal facility in each, can be estimated.

## 180.

The principle explained in the preceding article derives value also from this, that the numerical determination of the unknown quantities is reduced to a very expeditious algorithm, when the functions $V$, $V'$, $V''$, etc. are linear. Let us suppose

$$V - M = v = -m + ap + bq + cr + ds + \text{etc.}$$
$$V' - M' = v' = -m' + a'p + b'q + c'r + d's + \text{etc.}$$
$$V'' - M'' = v'' = -m'' + a''p + b''q + c''r + d''s + \text{etc.}$$

etc., and let us put

$$av + a'v' + a''v'' + \text{etc.} = P$$
$$bv + b'v' + b''v'' + \text{etc.} = Q$$
$$cv + c'v' + c''v'' + \text{etc.} = R$$
$$dv + d'v' + d''v'' + \text{etc.} = S$$

etc. Then the $\nu$ equations of article 177, from which the values of the unknown quantities must be determined, will, evidently, be the following: —

$$P = 0, \ Q = 0, \ R = 0, \ S = 0, \text{ etc.,}$$

provided we suppose the observations equally good; to which case we have shown in the preceding article how to reduce the others. We have, therefore, as many linear equations as there are unknown quantities to be determined, from which the values of the latter will be obtained by common elimination.

Let us see now, whether this elimination is always possible, or whether the solution can become indeterminate, or even impossible. It is known, from the theory of elimination, that the second or third case will occur when one of the equations

$$P = 0, \ Q = 0, \ R = 0, \ S = 0, \text{ etc.,}$$

being omitted, an equation can be formed from the rest, either identical with the omitted one or inconsistent with it, or, which amounts to the same thing, when it is possible to assign a linear function

$$\alpha P + \beta Q + \gamma R + \delta S + \text{etc.},$$

which is identically either equal to zero, or, at least, free from all the unknown quantities $p, q, r, s$, etc. Let us assume, therefore,

$$\alpha P + \beta Q + \gamma R + \delta S + \text{etc.} = \varkappa.$$

We at once have the identical equation

$$(v + m) v + (v' + m') v' + (v'' + m'') v'' + \text{etc.} = pP + qQ + rR + sS + \text{etc.}$$

If, accordingly, by the substitutions

$$p = \alpha x, q = \beta x, r = \gamma x, s = \delta x, \text{etc.}$$

we suppose the functions $v, v', v''$, to become respectively,

$$- m + \lambda x, - m' + \lambda' x, - m'' + \lambda'' x, \text{etc.},$$

we shall evidently have the identical equation

$$(\lambda\lambda + \lambda'\lambda' + \lambda''\lambda'' + \text{etc.}) xx - (\lambda m + \lambda' m' + \lambda'' m'' \text{ etc.}) x = \varkappa x,$$

that is,

$$\lambda\lambda + \lambda'\lambda' + \lambda''\lambda'' + \text{etc.} = 0, \varkappa + \lambda m + \lambda' m' + \lambda'' m'' + \text{etc.} = 0 :$$

hence it must follow that $\lambda = 0, \lambda' = 0, \lambda'' = 0$, etc. and also $\varkappa = 0$. Then it is evident, that all the functions $V, V' V''$, are such that their values are not changed, even if the quantities $p, q, r, s$, etc. receive any increments or decrements whatever, proportional to the numbers $\alpha, \beta, \gamma, \delta$, etc.: but we have already mentioned before, that cases of this kind, in which evidently the determination of the unknown quantities would not be possible, even if the true values of the functions $V, V', V''$, etc., should be given, do not belong to this subject.

Finally, we can easily reduce to the case here considered, all the others in which the functions $V, V', V''$, etc. are not linear. Letting, for instance, $\pi, \chi, \varrho, \sigma$, etc., denote approximate values of the unknown quantities $p, q, r, s$, etc., (which we shall easily obtain if at first we only use $\nu$ of the $\mu$ equations $V = M, V' = M', V'' = M''$, etc.), we will introduce in place of the unknown quantities the others, $p', q', r', s'$, etc., putting $p = \pi + p', q = \chi + q', r = \varrho + r', s = \sigma + s'$, etc.: the values of these new unknown quantities will evidently be so small that their squares and products may be neglected, by which means the equations become linear. If, after the calculation is completed, the values of the unknown quantities $p'$, $q'$, $r'$, $s'$, etc., prove, contrary to expectation, to be so great, as to make it appear unsafe to neglect the squares and products, a repetition of the same process (the corrected values of $p$, $q$, $r$, $s$, etc. being taken instead of $\pi$, $\chi$, $\varrho$, $\sigma$, etc.), will furnish an easy remedy.

## 181.

When we have only one unknown quantity $p$, for the determination of which the values of the functions $ap + n$, $a'p + n'$, $a''p + n''$, etc. have been found, respectively, equal to $M$, $M'$, $M''$, etc., and that, also, by means of observations equally exact, the most probable value of $p$ will be

$$A = \frac{am + a'm' + a''m'' + \text{etc.}}{aa + a'a' + a''a'' + \text{etc.}},$$

putting $m$, $m'$, $m''$, respectively, for $M - n$, $M' - n'$, $M'' - n''$, etc.

In order to estimate the degree of accuracy to be attributed to this value, let us suppose that the probability of an error $\varDelta$ in the observations is expressed by

$$\frac{h}{\sqrt{\pi}} e^{-hh\varDelta\varDelta}.$$

Hence the probability that the true value of $p$ is equal to $A + p'$ will be proportional to the function

$$e^{-hh\left((ap-m)^2+(a'p-m')^2+(a''p-m'')^2+\text{etc.}\right)}$$

if $A + p'$ is substituted for $p$. The exponent of this function can be reduced to the form,

$$-hh\left(aa + a'a' + a''a'' + \text{etc.}\right)\left(pp - 2pA + B\right),$$

in which $B$ is independent of $p$: therefore the function itself will be proportional to

$$e^{-hh(aa+a'a'+a''a''+\text{etc.})\,p'p'}.$$

It is evident, accordingly, that the same degree of accuracy is to be assigned to the value $A$ as if it had been found by a direct observation, the accuracy of which would be to the accuracy of the original observations as $h\sqrt{(aa+a'a'+a''a''+\text{etc.})}$ to $h$, or as $\sqrt{(aa + a'a' + a''a'' + \text{etc.})}$ to unity.

## 182.

It will be necessary to preface the discussion concerning the degree of accuracy to be assigned to the values of the unknown quantities, when there are several, with a more careful consideration of the function $vv + v'v' + v''v'' +$ etc., which we will denote by $W$.

I. Let us put

$$\tfrac{1}{2}\frac{d W}{d p} = p' = \lambda + \alpha p + \beta q + \gamma r + \delta s + \text{etc.},$$

also

$$W - \frac{p'p'}{\alpha} = W',$$

and it is evident that we have $p' = P$, and, since

$$\frac{d W'}{d p} = \frac{d W}{d p} - \frac{2 p'}{\alpha}\frac{d p'}{d p} = 0,$$

that the function $W'$ is independent of $p$.   The coefficient $\alpha = aa + a'a' + a''a'' +$ etc. will evidently always be a positive quantity.

II. In the same manner we will put

$$\tfrac{1}{2}\frac{d W'}{d q} = q' = \lambda' + \beta' q + \gamma' r + \delta' s + \text{etc.},$$

also

$$W' - \frac{q'q'}{\beta'} = W'',$$

and we shall have

$$q' = \tfrac{1}{2}\frac{d W}{d q} - \frac{p'}{\alpha}\frac{d p'}{d q} = Q - \frac{\beta}{\alpha}p', \text{ and } \frac{d W''}{d q} = 0,$$

whence it is evident that the function $W''$ is independent both of $p$ and $q$. This would not be so if $\beta'$ could become equal to zero.   But it is evident that $W'$ is derived from $vv + v'v' + v''v'' +$ etc., the quantity $p$ being eliminated from $v, v', v''$, etc., by means of the equation $p' = 0$; hence, $\beta'$ will be the sum of the coefficients of $qq$ in $vv, v'v', v''v''$, etc., after the elimination; each of these coefficients, in fact, is a square, nor can all vanish at once, except in the case excluded above, in which the unknown quantities remain indeterminate.   Thus it is evident that $\beta'$ must be a positive quantity.

III. By putting again,

$$\tfrac{1}{2}\frac{\mathrm{d}\,W''}{\mathrm{d}\,r}=r'=\lambda''+\gamma''r+\delta''s+\text{etc., and } W''-\frac{r'r'}{\gamma''}=W''',$$

we shall have

$$r'=R-\frac{\gamma}{\alpha}\,p'-\frac{\gamma'}{\beta'}\,q',$$

also $W'''$ independent of $p$, and $q$, as well as $r$. Finally, that the coefficient of $\gamma''$ must be positive is proved in the same manner as in II. In fact, it is readily perceived, that $\gamma''$ is the sum of the coefficients of $rr$ in $vv$, $v'v'$, $v''v''$, etc., after the quantities $p$ and $q$ have been eliminated from $v$, $v'$, $v''$, etc., by means of the equations $p'=0$, $q'=0$.

IV. In the same way, by putting

$$\tfrac{1}{2}\frac{\mathrm{d}\,W'''}{\mathrm{d}\,s}=s'=\lambda'''+\delta'''s+\text{etc.,}\quad W^{\mathrm{iv}}=W'''-\frac{s's'}{\delta'''},$$

we shall have

$$s'=S-\frac{\delta}{\alpha}p'-\frac{\delta'}{\beta'}q'-\frac{\delta''}{\gamma''}r',$$

$W^{\mathrm{iv}}$ independent of $p$, $q$, $r$, $s$, and $\delta'''$ a positive quantity.

V. In this manner, if besides $p$, $q$, $r$, $s$, there are still other unknown quantities, we can proceed further, so that at length we may have

$$W=\frac{1}{\alpha}\,p'p'+\frac{1}{\beta'}\,q'q'+\frac{1}{\gamma''}\,r'r'+\frac{1}{\delta'''}\,s's'+\text{etc.}+\text{Constant,}$$

in which all the coefficients will be positive quantities.

VI. Now the probability of any system of determinate values for the quantities $p$, $q$, $r$, $s$, etc. is proportional to the function $e^{-hhW}$; wherefore, the value of the quantity $p$ remaining indeterminate, the probability of a system of determinate values for the rest, will be proportional to the integral

$$\int e^{-hhW}\,\mathrm{d}p$$

extended from $p=-\infty$ to $p=+\infty$, which, by the theorem of LAPLACE, becomes

$$h^{-1}\alpha^{-\frac{1}{2}}\pi^{\frac{1}{2}}e^{-hh\left(\frac{1}{\beta'}\,q'q'+\frac{1}{\gamma''}\,rr+\frac{1}{\delta'''}\,s's'+\text{etc.}\right)};$$

therefore, this probability will be proportional to the function $e^{-hhW'}$. In the same manner, if, in addition, $q$ is treated as indeterminate, the probability of a system of determinate values for $r$, $s$, etc. will be proportional to the integral

$$\int e^{-hhW'}\, d\,q,$$

extended from $q=-\infty$ up to $q=+\infty$, which is

$$h^{-1}\beta'-\tfrac{1}{2}\pi^{\frac{1}{2}}e^{-hh\left(\frac{1}{\gamma''}rr+\frac{1}{\delta'''}s's'+\text{etc.}\right)};$$

or proportional to the function $e^{-hhW''}$. Precisely in the same way, if $r$ also is considered as indeterminate, the probability of the determinate values for the rest, $s$, etc. will be proportional to the function $e^{-hhW'''}$, and so on. Let us suppose the number of the unknown quantities to amount to four, for the same conclusion will hold good, whether it is greater or less. The most probable value of $s$ will be $-\frac{\lambda'''}{\delta'''}$, and the probability that this will differ from the truth by the quantity $\sigma$, will be proportional to the function $e^{-hh'''\sigma\sigma}$; whence we conclude that the measure of the relative precision to be attributed to that determination is expressed by $\sqrt{\delta'''}$, provided the measure of precision to be assigned to the original observations is put equal to unity.

## 183.

By the method of the preceding article the measure of precision is conveniently expressed for that unknown quantity only, to which the last place has been assigned in the work of elimination; in order to avoid which disadvantage, it will be desirable to express the coefficient $\delta'''$ in another manner. From the equations

$$P=p'$$

$$Q=q'+\frac{\beta}{\alpha}p'$$

$$R=r'+\frac{\gamma'}{\beta'}q'+\frac{\gamma}{\alpha}p'$$

$$S=s'+\frac{\delta''}{\gamma''}r''+\frac{\delta'}{\beta'}q'+\frac{\delta}{\alpha}p',$$

it follows, that $p'$, $q'$, $r'$, $s'$, can be thus expressed by means of $P$, $Q$, $R$, $S$,

$$p'=P$$

$$q'=Q+\mathfrak{A}P$$

$$r' = R + \mathfrak{B}'Q + \mathfrak{A}'P$$
$$s' = S + \mathfrak{C}''R + \mathfrak{B}''Q + \mathfrak{A}''P,$$

so that $\mathfrak{A}$, $\mathfrak{A}'$, $\mathfrak{B}'$, $\mathfrak{A}''$, $\mathfrak{B}''$, $\mathfrak{C}''$ may be determinate quantities. We shall have, therefore (by restricting the number of unknown quantities to four),

$$s = -\frac{\lambda'''}{\delta'''} + \frac{\mathfrak{A}''}{\delta'''}P + \frac{\mathfrak{B}''}{\delta'''}Q + \frac{\mathfrak{C}''}{\delta'''}R + \frac{1}{\delta'''}S.$$

Hence we deduce the following conclusion. The most probable values of the unknown quantities $p, q, r, s$, etc., to be derived by elimination from the equations

$$P = 0, \ \ Q = 0, \ R = 0, \ S = 0, \text{ etc.},$$

will, if $P$, $Q$, $R$, $S$, etc., are regarded for the time as indeterminate, be expressed in a linear form by the same process of elimination by means of $P$, $Q$, $R$, $S$, etc., so that we may have

$$p = L + AP + BQ + CR + DS + \text{ etc.}$$
$$q = L' + A'P + B'Q + C'R + D'S + \text{ etc.}$$
$$r = L'' + A''P + B''Q + C''R + D''S + \text{ etc.}$$
$$s = L''' + A'''P + B'''Q + C'''R + D'''S + \text{ etc.}$$
$$\text{etc.}$$

This being done, the most probable values of $p, q, r, s$, etc., will evidently be $L, L', L'', L'''$, etc., respectively, and the measure of precision to be assigned to these determinations respectively will be expressed by

$$\frac{1}{\sqrt{A}}, \ \frac{1}{\sqrt{B'}}, \ \frac{1}{\sqrt{C''}}, \ \frac{1}{\sqrt{D'''}}, \text{ etc.},$$

the precision of the original observations being put equal to unity. That which we have before demonstrated concerning the determination of the unknown quantity $s$ (for which $\frac{1}{\delta'''}$ answers to $D'''$) can be applied to all the others by the simple interchange of the unknown quantities.

## 184.

In order to illustrate the preceding investigations by an example, let us suppose that, by means of observations in which equal accuracy may be assumed, we have found

$$p - q + 2r = 3$$
$$3p + 2q - 5r = 5$$
$$4p + q + 4r = 21,$$

but from a fourth observation, to which is to be assigned one half the same accuracy only, there results

$$-2p + 6q + 6r = 28.$$

We will substitute in place of the last equation the following : —

$$-p + 3q + 3r = 14,$$

and we will suppose this to have resulted from an observation possessing equal accuracy with the former.   Hence we have

$$P = 27p + 6q \qquad - 88$$
$$Q = 6p + 15q + r \quad - 70$$
$$R = \qquad q + 54r - 107,$$

and hence by elimination,

$$19899\,p = 49154 + 809\,P - 324\,Q + 6\,R$$
$$737\,q = 2617 - 12\,P + 54\,Q - R$$
$$6633\,r = 12707 + 2\,P - 9\,Q + 123\,R.$$

The most probable values of the unknown quantities, therefore, will be

$$p = 2.470$$
$$q = 3.551$$
$$r = 1.916$$

and the relative precision to be assigned to these determinations, the precision of the original observations being put equal to unity, will be

$$\text{for } p \ldots \ldots \sqrt{\tfrac{19899}{809}} = 4.96$$

$$\text{for } q \ldots \ldots \sqrt{\tfrac{737}{54}} = 3.69$$

$$\text{for } r \ldots \ldots \sqrt{\tfrac{2211}{41}} = 7.34.$$

## 185.

The subject we have just treated might give rise to several elegant analytical investigations, upon which, however, we will not dwell, that we may not be too much diverted from our object. For the same reason we must reserve for another occasion the explanation of the devices by means of which the numerical calculation can be rendered more expeditious. I will add only a single remark. When the number of the proposed functions or equations is considerable, the computation becomes a little more troublesome, on this account chiefly, that the coefficients, by which the original equations are to be multiplied in order to obtain $P$, $Q$, $R$, $S$, etc., often involve inconvenient decimal fractions. If in such a case it does not seem worth while to perform these multiplications in the most accurate manner by means of logarithmic tables, it will generally be sufficient to employ in place of these multipliers others more convenient for calculation, and differing but little from them. This change can produce sensible errors in that case only in which the measure of precision in the determination of the unknown quantities proves to be much less than the precision of the original observations.

## 186.

In conclusion, the principle that the sum of the squares of the differences between the observed and computed quantities must be a minimum may, in the following manner, be considered independently of the calculus of probabilities.

When the number of unknown quantities is equal to the number of the observed quantities depending on them, the former may be so determined as exactly to satisfy the latter. But when the number of the former is less than that of the latter, an absolutely exact agreement cannot be obtained, unless the observations possess absolute accuracy. In this case care must be taken to establish the best possible agreement, or to diminish as far as practicable the differences. This idea, however, from its nature, involves something vague. For, although a system of values for the unknown quantities which makes *all* the differences respectively less than another system, is without doubt to be preferred to the latter, still the choice between two systems, one of which presents a better agreement in some observations, the other in others, is left in a measure to our judgment, and innumerable different principles can be proposed by which the former condition is satisfied.    Denoting the differences between observation and calculation by $\Delta$, $\Delta'$, $\Delta''$, etc., the first condition will be satisfied not only if $\Delta\Delta + \Delta'\Delta' + \Delta''\Delta'' +$ etc., is a minimum (which is our principle), but also if $\Delta^4 + \Delta'^4 + \Delta''^4 +$ etc., or $\Delta^6 + \Delta'^6 + \Delta''^6 +$ etc., or in general, if the sum of any of the powers with an even exponent becomes a minimum. But of all these principles ours is the most simple; by the others we should be led into the most complicated calculations.

Our principle, which we have made use of since the year 1795, has lately been published by LEGENDRE in the work *Nouvelles methodes pour la determination des orbites des cometes, Paris*, 1806, where several other properties of this principle have been explained, which, for the sake of brevity, we here omit.

If we were to adopt a power with an infinite even exponent, we should be led to that system in which the greatest differences become less than in any other system.

LAPLACE made use of another principle for the solution of linear equations the number of which is greater than the number of the unknown quantities, which had been previously proposed by BOSCOVICH, namely, that the sum of the errors themselves taken positively, be made a minimum.    It can be easily shown, that a system of values of unknown quantities, derived from this principle alone, must necessarily* exactly satisfy as many equations out of the number proposed, as there are unknown quantities, so that the remaining equations come under consideration only so far as they help to *determine the choice :* if, therefore, the equation $V = M$, for example, is of the number of those which are not satisfied, the system of values found according to this principle would in no respect be changed, even if any other value $N$ had been observed instead of $M$, provided that, denoting the computed value by $n$, the differences $M - n$, $N - n$, were affected by the same signs.    Besides, LAPLACE qualifies in some measure this principle by adding

---

* Except the special cases in which the problem remains, to some extent, indeterminate.

a new condition: he requires, namely, that the sum of the differences, the signs remaining unchanged, be equal to zero.   Hence it follows, that the number of equations exactly represented may be less by unity than the number of unknown quantities; but what we have before said will still hold good if there are only two unknown quantities.

## 187.

From these general discussions we return to our special subject for the sake of which they were undertaken.   Before the most accurate determination of the orbit from more observations than are absolutely requisite can be commenced, there should be an approximate determination which will nearly satisfy all the given observations.   The corrections to be applied to these approximate elements, in order to obtain the most exact agreement, will be regarded as the objects of the problem.   And when it can be assumed that these are so small that their squares and products may be neglected, the corresponding changes, produced in the computed geocentric places of a heavenly body, can be obtained by means of the differential formulas given in the Second Section of the First Book.   The computed places, therefore, which we obtain from the corrected elements, will be expressed by linear functions of the corrections of the elements, and their comparison with the observed places according to the principles before explained, will lead to the determination of the most probable values.   These processes are so simple that they require no further illustration, and it appears at once that any number of observations, however remote from each other, can be employed.   The same method may also be used in the correction of the *parabolic* orbits of comets, should we have a long series of observations and the best agreement be required.

## 188.

The preceding method is adapted principally to those cases in which the greatest accuracy is desired: but cases very frequently occur where we may, without hesitation, depart from it a little, provided that by so doing the calculation is considerably abridged, especially when the observations do not embrace a great interval of time; here the final determination of the orbit is not yet proposed. In such cases the following method may be employed with great advantage.

Let complete places $L$ and $L'$ be selected from the whole number of observations, and let the distances of the heavenly body from the earth be computed from the approximate elements for the corresponding times. Let three hypotheses then be framed with respect to these distances, the computed values being retained in the first, the first distance being changed in the second hypothesis, and the second in the third hypothesis; these changes can be made in proportion to the uncertainty presumed to remain in the distances. According to these three hypotheses, which we present in the following table,

|  | Hyp. I. | Hyp. II. | Hyp. III. |
|---|---|---|---|
| Distance * corresponding to the first place, | $D$ | $D + \delta$ | $D$ |
| Distance corresponding to the second place, | $D'$ | $D'$ | $D' + \delta$ |

let three sets of elements be computed from the two places $L$, $L'$, by the methods explained in the first book, and afterwards from each one of these sets the geocentric places of the heavenly body corresponding to the times of all the remaining observations. Let these be (the several longitudes and latitudes, or right ascensions and declinations, being denoted separately),

in the first set . . . . $M,$    $M',$    $M'',$    etc.
in the second set . . . $M + \alpha,$ $M' + \alpha',$ $M'' + \alpha'',$ etc.
in the third set . . . . $M + \beta,$ $M' + \beta',$ $M'' + \beta'',$ etc.

Let, moreover, the observed
places be respectively . . . . . $N,$    $N',$    $N'',$    etc.

Now, so far as proportional variations of the individual elements correspond

---

* It will be still more convenient to use, instead of the distances themselves, the logarithms of the curtate distances.

to small variations of the distances $D$, $D'$, as well as of the geocentric places computed from them, we can assume, that the geocentric places computed from the fourth system of elements, based on the distances from the earth $D + x\delta$. $D' + y\delta'$, are respectively $M + \alpha x + \beta y$, $M' + \alpha' x + \beta' y$, $M'' + \alpha'' x + \beta'' y$, etc. Hence, $x$, $y$, will be determined, according to the preceding discussions, in such a manner (the relative accuracy of the observations being taken into account), that these quantities may as far as possible agree with $N$, $N'$, $N''$, etc., respectively. The corrected system of elements can be derived either from $L$, $L'$ and the distances $D + x\delta$, $D' + x\delta'$, or, according to well-known rules, from the three first systems of elements by simple interpolation.

## 189.

This method differs from the preceding in this respect only, that it satisfies two geocentric places exactly, and then the remaining places as nearly as possible; while according to the other method no one observation has the preference over the rest, but the errors, as far as it can be done, are distributed among all. The method of the preceding article, therefore, is only not to be preferred to the former when, allowing some part of the errors to the places $L$, $L'$, it is possible to diminish considerably the errors in the remaining places: but yet it is generally easy, by a suitable choice of the observations $L$, $L'$, to provide that this difference cannot become very important. It will be necessary, of course, to take care that such observations are selected for $L$, $L'$, as not only possess the greatest accuracy, but also such that the elements derived from them and the distances are not too much affected by small variations in the geocentric places. It will not, therefore, be judicious to select observations distant from each other by a small interval of time, or those to which correspond nearly opposite or coincident heliocentric places.

# FOURTH SECTION.

## ON THE DETERMINATION OF ORBITS, TAKING INTO ACCOUNT THE PERTURBATIONS.

---

## 190.

THE perturbations which the motions of planets suffer from the influence of other planets, are so small and so slow that they only become sensible after a long interval of time; within a shorter time, or even within one or several entire revolutions, according to circumstances, the motion would differ so little from the motion exactly described, according to the laws of KEPLER, in a perfect ellipse, that observations cannot show the difference. As long as this is true, it would not be worth while to undertake prematurely the computation of the perturbations, but it will be sufficient to adapt to the observations what we may call an osculating conic section: but, afterwards, when the planet has been accurately observed for a longer time, the effect of the perturbations will show itself in such a manner, that it will no longer be possible to satisfy exactly all the observations by a purely elliptic motion; then, accordingly, a complete and permanent agreement cannot be obtained, unless the perturbations are properly connected with the elliptic motion.

Since the determination of the elliptic elements with which, in order that the observations may be exactly represented, the perturbations are to be combined, supposes a knowledge of the latter; so, inversely, the theory of the perturbations cannot be accurately settled unless the elements are already very nearly known: the nature of the case does not admit of this difficult task being accomplished with complete success at the first trial: but the perturbations and the elements can be brought to the highest degree of perfection only by alternate corrections

(274)

often repeated. Accordingly, the first theory of perturbations will be constructed upon those purely elliptical elements which have been approximately adjusted to the observations; a new orbit will afterwards be investigated, which, with the addition of these perturbations, may satisfy, as far as practicable, the observations. If this orbit differs considerably from the former, a second determination of the perturbations will be based upon it, and the corrections will be repeated alternately, until observations, elements, and perturbations agree as nearly as possible.

## 191.

Since the development of the theory of perturbations from given elements is foreign to our purpose, we will only point out here how an approximate orbit can be so corrected, that, joined with given perturbations, it may satisfy, in the best manner, the observations. This is accomplished in the most simple way by a method analogous to those which we have explained in articles 124, 165, 188. The numerical values of the perturbations will be computed from the equations, for the longitudes in orbit, for the radii vectores, and also for the heliocentric latitudes, for the times of all the observations which it is proposed to use, and which can either be three, or four, or more, according to circumstances: for this calculation the materials will be taken from the approximate elliptic elements upon which the theory of perturbations has been constructed. Then two will be selected from all the observations, for which the distances from the earth will be computed from the same approximate elements: these will constitute the first hypothesis, the second and third will be formed by changing these distances a little. After this, in each of the hypotheses, the heliocentric places and the distances from the sun will be determined from two geocentric places; from those, after the latitudes have been freed from the perturbations, will be deduced the longitude of the ascending node, the inclination of the orbit, and the longitudes in orbit. The method of article 110 with some modification is useful in this calculation, if it is thought worth while to take account of the secular variation of the longitude of the node and of the inclination. If $\beta$, $\beta'$, denote the heliocentric latitudes freed from the periodical perturbations; $\lambda$, $\lambda'$, the heliocentric longitudes; $\Omega$, $\Omega + \mathit{\Delta}$, the longitudes of the ascending node; $i, i + \delta$, the inclinations of the orbit; the equations can be conveniently given in the following form : —

$$\tan \beta = \tan i \sin (\lambda - \Omega),$$

$$\frac{\tan i}{\tan (i + \delta)} \tan \beta' = \tan i \sin (\lambda' - \mathit{\Delta} - \Omega).$$

This value of $\frac{\tan i}{\tan (i + \delta)}$ acquires all the requisite accuracy by substituting an approximate value for $i$: $i$ and $\Omega$ can afterwards be deduced by the common methods.

Moreover, the sum of the perturbations will be subtracted from the longitudes in orbit, and also from the two radii vectores, in order to produce purely elliptical values. But here also the effect, which the secular variations of the place of the perihelion and of the eccentricity exert upon the longitude in orbit and radius vector, and which is to be determined by the differential formulas of Section I. of the First Book, is to be combined directly with the periodical perturbations, provided the observations are sufficiently distant from each other to make it appear worth while to take account of it. The remaining elements will be determined from these longitudes in orbit and corrected radii vectores together with the corresponding times. Finally, from these elements will be computed the geocentric places for all the other observations. These being compared with the observed places, in the manner we have explained in article 188, that set of distances will be deduced, from which will follow the elements satisfying in the best possible manner all the remaining observations.

## 192.

The method explained in the preceding article has been principally adapted to the determination of the *first* orbit, including the perturbations: but as soon as the mean elliptic elements, and the equations of the perturbations have both become very nearly known, the most accurate determination will be very conveniently made with the aid of as many observations as possible by the method of article 187, which will not require particular explanation in this place. Now if the number of the best observations is sufficiently great, and a great interval of time is embraced, this method can also be made to answer in several cases for the more precise determination of the masses of the disturbing planets, at least of the larger planets. Indeed, if the mass of any disturbing planet assumed in the calculation of the perturbations does not seem sufficiently determined, besides the six unknown quantities depending on the corrections of the elements, yet another, $\mu$, will be introduced, putting the ratio of the correct mass to the assumed one as $1 + \mu$ to $1$; it will then be admissible to suppose the perturbations themselves to be changed in the same ratio, whence, evidently, in each one of the computed places a new linear term, containing $\mu$, will be produced, the development of which will be subject to no difficulty. The comparison of the computed places with the observed according to the principles above explained, will furnish, at the same time with the corrections of the elements, also the correction $\mu$. The masses of *several* planets even, which exert very considerable perturbations, can be more exactly determined in this manner. There is no doubt but that the motions of the new planets, especially Pallas and Juno, which suffer such great perturbations from Jupiter, may furnish in this manner after some decades of years, a most accurate determination of the mass of Jupiter; it may even be possible perhaps, hereafter, to ascertain, from the perturbations which it exerts upon the others, the mass of some one of these new planets.

# APPENDIX.

---

## 1.*

THE value of $t$ adopted in the Solar Tables of HANSEN and OLUFSEN, (Copenhagen, 1853,) is 365.2563582. Using this and the value of $\mu$,

$$\mu = \frac{1}{354936},$$

from the last edition of LAPLACE's *Système du Monde*, the computation of $k$ is

| | |
|---|---|
| log $2\pi$ . . . . . . . . | 0.7981798684 |
| Compl. log $t$ . . . . . . | 7.4374022154 |
| Compl. log $\sqrt{(1+\mu)}$ . . . | 9.9999993882 |
| log $k$ . . . . . . . . | 8.2355814720 |
| $k =$ . . . . . . . | 0.01720210016. |

## 11.

The following method of solving the equation

$$M = E - e \sin E,$$

is recommended by ENCKE, *Berliner Astronomisches Jahrbuch*, 1838.

Take any approximate value of $E$, as $\varepsilon$, and compute

$$M' = \varepsilon - e'' \sin \varepsilon,$$

---

* The numbering of the Notes of the Appendix designates the articles of the original work to which they pertain.

$e''$ being used to denote $e$ expressed in seconds, then we have

$$dM = dE\,(1 - e \cos E),$$

or

$$M - M' = E - \varepsilon - e''\,(\sin E - \sin \varepsilon)$$
$$= (E - \varepsilon)\,(1 - e \cos \varepsilon),$$

if $E - \varepsilon$ is regarded as a small quantity of the first order, and quantities of the second order are neglected for the present : — so that the correction of $\varepsilon$ is

$$x = \frac{M - M'}{1 - e \cos \varepsilon},$$

and a new approximate value of $\varepsilon$ is

$$\varepsilon + \frac{M - M'}{1 - e \cos \varepsilon},$$

with which we may proceed in the same manner until the true value is obtained. It is almost always unnecessary to repeat the calculation of $1 - e \cos \varepsilon$. Generally, if the first $\varepsilon$ is not too far from the truth, the first computed value of $1 - e \cos \varepsilon$ may be retained in all the trials.

This process is identical with that of article 11, for $\lambda$ is nothing more than

$$\lambda = \frac{d \log \sin E}{d E} = \frac{\cos E}{\sin E},$$

if we neglect the modulus of BRIGGS's system of logarithms, which would subsequently disappear of itself, and

$$\mu = \frac{d \log (e'' \sin E)}{d\,(e'' \sin E)} = \frac{1}{e \sin E},$$

therefore,

$$\frac{\mu}{\mu - \lambda} = \frac{1}{1 - e \cos E},$$

and

$$x = \frac{\mu}{\mu \mp \lambda}\,(M + e'' \sin \varepsilon - \varepsilon) = (M - M')\,\frac{\mu}{\mu \mp \lambda} = \frac{M - M'}{1 - e \cos E'},$$

and the double sign is to be used in such a way that $\lambda$ shall always have the same sign as $\cos E$. In the first approximations when the value of $\varepsilon$ differs so much from $E$ that the differences of the logarithms are uncertain, the method of this note will be found most convenient. But when it is desired to insure perfect agreement to the last decimal place, that of article 11 may be used with advantage.

As an illustration, take the data of the example in article 13.

Assume $\varepsilon = 326°$, and we find

| | | | |
|---|---|---|---|
| $\log \sin \varepsilon$ | $9.74756\,n$ | $\log \cos \varepsilon$ | $9.91857$ |
| $\log e''$ | $4.70415$ | $\log e$ | $9.38973$ |
| $\log e'' \sin \varepsilon$ | $4.45171\,n$ | $\log e \cos \varepsilon$ | $9.30830$ |

$$e'' \sin \varepsilon = -28295'' = -7° 51' 35'' \qquad 1 - e \cos \varepsilon = .79662$$

$$M' = \varepsilon - e'' \sin \varepsilon = 333° 51' 35'' \qquad \log(1 - e \cos \varepsilon) \quad 9.90125$$

$$M - M' = -4960'' \qquad\qquad \log M - M' \qquad 3.69548\,n$$

$$\frac{M - M'}{1 - e \cos \varepsilon} = -6226'' \qquad\qquad \log \frac{M - M'}{1 - e \cos \varepsilon} \qquad 3.79423\,n$$

$$= -1° 43' 46''.$$

And for a second approximation,

$$\varepsilon = 326° - 1° 43' 46'' = 324° 16' 14''$$

| | |
|---|---|
| $\log \sin \varepsilon$ | $9.7663820\,n$ |
| $\log e''$ | $4.7041513$ |
| $\log e'' \sin \varepsilon$ | $4.4705333\,n$ |

$$e'' \sin \varepsilon = -29548''.36 = -8° 12' 28''.36$$

$$M' = 332° 28' 42''.36 \qquad \log(1 - e \cos \varepsilon) \quad 9.90356$$

$$M - M' = +12''.41 \qquad\qquad \log(M - M') \qquad 1.09377$$

$$\frac{M - M'}{1 - e \cos \varepsilon} = +15''.50 \qquad\qquad \log \frac{M - M'}{1 - e \cos \varepsilon} \qquad 1.19021$$

which gives

$$E = 324° 16' 14'' + 15''.50 = 324° 16' 29''.50.$$

## 18.

Putting

$$q = \tfrac{1}{2} p = \text{perihelion distance,}$$

$$\varkappa = k \sqrt{\tfrac{1}{2}},$$

$$\log \varkappa = 8.0850664436,$$

$$\tau = t \sqrt{\frac{1 + \mu}{q^3}},$$

we have

$$\tan \tfrac{1}{2} v + \tfrac{1}{3} \tan^3 \tfrac{1}{2} v = \varkappa \tau,$$

$$\tau = \frac{1}{3 \varkappa} (3 \tan \tfrac{1}{2} v + \tan^3 \tfrac{1}{2} v);$$

a table may be computed from this formula, giving $v$ for values of $\tau$ as the argument, which will readily furnish the true anomaly corresponding to any time from the perihelion passage. Table II$a$ is such a table. It is taken from the first volume of *Annales de l' Observatoire Impériale de Paris*, (Paris, 1855,) and differs from that given in DELAMBRE's Astronomy, (Paris, 1814,) Vol. III., only in the intervals of the argument, the coefficients for interpolation, and the value of $k$ with which it was computed.

The true anomaly corresponding to any value of the argument is found by the formula

$$v = v_0 + A_1\,(\tau - \tau_0) + A_2\,(\tau - \tau_0)^2 + (\tau - \tau_0)^3\,A_3 + A_4\,(\tau - \tau_0)^4.$$

The signs of $A_1$, $A_2$, $A_3$, are placed before the logarithms of these quantities in the table.

BURCKHARDT's table, BOWDITCH's Appendix to the third volume of the *Mecanique Celeste*, is similar, except that $\log \tau$ is the argument instead of $\tau$.

Table II$a$ contains the true anomaly corresponding to the time from perihelion passage in a parabola, the perihelion distance of which is equal to the earth's mean distance from the sun, and the mass $\mu$ equal to zero. For if we put $q = 1$, $\mu = 0$, we have $\tau = t$.

By substituting the value of $\varkappa$ in the equation

$$\tau = \frac{1}{3\,\varkappa}\,(3 \tan \tfrac{1}{2} v + \tan^3 \tfrac{1}{2} v)$$

it becomes

$$\tau = 27.40389544\,(3 \tan \tfrac{1}{2} v + \tan^3 \tfrac{1}{2} v)$$
$$= 1.096155816\,(75 \tan \tfrac{1}{2} v + 25 \tan^3 \tfrac{1}{2} v;$$

and therefore, if we put $\varkappa' = 0.912279061$,

$$75 \tan \tfrac{1}{2} v + 25 \tan^3 \tfrac{1}{2} v = \varkappa' \tau$$
$$\log \varkappa' = 9.9601277069$$

BARKER's Table, explained in article 19, contains $\varkappa' \tau$ for the argument $v$. The *Mean daily motion* or the quantity $M$, therefore, of BARKER's Table may be obtained from table II$a$, for any value of $v$, by multiplying the corresponding value of $\tau$ by $\varkappa'$.

The following examples will serve to illustrate the use of the table.

Given, the perihelion distance $q = 0.1$; the time after perihelion passage $t = 6^d.590997$, to find the true anomaly.

Assuming $\mu = 0$, we find

$$\tau = 208.42561$$
$$\tau_0 = 200.$$
$$\tau - \tau_0 = \phantom{0}8.42561$$
$$v_0 = 110° \, 24' \, 46''.69$$
$$A_1 (\tau - \tau_0) = + 1° \, 14' \, 42''.42$$
$$A_2 (\tau - \tau_0)^2 = - \phantom{00}2' \, 20''.19$$
$$A_3 (\tau - \tau_0)^3 = + \phantom{0000000}4''.76$$
$$A_4 (\tau - \tau_0)^4 = - \phantom{0000000}0''.16$$
$$v = \overline{111° \, 37' \, 13''.52}$$

or

$$\tau = 208.42561$$
$$\tau_0 = 210.$$
$$\tau - \tau_0 = -1.57439$$
$$v_0 = 111° \, 50' \, 16''.87$$
$$A_1 (\tau - \tau_0) = - \phantom{0}12' \, 58''.96$$
$$A_2 (\tau - \tau_0)^2 = - \phantom{0000000}4''.35$$
$$A_3 (\tau - \tau_0)^3 = - \phantom{0000000}0''.03$$
$$A_4 (\tau - \tau_0)^4 = - \phantom{0000000}0''.00$$
$$v = \overline{111° \, 37' \, 13''.53}$$

The latter form of calculation is to be preferred because the value of $\tau - \tau_0$ is smaller, and therefore the terms depending on $(\tau - \tau_0)$, $(\tau - \tau_0)^2$, $(\tau - \tau_0)^3$, are smaller, and that depending on $(\tau - \tau_0)^4$ is insensible; and it is the only form of which all the appreciable terms are to be found in the table.

Beyond $\tau = 40000$, the limit of the table, we can use the formula,

$$v = 180° - [6.0947259] \left(\frac{1}{\tau}\right)^{\frac{1}{3}} - [6.87718] \left(\frac{1}{\tau}\right) - [7.313] \left(\frac{1}{\tau}\right)^{\frac{5}{3}}, \text{ etc.,}$$

in which the coefficients expressed in arc are given by their logarithms.

For $\tau = 40000$, for example, we have

$$v = 180° - 10° \, 6' \, 6''.87 - 3' \, 8''.41 - 0''.44$$
$$= 169° \, 50' \, 44''.28.$$

If $v$ is given, and it is required to find $\tau$, we have

$$\tau - \tau_0 = \frac{v - v_0}{A_1} - \frac{A_2}{A_1} (\tau - \tau_0)^2 - \frac{A_3}{A_1} (\tau - \tau_0)^3.$$

For a first approximation the terms depending on the square and third power of $\tau - \tau_0$ may be neglected, and the value of $\tau - \tau_0$ thus found can be corrected so as to exactly satisfy the equation.

If $v$ exceeds 169°, the formula

$$\tau = [1.9149336] \tan \tfrac{1}{2} v + [1.4378123] \tan^3 \tfrac{1}{2} v$$

may be used instead of the table.

Thus, for $v = 169° \, 50' \, 44''.28$,

|  | $\log \tan \tfrac{1}{2} v$ . . | 1.0513610 |
|---|---|---|
|  |  | 1.9149336 |
| 925.33 |  | 2.9662946 |
|  | $\log \tan^3 \tfrac{1}{2} v$ . . | 3.1540830 |
|  |  | 1.4378123 |
| 39074.67 |  | 4.5918953 |
| $\tau = 40000.00$ |  |  |

This method will often be found more convenient than the table, even where $v$ is less than 169°.

## 35.

Table V$a$ contains BESSEL'S table here referred to, in a slightly modified form; and also a similar table by POSSELT, for the coefficients $v'$ and $v''$ in the formula of article 34,

$$w = v + \delta v' + \delta\delta v'' + \delta^3 v''' + \text{etc.},$$

it is taken from ENCKE'S edition of OLBERS *Abhandlung über die leichteste und bequemste Methode die Bahn eines Cometen zu berechnen* (Weimar, 1847). The following explanation of its construction and use is taken from the same work, with such changes as are needed to adapt it to the notation of the preceding articles: —

If we put

$$\vartheta = \tan \tfrac{1}{2} w$$
$$\tau = \tan \tfrac{1}{2} v$$

the formulas of article 34 become

$$w = v + \frac{\frac{1}{2}\tau - \frac{1}{2}\tau^3 - \frac{2}{5}\tau^5}{(1+\tau^2)^2}\delta$$

$$+ \frac{\frac{3}{16}\tau - \frac{5}{16}\tau^3 - \frac{3}{16}\tau^5 - \frac{41}{560}\tau^7 + \frac{1}{35}\tau^9 + \frac{19}{350}\tau^{11}}{(1+\tau^2)^4}\delta^2$$

$$v = w + \frac{-\frac{1}{2}\vartheta + \frac{1}{2}\vartheta^3 + \frac{2}{5}\vartheta^5}{(1+\vartheta^2)^2}\delta$$

$$+ \frac{-\frac{1}{16}\vartheta - \frac{9}{16}\vartheta^3 + \frac{37}{80}\vartheta^5 + \frac{531}{560}\vartheta^7 + \frac{13}{35}\vartheta^9 + \frac{9}{350}\vartheta^{11}}{(1+\vartheta^2)^4}\delta^2$$

The second equation, in which $v$ is expressed in terms of $w$, is that given by BESSEL, *Monatliche Correspondenz*, Vol. XII., p. 197. He also gives the third coefficient of the series, but has computed a table of only the first two. POSSELT, in the *Zeitschrift für Astronomie und verwandte Wissenschaften*, Vol. V., p. 161, has given the first equation; he has also given three coefficients of the series, but a table of the second only, since BESSEL's table will give the first coefficient simply by changing the sign. POSSELT has changed the sign of the second coefficient also.

Instead of the logarithms as given in the tables of BESSEL and POSSELT, the corresponding numbers are given in table $Va$, and to avoid large numbers, 0.01 is taken as the unit of $\delta$.

Putting

$$\tan \tfrac{1}{2}x = \xi$$

the table contains

$$A = \frac{-\frac{1}{2}\xi + \frac{1}{2}\xi^3 + \frac{2}{5}\xi^5}{100\,(1+\xi^2)^2}\,206265$$

$$B = \frac{-\frac{1}{16}\xi - \frac{9}{16}\xi^3 + \frac{37}{80}\xi^5 + \frac{531}{560}\xi^7 + \frac{13}{35}\xi^9 + \frac{9}{350}\xi^{11}}{10000\,(1+\xi^2)^4}\,206265$$

$$B' = \frac{-\frac{3}{16}\xi + \frac{5}{16}\xi^3 + \frac{3}{16}\xi^5 + \frac{41}{560}\xi^7 - \frac{1}{35}\xi^9 - \frac{19}{350}\xi^{11}}{10000\,(1+\xi^2)^4}\,206265$$

So that when $x = w$ we have

$$v = w + A\,(100\,\delta) + B\,(100\,\delta)^2$$

And when $x = v$,

$$w = v - A\,(100\,\delta) - B'\,(100\,\delta)^2$$

It seems unnecessary to recompute the table in order to be certain of the accuracy of the last place, or to extend it further, as its use is limited. For absolute values of $\delta$ greater than 0.03, and for values of $x$ considerably greater than 90°, the terms here given would not be sufficient. In such cases the method of 37 and the following articles should be used.

*Example.* — For HALLEY'S comet,

$$\log \delta = 8.5099324, \text{ and } t = 63^d.43592, \text{ we have}$$

by table II*a*, $\qquad\qquad\qquad\qquad\qquad\qquad w = 99° \; 36' \; 55''.91$

and by table V*a*, $\quad A = + 417.45 \qquad$ 1st cor. $\qquad + 22' \; 30''.63$

$\qquad\qquad B = + \quad 3.111 \qquad$ 2d cor. $\qquad + \qquad 32''.57$

$$v = 99° \; 59' \; 59''.11$$

which, rigorously, should be 100°; so that $\delta$ is in this case too great.

Inversely, we find, for $v = 100°$,

$$v = 100° \; \; 0' \; 00''.00$$

$\quad A = + 426.78 \qquad$ 1st cor. $\qquad - \qquad 23' \; 0''.83$

$\quad B = + \quad 0.297 \qquad$ 2d cor. $\qquad - \qquad\qquad 3''.11$

$$w = \; 99° \; 36' \; 56''.06$$

which agrees nearly with the preceding value. The change of the table to the present form has been made under the supervision of D'ARREST.

## 39.

When table II*a* is used instead of BARKER'S table, $w$ is the value of $v$, which corresponds to the argument

$$\tau = \frac{\alpha t}{\varkappa B}.$$

## 40.

If we put

$$E_v = \frac{1}{\sqrt{(1 - \frac{3}{5} A + C)}}$$

$$E_r = \frac{1 - \frac{3}{5} A + C}{1 + \frac{1}{5} A + C}$$

the formulas for computing the true anomaly and radius vector are

$$\tan \tfrac{1}{2} v = E_v \, \gamma \tan \tfrac{1}{2} w$$

$$r = E_r \, q \sec^2 \tfrac{1}{2} v.$$

Table $I_a$ for the Ellipse contains $\log E_v$ and $\log E_r$ for the argument $A$, together with the logarithms of their differences corresponding to a change of a unit in the seventh decimal place of the argument. It was computed by Prof. J. S. HUBBARD, and has been used by him for several years. Since it was in type, a similar table, computed by Mr. A. MARTH, has appeared in the *Astronomische Nachrichten*, Vol. XLIII., p. 122. The example of article 43 will furnish an illustration of its use.

Formulas expressing the differentials of the true anomaly and radius vector in a very eccentric ellipse, in terms of the differentials of the time of perihelion passage, the perihelion distance and the eccentricity may be obtained from the equations of this article.

If we put $B = 1$, $C = 0$, we have, article 39,

$$\tan \tfrac{1}{2} w + \tfrac{1}{3} \tan^3 \tfrac{1}{2} w = \frac{\alpha t}{75}$$

which, by article 20, gives

$$\frac{d w}{2 \cos^4 \tfrac{1}{2} w} = \frac{\alpha}{75} d t - \frac{3}{2 q} \frac{\alpha t}{75} d q + \frac{t}{75} d \alpha.$$

We also have, article 40,

$$\log \tan \tfrac{1}{2} v = \log \tan \tfrac{1}{2} w - \tfrac{1}{2} \log \left(1 - \tfrac{4}{5} \beta \tan^2 \tfrac{1}{2} w\right) + \log \gamma$$

and, therefore,

$$\frac{d v}{2 \sin \tfrac{1}{2} v \cos \tfrac{1}{2} v} = \frac{\cos^2 \tfrac{1}{2} w \, d w}{2 \sin \tfrac{1}{2} w \cos^3 \tfrac{1}{2} w \left(1 - \tfrac{4}{5} A\right)} + \frac{d \gamma}{\gamma} + \frac{\tfrac{2}{5} A}{1 - \tfrac{4}{5} A} \frac{d \beta}{\beta}$$

$$\frac{d v}{\sin v} = \frac{\alpha \cos^2 \tfrac{1}{2} w}{75 \tan \tfrac{1}{2} w \left(1 - \tfrac{4}{5} A\right)} d t - \frac{3 \, \alpha t \cos^2 \tfrac{1}{2} w}{2 q \, 75 \tan \tfrac{1}{2} w \left(1 - \tfrac{4}{5} A\right)} d q$$

$$+ \frac{t \cos^2 \tfrac{1}{2} w}{75 \tan \tfrac{1}{2} w \left(1 - \tfrac{4}{5} A\right)} d a + \frac{d \gamma}{\gamma} + \frac{\tfrac{2}{5} A}{1 - \tfrac{4}{5} A} \frac{d \beta}{\beta}$$

which, by putting

$$K = \frac{\alpha \cos^2 \tfrac{1}{2} w}{75 \tan \tfrac{1}{2} w \left(1 - \tfrac{4}{5} A\right)}$$

$$L = \frac{3}{2 q}$$

$$M = \frac{9}{2 \left(1 + 9 e\right)}$$

$$N = \frac{4}{\left(1 + e\right) \left(1 + 9 e\right)}$$

$$O = \frac{\frac{2}{8}A}{1 - \frac{2}{8}A}$$

$$P = \frac{10}{(1-e)(1+9e)}$$

is reduced to

$$\frac{dv}{\sin v} = -KdT - KLt\,dq + [KMt - N - OP]\,de,$$

observing that $dt = -dT$, if $T$ denotes the time of perihelion passage.

If we differentiate the equation

$$r = \frac{q(1+e)}{1+e\cos v}$$

we find

$$dr = \frac{r}{q}\,dq + \frac{2\,q^2\sin^2\frac{1}{2}v}{q(1+e)^2}\,de + \frac{r^2 e\sin v}{q(1+e)}\,dv.$$

These formulas are given by NICOLAI, (*Monatliche Correspondenz*, Vol. XXVII., p. 212). The labor of using them is greatly abridged by the fact that $K$, $L$, $M$, etc., are computed once for all, and that the quantities needed for this purpose are those required for computing the true anomaly and radius vector.

If the ellipse so nearly approaches the parabola that, in the coefficients, we may assume

$$\tan \tfrac{1}{2} v = \gamma \tan \tfrac{1}{2} w$$

$$K = \frac{k\sqrt{2}\cos^2\frac{1}{2}v}{2\,q^{\frac{3}{2}}\tan\frac{1}{2}v}$$

the values of $dv$ and $dr$ assume a much more simple form. In this case we should have

$$K\sin v = \frac{k\sqrt{2}\cos^3\frac{1}{2}v\sin\frac{1}{2}v}{2\,q^{\frac{3}{2}}\tan\frac{1}{2}v} = \frac{k\sqrt{2}\cos^4\frac{1}{2}v}{q^{\frac{3}{2}}} = \frac{k\sqrt{2q}}{r^2}$$

$$(N+OP)\sin v = \left[\frac{4}{(1+e)(1+9e)} - \frac{20\tan^2\frac{1}{2}v}{\gamma(1+9e)^2}\right]\sin v$$

$$= \left[\frac{4+4\tan^2\frac{1}{2}v}{(1+e)(1+9e)}\right]\sin v = \frac{8\tan\frac{1}{2}v}{(1+e)(1+9e)}$$

and consequently,

$$dv = -\frac{k\sqrt{2q}}{r^2}\,dT - \frac{3kt}{r^2\sqrt{2q}}\,dq + \left[\frac{kt\sqrt{2q}}{r^2}\frac{9}{2(1+9e)} - \frac{8\tan\frac{1}{2}v}{(1+e)(1+9e)}\right]de.$$

This form is given by ENCKE (*Berliner Astronomisches Jahrbuch*, 1822, page 184.) If we put $e = 1$ in the coefficient of $de$ it becomes

$$\frac{dv}{de} = \tfrac{9}{20} \frac{k t \sqrt{2q}}{r^2} - \tfrac{2}{5} \tan \tfrac{1}{2} v.$$

If we substitute the value of $dv$ in the expression for $dr$ given above, it may be reduced to the form

$$dr = - \frac{k}{\sqrt{2q}} \sin v \, dT + \cos v \, dq + \left( \tfrac{9}{20} \frac{k t \sin v}{\sqrt{2q}} + \tfrac{1}{10} r \tan^2 \tfrac{1}{2} v \right) de.$$

## 41.

The time $t$ may be found from table II$a$, by multiplying the value of $\tau$ corresponding to $w$ by

$$\frac{\varkappa' B}{\alpha}.$$

## 45.

Table I$a$ for the hyperbola is similar to that for the ellipse, and contains $\log E_v$ and $\log E_r$ for the formulas

$$\tan \tfrac{1}{2} v = E_v \, \gamma \tan \tfrac{1}{2} w$$
$$r = E_r \sec^2 \tfrac{1}{2} v.$$

The differential formulas of article 40, of the Appendix, can be applied to the hyperbola also, by changing the sign of $A$ and of $1 - e$ in the coefficients.

## 56.

As the solution here referred to may sometimes be found more convenient than the one given in articles 53–57, the formulas sufficient for the use of practical computers are given below.

Using the notation of 50 and the following articles, the expressions for the rectangular coördinates referred to the equator are, —

$$(1) \quad \begin{aligned} x &= r \cos u \cos \Omega - r \sin u \sin \Omega \cos i \\ y &= r \cos u \sin \Omega \cos \varepsilon + r \sin u \cos \Omega \cos i \cos \varepsilon - r \sin u \sin i \sin \varepsilon \\ z &= r \cos u \sin \Omega \sin \varepsilon + r \sin u \cos \Omega \cos i \sin \varepsilon + r \sin u \sin i \cos \varepsilon \end{aligned}$$

which can be put in the form

$$x = r \sin a \sin (A + u)$$

(2)
$$y = r \sin b \sin (B + u)$$

$$z = r \sin c \sin (C + u)$$

or

$$x = r \sin a \sin A \cos u + r \sin a \cos A \sin u$$

(3)
$$y = r \sin b \sin B \cos u + r \sin b \cos B \sin u$$

$$z = r \sin c \sin C \cos u + r \sin c \cos C \sin u$$

equations (3), compared with (1) give

(4)
$$\sin a \sin A = \cos \Omega \qquad \sin a \cos A = - \sin \Omega \cos i$$

$$\sin b \sin B = \sin \Omega \cos \varepsilon \qquad \sin b \cos B = \cos \Omega \cos i \cos \varepsilon - \sin i \sin \varepsilon$$

$$\sin c \sin C = \sin \Omega \sin \varepsilon \qquad \sin c \cos C = \cos \Omega \cos i \sin \varepsilon + \sin i \cos \varepsilon.$$

By introducing the auxiliary angle $E$

$$\tan E = \frac{\tan i}{\cos \Omega}$$

we shall find

$$\cotan A = - \tan \Omega \cos i$$

$$\cotan B = \frac{\cos i \cos (E + \varepsilon)}{\tan \Omega \cos E \cos \varepsilon}$$

$$\cotan C = \frac{\cos i \sin (E + \varepsilon)}{\tan \Omega \cos E \sin \varepsilon}$$

$$\sin a = \frac{\cos \Omega}{\sin A} = - \frac{\sin \Omega \cos i}{\cos A}$$

$$\sin b = \frac{\sin \Omega \cos \varepsilon}{\sin B} = \frac{\cos \Omega \cos i \cos \varepsilon - \sin i \sin \varepsilon}{\cos B}$$

$$\sin c = \frac{\sin \Omega \sin \varepsilon}{\sin C} = \frac{\cos \Omega \cos i \sin \varepsilon + \sin i \cos \varepsilon}{\cos C}.$$

$\sin a$, $\sin b$, $\sin c$ are always positive, and the quadrants in which $A$, $B$, $C$ are to be taken, can be decided by means of equations (4).

The following relations between these constants, easily deducible from the foregoing, are added, and may be used as checks:

$$\tan i = \frac{\sin b \sin c \sin (C - B)}{\sin a \sin A}$$

$$\cos a = \sin \Omega \sin i$$
$$\cos b = -\cos \Omega \sin i \cos \varepsilon - \cos i \sin \varepsilon$$
$$\cos c = -\cos \Omega \sin i \sin \varepsilon + \cos i \cos \varepsilon$$
$$\sin^2 a + \sin^2 b + \sin^2 c = 2$$
$$\cos^2 a + \cos^2 b + \cos^2 c = 1$$
$$\cos (A - B) = -\cotan a \cotan b$$
$$\cos (B - C) = -\cotan b \cotan c$$
$$\cos (A - C) = -\cotan a \cotan c.$$

## 58.

If in the formulas of article 56 of the Appendix, the ecliptic is adopted as the fundamental plane, in which case $\varepsilon = 0$; and if we put

$$\pi = \quad \text{long. of the perihelion}$$
$$\sin a = k_x \quad A = K_x - (\pi - \Omega)$$
$$\sin b = k_y \quad B = K_y - (\pi - \Omega)$$
$$\sin c = k_z \quad C = K_z - (\pi - \Omega)$$

we shall have

$$k_x \sin (K_x - (\pi - \Omega)) = \cos \Omega$$
$$k_x \cos (K_x - (\pi - \Omega)) = -\sin \Omega \cos i$$
$$k_x \sin K_x = \cos \Omega \cos (\pi - \Omega) - \sin \Omega \sin (\pi - \Omega) \cos i$$
$$k_x \cos K_x = -[\cos \Omega \sin (\pi - \Omega) + \sin \Omega \cos (\pi - \Omega) \cos i]$$

which can easily be reduced to the form,

$$k_x \sin K_x = \cos^2 \tfrac{1}{2} i \cos \pi + \sin^2 \tfrac{1}{2} i \cos (\pi - 2 \Omega)$$
$$k_x \cos K_x = -[\cos^2 \tfrac{1}{2} i \sin \pi + \sin^2 \tfrac{1}{2} i \sin (\pi - 2 \Omega)]$$

and in like manner we should find

$$k_y \sin K_y = \cos^2 \tfrac{1}{2} i \sin \pi - \sin^2 \tfrac{1}{2} i \sin (\pi - 2 \Omega)$$
$$k_y \cos K_y = \cos^2 \tfrac{1}{2} i \cos \pi - \sin^2 \tfrac{1}{2} i \cos (\pi - 2 \Omega)$$
$$k_z \sin K_z = \sin i \sin (\pi - \Omega)$$
$$k_z \cos K_z = \sin i \sin (\pi - \Omega)$$

If these values are substituted in the general expression for coördinates,

$$a\,k\cos\varphi\cos K\sin E + a\,k\sin K(\cos E - e)$$

and if we put

$$a\cos\varphi = b$$

$$a\cos^2\tfrac{1}{2}i\cos\pi\left[1 + \tan^2\tfrac{1}{2}i\,\frac{\cos(\pi - 2\,\Omega)}{\cos\pi}\right] = A$$

$$-b\cos^2\tfrac{1}{2}i\sin\pi\left[1 + \tan^2\tfrac{1}{2}i\,\frac{\sin(\pi - 2\,\Omega)}{\sin\pi}\right] = B$$

$$a\cos^2\tfrac{1}{2}i\sin\pi\left[1 - \tan^2\tfrac{1}{2}i\,\frac{\sin(\pi - 2\,\Omega)}{\sin\pi}\right] = A'$$

$$b\cos^2\tfrac{1}{2}i\cos\pi\left[1 - \tan^2\tfrac{1}{2}i\,\frac{\cos(\pi - 2\,\Omega)}{\cos\pi}\right] = B'$$

$$a\sin i\sin(\pi - \Omega) = A''$$
$$b\sin i\cos(\pi - \Omega) = B''$$

the coördinates will be

$$x = A\ (\cos E - e) + B\ \sin E = A\ (1 - e\sec E) + B\ \sin E$$
$$y = A'\ (\cos E - e) + B'\ \sin E = A'\ (1 - e\sec E) + B'\ \sin E$$
$$z = A''(\cos E - e) + B''\sin E = A''(1 - e\sec E) + B''\sin E.$$

If the equator is adopted as the fundamental plane instead of the ecliptic, the same formulas may be used, if $\Omega$, $\pi$, and $i$ are referred to the equator by the method of article 55. Thus, if $\Omega_\varepsilon$ denote the right ascension of the node on the equator, for $\Omega$, $\pi$, and $i$, we must use $\Omega_\varepsilon$, $\Omega_\varepsilon + (\pi - \Omega) - \varDelta$, and $\imath$ respectively.

This form has been given to the computation of coördinates by Prof. PEIRCE, and is designed to be used with ZECH's *Tables of Addition and Subtraction Logarithms.*

*Example.* — The data of the example of articles 56 and 58, furnish $\Omega = 158° 30' 50''.43$, $\pi = 122° 12' 23''.55$, $i = 11° 43' 52''.89$ when the equator is adopted as the fundamental plane; and also log $b = 0.4288533$.

Whence we find

| | | | |
|---|---|---|---|
| log cos $(\pi - 2\,\Omega)$ | 9.9853041 $n$ | log sin $(\pi - 2\,\Omega)$ | 9.4079143 |
| log sec $\pi$ | 0.2732948 $n$ | log cosec $\pi$ | 0.0725618 |
| log tan$^2\tfrac{1}{2}i$ | 8.0234332 | log tan$^2\tfrac{1}{2}i$ | 8.0234332 |
| log $c$ | 8.2820321 | log $c'$ | 7.5039093 |

| | | | |
|---|---|---|---|
| *add.* $\log \frac{1}{c}$ | 0.0082354 | *C. sub.* $\log \frac{1}{c}$ | 9.9916052 |
| $\log \cos \pi$ | 9.7267052 $n$ | $\log \cos \pi$ | 9.7267052 |
| $\log \cos^2 \frac{1}{2} i$ | 9.9954404 | $\log \cos^2 \frac{1}{2} i$ | 9.9954404 |
| $\log \alpha$ | 0.4423790 | $\log b$ | 0.4288533 |
| $\log A$ | 0.1727600 $n$ | $\log B'$ | 0.1426041 $n$ |
| | | | |
| *add.* $\log \frac{1}{c'}$ | 0.0013836 | *C. sub.* $\log \frac{1}{c'}$ | 9.9986120 |
| $\log \sin \pi$ | 9.9274382 | $\log \sin \pi$ | 9.9274382 |
| $\log \cos^2 \frac{1}{2} i$ | 9.9954404 | $\log \cos^2 \frac{1}{2} i$ | 9.9954404 |
| $\log b$ | 0.4288533 | $\log a$ | 0.4423790 |
| $\log B$ | 0.3531155 $n$ | $\log A'$ | 0.3638696 |

This method may also be used to compute $k$ and $K$ for the general formula of article 57. Thus: —

| | | | |
|---|---|---|---|
| *add.* $\log \frac{1}{c}$ | 0.0082354 | *C. sub.* $\log \frac{1}{c}$ | 9.9916052 |
| $\log \cos \pi$ | 9.7267052 $n$ | $\log \cos \pi$ | 9.7267052 $n$ |
| $\log \cos^2 \frac{1}{2} i$ | 9.9954404 | $\log \cos^2 \frac{1}{2} i$ | 9.9954404 |
| $\log k_x \sin K_x$ | 9.7303810 $n$ | $\log k_y \cos K_y$ | 9.7137508 $n$ |
| | | | |
| *add.* $\log \frac{1}{c}$ | 0.0013836 | *C. sub.* $\log \frac{1}{c}$ | 9.9986120 |
| $\log \sin \pi$ . | 9.9274382 | $\log \sin \pi$ | 9.9274382 |
| $\log \cos^2 \frac{1}{2} i$ | 9.9954404 | $\log \cos^2 \frac{1}{2} i$ . | 9.9954404 |
| $\log k_x \cos K_x$ | 9.9242622 $n$ | $\log k_y \sin K_y$ | 9.9214906 |
| | | | |
| $\log \tan K_x$ | 9.8061188 | $\log \tan K_y$ | 0.2077398 $n$ |
| $\log \cos K_x$ | 9.9254698 $n$ | $\log \sin K_y$ | 9.9294058 |

$$\log k_x = 9.9987924 \qquad\qquad \log k_y = 9.9920848$$
$$K_x = 212° 36' 56''.1 \qquad\qquad K_y = 121° 47' 28''.1$$

It will not be necessary to extend the example to the final expressions for $x, y, z,$ as illustrations of similar applications of the Addition and Subtraction Logarithms are given in the directions accompanying ZECH's Tables.

## 59.

If $r$, $b$, and $l$ denote the radius vector, the heliocentric latitude and longitude of any planet, the rectangular coördinates referred to three axes, — of which that of $x$ is directed towards the vernal equinox, that of $z$, parallel to the earth's axis, and that of $y$, 90° of right ascension in advance of $x$, — will be as in case II.

$$x = r \cos b \cos l$$
$$y = r \cos b \sin l \cos \varepsilon - r \sin b \sin \varepsilon$$
$$z = r \cos b \sin \varepsilon \sin l + r \sin b \cos \varepsilon$$

and by putting

$$\cos u = \cos b \cos l$$
$$\sin u = \frac{\sin b}{\sin \theta} = \frac{\sin l \cos b}{\cos \theta}$$
$$\tan \theta = \frac{\tan b}{\sin l}$$

they assume the following forms convenient for computation : —

$$x = r \cos u$$
$$y = r \sin u \cos (\theta + \varepsilon)$$
$$z = r \sin u \sin (\theta + \varepsilon).$$

## 74.

The following are the solutions and examples from the *Monatliche Correspondenz* referred to in this article, adopting the notation of article 74, and using $L'$ to denote the longitude of the Sun.

Given, $\Omega$, $L'$, $l$, $b$, $i$, $R$, to find $u$, $r$, $\varDelta$, and the auxiliary angles $A$, $B$, $C$, etc.

### I.

1. $\dfrac{\cos (L' - \Omega) \tan b}{\sin (L' - l)} = \tan A$    $\dfrac{\sin A \tan (L' - \Omega)}{\sin (A + i)} = \tan u$

2. $\dfrac{\sin (L' - l) \tan i}{\cos (L' - \Omega)} = \tan B$    $\dfrac{\cos B \sin b \tan (L' - \Omega)}{\sin (B + b) \cos i} = \tan u$

3. $\dfrac{\sin (L' - \Omega) \tan b}{\sin (L' - l) \tan i} = \tan C$    $\dfrac{\sin C \sin (L' - \Omega)}{\sin (C + L' - \Omega) \cos i} = \tan u$

4. $\dfrac{\cos (L' - \Omega) \tan b}{\cos (L' - l) \tan i} = \tan D$    $\dfrac{\sin D \tan (L' - \Omega) \cos (L' - l)}{\sin (D + L' - l) \cos i} = \tan u$

The angle $u$ is to be taken between $0°$ and $180°$ when $b$ is positive, and between $180°$ and $360°$ when $b$ is negative. When $b = 0°$, the body is in one of the nodes of its orbit, in the ascending node when $\sin(L' - l)$ and $\sin(l - \Omega)$ have the same sign; and in the descending node when they have opposite signs.

It is immaterial in which of the two quadrants that give the same tangent, the auxiliary angles $A, B, C$, etc., are taken. In the following examples they are always taken between $+90°$ and $-90°$.

## II.

5. $\quad \dfrac{\tan b}{\sin(l - \Omega)} = \tan E \qquad\qquad \dfrac{\sin E \sin(L' - \Omega)}{\sin(i - E)\sin u} = \dfrac{r}{R}$

6. $\quad \tan i \sin(l - \Omega) = \tan F \qquad\qquad \dfrac{\cos F \sin(L' - \Omega)\sin b}{\sin(F - b)\sin u \cos i} = \dfrac{r}{R}$

7. $\quad \cos i \tan u = \tan G \qquad\qquad \dfrac{\cos G \sin(L' - l)}{\sin(l - \Omega - G)\cos u} = \dfrac{r}{R}$

8. $\quad \dfrac{\tan(l - \Omega)}{\cos i} = \tan H \qquad\qquad \dfrac{\sin H \sin(L' - l)}{\sin(H - u)\sin(l - \Omega)} = \dfrac{r}{R}$

9. $\quad \dfrac{\tan b}{\sin i \cos(l - \Omega)}\tan I \qquad\qquad \dfrac{\sin I \cos(L' - \Omega)}{\sin(u - I)} = \dfrac{r}{R}$

10. $\quad \sin i \cos(l - \Omega)\tan u = \tan K \qquad\qquad \dfrac{\cos K \sin b \cos(L' - \Omega)}{\sin(K - b)\cos u} = \dfrac{r}{R}$

11. $\quad \dfrac{\sin C \sin(L - l)}{\cos(C + L' - l)\tan(L' - \Omega)\cos i} = \tan L \qquad\qquad \dfrac{\sin L}{\sin(u - L)\cos(L' - \Omega)} = \dfrac{r}{R}$

12. $\quad \dfrac{\sin D \cos(L' - \Omega)}{\cos(D + L' - \Omega)\cos i} = \tan M \qquad\qquad \dfrac{\sin M}{\sin(u - M)\cos(L' - \Omega)} = \dfrac{r}{R}$

## III.

13. $\quad \dfrac{r \sin u \sin i}{\sin b} = \varDelta$

14. $\quad \dfrac{R \sin E \sin(L' - \Omega)\sin i}{\sin(i - E)\sin b} = \dfrac{R \cos E \sin(L' - \Omega)\sin i}{\sin(i - E)\sin(l - \Omega)\cos b} = \varDelta$

15. $\quad \dfrac{R \cos F \sin(L' - \Omega)\tan i}{\sin(F - b)} = \dfrac{R \sin F \sin(L' - \Omega)\sin(l - \Omega)}{\sin(F - b)} = \varDelta$

Other expressions for $\varDelta$ may be obtained by combining 13 with all the formulas II.

Examples: —

Given, $\Omega = 80°\,59'\,12''.07$, $L' = 281°\,1'\,34''.99$, $l = 53°\,23'\,2''.46$, $i = 10°\,37'\,9''.55$, $b = -3°\,6'\,33''.561$, $\log R = 9.9926158$.

### 1°.

| | | | |
|---|---|---|---|
| log tan $b$ | 8.7349698 $n$ | log sin $A$ | 8.8381955 $n$ |
| log cos $(L' - \Omega)$ | 9.9728762 $n$ | log tan $(L' - \Omega)$ | 9.5620014 |
| $C$ log sin $(L' - b)$ | 0.1313827 $n$ | $C$ log sin $(A + i)$ | 0.9350608 |
| log tan $A$ | 8.8392287 $n$ | log tan $u$ | 9.3352577 $n$ |

$$A = -\ 3°\ 57'\ 2''.136$$
$$A + i = \quad 6°\ 40'\ 7''.414$$

$$u = -\ 12°\ 12'\ 37''.942$$

### 2°.

| | | | |
|---|---|---|---|
| log sin $(L' - l)$ | 9.8686173 $n$ | log cos $B$ | 9.9953277 |
| log tan $i$ | 9.2729872 | log sin $b$ | 8.7343300 $n$ |
| $C$. log cos $(L' - \Omega)$ | 0.0271238 $n$ | log tan $(L' - \Omega)$ | 9.5620014 |
| log tan $B$ | 9.1687283 | $C$. log sin $(B + b)$ | 1.0360961 |
| | | $C$. log cos $i$ | 0.0075025 |
| | | log tan $u$ | 9.3352577 $n$ |

$$B = 8°\ 23'\ 21''.888$$
$$B + b = 5°\ 16'\ 48''.327$$

### 3°.

| | | | |
|---|---|---|---|
| log sin $(L' - \Omega)$ | 9.5348776 $n$ | log sin $C$ | 9.1243583 $n$ |
| log tan $b$ | 8.7349698 $n$ | log sin $(L' - \Omega)$ | 9.5348776 $n$ |
| $a$. log sin $(L' - l)$ | 0.1313827 $n$ | $C$. log sin $(C + L' - \Omega)$ | 0.6685194 $n$ |
| $C$. log tan $i$ | 0.7270128 | $C$. log cos $i$ | 0.0075025 |
| log tan $C$ | 9.1282429 $n$ | log tan $u$ | 9.3352578 $n$ |

$$C = -\ 7°\ 39'\ 7''.058$$
$$C + L' - \Omega = 192°\ 23'\ 15''.864$$

### 4°.

| | | | |
|---|---|---|---|
| log cos $(L' - \Omega)$ | 9.9728762 $n$ | log sin $D$ | 9.5735295 $n$ |
| log tan $b$ | 8.7349698 $n$ | log tan $(L' - \Omega)$ | 9.5620014 |
| $C$. log cos $(L' - l)$ | 0.1714973 $n$ | log cos $(L' - l)$ | 9.8285027 $n$ |
| $C$. log tan $i$ | 0.7270128 | $C$. log sin $(D + L' - l)$ | 0.3637217 $n$ |
| log tan $D$ | 9.6063561 $n$ | $C$. log cos $i$ | 0.0075025 |
| | | log tan $u$ | 9.3352578 $n$ |

$$D = -\ 21°\ 59'\ 51''.182$$
$$D + L' - l = 205°\ 38'\ 41''.348$$

### 5°.

| | | | |
|---|---|---|---|
| $\log \tan b$ | $8.7349698\,n$ | $\log \sin E$ | $9.0661081$ |
| $\log \sin (l - \Omega)$ | $9.6658973\,n$ | $\log \sin (L' - \Omega)$ | $9.5348776\,n$ |
| $\log \tan E$ | $9.0690725$ | $C.\log \sin (i - E)$ | $1.1637907$ |
| $E = 6° 41' 12''.412$ | | $C.\log \sin u$ | $0.6746802\,n$ |
| $i - E = 3° 55' 57''.138$ | | $\log \dfrac{r}{R}$ | $0.4394566$ |

$$\log r = \log R + \log \frac{r}{R} = 0.4320724$$

### 6°.

| | | | |
|---|---|---|---|
| $\log \tan i$ | $9.2729872$ | $\log \cos F$ | $9.9983674$ |
| $\log \sin (l - \Omega)$ | $9.6658973\,n$ | $\log \sin b$ | $8.7343300\,n$ |
| $\log \tan F$ | $8.9388845\,n$ | $\log \sin (L' - \Omega)$ | $9.5348776\,n$ |
| $F = -4° 57' 53''.955$ | | $C.\log \sin (F - b)$ | $1.4896990\,n$ |
| $F - b = -1° 51' 20''.394$ | | $C.\log \sin u$ | $0.6746802\,n$ |
| | | $C.\log \cos i$ | $0.0075025\,n$ |
| | | $\log \dfrac{r}{R}$ | $0.4394567$ |

### 7°.

| | | | |
|---|---|---|---|
| $\log \cos i$ | $9.9924975$ | $\log \cos G$ | $9.9903922$ |
| $\log \tan u$ | $9.3352577\,n$ | $\log \sin (L' - l)$ | $9.8686173\,n$ |
| $\log \tan G$ | $9.3277552\,n$ | $C.\log \sin (l - \Omega - G)$ | $0.5705092\,n$ |
| $G = -12° 0' 27''.118$ | | $C.\log \cos u$ | $0.0099379$ |
| $l - \Omega - G = -15° 35' 42''.492$ | | $\log \dfrac{r}{R}$ | $0.4394566$ |

### 8°.

| | | | |
|---|---|---|---|
| $\log \tan (l - \Omega)$ | $9.7183744\,n$ | $\log \sin H$ | $9.6717672\,n$ |
| $\log \cos i$ | $9.9924975$ | $\log \sin (L' - l)$ | $9.8686173\,n$ |
| $\log \tan H$ | $9.7258769\,n$ | $C.\log \sin (H - u)$ | $0.5649695\,n$ |
| $H = -28° 0' 39''.879$ | | $C.\log \sin (l - \Omega)$ | $0.3341027\,n$ |
| $H - u = -15° 48' 1''.937$ | | $\log \dfrac{r}{R}$ | $0.4394567$ |

## 9°.

| | | | |
|---|---|---|---|
| $\log \tan b$ | $8.7349698\,n$ | $\log \sin I$ | $9.4991749\,n$ |
| $C.\log \sin i$ | $0.7345153$ | $\log \sin (L' - \Omega)$ | $9.9728762\,n$ |
| $C.\log \cos (l - \Omega)$ | $0.0542771$ | $C.\log \sin (u - I)$ | $0.9674054$ |
| $\log \tan I$ | $9.5237622\,n$ | $\log \dfrac{r}{R}$ | $0.4394565$ |

$$I = -18°\,23'\,55''.334$$
$$u - I = \phantom{-}6°\,11'\,17''.392$$

## 10°.

| | | | |
|---|---|---|---|
| $\log \sin i$ | $9.2654847$ | $\log \cos K$ | $9.9997290$ |
| $\log \cos (l - \Omega)$ | $9.9475229$ | $\log \sin b$ | $8.7343300\,n$ |
| $\log \tan u$ | $9.3352577\,n$ | $\log \cos (L' - \Omega)$ | $9.9728762\,n$ |
| $\log \tan K$ | $8.5482653\,n$ | $C.\log \sin (K - b)$ | $1.7225836$ |
| $K = -2°\,1'\,26''.344$ | | $C.\log \cos u$ | $0.0099379$ |
| $K - b = \phantom{-}1°\,5'\,\phantom{0}7''.217$ | | $\log \dfrac{r}{R}$ | $0.4394567$ |

## 11°.

$$C + L' - l = 219°\,59'\,25''.474$$

| | | | |
|---|---|---|---|
| $\log \sin C$ | $9.1243583\,n$ | $\log \sin L$ | $9.5279439\,n$ |
| $\log \sin (L' - l)$ | $9.8686173\,n$ | $C.\log \sin (u - L)$ | $0.8843888$ |
| $C.\log \cos (C + L' - l)$ | $0.1156850\,n$ | $C.\log \cos (L' - \Omega)$ | $0.0271238\,n$ |
| $C.\log \tan (L' - \Omega)$ | $0.4379986$ | $\log \dfrac{r}{R}$ | $0.4394565$ |
| $C.\log \cos i$ | $0.0075025$ | | |
| $\log \tan L$ | $9.5541617\,n$ | | |

$$L = -19°\,42'\,32''.533$$
$$u - L = \phantom{-}7°\,29'\,54''.591$$

## 12°.

| | |
|---|---|
| $D + L' - \Omega = 178°\,2'\,31''.738$ | |
| $\log \sin D$ | $9.5735295\,n$ |
| $\log \cos (L' - \Omega)$ | $9.9728762\,n$ |
| $C.\log \cos (D + L' - \Omega)$ | $0.0002536\,n$ |
| $C.\log \cos i$ | $0.0075025$ |
| $\log \tan M (= L)$ | $9.5541618\,n$ |

## 13°.

| | |
|---|---|
| $\log r$ | $0.4320724$ |
| $\log \sin u$ | $9.3253198\,n$ |
| $\log \sin i$ | $9.2654847$ |
| $C.\log \sin b$ | $1.2656700\,n$ |
| $\log \varDelta$ | $0.2885469$ |

## 76.

If in the equations of article 60,

$$x - X = \varDelta \cos \delta \cos \alpha$$
$$y - Y = \varDelta \cos \delta \sin \alpha$$
$$z - Z = \varDelta \sin \delta$$

$\alpha$ denoting the right ascension, and $\delta$ the declination, we suppose $X, Y, Z$ known, we have

$$d\,x = \cos \alpha \cos \delta \, d\varDelta - \varDelta \sin \alpha \cos \delta \, d\alpha - \varDelta \cos \alpha \sin \delta \, d\delta$$
$$d\,y = \sin \alpha \cos \delta \, d\varDelta + \varDelta \cos \alpha \cos \delta \, d\alpha - \varDelta \sin \alpha \sin \delta \, d\delta$$
$$d\,z = \sin \delta \, d\varDelta + \varDelta \cos \delta \, d\delta.$$

Multiply the first of these by $\sin \alpha$, and subtract from it the second multiplied by $\cos \alpha$, and we find

$$\varDelta \cos \delta \, d\alpha = -\, d\,x \sin \alpha + d\,y \sin \alpha.$$

Multiply the first by $\cos \alpha$ and add to it the second multiplied by $\sin \alpha$, and we find

$$d\,x \cos \alpha + d\,y \sin \alpha = \cos \delta \, d\varDelta - \varDelta \sin \delta \, d\delta.$$

Multiply this equation by $-\sin \delta$ and add it to the third of the differential equations above multiplied by $\cos \delta$ and we find

$$-\, d\,x \cos \alpha \sin \delta - d\,y \sin \alpha \sin \delta + d\,z \cos \delta = \varDelta \, d\delta$$

and, therefore,

$$\cos \delta \, d\alpha = -\, \frac{\sin \alpha}{\varDelta} d\,x + \frac{\cos \alpha}{\varDelta} d\,y$$

$$d\delta = -\, \frac{\cos \alpha \sin \delta}{\varDelta} d\,x - \frac{\sin \alpha \sin \delta}{\varDelta} d\,y + \frac{\cos \delta}{\varDelta} d\,z.$$

From the formulas of article 56 of the Appendix are obtained

$$\frac{d\,x}{d\,r} = \frac{x}{r}, \ \frac{d\,y}{d\,r} = \frac{y}{r}, \ \frac{d\,z}{d\,r} = \frac{z}{r},$$

$$\frac{d\,x}{d\,u} = x \cotan (A + u), \ \frac{d\,y}{d\,u} = y \cotan (B + u), \ \frac{d\,z}{d\,u} = z \cotan (C + u)$$

$$\frac{d\,x}{d\,i} = x \sin u \cos \alpha, \ \frac{d\,y}{d\,i} = r \sin u \cos b, \ \frac{d\,z}{d\,i} = r \sin u \cos c,$$

and the partial differentials

$$\frac{d\,x}{d\,\Omega} = -\, y \cos \varepsilon - z \sin \varepsilon, \ \frac{d\,y}{d\,\Omega} = x \cos \varepsilon, \ \frac{d\,z}{d\,\Omega} = x \sin \varepsilon$$

whence

$$dx = \frac{x}{r} dr + x \cotan (A+u) dv + x \cotan (A+u) d\pi$$
$$- [x \cotan (A+u) + y \cos \varepsilon + z \sin \varepsilon] d\Omega + r \sin u \cos a \, di$$

$$dy = \frac{y}{r} dr + y \cotan (B+u) dv + y \cotan (B+u) d\pi$$
$$- [y \cotan (B+u) - x \cos \varepsilon] d\Omega + r \sin u \cos b \, di$$

$$dz = \frac{z}{r} dr - z \cotan (C+u) dv + z \cotan (C+u) d\pi$$
$$- [z \cotan (C+u) - x \sin \varepsilon] d\Omega + r \sin u \cos c \, di.$$

These formulas, as well as those of 56 may be found in a small treatise *Ueber die Differentialformeln für Cometen-Bahnen*, etc., by G. D. E. WEYER, (Berlin, 1852). They are from BESSEL's *Abhandlung über den Olbers'schen Cometen*.

## 90.

GAUSS, in the *Berliner Astronomisches Jahrbuch* for 1814, p. 256, has given another method of computing $\xi$, and also $\zeta$ of article 100. It is as follows: —

We have

$$\xi = x - \frac{5}{6} + \frac{10}{9X} = \frac{x X - \frac{5}{6} X + \frac{10}{9}}{X}.$$

This fraction, by substituting for $X$ the series of article 90, is readily transformed into

$$\xi = \frac{8}{105} x^2 \left( 1 + \frac{2 \cdot 8}{9} x + \frac{3 \cdot 8 \cdot 10}{9 \cdot 11} x^2 + \frac{4 \cdot 8 \cdot 10 \cdot 12}{9 \cdot 11 \cdot 13} x^3 + \frac{5 \cdot 8 \cdot 10 \cdot 12 \cdot 14}{9 \cdot 11 \cdot 13 \cdot 15} x^4 + \text{etc.} \right)$$

Therefore, if we put

$$A = 1 + \frac{2 \cdot 8}{9} x + \frac{3 \cdot 8 \cdot 10}{9 \cdot 11} x^2 + \text{etc.},$$

we shall have

$$x X - \tfrac{5}{6} X + \tfrac{10}{9} = \tfrac{8}{105} A x^2$$

$$X = \frac{\frac{5}{6} (1 - \frac{12}{175} A x^2)}{1 - \frac{6}{5} x}$$

$$\xi = \frac{\frac{2}{35} A x^2 (1 - \frac{6}{5} x)}{1 - \frac{12}{175} A x^2}$$

by means of which $\xi$ can always be found easily and accurately.

For $\zeta$, article 100, it is only necessary to write $z$ in place of $x$ in the preceding formulas.

$A$ may be computed more conveniently by the following formula:—

$$A = (1-x)^{-\frac{3}{2}}\left(1 + \frac{1.5}{2.9}x + \frac{1.3.5.7}{2.4.9.11}x^2 + \frac{1.3.5.5.7.9}{2.4.6.9.11.13}x^3 + \text{etc.}\right)$$

## 142.

PROF. ENCKE, on the 13th of January, 1848, read a paper before the Royal Academy of Sciences at Berlin, entitled *Ueber den Ausnahmefall einer doppelten Bahnbestimmung aus denselben drei geocentrischen Oertern*, in which he entered into a full discussion of the origin of the ambiguous case here mentioned, and the manner in which it is to be explained. The following paragraphs, containing useful instructions to the practical computer, embody the results of his investigation:—

By putting

$$m = c\,Q \sin \omega$$
$$q = (\omega + \sigma),$$

Equation IV., 141, becomes, for $r' > R'$

$$m \sin^4 z = \sin(z - q)$$

and for $r' < R'$

$$m \sin^4 z = \sin(z + q)$$

$m$ is always positive.

The number and the limits of the roots of this equation may be found by examining both forms.

Take the first form, and consider the curves, the equations of which are

$$y = m \sin^4 z, \quad y' = \sin(z - q)$$

$y$ and $y'$ being ordinates, and $z$ abscissas.

The first differential coefficients are

$$\frac{dy}{dz} = 4\,m \sin^3 z \cos z, \quad \frac{dy'}{dz} = \cos(z - q),$$

There will, therefore, be a contact of the curves when we have

$$m \sin^4 z = \sin (z - q)$$

and

$$4 \, m \sin^3 z \cos z = \cos (z - q)$$

or when

$$4 \sin (z - q) \cos z = \cos (z - q) \sin z$$

which may be more simply written

$$\sin (2 z - q) = \tfrac{5}{3} \sin q.$$

When the value of $z$ deduced from this equation satisfies

$$m \sin^4 z = \sin (z - q)$$

then there is a contact of the curves, or the equation has two equal roots. These equal roots constitute the limits of possibility of intersection of the curves, or the limits of the real roots of the equation.

For the delineation of both curves it is only necessary to regard values of $z - q$ between 0° and 180°, since for values between 180° and 360° the solution is impossible; and beyond 360° these periods are repeated.

The curve

$$y' = \sin (z - q)$$

is the simple sine-curve, always on the positive side of $y'$, and concave to the axis of abscissas, and has a maximum for

$$z - q = 90°.$$

The curve

$$y = \sin^4 z$$

is of the fourth order, and since it gives

$$\frac{d y}{d z} = 4 \, m \sin^3 z \cos z = m \sin 2 z - \tfrac{1}{2} m \sin 4 z$$

$$\frac{d^2 y}{d z^2} = 12 \, m \sin^2 z \cos^2 z - 4 \, m \sin^4 z$$

$$= 4 \, m \sin^2 z \, (1 + 2 \cos 2 z) = 2 \, m \, (\cos 2 z - \cos 4 z)$$

$$\frac{d^3 y}{d z^3} = - 4 \, m \, (\sin 2 z - 2 \sin 4 z)$$

$$\frac{d^4 y}{d z^4} = - 8 \, m \, (\cos 2 z - 4 \cos 4 z)$$

it has a maximum for

$$z = 90°$$

and a point of contrary flexure for

$$z = 60°, \quad \text{and } z = 120°.$$

From $z = 0°$ to $z = 60°$, it is convex to the axis of abscissas, from $60°$ to $120°$ it is concave, and convex from $120°$ to $180°$.

For osculation, the three equations,

$$m \sin^4 z = \sin (z - q)$$
$$4 m \sin^3 z \cos z = \cos (z - q)$$
$$4 m \sin^2 z (1 + 2 \cos 2 z) = - \sin (z - q)$$

must coexist, or

$$m \sin^4 z = \sin (z - q)$$
$$\sin (2 z - q) = \tfrac{5}{3} \sin q$$
$$\cos 2 z = - \tfrac{3}{5}.$$

In this case we should have

$$\sin (2 z - q) = \tfrac{4}{5} \cos q + \tfrac{3}{5} \sin q,$$

consequently,

$$\tan q = \tfrac{3}{4}$$

and

$$\sin q = \tfrac{3}{5},$$

or

$$z = 45° + \tfrac{1}{2} \sin^{-1} \tfrac{3}{5}.$$

From these considerations we infer that for the equation

$$m \sin^4 z = \sin (z - q)$$

or even when it is in the form

$$m^2 \sin^8 z - 2 m \cos q \sin^5 z + \sin^2 z - \sin^2 q = 0$$

of the eighth degree, there can only be four real roots; because, in the whole period from $z - q = 0°$ to $z - q = 360°$, only four intersections of the two curves are possible on the positive side of the axis of ordinates.

Of these, three are between $z = 0°$ and $z = 180°$, and one between $180°$ and $180° + q$; or, inversely, one between $0°$ and $180°$, and three between $180°$ and $180° + q$; consequently, there are three positive and one negative roots, or three negative and one positive roots for $\sin z$.

Contact of the curves can exist only when for a given value of $q$,

$$z' = \tfrac{1}{2} q + \tfrac{1}{2} \sin^{-1} \tfrac{5}{3} \sin q$$

and

$$m' = \frac{\sin (z' - q)}{\sin^4 z'}.$$

If the contact of the curve of the fourth order with the sine-curve is without the latter, then will $m'$ constitute the upper limit, — for $m$ greater than this values of the roots will be impossible. There would then remain only one positive and one negative root.

If the contact is within the sine-curve, then will the corresponding $m''$ constitute the lower limit, and for $m$ less than this, the roots again would be reduced to two, one positive and one negative.

If $q$ is taken negative, or if we adopt the form

$$m \sin^4 2 = \sin (z + q)$$

$180° - z$ must be substituted for $z$.

The equation

$$m^2 \sin^8 z - 2 m \cos q \sin^5 z + \sin^2 z - \sin^2 q = 0$$

shows, moreover, according to the rule of DESCARTES, that, of the four real roots three can be positive only . when $q$, without regard to sign is less than $90°$, because $m$ is always regarded as positive. For $q$ greater than $90°$, there is always only one real positive root. Now since one real root must always correspond to the orbit of the Earth, that is, to $r' = R'$; and since $\sin \delta'$, in the equation, article 141, —

$$\sin z = \frac{R' \sin \delta'}{r'}$$

is always positive, so that it can be satisfied by none but positive values of $z$; an orbit can correspond to the observations only when three real roots are positive, or when $q$ without regard to its sign is less than $90°$. These limits are still more narrowly confined, because, also, there can be four real roots only when $m$ lies between $m'$ and $m''$, and when we have

$$\tfrac{5}{3} \sin q < 1, \text{ or } \sin q < \tfrac{3}{5}, \quad q < 36° \, 52' \, 11''.64$$

in order that a real value of $z'$ may be possible.

Then the following are the conditions upon which it is possible to find a planet's orbit different from that of the earth, which shall satisfy three complete observations.

*First.* The equation

$$m \sin^4 z = \sin (z + q)$$

must have four real roots. The conditions necessary for this are, that we must have, without regard to sign,

$$\sin q < \tfrac{3}{5}$$

and $m$ must lie between the limits $m'$ and $m''$.

*Second.* Of these four real roots three must be positive and one negative.

For this it is necessary that $\cos q$ should remain positive for all four of those values for which

$$\sin q < \pm \tfrac{3}{5},$$

the two in the second and third quadrants are excluded, and only values between $- 36°\ 52'$ and $+ 36°\ 52'$ are to be retained.

If both these conditions are satisfied, of the three real positive roots, one must always correspond to the Earth's orbit, and consequently will not satisfy the problem. And generally there will be no doubt which of the other two will give a solution of the problem. And since by the meaning of the symbols, articles 139, 140, we have

$$\frac{\sin z}{R} = \frac{\sin (\delta' - z)}{\varrho'} = \frac{\sin \delta'}{r'}$$

not only must $z$ and $\delta'$ be always less than $180°$, but, also, $\sin (\delta' - z)$ must be positive, or we must have

$$\delta' > z.$$

If, therefore, we arrange the three real positive roots in the order of their absolute magnitudes, there may be three distinct cases. Either the smallest root approaches most nearly the value of $\delta'$, and corresponds, therefore, to the Earth's orbit, in which case the problem is impossible; because the condition $\delta' > z$ can never be fulfilled. Or the middle root coincides with $\delta'$, then will the problem be solved only by the smallest root. Or, finally, the greatest of the three roots differs least from $\delta'$. in which case the choice must lie between the two smaller

39

roots. Each of these will give a planetary orbit, because each one fulfils all the conditions, and it will remain to be determined, from observations other than the three given ones, which is the true solution.

As the value of $m$ must lie between the two limits $m'$ and $m''$, so also must all four of the roots lie between those roots as limits which correspond to $m'$ and $m''$. In Table IV $a$. are found, therefore, for the argument $q$ from degree to degree, the roots corresponding to the limits, arranged according to their magnitude, and distinguished by the symbols $z^{\mathrm{I}}, z^{\mathrm{II}}, z^{\mathrm{III}}, z^{\mathrm{IV}}$. For every value of $m$ which gives a possible solution, these roots will lie within the quantities given both for $m'$ and $m''$, and we shall be enabled in this manner, if $\delta'$ is found, to discern at the first glance, whether or not, for a given $m$ and $q$, the paradoxical case of a double orbit can occur. It must, to be sure, be considered that, strictly speaking, $\delta'$ would only agree exactly with one of the $z$'s, when the corrections of $P$ and $Q$ belonging to the earth's orbit had been employed, and, therefore, a certain difference even beyond the extremest limit might be allowed, if the intervals of time should be very great.

The root $z^{\mathrm{IV}}$, for which $\sin z$ is negative, always falls out, and is only introduced here for the sake of completeness. Both parts of this table might have been blended in one with the proviso of putting in the place of $z$ its supplement; for the sake of more rapid inspection, however, the two forms $\sin (z - q)$ and $\sin (z + q)$ have been separated, so that $q$ is always regarded as positive in the table.

To explain the use of Table IV $a$. two cases are added ; one, the example of Ceres in this Appendix, and the other, the exceptional case that occurred to Dr. Gould, in his computation of the orbit of the fifth comet of the year 1847, an account of which is given in his *Astronomical Journal,* Vol. I., No. 19.

I. In our example of Ceres, the final equation in the first hypothesis is

$$[0.9112987] \sin^4 z = \sin (z - 7° 49' 2''.0)$$
and
$$\delta' = 24° 19' 53''.34$$

the factor in brackets being the logarithm. By the table, the numerical factor lies between $m'$ and $m''$, and this $\delta'$ answers to $z^{\mathrm{II}}$, concerning which there can be no hesitation, since $z^{\mathrm{II}}$ must lie between $10° 27'$ and $87° 34'$. Accordingly, we have only to choose for the $z^I$ which occurs in this case, and which, as we perceive, is to be sought between $7° 50'$ and $10° 27'$.

The root is in fact

$$z^I = 7° 59' 30''.3,$$

and the remaining roots,

$$z^{II} = 26\ 24\ \ 3$$
$$z^{III} = 148\ \ 2\ 35$$
$$z^{IV} = 187\ 40\ \ 9$$

are all found within the limits of the table.

2. In the case of the fifth comet of 1847, Dr. Gould derived from his first hypothesis the equation

$$[9.7021264]\ \sin^4 z = \sin(z + 32° 53' 28''.5).$$

He had also

$$\delta' = 133° 0' 31''.$$

Then we have $\sin q < \frac{3}{5}$, and the inspection of the table shows that the factor in the parenthesis lies between $m'$ and $m''$; therefore, there will be four real roots. of which three will be positive. The given $\delta'$ approximates here most nearly to $z^{III}$, about which, at any rate, there can be no doubt.

Consequently, the paradoxical case of the determination of a double orbit occurs here, and the two possible values of $z$ will lie between

$$88° 29' - 105° 59'$$

and

$$105\ 59\ - 131\ \ 7$$

In fact, the four roots are,

$$z^I = \ \ 95° 31' 43''.5$$
$$z^{II} = 117\ \ 31\ 13\ .1$$
$$z^{III} = 137\ \ 38\ 16\ .7$$
$$z^{IV} = 329\ \ 58\ 35\ .5.$$

By a small decrease of $m$ without changing $q$, or by a small decrease of $q$ without changing $m$, a point of osculation will be obtained corresponding to nearly a mean between the second and third roots; and on the contrary, by a small increase of $m$ without changing $q$, or a small increase of $q$ without changing $m$, a point of osculation is obtained corresponding to nearly a mean between the first and second roots.

We have, therefore, the choice between the two orbits. The root used by Dr. GOULD was $z^{\text{II}}$, which gave him an ellipse of very short period. The other observations showed him that this was not the real orbit. M. D'ARREST was involved in a similar difficulty with the same comet, and arrived also at an ellipse. An ellipse of eighty-one years resulted from the use of the other root.

"Finally, both forms of the table show that the exceptional case can never occur when $\delta' < 63° \, 26'$.

"It will also seldom occur when $\delta' < 90°$. For then it can only take place with the first form $\sin (z - q)$, and since here for all values of $q$ either the limits are very narrow, or one of the limits approximates very nearly to 90°, so it will be perceived that the case where there are two possible roots for $\delta' < 90°$ will very seldom happen. For the smaller planets, therefore, which for the most part are discovered near opposition, there is rarely occasion to look at the table. For the comets we shall have more frequently $\delta' > 90°$; still, even here, on account of the proximity to the sun, $\delta' > 150°$ can, for the most part, be excluded. Consequently, it will be necessary, in order that the exceptional case should occur, that we should have in general, the combination of the conditions $\delta' > 90°$ and $q$ between 0° and 32° in the form $\sin (z - q)$, or between 22° and 36° 52' in the form $\sin (z + q)$."

---

Professor PEIRCE has communicated to the American Academy several methods of exhibiting the geometrical construction of this celebrated equation, and of others which, like this, involve two parameters, some of which are novel and curious. In order to explain them, let us resume the fundamental equation,

$$m \sin^4 z = \sin (z - q).$$

1. The first method of representation is by logarithmic curves; the logarithm of the given equation is

$$\log m + 4 \log \sin z = \log \sin (z - q).$$

If we construct the curve

$$y = 4 \log \sin z,$$

and also the same curve on another scale, in which $y$ is reduced to one fourth of its value, so that

$$y = \log \sin z,$$

it is plain that if the second curve is removed parallel to itself by a distance equal to $q$ in the direction of the axis of $z$, and by a distance equal to $-\log m$ in the direction of the axis of $y$, the value of $z$ on the first curve where the two curves intersect each other will be a root of the given equation; for, since the point of intersection is on the first curve, its coördinates satisfy the equation,

$$y = 4 \log \sin z,$$

and because it is on the second curve its coördinates satisfy the equation,

$$y + \log m = \log \sin (z - q);$$

and by eliminating $y$ from these two equations we return to the original equation,

$$m \sin^4 z = \sin (z - q).$$

A diagram constructed on this principle is illustrated by figure 5, and it will be readily seen how, by moving one curve upon the other, according to the changeable values of $q$ and $m$, the points of intersection will be exhibited, and also the limits at which they become points of osculation.

On this and all the succeeding diagrams, we may remark, once for all, that two cases are shown, one of which is the preceding example of the planet Ceres, in which the four roots of the equation will correspond in all the figures to the four points of intersection $D, D', D'', D'''$, and the other of which is the very remarkable case that occurred to Dr. Gould, approaching the two limits of the osculation of the second order, the details of which are given in No. 19 of his *Astronomical Journal*, and the points of which are marked on all our diagrams $G, G', G'', G'''$.

2. The second method of representation is by a fixed curve and straight line, as follows.

(*a.*) The fundamental equation, developed in its second member, and divided by $m \cos z$, assumes the form

$$\frac{\sin^4 z}{\cos z} = \frac{\cos q}{m} (\tan z - \tan q)$$

By putting

$$x = \tan z, \ b = \tan q, \ a = \frac{\cos q}{m}$$

the roots of the equation will correspond to the points of intersection of the curve

$$y = \frac{\sin^4 z}{\cos z} = \frac{x^4}{(1 + x^2)^{\frac{3}{2}}}$$

with the straight line

$$y = a\,(x - b). \quad \text{[Figs. 6 and 6'.]}$$

It will be perceived that the curve line, in this as in all the following cases under this form, is not affected by any change in the values of $m$ and $q$, and that the position of the straight line is determined by its cutting the axis of $x$ at the distance $\tan q$ from the origin, and the axis of $y$ at the distance $-\frac{\sin q}{m}$ from the origin. The tangent of its inclination to the axis is obviously equal to $\frac{\cos q}{m}$, which may in some cases answer more conveniently for determining its position than its intersection with the axis of $y$.

(b.) The development of the fundamental equation divided by $m \sin z$, is

$$\sin^3 z = \frac{\sin q}{m}\,(\cotan q - \cotan z)\,;$$

and by putting

$$x = \cotan z$$
$$b = \cotan q$$
$$a = \frac{\sin q}{m}$$

the roots of the equation correspond to the intersection of the curve

$$y = \sin^3 z = (1 + x^2)^{-\frac{3}{2}}$$

with the straight line

$$y = a\,(b - x). \quad \text{[Fig. 7.]}$$

The position of the straight line is determined by its cutting the axis of $x$ at a distance equal to $\cotan q$ from the origin, and the axis of $y$ at a distance equal to $\frac{\cos q}{m}$ from the origin. This form of construction is identical with that given by M. Binet in the *Journal de l'Ecole Polytechnique*, 20 Cahier, Tome XIII. p. 285. His method of fixing the position of the straight line is not strictly accurate. This mode of representation is not surpassed by either of the others under this form.

(c.) The fourth root of the fundamental equation developed, and divided by $\cos (z - q)$, assumes the form

$$\sqrt[4]{m \cos q\,(\tan (z - q) + \tan q)} = \frac{\sqrt[4]{(\sin (z - q))}}{\cos (z - q)}.$$

By putting

$$x = \tan (z - q)$$
$$b = \tan q$$
$$a = \sqrt[4]{m} \cos q$$

the roots of the equation correspond to the intersection of the curve

$$y = \frac{\sqrt[4]{(\sin (z - q))}}{\cos (z - q)} = x^{\frac{1}{4}} (1 + x^2)^{\frac{3}{8}}$$

with the straight line

$$y = a (x + b). \quad [\text{Fig. 8.}]$$

The straight line cuts the axis of $x$ at a distance equal to $- \tan q$, and the axis of $y$ at a distance equal to $\sqrt[4]{m} \sin q$, from the origin.

(*d*.) The development of the fourth root of the fundamental equation divided by $\sin (z - q)$ is,

$$\sqrt[4]{m} \sin q (\cotan (z - q) + \cotan q) = \cosec (z - q)^{\frac{3}{4}}.$$

By putting

$$x = \cotan (z - q)$$
$$b = \cotan q$$
$$a = \sqrt[4]{m} \sin q$$

the roots of the equation correspond to the intersection of the curve

$$y = (1 + x^2)^{\frac{3}{8}}$$

with the straight line

$$y = a (x + b). \quad [\text{Figs. 9 and 9'.}]$$

The straight line cuts the axis of $x$ at a distance equal to $- \cotan q$, and the axis of $y$ at a distance equal to $\sqrt[4]{m} \cos q$, from the origin.

(*e*.) From the reciprocal of the fundamental equation multiplied by $m$, its roots may be seen to correspond to the intersection of the curve

$$r = \cosec^4 z$$

with the straight line

$$r = m \cosec (z - q). \quad [\text{Figs. 10 and 10'.}]$$

Both these equations are referred to polar coördinates, of which $r$ is the radius vector, $z$ the angle which the radius vector makes with the polar axis, $m$ the distance of the straight line from the origin, and $q$ the inclination of the line to the polar axis.

($f$). From the reciprocal of the fourth root of the fundamental equation, its roots may be seen to correspond to the intersection of the curve

$$r = \operatorname{cosec}^{\frac{1}{4}} \varphi$$

with the straight line

$$r = \sqrt[4]{\frac{1}{m}} \operatorname{cosec} (\varphi + q),$$

in which

$$\varphi = z - q. \quad [\text{Fig. 11.}]$$

Both these equations are referred to polar coördinates, of which $\varphi$ is the angle which the radius vector $r$ makes with the polar axis, $\sqrt[4]{\frac{1}{m}}$ the distance of the straight line from the origin, and $q$ the inclination of the line to the polar axis.

3. The third method of representation is by a curve and a circle.

($a$.) The roots of the fundamental equation correspond to the intersection of the curve

$$r = \sin^4 z$$

with the circle

$$r = \frac{1}{m} \sin (z - z). \quad [\text{Fig. 12.}].$$

Both these equations are referred to polar coördinates, of which $r$ is the radius vector, $z$ the angle which the radius vector makes with the polar axis, $\frac{1}{m}$ the radius of the circle which passes through the origin, and $90° + q$ is the angle which the diameter drawn to the origin makes with the polar axis.

($b$.) From the fourth root of the fundamental equation it appears that its roots correspond to the intersection of the equation

$$r = \sqrt[4]{\ } \sin \varphi$$

with the circle

$$r = \sqrt[4]{\ } m \sin (\varphi + q) \quad [\text{Fig. 13}],$$

in which $\varphi = (z - q)$ is the inclination of the radius vector to the polar axis, $\sqrt[4]{\ } m$ is the diameter of the circle which passes through the origin, and $90° - q$ is the inclination of the diameter drawn through the origin of the polar axis.

In these last two delineations the curve $I\,K\,I'\,K'\,I''$ incloses a space, within which the centre of the circle must be contained, in order that there should be four real roots, and therefore that there should be a possible orbit. The curve itself corresponds to the limiting points of osculation denoted by Professor Encke's $m'$ and $m''$, and the points $K$ and $K'$ correspond to the extreme points of osculation of the second order, for which Encke has given the values $q = \mp 36° 52'$ and $m' = 4.2976$, and $m'' = 9.9999$.

On the delineations, $S$ is the centre of the circle for our example of Ceres, and $S'$ the same for Dr. Gould's exceptional case. A careful examination of the singular position of the point $S'$ will illustrate the peculiar difficulties attending the solution of this rare example.

## 159.

We add another example, which was prepared with great care to illustrate the Method of Computing an Orbit from three observations published in pamphlet form for the use of the American Ephemeris and Nautical Almanac in 1852. It furnishes an illustration of the case of the determination of two orbits from the same three geocentric places, referred to in article 142.

We take the following observations, made at the Greenwich Observatory, from the volume for the year 1845, p. 36.

| Mean Time, Greenwich. | Apparent Right Ascension. | Apparent Declination. |
|---|---|---|
| *m. h. s.*<br>1845. July 30, 14 5 10.8<br>Sept. 6, 11 5 56.8<br>Oct. 14, 8 19 35.9 | 339 51 15.15<br>332 22 39.30<br>328 7 51.45 | S. 23 31 34.60<br>27 10 23.13<br>26 49 57.23 |

From the *Nautical Almanac* for the same year, we obtain

| Date. | Longitude of the Sun from App. Equinox. | Nutation. | Distance from the Earth. | Latitude of the Sun. | Apparent Obliquity of the Ecliptic. |
|---|---|---|---|---|---|
| July 30.<br>Sept. 6.<br>Oct. 14. | 127 40 11.32<br>164 9 40.85<br>201 21 12.49 | +14.99<br>+14.06<br>+12.16 | 0.0064168<br>0.0031096<br>9.9984688 | −0.17<br>+0.21<br>+0.53 | 23 27 28.13<br>28.41<br>28.05 |

The computation is arranged as if the orbit were wholly unknown, on which account we are not at liberty to free the places of Ceres from parallax, but must transfer it to the places of the earth.

40

Reducing the observed places of the planet from the equator to the ecliptic, we find

| Date. | App. Longitude of Ceres. | App. Latitude of Ceres. |
|---|---|---|
| July 30. | 332° 28′ 28″.02 | S. 13° 54′ 52″.47 |
| Sept. 6. | 324 35 58.87 | 14 45 30.00 |
| Oct. 14. | 321 4 54.55 | 13 5 35.33 |

And also,

| Date. | Longitude of Zenith. | Latitude of Zenith. |
|---|---|---|
| July 30. | 11° 6′ | N. 53° 26′ |
| Sept. 6. | 4 49 | 56 22 |
| Oct. 14. | 1 4 | 58 4 |

The method of article 72 gives

| Date. | Reduction of Longitude. | Reduction of Distance. | Reduction of Time. |
|---|---|---|---|
| July 30. | +16″.32 | +0.0001368 | —0.070 |
| Sept. 6. | — 7.10 | 1421 | —0.065 |
| Oct. 14. | —26.95 | 0907 | —0.071 |

The reduction of time is merely added to show that it is wholly insensible.

All the longitudes, both of the planet and of the earth, are to be reduced to the mean vernal equinox for the beginning of the year 1845, which is taken as the epoch; the nutation, therefore, being applied, we are still to subtract the precession, which for the three observations is 28″.99, 34″.20, and 39″.41, respectively; so that for the first observation it is necessary to add — 43″.98, for the second, — 48″.26, and for the third, — 51″.57.

Finally, the latitudes and longitudes of Ceres are to be freed from the aberration of the fixed stars, by subtracting from the longitudes 18″.76, 19″.69, and 10″.40, respectively, and adding to the latitudes — 2.02, + 1.72, and + 4.02, numbers which are obtained from the following formulas of Prof. PEIRCE : —

$$\delta \alpha = m \cos (\odot - \alpha) \sec \beta$$
$$\delta \beta = m \sin (\odot - \alpha) \sin \alpha ;$$

where $\odot$ = sun's longitude, and $m$ = aberration of $\odot$.

The longitudes of the sun were corrected for aberration by adding $20''.06$, $20''.21$, and $20''.43$, respectively, to the numbers given in the *Nautical Almanac*.

These reductions having been made, the correct data of the problem are as follows : —

Times of observation.

| For Washington Meridian. | July 30.  372903. | Sept. 6.  248435. | Oct. 14.  132915. |
|---|---|---|---|
| Ceres's long. $\alpha$, $\alpha'$, $\alpha''$ | $330°\ 27'\ 25''.28$ | $324\ 34\ \ 50.92$ | $321\ \ 3\ \ 52.58$ |
| latitudes $\beta$, $\beta'$, $\beta''$ | $-\ 13\ \ 54\ \ 54\ .49$ | $-\ 14\ 45\ \ 28.28$ | $-\ 13\ \ 5\ \ 31.31$ |
| Earth's long. $l$, $l'$, $l''$ | $307\ \ 39\ \ 43\ .66$ | $344\ \ 8\ \ 45.49$ | $21\ 19\ 53.97$ |
| logs. of dist. $R$, $R'$, $R''$ | $0.0064753$ | $0.0031709$ | $9.9985083$ |

By the formulas of Arts. 136 and 137, we find

| | | | |
|---|---|---|---|
| $\gamma$, $\gamma'$, $\gamma''$ . . . . . | $329°\ 25'\ 34''.81$ | $218°\ 11'\ 22''.38$ | $194\ \ 59\ \ 35\ .15$ |
| $\delta$, $\delta'$, $\delta''$ . . . . . | $28\ \ 12\ \ 56\ .84$ | $24\ \ 19\ 53\ .34$ | $61\ \ 6\ \ 50.78$ |
| log $\delta$, $\delta'$, $\delta''$ sines | $9.6746717$ | $9.6149131$ | $9.9422976$ |
| $A'\,D$, $A\,D'$, $A\,D''$ | $199°\ 45'\ 41''.00$ | $204°\ \ 8'\ 25''.14$ | $203°\ 56'\ 46''.56$ |
| $A''\,D$, $A''\,D'$, $A'\,D''$, | $233\ \ 54\ \ 11\ .72$ | $233\ \ 31\ 23\ .54$ | $199\ \ 30\ 24\ .04$ |
| $\varepsilon$, $\varepsilon'$, $\varepsilon''$, | $27\ \ 32\ \ 45\ .72$ | $142\ \ 37\ 25\ .44$ | $115\ \ 4\ \ 41\ .10$ |
| log $\varepsilon$, $\varepsilon'$, $\varepsilon''$ sines, . | $9.6650753$ | $9.7832221$ | $9.956992$ |
| log sin $\frac{1}{2}\,\varepsilon'$ | | $9.9764767$ | |
| log cos $\frac{1}{2}\,\varepsilon'$ | | $9.5057153$ | |

And by article 138,

$$\log T \sin t \ . \ . \ . \ . \ \ 6.2654993\,n$$
$$\log T \cos t \qquad\quad 9{,}2956278\,n$$

wherefore

$$t = 180°\ \ 3'\ 12''.63,\ \log T\ .\ .\ .\ \ 9.2956280$$
$$t + \gamma' = \ 38°\ 14'\ 35''.01,\ \log \sin (t + \gamma')\ \ 9.7916898$$
$$\log S\ .\ .\ .\ .\ .\ .\ \ 8.6990834$$
$$\log T \sin (t + \gamma)\ .\ .\ \ \underline{9.0873178}$$

Whence

$$\log \tan (\delta' - \sigma)\ .\ .\ .\ \ 9.6117656$$
$$\delta' - \sigma = 22°\ 14'\ 47''.47 \text{ and } \sigma = 2°\ 5'\ 5''.87.$$

By articles 140–143, we find

$$
\begin{array}{llll}
A'' D' - \delta'' & = 172^\circ\ 24'\ 32''.76 & \log \sin 9.1208995 & \log \cos 9.9961773\,n \\
A D' - \delta & = 175\ \ 55\ \ 28\ .30 & 8.8516890 & 9.9989004\,n \\
A'' D - \delta'' & = 172\ \ 47\ \ 20\ .94 & 9.0987168 & \\
A D - \delta' + \sigma & = 177\ \ 30\ \ 53\ .53 & 8.6370904 & \\
A D'' - \delta & = 175\ \ 43\ \ 49\ .72 & 8.8718546 & \\
A' D'' - \delta' + \sigma & = 177\ \ 15\ \ 36\ .57 & 8.6794373 &
\end{array}
$$

$$\log a \ \ . \ \ . \ \ . \ \ . \ \ . \ \ 0.0095516,\ a = 1.0222370$$

$$\log b \ \ . \ \ . \ \ . \ \ . \ \ . \ \ 0.1389045.$$

Formula 13, which serves as a check, would give $\log b = 0.1389059$. We prefer the latter value, because $\sin (A' D - \delta' + \sigma)$ is less than $\sin (A' D'' - \delta' + \sigma)$.

The interval of the time (not corrected) between the second and third observations is 37.884480 days, and between the first and second 37.875532 days. The logarithms of these numbers are 1.5784613 and 1.5783587; the logarithm of $k$ is 8.2355814; whence $\log \theta = 9.8140427$, $\log \theta'' = 9.8139401$.

We shall put, therefore, for the first hypothesis

$$x = \log P = \frac{\theta''}{\theta} = 9.9998974$$

$$y = \log Q = \theta\,\theta'' = 9.6269828$$

and we find

$$\omega = 5^\circ\ 43'\ 56''.13$$

$$\omega + \sigma = 7\ \ 49\ \ \ 2\ .00$$

$$\log Q\, c \sin \omega = 0.9112987$$

It is found, by a few trials, that the equation

$$Q\, c \sin \omega \sin^4 z = \sin (z + 7^\circ\ 49'\ 2''.00)$$

is satisfied by the value

$$z = 7^\circ\ 59'\ 30''.30,$$

whence $\log \sin z = 9.1431101$, and

$$r' = \frac{R' \sin \delta'}{\sin z} = 0.474939.$$

Besides this solution, the equation admits of three others, —

$$z = \phantom{0}26° 24' \phantom{0}3''$$
$$z = 148 \phantom{00} 2 \phantom{0} 35$$
$$z = 187 \phantom{0} 40 \phantom{00} 9$$

The third must be rejected, because sin $z$ is negative; the second, because $z$ is greater than $\delta'$; the first answers to the approximation to the orbit of the earth, of which we have spoken in article 142.*

The manner of making these trials is as follows. On looking at the table of sines we are led to take for a first approximation for one of the values, $z = 8°$ nearly, or $8° + x$. Then we have

$$\log \sin z \phantom{....} \ldots \ldots \ldots \phantom{.} 9.14356 + 89\,x$$
$$\log \sin^4 z \phantom{.} \ldots \ldots \ldots \phantom{.} 6.57424 + 356\,x$$
$$\log Q\,c \sin \omega \ldots \ldots \ldots \phantom{.} 0.91130$$

$$\overline{\log \sin (z - \omega - \sigma) \phantom{.} \ldots \phantom{.} 7.48554 + 356\,x}$$
$$z - \omega - \sigma = 0° \phantom{0} 10' \phantom{0} 52'' + \tfrac{356}{4139}\,x$$
$$\omega + \sigma = 7 \phantom{00} 49 \phantom{000} 3$$
$$z = 7 \phantom{00} 59 \phantom{0} 55 + \tfrac{1}{12}\,x, \text{ nearly} = 8° + x.$$

For the second approximation, we make

$$z = 7° 59' 30'' + x'; \text{ and have}$$

$$\log \sin z \phantom{.} \ldots \ldots \phantom{.} 9.1431056 + 150\,x'$$
$$\log \sin^4 z \ldots \ldots \phantom{.} 6.5724224 + 600\,x',$$
$$Q\,c \sin \omega \ldots \ldots \phantom{.} 0.9112987$$

$$\overline{\log \sin (z - \omega - \sigma) \phantom{.} \ldots \phantom{.} 7.4837211 + 600\,x'}$$
$$z - \omega - \sigma = 0° \phantom{0} 10' \phantom{0} 28''.27 + \tfrac{1}{10}\,x' \text{ nearly.}$$
$$\omega + \sigma = 7 \phantom{0} 49 \phantom{00} 2.\,00$$
$$z = 7 \phantom{0} 59 \phantom{0} 30.\,27 + \tfrac{1}{10}\,x' = 7° 59' 30''.30.$$

The process is the same for the other roots.

---

* See article 142 of the Appendix.

Again, by art. 143 we obtain

$$\zeta = 185° \ 10' \ 31''.78$$
$$\zeta'' = 189 \ \ 25 \ \ 30 \ .25$$
$$\log r = 0.4749722$$
$$\log r'' = 0.4744748$$
$$\tfrac{1}{2}(u'' + u) = 264° \ 21' \ 48''.61$$
$$\tfrac{1}{2}(u'' - u) = 288 \ \ 49 \ \ \ 5 \ .19$$
$$2f \ \ = \ \ \ 6 \ \ 57 \ \ \ 7 \ .46$$
$$2f'' \ = \ \ \ 6 \ \ 56 \ \ 32 \ .68$$

The sum $2f + 2f''$, which is a check, only differs by $0''.20$ from $2f'$, and the equation

$$P = \frac{r \sin 2f''}{r'' \sin 2f} = \frac{n''}{n}$$

is sufficiently satisfied by distributing this $0''.2$ equally between $2f$ and $2f''$, so that $2f = 6°59'7''.36$, and $2f'' = 6°56'32''.58$.

Now, in order that the times may be corrected for aberration, the distances $\varrho$, $\varrho'$, $\varrho''$ must be computed by the formulas of Art. 145, and then multiplied into the time $493^s$ or $0^d.005706$, as follows: —

$$
\begin{array}{ll}
\log r \ \ . \ . \ . \ . \ . \ . \ . & 0.47497 \\
\log \sin (\mathrm{A\,D} - \zeta) \ . \ . \ . \ . & 9.51187 \\
\text{comp. } \log \sin \delta \ . \ . \ . \ . \ . & 0.32533 \\
\hline
\log \varrho & 0.31217 \\
\log \text{const} & 7.76054 \, * \\
\hline
\log \text{ of reduction} & 8.07271 \\
\ \ \ \ \ \ \text{Reduction} = 0.011823 \\
\\
\log r', & 0.47497 \\
\log \sin (\delta - z) & 9.44921 \\
\text{comp } \log \sin \delta', & 0.38509 \\
\hline
\log \text{ of reduction} & 0.30927 \\
\ \ \ \ \ \ \text{Reduction, } 0.011744.
\end{array}
$$

---

* The constant of aberration is that of M. Struve.

$$\log r'' \quad . \quad . \quad . \quad . \quad . \quad . \quad . \quad . \quad 0.47447$$

$$\log \sin (A'' D' - \zeta'') \quad . \quad . \quad . \quad 9.84253$$

$$\log \sin \delta'' \quad . \quad . \quad . \quad . \quad . \quad . \quad . \quad 0.05770$$

$$\log \text{ of reduction} \quad . \quad . \quad . \quad . \quad 0.37470$$

Reduction $= 0.013653$

| Observations. | Corrected Times. | Intervals. | Logarithms. |
|---|---|---|---|
| I. | July 30. 361080 | | |
| II. | Sept. 6. 236691 | 37.875611 | 1.5783596 |
| III. | Oct. 14. 119260 | 37.882569 | 1.5784395 |

Hence the corrected logarithms of the quantities $\theta$, $\theta''$ become 9.8140209, and 9.8139410.

We are now, according to the precept of Art. 146, to commence the determination of the elements from the quantities $f$, $r'$, $r''$, $\theta$, and to continue the calculation so far as to obtain $\eta$, and again from the quantities $f''$, $r$, $r'$, $\theta''$ so as to obtain $\eta''$.

$$\log \eta \quad . \quad . \quad . \quad . \quad . \quad 0.0011576$$

$$\log \eta'' \quad . \quad . \quad . \quad . \quad . \quad 0.0011552$$

$$\log P' \quad . \quad . \quad . \quad . \quad 9.9999225$$

$$\log Q' \quad . \quad . \quad . \quad . \quad 9.6309476$$

From the first hypothesis, therefore, there results $X = 0.0000251$, and $Y = 0.0029648$.

In the second hypothesis, we assign to $P$ and $Q$ the values which we find in the first hypothesis for $P'$ and $Q'$. We put, therefore,

$$x = \log P = 9.9999225,$$

$$y = \log Q = 9.6309476.$$

Since the computation is to be performed in precisely the same manner as in the first hypothesis, it is sufficient to set down here its principal results: —

| | | | |
|---|---|---|---|
| $\omega$ . . . . . . . . . 5° 43′ 56″.10 | $z$ . . . . . . . . . . 7° 59′ 34″ 98 |
| $\omega + \sigma$ . . . . . . 7 49 1 .97 | $\log r'$ . . . . . . . 0.4749037 |
| $\log Q c \sin \omega$ . . . . . 0.9142633 | $\log \dfrac{n' r'}{n}$ . . . . . . 0.7724177 |

| | | | | |
|---|---|---|---|---|
| $\log \frac{n'\,r'}{n''}$ . . . . . . . . | 0.7724952 | $\frac{1}{2}(u'+u)$ . . . . | 264° 21′ 50″.64 |
| $\zeta$ . . . . . . . . . | 185° 10′ 39″ 64 | $\frac{1}{2}(u''-u)$ . . . . | 288 49 5 .57 |
| $\zeta''$ . . . . . . . | 189 25 42 .36 | $2f'$ . . . . . . . | .13 53 58 82 |
| $\log r$ . . . . . . . | 0.4748696 | $2f$ . . . . . . . | 6 57 15 58 |
| $\log r''$ . . . . . . . | 0.4743915 | $2f''$ . . . . . . . | 6 56 43 41 |

In this case we distribute the difference 0″.17 so as to make $2f = 6° 51′ 15″.49$ and $2f'' = 6° 56′ 43″.33$.

It would not be worth while to compute anew the reductions of the time on account of the aberration, for they scarcely differ 1″ from those which we derived from the first hypothesis.

Further computations furnish

$\log \eta = 0.0011582$, $\log \eta'' = 0.0011558$, whence are deduced
$$\log P' = 9.9999225, \quad X = 0.0000000$$
$$\log Q' = 9.6309955, \quad Y = 0.0000479.$$

From which it is apparent how much more exact the second hypothesis is than the first.

For the sake of completing the example, we will still construct the third hypothesis, in which we shall adopt the values of $P'$ and $Q'$ derived from the second hypothesis for the values of $P$ and $Q$.

Putting, therefore,
$$x = \log P = 9.9999225$$
$$y = \log Q = 9.6309955$$

the following are obtained for the most important parts of the computation : —

| | | | | |
|---|---|---|---|---|
| $\omega$ . . . . . . . . . | 5° 43′ 56″.10 | $\zeta''$ . . . . . . . | 189° 25′ 42″.45 |
| $\omega + \sigma$ . . . . . . . | 7 49 1 .97 | $\log r$ . . . . . . | 0.4748690 |
| $\log Q\,c \sin \omega$ . . . . | 0.9143111 | $\log r''$ . . . . . . | 0.4743909 |
| $z$ . . . . . . . . | 7° 59′ 35″.02 | $\frac{1}{2}(u''+u)$ . . . . | 264° 21′ 50″.64 |
| $\log r'$ . . . . . . . | 0.4749031 | $\frac{1}{2}(u''-u)$ . . . . | 288 49 5 .57 |
| $\log \frac{n'\,r'}{n}$ . . . . . . | 0.7724168 | $2f'$ . . . . . . | 13 53 58 .94 |
| $\log \frac{n'\,r'}{n''}$ . . . . . . | 0.7724943 | $2f$ . . . . . . . | 6 57 15 .65 |
| $\zeta$ . . . . . . . . | 185° 10′ 39″.69 | $2f''$ . . . . . . | 6 56 43 .49 |

The difference $0''.2$ between $2f'$ and $2f + 2f''$ is divided as in the first hypothesis, making $2f = 6° 57' 15''.55$, and $2f'' = 6° 56' 43''.39$.

All these numbers differ so little from those given by the second hypothesis that it may safely be concluded that the third hypothesis requires no further correction; if the computation should be continued as in the preceding hypotheses, the result would be $X = 0.0000000$, $Y = 0.0000001$, which last value must be regarded as of no consequence, and not exceeding the unavoidable uncertainty belonging to the last decimal figure.

We are, therefore, at liberty to proceed to the determination of the elements from $2f'$, $r$, $r''$, $\theta'$ according to the methods contained in articles 88–97.

The elements are found to be as follows : —

| | |
|---|---|
| Epoch of the mean longitude, 1845, . . . . . | $278° 47' 13''.79$ |
| Mean daily motion, . . . . . . . . | $771''.5855$ |
| Longitude of the perihelion, . . . . . . | $148° 27' 49''.70$ |
| Angle of eccentricity, . . . . . . . . | $4\ 33\ 28\ .35$ |
| Logarithm of the major semi-axis . . . . | $0.4417481$ |
| Longitude of the ascending node, . . . . | $80° 46' 36''.94$ |
| Inclination of the orbit, . . . . . . . . | $10\ 37\ \ \ 7\ .98$ |

The computation of the middle place from these elements gives

$$\alpha' = 324° 34' 51''.05, \quad \beta' = -14° 45' 28''.31$$

which differ but little from the observed values

$$\alpha' = 324° 34' 50''.92, \quad \beta' = -14° 45' 28''.28.$$

41

## FORMULAS FOR COMPUTING THE ORBIT OF A COMET.

Given

| | |
|---|---|
| Mean times of the observations in days, | $t'$, $t''$, $t'''$ |
| Observed longitudes of the comet, | $\alpha'$, $\alpha''$, $\alpha'''$ |
| Observed latitudes of the comet, | $\beta'$, $\beta''$, $\beta'''$ |
| Longitudes of the sun, | $A'$, $A''$, $A'''$ |
| Distances of the sun from the earth, | $R'$, $R''$, $R'''$ |

Required

The curtate distances from the earth, $\qquad\qquad \varrho'$, $\varrho''$, $\varrho'''$

Compute

### I.

$$m = \frac{\tan \beta''}{\sin (\alpha'' - A'')} \qquad M = \frac{t''' - t''}{t'' - t'} \frac{m \sin (\alpha' - A'') - \tan \beta'}{\tan \beta''' - m \sin (\alpha''' - A'')}$$

and by means of this, approximately,

$$\varrho''' = M \varrho'.$$

### II.

$$R''' \cos (A''' - A') - R' = g \cos (G - A')$$
$$R''' \sin (A''' - A') = g \sin (G - A')$$

$g$ is the chord of the earth's orbit between the first and third places of the earth. $G$ the longitude of the first place of the earth as seen from the third place.

### III.

$$M - \cos (\alpha''' - \alpha') = h \cos \zeta \cos (H - \alpha''')$$
$$\sin (\alpha''' - \alpha') = h \cos \zeta \sin (H - \alpha''')$$
$$M \tan \beta''' - \tan \beta' = h \sin \zeta.$$

$h$ is always positive. If $N$ is a point, the coördinates of which, referred to the third place of the earth, are

$$\varrho' \cos \alpha', \quad \varrho' \sin \alpha', \quad \varrho \tan \beta,$$

then are

$$h \varrho', \quad H, \quad \zeta,$$

the polar coördinates of the third place of the comet, (that is, the distance, longitude and latitude,) referred to the point $N$ as the origin.

## IV.

$$\cos \zeta \cos (G - H) = \cos \varphi \qquad g \sin \varphi = A$$
$$\cos \beta' \cos (\alpha' - A') = \cos \psi' \qquad R' \sin \psi' = B'$$
$$\cos \beta''' \cos (\alpha''' - A''') = \cos \psi''' \qquad R''' \sin \psi''' = B'''$$

By means of $\varphi$, $\psi'$, $\psi'''$, $A$, $B'$, $B'''$, Olbers's formulas, become :—

$$k^2 = (h \varrho' - g \cos \varphi)^2 + A^2$$
$$r'^2 = (\varrho' \sec \beta' - R' \cos \psi')^2 + B'^2$$
$$r'''^2 = (M \varrho' \sec \beta''' - R''' \cos \psi''')^2 + B'''^2$$

The computation would be somewhat easier by

## V.

$$h \cos \beta' = f', \qquad g \cos \varphi - f' R' \cos \psi' = c'$$
$$\frac{h \cos \beta'''}{M} = f''' \qquad g \cos \psi - f''' R''' \cos \psi''' = c'''$$

$$k^2 = u^2 + A^2$$
$$r'^2 = \left(\frac{u + c'}{f'}\right)^2 + B'^2$$
$$r'''^2 = \left(\frac{u + c'''}{f'''}\right)^2 + B'''^2$$

in which

$$u = h \varrho' - g \cos \varphi$$

## VI.

A value of $u$ is to be found by trial which will satisfy the equation

$$(r' + r''' + k)^{\frac{3}{2}} - (r' + r''' - k)^{\frac{3}{2}} = \frac{t''' - t'}{m'},$$

in which

$$\log m' = 0.9862673$$

If no approximate value for $\varrho'$ or for $r'$ or $r'''$ is otherwise known, by means of which an approximate value of $u$ can be found, we may begin with

$$u = \pm \sqrt{\left[\left(\frac{t''' - t'}{41}\right)^2 - A^2\right]}$$

This trial will be facilitated by Table III$a$, which gives $\mu$ corresponding to

$$\eta = \frac{\varkappa\,(t''' - t')}{(r' + r''')^{\frac{3}{2}}},$$

by means of which is found $k$, which corresponds rigorously to $r$, $r'''$, and $t''' - t'$: —

$$k = \frac{\varkappa\,(t''' - t')}{(r' + r''')^{\frac{1}{2}}}\,\mu,$$

in which

$$\log \varkappa = 8.5366114.$$

The process may be as follows: For any value of $u$ compute $k$, $r'$, $r'''$, by V, and with $r'$, $r'''$, compute $\eta$, with which $\mu$ is to be taken from Table III$a$, and a value of $k$ is to be computed which corresponds to the $r'$, $r'''$, $t''' - t'$ used. And $u$ is to be changed until the second value of $k$ shall agree exactly with that computed by V.

Then we have

$$\varrho' = \frac{u + g \cos \varphi}{h}$$

$$\varrho''' = M \varrho'.$$

## VII.

$$\varrho' \cos (\alpha' - A') - R' = r' \cos b' \cos (l - A')$$
$$\varrho' \sin (\alpha' - A') = r' \cos b' \sin (l - A')$$
$$\varrho' \tan \beta' = r' \sin b'$$
$$\varrho''' \cos (\alpha''' - A''') - R'' = r''' \cos b''' \cos (l'' - A''')$$
$$\varrho''' \sin (\alpha''' - A''') = r''' \cos b''' \sin (l'' - A''')$$
$$\varrho''' \tan \beta''' = r''' \sin b'''.$$

### FIRST CONTROL.

The values of $r'$, $r'''$, obtained from these formulas, must agree exactly with those before computed.

$l$, $b'$; $l''$, $b'''$, are heliocentric longitudes and latitudes of the comet.

The motion is direct when $l''' - l$ is positive, and retrograde when $l'' - l$ is negative.

## VIII.

$$\pm \tan b' = \tan i \sin (l' - \Omega)$$

$$\pm \frac{\tan b''' - \tan b' \cos (l''' - l')}{\sin (l''' - l')} = \tan i \cos (l - \Omega)$$

$i$ the inclination is always positive, and less than 90°. The upper signs are to be used when the motion is direct; the lower when it is retrograde.

## IX.

$$\frac{\tan (l' - \Omega)}{\cos i} = \tan (L' - \Omega), \quad \frac{\tan (l''' - \Omega)}{\cos i} = \tan (L''' - \Omega).$$

$L'$ and $L'''$ are the longitudes in orbit.

### SECOND CONTROL.

The value of $k$ before computed must be exactly

$$k = \sqrt{[r'^2 + r'''^2 - 2 r' r''' \cos (L''' - L')]}.$$

## X.

$$\frac{1}{\sqrt{r'}} = \frac{\cos \frac{1}{2} (L' - \pi)}{\sqrt{q}}$$

$$\frac{\cos (L''' - L')}{\sqrt{r'}} - \frac{\operatorname{cosec} \frac{1}{2} (L''' - L')}{\sqrt{r'''}} = \frac{\sin \frac{1}{2} (L' - \pi)}{\sqrt{q}}$$

$\pi$, the longitude of the perihelion, is counted from a point in the orbit from which the distance, in the direction of the order of the signs, to the ascending node, is equal to the longitude of the ascending node.

## XI.

The true anomalies are

$$v' = L' - \pi, \quad v''' = L''' - \pi.$$

With these the corresponding $M'$ and $M'''$ are to be taken from BARKER's Table, and we have then the time of perihelion passage

$$T = t' \mp M' q^{\frac{3}{2}} n = t''' \mp M''' q^{\frac{3}{2}} n,$$

in which $M'$ and $M''''$ have the sign of $v'$ and $v'''$; the constant $\log n$ is

$$\log n = 0.0398723 .$$

The upper signs serve for direct, the lower for retrograde motion.

For the use of Table II$a$ instead of BARKER's Table, see Article 18 of the Appendix.

### THIRD CONTROL.

The two values of $T$, from $t'$, and $t'''$, must agree exactly.

## XII.

With $T$, $q$, $\pi$, $\Omega$, $i$, $l''$, $A''$, $R''$, compute $\alpha''$ and $\beta''$, and compare them with the observed values.  And also compute with these values the formula

$$m = \frac{\tan \beta''}{\sin (\alpha'' - A'')} .$$

If this value agrees with that of $m$ of formulas I., the orbit is exactly determined according to the principles of Olbers's Method.  That is, while it satisfies exactly the two extreme places of the comet, it agrees with the observations in the great circle which connects the middle place of the Comet with the middle place of the Sun.

If a difference is found, $M$ can be changed until the agreement is complete.

# TABLES.

TABLE I. (See articles 42, 45.) 1

| A | ELLIPSE. | | | | HYPERBOLA. | | |
|---|---|---|---|---|---|---|---|
| | Log B | C | T | | Log B | C | T |
| 0.000 | 0 | 0 | 0.00000 | | 0 | 0 | 0.00000 |
| .001 | 0 | 0 | .00100 | | 0 | 0 | .00100 |
| .002 | 0 | 2 | .00200 | | 0 | 2 | .00200 |
| .003 | 1 | 4 | .00301 | | 1 | 4 | .00299 |
| .004 | 1 | 7 | .00401 | | 1 | 7 | .00399 |
| 0.005 | 2 | 11 | 0.00502 | | 2 | 11 | 0.00498 |
| .006 | 3 | 16 | .00603 | | 3 | 16 | .00597 |
| .007 | 4 | 22 | .00704 | | 4 | 22 | .00696 |
| .008 | 5 | 29 | .00805 | | 5 | 29 | .00795 |
| .009 | 6 | 37 | .00907 | | 6 | 37 | .00894 |
| 0.010 | 7 | 46 | 0.01008 | | 7 | 46 | 0.00992 |
| .011 | 9 | 56 | .01110 | | 9 | 55 | .01090 |
| .012 | 11 | 66 | .01212 | | 11 | 66 | .01189 |
| .013 | 13 | 78 | .01314 | | 13 | 77 | .01287 |
| .014 | 15 | 90 | .01416 | | 15 | 89 | .01384 |
| 0.015 | 17 | 103 | 0.01518 | | 17 | 102 | 0.01482 |
| .016 | 19 | 118 | .01621 | | 19 | 116 | .01580 |
| .017 | 22 | 133 | .01723 | | 21 | 131 | .01677 |
| .018 | 24 | 149 | .01826 | | 24 | 147 | .01774 |
| .019 | 27 | 166 | .01929 | | 27 | 164 | .01872 |
| 0.020 | 30 | 184 | 0.02032 | | 30 | 182 | 0.01968 |
| .021 | 33 | 203 | .02136 | | 33 | 200 | .02065 |
| .022 | 36 | 223 | .02239 | | 36 | 220 | .02162 |
| .023 | 40 | 244 | .02343 | | 39 | 240 | .02258 |
| .024 | 43 | 265 | .02447 | | 43 | 261 | .02355 |
| 0.025 | 47 | 288 | 0.02551 | | 46 | 283 | 0.02451 |
| .026 | 51 | 312 | .02655 | | 50 | 306 | .02547 |
| .027 | 55 | 336 | .02760 | | 54 | 330 | .02643 |
| .028 | 59 | 362 | .02864 | | 58 | 355 | .02739 |
| .029 | 63 | 388 | .02969 | | 62 | 381 | .02834 |
| 0.030 | 67 | 416 | 0.03074 | | 67 | 407 | 0.02930 |
| .031 | 72 | 444 | .03179 | | 71 | 435 | .03025 |
| .032 | 77 | 473 | .03284 | | 76 | 463 | .03120 |
| .033 | 82 | 503 | .03389 | | 80 | 492 | .03215 |
| .034 | 87 | 535 | .03495 | | 85 | 523 | .03310 |
| 0.035 | 92 | 567 | 0.03601 | | 91 | 554 | 0.03404 |
| .036 | 97 | 600 | .03707 | | 96 | 585 | .03499 |
| .037 | 103 | 634 | .03813 | | 101 | 618 | .03593 |
| .038 | 108 | 669 | .03919 | | 107 | 652 | .03688 |
| .039 | 114 | 704 | .04025 | | 112 | 686 | .03782 |
| .040 | 120 | 741 | .04132 | | 118 | 722 | .03876 |

| | ELLIPSE. | | | | HYPERBOLA. | | |
|---|---|---|---|---|---|---|---|
| A | Log B | C | T | | Log B | C | T |
| 0.040 | 120 | 741 | 0.041319 | | 118 | 722 | 0.038757 |
| .041 | 126 | 779 | .042387 | | 124 | 758 | .039695 |
| .042 | 133 | 818 | .043457 | | 130 | 795 | .040632 |
| .043 | 139 | 858 | .044528 | | 136 | 833 | .041567 |
| .044 | 146 | 898 | .045601 | | 143 | 872 | .042500 |
| 0.045 | 152 | 940 | 0.046676 | | 149 | 912 | 0.043432 |
| .046 | 159 | 982 | .047753 | | 156 | 953 | .044363 |
| .047 | 166 | 1026 | .048831 | | 163 | 994 | .045292 |
| .048 | 173 | 1070 | .049911 | | 170 | 1037 | .046220 |
| .049 | 181 | 1116 | .050993 | | 177 | 1080 | .047147 |
| 0.050 | 188 | 1162 | 0.052077 | | 184 | 1124 | 0.048072 |
| .051 | 196 | 1210 | .053163 | | 191 | 1169 | .048995 |
| .052 | 204 | 1258 | .054250 | | 199 | 1215 | .049917 |
| .053 | 212 | 1307 | .055339 | | 207 | 1262 | .050838 |
| .054 | 220 | 1358 | .056430 | | 215 | 1310 | .051757 |
| 0.055 | 228 | 1409 | 0.057523 | | 223 | 1358 | 0.052675 |
| .056 | 236 | 1461 | .058618 | | 231 | 1407 | .053592 |
| .057 | 245 | 1514 | .059714 | | 239 | 1458 | .054507 |
| .058 | 254 | 1568 | .060812 | | 247 | 1509 | .055420 |
| .059 | 263 | 1623 | .061912 | | 256 | 1561 | .056332 |
| 0.060 | 272 | 1679 | 0.063014 | | 265 | 1614 | 0.057243 |
| .061 | 281 | 1736 | .064118 | | 273 | 1667 | .058152 |
| .062 | 290 | 1794 | .065223 | | 282 | 1722 | .059060 |
| .063 | 300 | 1853 | .066331 | | 291 | 1777 | .059967 |
| .064 | 309 | 1913 | .067440 | | 301 | 1833 | .060872 |
| 0.065 | 319 | 1974 | 0.068551 | | 310 | 1891 | 0.061776 |
| .066 | 329 | 2036 | .069664 | | 320 | 1949 | .062678 |
| .067 | 339 | 2099 | .070779 | | 329 | 2007 | .063579 |
| .068 | 350 | 2163 | .071896 | | 339 | 2067 | .064479 |
| .069 | 360 | 2228 | .073014 | | 349 | 2128 | .065377 |
| 0.070 | 371 | 2294 | 0.074135 | | 359 | 2189 | 0.066274 |
| .071 | 381 | 2360 | .075257 | | 370 | 2251 | .067170 |
| .072 | 392 | 2428 | .076381 | | 380 | 2314 | .068064 |
| .073 | 403 | 2497 | .077507 | | 390 | 2378 | .068957 |
| .074 | 415 | 2567 | .078635 | | 401 | 2443 | .069848 |
| 0.075 | 426 | 2638 | 0.079765 | | 412 | 2509 | 0.070738 |
| .076 | 437 | 2709 | .080897 | | 423 | 2575 | .071627 |
| .077 | 449 | 2782 | .082030 | | 434 | 2643 | .072514 |
| .078 | 461 | 2856 | .083166 | | 445 | 2711 | .073400 |
| .079 | 473 | 2930 | .084303 | | 457 | 2780 | .074285 |
| .080 | 485 | 3006 | .085443 | | 468 | 2850 | .075168 |

# TABLE I.

3

| A | ELLIPSE. | | | | HYPERBOLA. | | |
|---|---|---|---|---|---|---|---|
| | Log B | C | T | | Log B | C | T |
| 0.080 | 485 | 3006 | 0.085443 | | 468 | 2850 | 0.075168 |
| .081 | 498 | 3083 | .086584 | | 480 | 2921 | .076050 |
| .082 | 510 | 3160 | .087727 | | 492 | 2992 | .076930 |
| .083 | 523 | 3239 | .088872 | | 504 | 3065 | .077810 |
| .084 | 535 | 3319 | .090019 | | 516 | 3138 | .078688 |
| 0.085 | 548 | 3399 | 0.091168 | | 528 | 3212 | 0.079564 |
| .086 | 561 | 3481 | .092319 | | 540 | 3287 | .080439 |
| .087 | 575 | 3564 | .093472 | | 553 | 3363 | .081313 |
| .088 | 588 | 3647 | .094627 | | 566 | 3440 | .082186 |
| .089 | 602 | 3732 | .095784 | | 578 | 3517 | .083057 |
| 0.090 | 615 | 3818 | 0.096943 | | 591 | 3595 | 0.083927 |
| .091 | 629 | 3904 | .098104 | | 604 | 3674 | .084796 |
| .092 | 643 | 3992 | .099266 | | 618 | 3754 | .085663 |
| .093 | 658 | 4081 | .100431 | | 631 | 3835 | .086529 |
| .094 | 672 | 4170 | .101598 | | 645 | 3917 | .087394 |
| 0.095 | 687 | 4261 | 0.102766 | | 658 | 3999 | 0.088257 |
| .096 | 701 | 4353 | .103937 | | 672 | 4083 | .089119 |
| .097 | 716 | 4446 | .105110 | | 686 | 4167 | .089980 |
| .098 | 731 | 4539 | .106284 | | 700 | 4252 | .090840 |
| .099 | 746 | 4634 | .107461 | | 714 | 4338 | .091698 |
| 0.100 | 762 | 4730 | 0.108640 | | 728 | 4424 | 0.092555 |
| .101 | 777 | 4826 | .109820 | | 743 | 4512 | .093410 |
| .102 | 793 | 4924 | .111003 | | 758 | 4600 | .094265 |
| .103 | 809 | 5023 | .112188 | | 772 | 4689 | .095118 |
| .104 | 825 | 5123 | .113375 | | 787 | 4779 | .095969 |
| 0.105 | 841 | 5224 | 0.114563 | | 802 | 4870 | 0.096820 |
| .106 | 857 | 5325 | .115754 | | 817 | 4962 | .097669 |
| .107 | 873 | 5428 | .116947 | | 833 | 5054 | .098517 |
| .108 | 890 | 5532 | .118142 | | 848 | 5148 | .099364 |
| .109 | 907 | 5637 | .119339 | | 864 | 5242 | .100209 |
| 0.110 | 924 | 5743 | 0.120538 | | 880 | 5337 | 0.101053 |
| .111 | 941 | 5850 | .121739 | | 895 | 5432 | .101896 |
| .112 | 958 | 5958 | .122942 | | 911 | 5529 | .102738 |
| .113 | 975 | 6067 | .124148 | | 928 | 5626 | .103578 |
| .114 | 993 | 6177 | .125355 | | 944 | 5724 | .104417 |
| 0.115 | 1011 | 6288 | 0.126564 | | 960 | 5823 | 0.105255 |
| .116 | 1029 | 6400 | .127776 | | 977 | 5923 | .106092 |
| .117 | 1047 | 6513 | .128989 | | 994 | 6024 | .106927 |
| .118 | 1065 | 6627 | .130205 | | 1010 | 6125 | .107761 |
| .119 | 1083 | 6742 | .131423 | | 1027 | 6228 | .108594 |
| .120 | 1102 | 6858 | .132643 | | 1045 | 6331 | .109426 |

| | ELLIPSE. | | | | HYPERBOLA. | | |
|---|---|---|---|---|---|---|---|
| A | Log B | C | T | | Log B | C | T |
| 0.120 | 1102 | 6858 | 0.132643 | | 1045 | 6331 | 0.109426 |
| .121 | 1121 | 6976 | .133865 | | 1062 | 6435 | .110256 |
| .122 | 1139 | 7094 | .135089 | | 1079 | 6539 | .111085 |
| .123 | 1158 | 7213 | .136315 | | 1097 | 6645 | .111913 |
| .124 | 1178 | 7334 | .137543 | | 1114 | 6751 | .112740 |
| 0.125 | 1197 | 7455 | 0.138774 | | 1132 | 6858 | 0.113566 |
| .126 | 1217 | 7577 | .140007 | | 1150 | 6966 | .114390 |
| .127 | 1236 | 7701 | .141241 | | 1168 | 7075 | .115213 |
| .128 | 1256 | 7825 | .142478 | | 1186 | 7185 | .116035 |
| .129 | 1276 | 7951 | .143717 | | 1205 | 7295 | .116855 |
| 0.130 | 1296 | 8077 | 0.144959 | | 1223 | 7406 | 0.117675 |
| .131 | 1317 | 8205 | .146202 | | 1242 | 7518 | .118493 |
| .132 | 1337 | 8334 | .147448 | | 1261 | 7631 | .119310 |
| .133 | 1358 | 8463 | .148695 | | 1280 | 7745 | .120126 |
| .134 | 1378 | 8594 | .149945 | | 1299 | 7859 | .120940 |
| 0.135 | 1399 | 8726 | 0.151197 | | 1318 | 7974 | 0.121754 |
| .136 | 1421 | 8859 | .152452 | | 1337 | 8090 | .122566 |
| .137 | 1442 | 8993 | .153708 | | 1357 | 8207 | .123377 |
| .138 | 1463 | 9128 | .154967 | | 1376 | 8325 | .124186 |
| .139 | 1485 | 9264 | .156228 | | 1396 | 8443 | .124995 |
| 0.140 | 1507 | 9401 | 0.157491 | | 1416 | 8562 | 0.125802 |
| .141 | 1529 | 9539 | .158756 | | 1436 | 8682 | .126609 |
| .142 | 1551 | 9678 | .160024 | | 1456 | 8803 | .127414 |
| .143 | 1573 | 9819 | .161294 | | 1476 | 8925 | .128217 |
| .144 | 1596 | 9960 | .162566 | | 1497 | 9047 | .129020 |
| 0.145 | 1618 | 10102 | 0.163840 | | 1517 | 9170 | 0.129822 |
| .146 | 1641 | 10246 | .165116 | | 1538 | 9294 | .130622 |
| .147 | 1664 | 10390 | .166395 | | 1559 | 9419 | .131421 |
| .148 | 1687 | 10536 | .167676 | | 1580 | 9545 | .132219 |
| .149 | 1710 | 10683 | .168959 | | 1601 | 9671 | .133016 |
| 0.150 | 1734 | 10830 | 0.170245 | | 1622 | 9798 | 0.133812 |
| .151 | 1757 | 10979 | .171533 | | 1643 | 9926 | .134606 |
| .152 | 1781 | 11129 | .172823 | | 1665 | 10055 | .135399 |
| .153 | 1805 | 11280 | .174115 | | 1686 | 10185 | .136191 |
| .154 | 1829 | 11432 | .175410 | | 1708 | 10315 | .136982 |
| 0.155 | 1854 | 11585 | 0.176707 | | 1730 | 10446 | 0.137772 |
| .156 | 1878 | 11739 | .178006 | | 1752 | 10578 | .138561 |
| .157 | 1903 | 11894 | .179308 | | 1774 | 10711 | .139349 |
| .158 | 1927 | 12051 | .180612 | | 1797 | 10844 | .140135 |
| .159 | 1952 | 12208 | .181918 | | 1819 | 10978 | .140920 |
| .160 | 1977 | 12366 | .183226 | | 1842 | 11113 | .141704 |

TABLE I. 5

| A | ELLIPSE. | | | | HYPERBOLA. | | |
| | Log B | C | T | | Log B | C | T |
|---|---|---|---|---|---|---|---|
| 0.160 | 1977 | 12366 | 0.183226 | | 1842 | 11113 | 0.141704 |
| .161 | 2003 | 12526 | .184537 | | 1864 | 11249 | .142487 |
| .162 | 2028 | 12686 | .185850 | | 1887 | 11386 | .143269 |
| .163 | 2054 | 12848 | .187166 | | 1910 | 11523 | .144050 |
| .164 | 2080 | 13011 | .188484 | | 1933 | 11661 | .144829 |
| 0.165 | 2106 | 13175 | 0.189804 | | 1956 | 11800 | 0.145608 |
| .166 | 2132 | 13340 | .191127 | | 1980 | 11940 | .146385 |
| .167 | 2158 | 13506 | .192452 | | 2003 | 12081 | .147161 |
| .168 | 2184 | 13673 | .193779 | | 2027 | 12222 | .147937 |
| .169 | 2211 | 13841 | .195109 | | 2051 | 12364 | .148710 |
| 0.170 | 2238 | 14010 | 0.196441 | | 2075 | 12507 | 0.149483 |
| .171 | 2265 | 14181 | .197775 | | 2099 | 12651 | .150255 |
| .172 | 2292 | 14352 | .199112 | | 2123 | 12795 | .151026 |
| .173 | 2319 | 14525 | .200451 | | 2147 | 12940 | .151795 |
| .174 | 2347 | 14699 | .201793 | | 2172 | 13086 | .152564 |
| 0.175 | 2374 | 14873 | 0.203137 | | 2196 | 13233 | 0.153331 |
| .176 | 2402 | 15049 | .204484 | | 2221 | 13380 | .154097 |
| .177 | 2430 | 15226 | .205832 | | 2246 | 13529 | .154862 |
| .178 | 2458 | 15404 | .207184 | | 2271 | 13678 | .155626 |
| .179 | 2486 | 15583 | .208538 | | 2296 | 13827 | .156389 |
| 0.180 | 2515 | 15764 | 0.209894 | | 2321 | 13978 | 0.157151 |
| .181 | 2543 | 15945 | .211253 | | 2346 | 14129 | .157911 |
| .182 | 2572 | 16128 | .212614 | | 2372 | 14281 | .158671 |
| .183 | 2601 | 16311 | .213977 | | 2398 | 14434 | .159429 |
| .184 | 2630 | 16496 | .215343 | | 2423 | 14588 | .160187 |
| 0.185 | 2660 | 16682 | 0.216712 | | 2449 | 14742 | 0.160943 |
| .186 | 2689 | 16868 | .218083 | | 2475 | 14898 | .161698 |
| .187 | 2719 | 17057 | .219456 | | 2502 | 15054 | .162453 |
| .188 | 2749 | 17246 | .220832 | | 2528 | 15210 | .163206 |
| .189 | 2779 | 17436 | .222211 | | 2554 | 15368 | .163958 |
| 0.190 | 2809 | 17627 | 0.223592 | | 2581 | 15526 | 0.164709 |
| .191 | 2839 | 17820 | .224975 | | 2608 | 15685 | .165458 |
| .192 | 2870 | 18013 | .226361 | | 2634 | 15845 | .166207 |
| .193 | 2900 | 18208 | .227750 | | 2661 | 16005 | .166955 |
| .194 | 2931 | 18404 | .229141 | | 2688 | 16167 | .167702 |
| 0.195 | 2962 | 18601 | 0.230535 | | 2716 | 16329 | 0.168447 |
| .196 | 2993 | 18799 | .231931 | | 2743 | 16491 | .169192 |
| .197 | 3025 | 18998 | .233329 | | 2771 | 16655 | .169935 |
| .198 | 3056 | 19198 | .234731 | | 2798 | 16819 | .170678 |
| .199 | 3088 | 19400 | .236135 | | 2826 | 16984 | .171419 |
| .200 | 3120 | 19602 | .237541 | | 2854 | 17150 | .172159 |

# TABLE I.

| | ELLIPSE. | | | | HYPERBOLA. | | |
|---|---|---|---|---|---|---|---|
| A | Log B | C | T | | Log B | C | T |
| 0.200 | 3120 | 19602 | 0.237541 | | 2854 | 17150 | 0.172159 |
| .201 | 3152 | 19806 | .238950 | | 2882 | 17317 | .172899 |
| .202 | 3184 | 20011 | .240361 | | 2910 | 17484 | .173637 |
| .203 | 3216 | 20217 | .241776 | | 2938 | 17652 | .174374 |
| .204 | 3249 | 20424 | .243192 | | 2967 | 17821 | .175110 |
| 0.205 | 3282 | 20632 | 0.244612 | | 2995 | 17991 | 0.175845 |
| .206 | 3315 | 20842 | .246034 | | 3024 | 18161 | .176579 |
| .207 | 3348 | 21052 | .247458 | | 3053 | 18332 | .177312 |
| .208 | 3381 | 21264 | .248885 | | 3082 | 18504 | .178044 |
| .209 | 3414 | 21477 | .250315 | | 3111 | 18677 | .178775 |
| 0.210 | 3448 | 21690 | 0.251748 | | 3140 | 18850 | 0.179505 |
| .211 | 3482 | 21905 | .253183 | | 3169 | 19024 | .180234 |
| .212 | 3516 | 22122 | .254620 | | 3199 | 19199 | .180962 |
| .213 | 3550 | 22339 | .256061 | | 3228 | 19375 | .181688 |
| .214 | 3584 | 22557 | .257504 | | 3258 | 19551 | .182414 |
| 0.215 | 3618 | 22777 | 0.258950 | | 3288 | 19728 | 0.183139 |
| .216 | 3653 | 22998 | .260398 | | 3318 | 19906 | .183863 |
| .217 | 3688 | 23220 | .261849 | | 3348 | 20084 | .184585 |
| .218 | 3723 | 23443 | .263303 | | 3378 | 20264 | .185307 |
| .219 | 3758 | 23667 | .264759 | | 3409 | 20444 | .186028 |
| 0.220 | 3793 | 23892 | 0.266218 | | 3439 | 20625 | 0.186747 |
| .221 | 3829 | 24119 | .267680 | | 3470 | 20806 | .187466 |
| .222 | 3865 | 24347 | .269145 | | 3500 | 20988 | .188184 |
| .223 | 3900 | 24576 | .270612 | | 3531 | 21172 | .188900 |
| .224 | 3936 | 24806 | .272082 | | 3562 | 21355 | .189616 |
| 0.225 | 3973 | 25037 | 0.273555 | | 3594 | 21540 | 0.190331 |
| .226 | 4009 | 25269 | .275031 | | 3625 | 21725 | .191044 |
| .227 | 4046 | 25502 | .276509 | | 3656 | 21911 | .191757 |
| .228 | 4082 | 25737 | .277990 | | 3688 | 22098 | .192468 |
| .229 | 4119 | 25973 | .279474 | | 3719 | 22285 | .193179 |
| 0.230 | 4156 | 26210 | 0.280960 | | 3751 | 22473 | 0.193889 |
| .231 | 4194 | 26448 | .282450 | | 3783 | 22662 | .194597 |
| .232 | 4231 | 26687 | .283942 | | 3815 | 22852 | .195305 |
| .233 | 4269 | 26928 | .285437 | | 3847 | 23042 | .196012 |
| .234 | 4306 | 27169 | .286935 | | 3880 | 23234 | .196717 |
| 0.235 | 4344 | 27412 | 0.288435 | | 3912 | 23425 | 0.197422 |
| .236 | 4382 | 27656 | .289939 | | 3945 | 23618 | .198126 |
| .237 | 4421 | 27901 | .291445 | | 3977 | 23811 | .198829 |
| .238 | 4459 | 28148 | .292954 | | 4010 | 24005 | .199530 |
| .239 | 4498 | 28395 | .294466 | | 4043 | 24200 | .200231 |
| .240 | 4537 | 28644 | .295980 | | 4076 | 24396 | .200931 |

TABLE I. 7

| A | ELLIPSE. | | | | HYPERBOLA. | | |
|---|---|---|---|---|---|---|---|
| | Log B | C | T | | Log B | C | T |
| 0.240 | 4537 | 28644 | 0.295980 | | 4076 | 24396 | 0.200931 |
| .241 | 4576 | 28894 | .297498 | | 4110 | 24592 | .201630 |
| .242 | 4615 | 29145 | .299018 | | 4143 | 24789 | .202328 |
| .243 | 4654 | 29397 | .300542 | | 4176 | 24987 | .203025 |
| .244 | 4694 | 29651 | .302068 | | 4210 | 25185 | .203721 |
| 0.245 | 4734 | 29905 | 0.303597 | | 4244 | 25384 | 0.204416 |
| .246 | 4774 | 30161 | .305129 | | 4277 | 25584 | .205110 |
| .247 | 4814 | 30418 | .306664 | | 4311 | 25785 | .205803 |
| .248 | 4854 | 30676 | .308202 | | 4346 | 25986 | .206495 |
| .249 | 4894 | 30935 | .309743 | | 4380 | 26188 | .207186 |
| 0.250 | 4935 | 31196 | 0.311286 | | 4414 | 26391 | 0.207876 |
| .251 | 4976 | 31458 | .312833 | | 4449 | 26594 | .208565 |
| .252 | 5017 | 31721 | .314382 | | 4483 | 26799 | .209254 |
| .253 | 5058 | 31985 | .315935 | | 4518 | 27004 | .209941 |
| .254 | 5099 | 32250 | .317490 | | 4553 | 27209 | .210627 |
| 0.255 | 5141 | 32517 | 0.319048 | | 4588 | 27416 | 0.211313 |
| .256 | 5182 | 32784 | .320610 | | 4623 | 27623 | .211997 |
| .257 | 5224 | 33053 | .322174 | | 4658 | 27830 | .212681 |
| .258 | 5266 | 33323 | .323741 | | 4694 | 28039 | .213364 |
| .259 | 5309 | 33595 | .325312 | | 4729 | 28248 | .214045 |
| 0.260 | 5351 | 33867 | 0.326885 | | 4765 | 28458 | 0.214726 |
| .261 | 5394 | 34141 | .328461 | | 4801 | 28669 | .215406 |
| .262 | 5436 | 34416 | .330041 | | 4838 | 28880 | .216085 |
| .263 | 5479 | 34692 | .331623 | | 4873 | 29092 | .216763 |
| .264 | 5522 | 34970 | .333208 | | 4909 | 29305 | .217440 |
| 0.265 | 5566 | 35248 | 0.334797 | | 4945 | 29519 | 0.218116 |
| .266 | 5609 | 35528 | .336388 | | 4981 | 29733 | .218791 |
| .267 | 5653 | 35809 | .337983 | | 5018 | 29948 | .219465 |
| .268 | 5697 | 36091 | .339580 | | 5055 | 30164 | .220138 |
| .269 | 5741 | 36375 | .341181 | | 5091 | 30380 | .220811 |
| 0.270 | 5785 | 36659 | 0.342785 | | 5128 | 30597 | 0.221482 |
| .271 | 5829 | 36945 | .344392 | | 5165 | 30815 | .222153 |
| .272 | 5874 | 37232 | .346002 | | 5202 | 31033 | .222822 |
| .273 | 5919 | 37521 | .347615 | | 5240 | 31253 | .223491 |
| .274 | 5964 | 37810 | .349231 | | 5277 | 31473 | .224159 |
| 0.275 | 6009 | 38101 | 0.350850 | | 5315 | 31693 | 0.224826 |
| .276 | 6054 | 38393 | .352473 | | 5352 | 31915 | .225492 |
| .277 | 6100 | 38686 | .354098 | | 5390 | 32137 | .226157 |
| .278 | 6145 | 38981 | .355727 | | 5428 | 32359 | .226821 |
| .279 | 6191 | 39277 | .357359 | | 5466 | 32583 | .227484 |
| .280 | 6237 | 39573 | .358994 | | 5504 | 32807 | .228147 |

# TABLE I.

| A | ELLIPSE. | | | | HYPERBOLA. | | |
|---|---|---|---|---|---|---|---|
| | Log B | C | T | | Log B | C | T |
| 0.280 | 6237 | 39573 | 0.358994 | | 5504 | 32807 | 0.228147 |
| .281 | 6283 | 39872 | .360632 | | 5542 | 33032 | .228808 |
| .282 | 6330 | 40171 | .362274 | | 5581 | 33257 | .229469 |
| .283 | 6376 | 40472 | .363918 | | 5619 | 33484 | .230128 |
| .284 | 6423 | 40774 | .365566 | | 5658 | 33711 | .230787 |
| 0.285 | 6470 | 41077 | 0.367217 | | 5697 | 33938 | 0.231445 |
| .286 | 6517 | 41381 | .368871 | | 5736 | 34167 | .232102 |
| .287 | 6564 | 41687 | .370529 | | 5775 | 34396 | .232758 |
| .288 | 6612 | 41994 | .372189 | | 5814 | 34626 | .233413 |
| .289 | 6660 | 42302 | .373853 | | 5853 | 34856 | .234068 |
| 0.290 | 6708 | 42611 | 0.375521 | | 5893 | 35087 | 0.234721 |
| .291 | 6756 | 42922 | .377191 | | 5932 | 35319 | .235374 |
| .292 | 6804 | 43233 | .378865 | | 5972 | 35552 | .236025 |
| .293 | 6852 | 43547 | .380542 | | 6012 | 35785 | .236676 |
| .294 | 6901 | 43861 | .382222 | | 6052 | 36019 | .237326 |
| 0.295 | 6950 | 44177 | 0.383906 | | 6092 | 36253 | 0.237975 |
| .296 | 6999 | 44493 | .385593 | | 6132 | 36489 | .238623 |
| .297 | 7048 | 44812 | .387283 | | 6172 | 36725 | .239271 |
| .298 | 7097 | 45131 | .388977 | | 6213 | 36961 | .239917 |
| .299 | 7147 | 45452 | .390673 | | 6253 | 37199 | .240563 |
| .300 | 7196 | 45774 | .392374 | | 6294 | 37437 | .241207 |

TABLE II. (See Article 93.) 9

| h | log y y | h | log y y | h | log y y |
|---|---------|---|---------|---|---------|
| 0.0000 | 0.0000000 | 0.0040 | 0.0038332 | 0.0080 | 0.0076133 |
| .0001 | .0000965 | .0041 | .0039284 | .0081 | .0077071 |
| .0002 | .0001930 | .0042 | .0040235 | .0082 | .0078009 |
| .0003 | .0002894 | .0043 | .0041186 | .0083 | .0078947 |
| .0004 | .0003858 | .0044 | .0042136 | .0084 | .0079884 |
| 0.0005 | 0.0004821 | 0.0045 | 0.0043086 | 0.0085 | 0.0080821 |
| .0006 | .0005784 | .0046 | .0044036 | .0086 | .0081758 |
| .0007 | .0006747 | .0047 | .0044985 | .0087 | .0082694 |
| .0008 | .0007710 | .0048 | .0045934 | .0088 | .0083630 |
| .0009 | .0008672 | .0049 | .0046883 | .0089 | .0084566 |
| 0.0010 | 0.0009634 | 0.0050 | 0.0047832 | 0.0090 | 0.0085502 |
| .0011 | .0010595 | .0051 | .0048780 | .0091 | .0086437 |
| .0012 | .0011556 | .0052 | .0049728 | .0092 | .0087372 |
| .0013 | .0012517 | .0053 | .0050675 | .0093 | .0088306 |
| .0014 | .0013478 | .0054 | .0051622 | .0094 | .0089240 |
| 0.0015 | 0.0014438 | 0.0055 | 0.0052569 | 0.0095 | 0.0090174 |
| .0016 | .0015398 | .0056 | .0053515 | .0096 | .0091108 |
| .0017 | .0016357 | .0057 | .0054462 | .0097 | .0092041 |
| .0018 | .0017316 | .0058 | .0055407 | .0098 | .0092974 |
| .0019 | .0018275 | .0059 | .0056353 | .0099 | .0093906 |
| 0.0020 | 0.0019234 | 0.0060 | 0.0057298 | 0.0100 | 0.0094838 |
| .0021 | .0020192 | .0061 | .0058243 | .0101 | .0095770 |
| .0022 | .0021150 | .0062 | .0059187 | .0102 | .0096702 |
| .0023 | .0022107 | .0063 | .0060131 | .0103 | .0097633 |
| .0024 | .0023064 | .0064 | .0061075 | .0104 | .0098564 |
| 0.0025 | 0.0024021 | 0.0065 | 0.0062019 | 0.0105 | 0.0099495 |
| .0026 | .0024977 | .0066 | .0062962 | .0106 | .0100425 |
| .0027 | .0025933 | .0067 | .0063905 | .0107 | .0101355 |
| .0028 | .0026889 | .0068 | .0064847 | .0108 | .0102285 |
| .0029 | .0027845 | .0069 | .0065790 | .0109 | .0103215 |
| 0.0030 | 0.0028800 | 0.0070 | 0.0066732 | 0.0110 | 0.0104144 |
| .0031 | .0029755 | .0071 | .0067673 | .0111 | .0105073 |
| .0032 | .0030709 | .0072 | .0068614 | .0112 | .0106001 |
| .0033 | .0031663 | .0073 | .0069555 | .0113 | .0106929 |
| .0034 | .0032617 | .0074 | .0070496 | .0114 | .0107857 |
| 0.0035 | 0.0033570 | 0.0075 | 0.0071436 | 0.0115 | 0.0108785 |
| .0036 | .0034523 | .0076 | .0072376 | .0116 | .0109712 |
| .0037 | .0035476 | .0077 | .0073316 | .0117 | .0110639 |
| .0038 | .0036428 | .0078 | .0074255 | .0118 | .0111565 |
| .0039 | .0037380 | .0079 | .0075194 | .0119 | .0112491 |
| .0040 | .0038332 | .0080 | .0076133 | .0120 | .0113417 |

# TABLE II.

| h | log y y | h | log y y | h | log y y |
|---|---|---|---|---|---|
| 0.0120 | 0.0113417 | 0.0160 | 0.0150202 | 0.0200 | 0.0186501 |
| .0121 | .0114343 | .0161 | .0151115 | .0201 | .0187403 |
| .0122 | .0115268 | .0162 | .0152028 | .0202 | .0188304 |
| .0123 | .0116193 | .0163 | .0152941 | .0203 | .0189205 |
| .0124 | .0117118 | .0164 | .0153854 | .0204 | .0190105 |
| 0.0125 | 0.0118043 | 0.0165 | 0.0154766 | 0.0205 | 0.0191005 |
| .0126 | .0118967 | .0166 | .0155678 | .0206 | .0191905 |
| .0127 | .0119890 | .0167 | .0156589 | .0207 | .0192805 |
| .0128 | .0120814 | .0168 | .0157500 | .0208 | .0193704 |
| .0129 | .0121737 | .0169 | .0158411 | .0209 | .0194603 |
| 0.0130 | 0.0122660 | 0.0170 | 0.0159322 | 0.0210 | 0.0195502 |
| .0131 | .0123582 | .0171 | .0160232 | .0211 | .0196401 |
| .0132 | .0124505 | .0172 | .0161142 | .0212 | .0197299 |
| .0133 | .0125427 | .0173 | .0162052 | .0213 | .0198197 |
| .0134 | .0126348 | .0174 | .0162961 | .0214 | .0199094 |
| 0.0135 | 0.0127269 | 0.0175 | 0.0163870 | 0.0215 | 0.0199992 |
| .0136 | .0128190 | .0176 | .0164779 | .0216 | .0200889 |
| .0137 | .0129111 | .0177 | .0165688 | .0217 | .0201785 |
| .0138 | .0130032 | .0178 | .0166596 | .0218 | .0202682 |
| .0139 | .0130952 | .0179 | .0167504 | .0219 | .0203578 |
| 0.0140 | 0.0131871 | 0.0180 | 0.0168412 | 0.0220 | 0.0204474 |
| .0141 | .0132791 | .0181 | .0169319 | .0221 | .0205369 |
| .0142 | .0133710 | .0182 | .0170226 | .0222 | .0206264 |
| .0143 | .0134629 | .0183 | .0171133 | .0223 | .0207159 |
| .0144 | .0135547 | .0184 | .0172039 | .0224 | .0208054 |
| 0.0145 | 0.0136465 | 0.0185 | 0.0172945 | 0.0225 | 0.0208948 |
| .0146 | .0137383 | .0186 | .0173851 | .0226 | .0209842 |
| .0147 | .0138301 | .0187 | .0174757 | .0227 | .0210736 |
| .0148 | .0139218 | .0188 | .0175662 | .0228 | .0211630 |
| .0149 | .0140135 | .0189 | .0176567 | .0229 | .0212523 |
| 0.0150 | 0.0141052 | 0.0190 | 0.0177471 | 0.0230 | 0.0213416 |
| .0151 | .0141968 | .0191 | .0178376 | .0231 | .0214309 |
| .0152 | .0142884 | .0192 | .0179280 | .0232 | .0215201 |
| .0153 | .0143800 | .0193 | .0180183 | .0233 | .0216093 |
| .0154 | .0144716 | .0194 | .0181087 | .0234 | .0216985 |
| 0.0155 | 0.0145631 | 0.0195 | 0.0181990 | 0.0235 | 0.0217876 |
| .0156 | .0146546 | .0196 | .0182893 | .0236 | .0218768 |
| .0157 | .0147460 | .0197 | .0183796 | .0237 | .0219659 |
| .0158 | .0148374 | .0198 | .0184698 | .0238 | .0220549 |
| .0159 | .0149288 | .0199 | .0185600 | .0239 | .0221440 |
| .0160 | .0150202 | .0200 | .0186501 | .0240 | .0222330 |

TABLE II. 11

| h | log y y | h | log y y | h | log y y |
|---|---|---|---|---|---|
| 0.0240 | 0.0222330 | 0.0280 | 0.0257700 | 0.0320 | 0.0292626 |
| .0241 | .0223220 | .0281 | .0258579 | .0321 | .0293494 |
| .0242 | .0224109 | .0282 | .0259457 | .0322 | .0294361 |
| .0243 | .0224998 | .0283 | .0260335 | .0323 | .0295228 |
| .0244 | .0225887 | .0284 | .0261213 | .0324 | .0296095 |
| 0.0245 | 0.0226776 | 0.0285 | 0.0262090 | 0.0325 | 0.0296961 |
| .0246 | .0227664 | .0286 | .0262967 | .0326 | .0297827 |
| .0247 | .0228552 | .0287 | .0263844 | .0327 | .0298693 |
| .0248 | .0229440 | .0288 | .0264721 | .0328 | .0299559 |
| .0249 | .0230328 | .0289 | .0265597 | .0329 | .0300424 |
| 0.0250 | 0.0231215 | 0.0290 | 0.0266473 | 0.0330 | 0.0301290 |
| .0251 | .0232102 | .0291 | .0267349 | .0331 | .0302154 |
| .0252 | .0232988 | .0292 | .0268224 | .0332 | .0303019 |
| .0253 | .0233875 | .0293 | .0269099 | .0333 | .0303883 |
| .0254 | .0234761 | .0294 | .0269974 | .0334 | .0304747 |
| 0.0255 | 0.0235647 | 0.0295 | 0.0270849 | 0.0335 | 0.0305611 |
| .0256 | .0236532 | .0296 | .0271723 | .0336 | .0306475 |
| .0257 | .0237417 | .0297 | .0272597 | .0337 | .0307338 |
| .0258 | .0238302 | .0298 | .0273471 | .0338 | .0308201 |
| .0259 | .0239187 | .0299 | .0274345 | .0339 | .0309064 |
| 0.0260 | 0.0240071 | 0.0300 | 0.0275218 | 0.0340 | 0.0309926 |
| .0261 | .0240956 | .0301 | .0276091 | .0341 | .0310788 |
| .0262 | .0241839 | .0302 | .0276964 | .0342 | .0311650 |
| .0263 | .0242723 | .0303 | .0277836 | .0343 | .0312512 |
| .0264 | .0243606 | .0304 | .0278708 | .0344 | .0313373 |
| 0.0265 | 0.0244489 | 0.0305 | 0.0279580 | 0.0345 | 0.0314234 |
| .0266 | .0245372 | .0306 | .0280452 | .0346 | .0315095 |
| .0267 | .0246254 | .0307 | .0281323 | .0347 | .0315956 |
| .0268 | .0247136 | .0308 | .0282194 | .0348 | .0316816 |
| .0269 | .0248018 | .0309 | .0283065 | .0349 | .0317676 |
| 0.0270 | 0.0248900 | 0.0310 | 0.0283936 | 0.0350 | 0.0318536 |
| .0271 | .0249781 | .0311 | .0284806 | .0351 | .0319396 |
| .0272 | .0250662 | .0312 | .0285676 | .0352 | .0320255 |
| .0273 | .0251543 | .0313 | .0286546 | .0353 | .0321114 |
| .0274 | .0252423 | .0314 | .0287415 | .0354 | .0321973 |
| 0.0275 | 0.0253303 | 0.0315 | 0.0288284 | 0.0355 | 0.0322831 |
| .0276 | .0254183 | .0316 | .0289153 | .0356 | .0323689 |
| .0277 | .0255063 | .0317 | .0290022 | .0357 | .0324547 |
| .0278 | .0255942 | .0318 | .0290890 | .0358 | .0325405 |
| .0279 | .0256821 | .0319 | .0291758 | .0359 | .0326262 |
| .0280 | .0257700 | .0320 | .0292626 | .0360 | .0327120 |

# TABLE II.

| h | log y y | h | log y y | h | log y y |
|---|---------|---|---------|---|---------|
| 0.0360 | 0.0327120 | 0.040 | 0.0361192 | 0.080 | 0.0681057 |
| .0361 | .0327976 | .041 | .0369646 | .081 | .0688612 |
| .0362 | .0328833 | .042 | .0378075 | .082 | .0696146 |
| .0363 | .0329689 | .043 | .0386478 | .083 | .0703661 |
| .0364 | .0330546 | .044 | .0394856 | .084 | .0711157 |
| 0.0365 | 0.0331401 | 0.045 | 0.0403209 | 0.085 | 0.0718633 |
| .0366 | .0332257 | .046 | .0411537 | .086 | .0726090 |
| .0367 | .0333112 | .047 | .0419841 | .087 | .0733527 |
| .0368 | .0333967 | .048 | .0428121 | .088 | .0740945 |
| .0369 | .0334822 | .049 | .0436376 | .089 | .0748345 |
| 0.0370 | 0.0335677 | 0.050 | 0.0444607 | 0.090 | 0.0755725 |
| .0371 | .0336531 | .051 | .0452814 | .091 | .0763087 |
| .0372 | .0337385 | .052 | .0460997 | .092 | .0770430 |
| .0373 | .0338239 | .053 | .0469157 | .093 | .0777754 |
| .0374 | .0339092 | .054 | .0477294 | .094 | .0785060 |
| 0.0375 | 0.0339946 | 0.055 | 0.0485407 | 0.095 | 0.0792348 |
| .0376 | .0340799 | .056 | .0493496 | .096 | .0799617 |
| .0377 | .0341651 | .057 | .0501563 | .097 | .0806868 |
| .0378 | .0342504 | .058 | .0509607 | .098 | .0814101 |
| .0379 | .0343356 | .059 | .0517628 | .099 | .0821316 |
| 0.0380 | 0.0344208 | 0.060 | 0.0525626 | 0.100 | 0.0828513 |
| .0381 | .0345059 | .061 | .0533602 | .101 | .0835693 |
| .0382 | .0345911 | .062 | .0541556 | .102 | .0842854 |
| .0383 | .0346762 | .063 | .0549488 | .103 | .0849999 |
| .0384 | .0347613 | .064 | .0557397 | .104 | .0857125 |
| 0.0385 | 0.0348464 | 0.065 | 0.0565285 | 0.105 | 0.0864235 |
| .0386 | .0349314 | .066 | .0573150 | .106 | .0871327 |
| .0387 | .0350164 | .067 | .0580994 | .107 | .0878401 |
| .0388 | .0351014 | .068 | .0588817 | .108 | .0885459 |
| .0389 | .0351864 | .069 | .0596618 | .109 | .0892500 |
| 0.0390 | 0.0352713 | 0.070 | 0.0604398 | 0.110 | 0.0899523 |
| .0391 | .0353562 | .071 | .0612157 | .111 | .0906530 |
| .0392 | .0354411 | .072 | .0619895 | .112 | .0913520 |
| .0393 | .0355259 | .073 | .0627612 | .113 | .0920494 |
| .0394 | .0356108 | .074 | .0635308 | .114 | .0927451 |
| 0.0395 | 0.0356956 | 0.075 | 0.0642984 | 0.115 | 0.0934391 |
| .0396 | .0357804 | .076 | .0650639 | .116 | .0941315 |
| .0397 | .0358651 | .077 | .0658274 | .117 | .0948223 |
| .0398 | .0359499 | .078 | .0665888 | .118 | .0955114 |
| .0399 | .0360346 | .079 | .0673483 | .119 | .0961990 |
| .0400 | .0361192 | .080 | .0681057 | .120 | .0968849 |

TABLE II.                                                      13

| h | log y y | h | log y y | h | log y y |
|---|---------|---|---------|---|---------|
| 0.120 | 0.0968849 | 0.160 | 0.1230927 | 0.200 | 0.1471869 |
| .121 | .0975692 | .161 | .1237192 | .201 | .1477653 |
| .122 | .0982520 | .162 | .1243444 | .202 | .1483427 |
| .123 | .0989331 | .163 | .1249682 | .203 | .1489189 |
| .124 | .0996127 | .164 | .1255908 | .204 | .1494940 |
| 0.125 | 0.1002907 | 0.165 | 0.1262121 | 0.205 | 0.1500681 |
| .126 | .1009672 | .166 | .1268321 | .206 | .1506411 |
| .127 | .1016421 | .167 | .1274508 | .207 | .1512130 |
| .128 | .1023154 | .168 | .1280683 | .208 | .1517838 |
| .129 | .1029873 | .169 | .1286845 | .209 | .1523535 |
| 0.130 | 0.1036576 | 0.170 | 0.1292994 | 0.210 | 0.1529222 |
| .131 | .1043264 | .171 | .1299131 | .211 | .1534899 |
| .132 | .1049936 | .172 | .1305255 | .212 | .1540565 |
| .133 | .1056594 | .173 | .1311367 | .213 | .1546220 |
| .134 | .1063237 | .174 | .1317466 | .214 | .1551865 |
| 0.135 | 0.1069865 | 0.175 | 0.1323553 | 0.215 | 0.1557499 |
| .136 | .1076478 | .176 | .1329628 | .216 | .1563123 |
| .137 | .1083076 | .177 | .1335690 | .217 | .1568737 |
| .138 | .1089660 | .178 | .1341740 | .218 | .1574340 |
| .139 | .1096229 | .179 | .1347778 | .219 | .1579933 |
| 0.140 | 0.1102783 | 0.180 | 0.1353804 | 0.220 | 0.1585516 |
| .141 | .1109323 | .181 | .1359818 | .221 | .1591089 |
| .142 | .1115849 | .182 | .1365821 | .222 | .1596652 |
| .143 | .1122360 | .183 | .1371811 | .223 | .1602204 |
| .144 | .1128857 | .184 | .1377789 | .224 | .1607747 |
| 0.145 | 0.1135340 | 0.185 | 0.1383755 | 0.225 | 0.1613279 |
| .146 | .1141809 | .186 | .1389710 | .226 | .1618802 |
| .147 | .1148264 | .187 | .1395653 | .227 | .1624315 |
| .148 | .1154704 | .188 | .1401585 | .228 | .1629817 |
| .149 | .1161131 | .189 | .1407504 | .229 | .1635310 |
| 0.150 | 0.1167544 | 0.190 | 0.1413412 | 0.230 | 0.1640793 |
| .151 | .1173943 | .191 | .1419309 | .231 | .1646267 |
| .152 | .1180329 | .192 | .1425194 | .232 | .1651730 |
| .153 | .1186701 | .193 | .1431068 | .233 | .1657184 |
| .154 | .1193059 | .194 | .1436931 | .234 | .1662628 |
| 0.155 | 0.1199404 | 0.195 | 0.1442782 | 0.235 | 0.1668063 |
| .156 | .1205735 | .196 | .1448622 | .236 | .1673488 |
| .157 | .1212053 | .197 | .1454450 | .237 | .1678903 |
| .158 | .1218357 | .198 | .1460268 | .238 | .1684309 |
| .159 | .1224649 | .199 | .1466074 | .239 | .1689705 |
| .160 | .1230927 | .200 | .1471869 | .240 | .1695092 |

| h | log y y | h | log y y | h | log y y |
|---|---------|---|---------|---|---------|
| 0.240 | 0.1695092 | 0.280 | 0.1903220 | 0.320 | 0.2098315 |
| .241 | .1700470 | .281 | .1908249 | .321 | .2103040 |
| .242 | .1705838 | .282 | .1913269 | .322 | .2107759 |
| .243 | .1711197 | .283 | .1918281 | .323 | .2112470 |
| .244 | .1716547 | .284 | .1923286 | .324 | .2117174 |
| | | | | | |
| 0.245 | 0.1721887 | 0.285 | 0.1928282 | 0.325 | 0.2121871 |
| .246 | .1727218 | .286 | .1933271 | .326 | .2126562 |
| .247 | .1732540 | .287 | .1938251 | .327 | .2131245 |
| .248 | .1737853 | .288 | .1943224 | .328 | .2135921 |
| .249 | .1743156 | .289 | .1948188 | .329 | .2140591 |
| | | | | | |
| 0.250 | 0.1748451 | 0.290 | 0.1953145 | 0.330 | 0.2145253 |
| .251 | .1753736 | .291 | .1958094 | .331 | .2149909 |
| .252 | .1759013 | .292 | .1963035 | .332 | .2154558 |
| .253 | .1764280 | .293 | .1967968 | .333 | .2159200 |
| .254 | .1769538 | .294 | .1972894 | .334 | .2163835 |
| | | | | | |
| 0.255 | 0.1774788 | 0.295 | 0.1977811 | 0.335 | 0.2168464 |
| .256 | .1780029 | .296 | .1982721 | .336 | .2173085 |
| .257 | .1785261 | .297 | .1987624 | .337 | .2177700 |
| .258 | .1790484 | .298 | .1992518 | .338 | .2182308 |
| .259 | .1795698 | .299 | .1997406 | .339 | .2186910 |
| | | | | | |
| 0.260 | 0.1800903 | 0.300 | 0.2002285 | 0.340 | 0.2191505 |
| .261 | .1806100 | .301 | .2007157 | .341 | .2196093 |
| .262 | .1811288 | .302 | .2012021 | .342 | .2200675 |
| .263 | .1816467 | .303 | .2016878 | .343 | .2205250 |
| .264 | .1821638 | .304 | .2021727 | .344 | .2209818 |
| | | | | | |
| 0.265 | 0.1826800 | 0.305 | 0.2026569 | 0.345 | 0.2214380 |
| .266 | .1831953 | .306 | .2031403 | .346 | .2218935 |
| .267 | .1837098 | .307 | .2036230 | .347 | .2223483 |
| .268 | .1842235 | .308 | .2041050 | .348 | .2228025 |
| .269 | .1847363 | .309 | .2045862 | .349 | .2232561 |
| | | | | | |
| 0.270 | 0.1852483 | 0.310 | 0.2050667 | 0.350 | 0.2237090 |
| .271 | .1857594 | .311 | .2055464 | .351 | .2241613 |
| .272 | .1862696 | .312 | .2060254 | .352 | .2246130 |
| .273 | .1867791 | .313 | .2065037 | .353 | .2250640 |
| .274 | .1872877 | .314 | .2069813 | .354 | .2255143 |
| | | | | | |
| 0.275 | 0.1877955 | 0.315 | 0.2074581 | 0.355 | 0.2259640 |
| .276 | .1883024 | .316 | .2079342 | .356 | .2264131 |
| .277 | .1888085 | .317 | .2084096 | .357 | .2268615 |
| .278 | .1893138 | .318 | .2088843 | .358 | .2273093 |
| .279 | .1898183 | .319 | .2093582 | .359 | .2277565 |
| .280 | .1903220 | .320 | .2098315 | .360 | .2282031 |

TABLE II. 15

| h | log y y | h | log y y | h | log y y |
|---|---|---|---|---|---|
| 0.360 | 0.2282031 | 0.400 | 0.2455716 | 0.440 | 0.2620486 |
| .361 | .2286490 | .401 | .2459940 | .441 | .2624499 |
| .362 | .2290943 | .402 | .2464158 | .442 | .2628507 |
| .363 | .2295390 | .403 | .2468371 | .443 | .2632511 |
| .364 | .2299831 | .404 | .2472578 | .444 | .2636509 |
| | | | | | |
| 0.365 | 0.2304265 | 0.405 | 0.2476779 | 0.445 | 0.2640503 |
| .366 | .2308694 | .406 | .2480975 | .446 | .2644492 |
| .367 | .2313116 | .407 | .2485166 | .447 | .2648475 |
| .368 | .2317532 | .408 | .2489351 | .448 | .2652454 |
| .369 | .2321942 | .409 | .2493531 | .449 | .2656428 |
| | | | | | |
| 0.370 | 0.2326346 | 0.410 | 0.2497705 | 0.450 | 0.2660397 |
| .371 | .2330743 | .411 | .2501874 | .451 | .2664362 |
| .372 | .2335135 | .412 | .2506038 | .452 | .2668321 |
| .373 | .2339521 | .413 | .2510196 | .453 | .2672276 |
| .374 | .2343900 | .414 | .2514349 | .454 | .2676226 |
| | | | | | |
| 0.375 | 0.2348274 | 0.415 | 0.2518496 | 0.455 | 0.2680171 |
| .376 | .2352642 | .416 | .2522638 | .456 | .2684111 |
| .377 | .2357003 | .417 | .2526775 | .457 | .2688046 |
| .378 | .2361359 | .418 | .2530906 | .458 | .2691977 |
| .379 | .2365709 | .419 | .2535032 | .459 | .2695903 |
| | | | | | |
| 0.380 | 0.2370053 | 0.420 | 0.2539153 | 0.460 | 0.2699824 |
| .381 | .2374391 | .421 | .2543269 | .461 | .2703741 |
| .382 | .2378723 | .422 | .2547379 | .462 | .2707652 |
| .383 | .2383050 | .423 | .2551485 | .463 | .2711559 |
| .384 | .2387370 | .424 | .2555584 | .464 | .2715462 |
| | | | | | |
| 0.385 | 0.2391685 | 0.425 | 0.2559679 | 0.465 | 0.2719360 |
| .386 | .2395993 | .426 | .2563769 | .466 | .2723253 |
| .387 | .2400296 | .427 | .2567853 | .467 | .2727141 |
| .388 | .2404594 | .428 | .2571932 | .468 | .2731025 |
| .389 | .2408885 | .429 | .2576006 | .469 | .2734904 |
| | | | | | |
| 0.390 | 0.2413171 | 0.430 | 0.2580075 | 0.470 | 0.2738778 |
| .391 | .2417451 | .431 | .2584139 | .471 | .2742648 |
| .392 | .2421725 | .432 | .2588198 | .472 | .2746513 |
| .393 | .2425994 | .433 | .2592252 | .473 | .2750374 |
| .394 | .2430257 | .434 | .2596300 | .474 | .2754230 |
| | | | | | |
| 0.395 | 0.2434514 | 0.435 | 0.2600344 | 0.475 | 0.2758082 |
| .396 | .2438766 | .436 | .2604382 | .476 | .2761929 |
| .397 | .2443012 | .437 | .2608415 | .477 | .2765771 |
| .398 | .2447252 | .438 | .2612444 | .478 | .2769609 |
| .399 | .2451487 | .439 | .2616467 | .479 | .2773443 |
| .400 | .2455716 | .440 | .2620486 | .480 | .2777272 |

# TABLE II.

| h | log y y | h | log y y | h | log y y |
|---|---------|---|---------|---|---------|
| 0.480 | 0.2777272 | 0.520 | 0.2926864 | 0.560 | 0.3069938 |
| .481 | .2781096 | .521 | .2930518 | .561 | .3073437 |
| .482 | .2784916 | .522 | .2934168 | .562 | .3076931 |
| .483 | .2788732 | .523 | .2937813 | .563 | .3080422 |
| .484 | .2792543 | .524 | .2941455 | .564 | .3083910 |
| 0.485 | 0.2796349 | 0.525 | 0.2945092 | 0.565 | 0.3087394 |
| .486 | .2800151 | .526 | .2948726 | .566 | .3090874 |
| .487 | .2803949 | .527 | .2952355 | .567 | .3094350 |
| .488 | .2807743 | .528 | .2955981 | .568 | .3097823 |
| .489 | .2811532 | .529 | .2959602 | .569 | .3101292 |
| 0.490 | 0.2815316 | 0.530 | 0.2963220 | 0.570 | 0.3104758 |
| .491 | .2819096 | .531 | .2966833 | .571 | .3108220 |
| .492 | .2822872 | .532 | .2970443 | .572 | .3111678 |
| .493 | .2826644 | .533 | .2974049 | .573 | .3115133 |
| .494 | .2830411 | .534 | .2977650 | .574 | .3118584 |
| 0.495 | 0.2834173 | 0.535 | 0.2981248 | 0.575 | 0.3122031 |
| .496 | .2837932 | .536 | .2984842 | .576 | .3125475 |
| .497 | .2841686 | .537 | .2988432 | .577 | .3128915 |
| .498 | .2845436 | .538 | .2992018 | .578 | .3132352 |
| .499 | .2849181 | .539 | .2995600 | .579 | .3135785 |
| 0.500 | 0.2852923 | 0.540 | 0.2999178 | 0.580 | 0.3139215 |
| .501 | .2856660 | .541 | .3002752 | .581 | .3142641 |
| .502 | .2860392 | .542 | .3006323 | .582 | .3146064 |
| .503 | .2864121 | .543 | .3009890 | .583 | .3149483 |
| .504 | .2867845 | .544 | .3013452 | .584 | .3152898 |
| 0.505 | 0.2871565 | 0.545 | 0.3017011 | 0.585 | 0.3156310 |
| .506 | .2875281 | .546 | .3020566 | .586 | .3159719 |
| .507 | .2878992 | .547 | .3024117 | .587 | .3163124 |
| .508 | .2882700 | .548 | .3027664 | .588 | .3166525 |
| .509 | .2886403 | .549 | .3031208 | .589 | .3169923 |
| 0.510 | 0.2890102 | 0.550 | 0.3034748 | 0.590 | 0.3173318 |
| .511 | .2893797 | .551 | .3038284 | .591 | .3176709 |
| .512 | .2897487 | .552 | .3041816 | .592 | .3180096 |
| .513 | .2901174 | .553 | .3045344 | .593 | .3183481 |
| .514 | .2904856 | .554 | .3048869 | .594 | .3186861 |
| 0.515 | 0.2908535 | 0.555 | 0.3052390 | 0.595 | 0.3190239 |
| .516 | .2912209 | .556 | .3055907 | .596 | .3193612 |
| .517 | .2915879 | .557 | .3059420 | .597 | .3196983 |
| .518 | .2919545 | .558 | .3062930 | .598 | .3200350 |
| .519 | .2923207 | .559 | .3066436 | .599 | .3203714 |
| .520 | .2926864 | .560 | .3069938 | .600 | .3207074 |

TABLE III. (See Articles 90, 100.) 17

| x or z | $\xi$ | $\zeta$ | x or z | $\xi$ | $\zeta$ |
|---|---|---|---|---|---|
| 0.000 | 0.0000000 | 0.0000000 | 0.040 | 0.0000936 | 0.0000894 |
| .001 | .0000001 | .0000001 | .041 | .0000984 | .0000938 |
| .002 | .0000002 | .0000002 | .042 | .0001033 | .0000984 |
| .003 | .0000005 | .0000005 | .043 | .0001084 | .0001031 |
| .004 | .0000009 | .0000009 | .044 | .0001135 | .0001079 |
| 0.005 | 0.0000014 | 0.0000014 | 0.045 | 0.0001188 | 0.0001128 |
| .006 | .0000021 | .0000020 | .046 | .0001242 | .0001178 |
| .007 | .0000028 | .0000028 | .047 | .0001298 | .0001229 |
| .008 | .0000037 | .0000036 | .048 | .0001354 | .0001281 |
| .009 | .0000047 | .0000046 | .049 | .0001412 | .0001334 |
| 0.010 | 0.0000058 | 0.0000057 | 0.050 | 0.0001471 | 0.0001389 |
| .011 | .0000070 | .0000069 | .051 | .0001532 | .0001444 |
| .012 | .0000083 | .0000082 | .052 | .0001593 | .0001500 |
| .013 | .0000097 | .0000096 | .053 | .0001656 | .0001558 |
| .014 | .0000113 | .0000111 | .054 | .0001720 | .0001616 |
| 0.015 | 0.0000130 | 0.0000127 | 0.055 | 0.0001785 | 0.0001675 |
| .016 | .0000148 | .0000145 | .056 | .0001852 | .0001736 |
| .017 | .0000167 | .0000164 | .057 | .0001920 | .0001798 |
| .018 | .0000187 | .0000183 | .058 | .0001989 | .0001860 |
| .019 | .0000209 | .0000204 | .059 | .0002060 | .0001924 |
| 0.020 | 0.0000231 | 0.0000226 | 0.060 | 0.0002131 | 0.0001988 |
| .021 | .0000255 | .0000249 | .061 | .0002204 | .0002054 |
| .022 | .0000280 | .0000273 | .062 | .0002278 | .0002121 |
| .023 | .0000306 | .0000298 | .063 | .0002354 | .0002189 |
| .024 | .0000334 | .0000325 | .064 | .0002431 | .0002257 |
| 0.025 | 0.0000362 | 0.0000352 | 0.065 | 0.0002509 | 0.0002327 |
| .026 | .0000392 | .0000381 | .066 | .0002588 | .0002398 |
| .027 | .0000423 | .0000410 | .067 | .0002669 | .0002470 |
| .028 | .0000455 | .0000441 | .068 | .0002751 | .0002543 |
| .029 | .0000489 | .0000473 | .069 | .0002834 | .0002617 |
| 0.030 | 0.0000523 | 0.0000506 | 0.070 | 0.0002918 | 0.0002691 |
| .031 | .0000559 | .0000539 | .071 | .0003004 | .0002767 |
| .032 | .0000596 | .0000575 | .072 | .0003091 | .0002844 |
| .033 | .0000634 | .0000611 | .073 | .0003180 | .0002922 |
| .034 | .0000674 | .0000648 | .074 | .0003269 | .0003001 |
| 0.035 | 0.0000714 | 0.0000686 | 0.075 | 0.0003360 | 0.0003081 |
| .036 | .0000756 | .0000726 | .076 | .0003453 | .0003162 |
| .037 | .0000799 | .0000766 | .077 | .0003546 | .0003244 |
| .038 | .0000844 | .0000807 | .078 | .0003641 | .0003327 |
| .039 | .0000889 | .0000850 | .079 | .0003738 | .0003411 |
| .040 | .0000936 | .0000894 | .080 | .0003835 | .0003496 |

# TABLE III.

| x or z | $\xi$ | $\zeta$ | x or z | $\xi$ | $\zeta$ |
|---|---|---|---|---|---|
| 0.080 | 0.0003835 | 0.0003496 | 0.120 | 0.0008845 | 0.0007698 |
| .081 | .0003934 | .0003582 | .121 | .0008999 | .0007822 |
| .082 | .0004034 | .0003669 | .122 | .0009154 | .0007948 |
| .083 | .0004136 | .0003757 | .123 | .0009311 | .0008074 |
| .084 | .0004239 | .0003846 | .124 | .0009469 | .0008202 |
| 0.085 | 0.0004343 | 0.0003936 | 0.125 | 0.0009628 | 0.0008330 |
| .086 | .0004448 | .0004027 | .126 | .0009789 | .0008459 |
| .087 | .0004555 | .0004119 | .127 | .0009951 | .0008590 |
| .088 | .0004663 | .0004212 | .128 | .0010115 | .0008721 |
| .089 | .0004773 | .0004306 | .129 | .0010280 | .0008853 |
| 0.090 | 0.0004884 | 0.0004401 | 0.130 | 0.0010447 | 0.0008986 |
| .091 | .0004996 | .0004496 | .131 | .0010615 | .0009120 |
| .092 | .0005109 | .0004593 | .132 | .0010784 | .0009255 |
| .093 | .0005224 | .0004691 | .133 | .0010955 | .0009390 |
| .094 | .0005341 | .0004790 | .134 | .0011128 | .0009527 |
| 0.095 | 0.0005458 | 0.0004890 | 0.135 | 0.0011301 | 0.0009665 |
| .096 | .0005577 | .0004991 | .136 | .0011477 | .0009803 |
| .097 | .0005697 | .0005092 | .137 | .0011654 | .0009943 |
| .098 | .0005819 | .0005195 | .138 | .0011832 | .0010083 |
| .099 | .0005942 | .0005299 | .139 | .0012012 | .0010224 |
| 0.100 | 0.0006066 | 0.0005403 | 0.140 | 0.0012193 | 0.0010366 |
| .101 | .0006192 | .0005509 | .141 | .0012376 | .0010509 |
| .102 | .0006319 | .0005616 | .142 | .0012560 | .0010653 |
| .103 | .0006448 | .0005723 | .143 | .0012745 | .0010798 |
| .104 | .0006578 | .0005832 | .144 | .0012933 | .0010944 |
| 0.105 | 0.0006709 | 0.0005941 | 0.145 | 0.0013121 | 0.0011091 |
| .106 | .0006842 | .0006052 | .146 | .0013311 | .0011238 |
| .107 | .0006976 | .0006163 | .147 | .0013503 | .0011387 |
| .108 | .0007111 | .0006275 | .148 | .0013696 | .0011536 |
| .109 | .0007248 | .0006389 | .149 | .0013891 | .0011686 |
| 0.110 | 0.0007386 | 0.0006503 | 0.150 | 0.0014087 | 0.0011838 |
| .111 | .0007526 | .0006618 | .151 | .0014285 | .0011990 |
| .112 | .0007667 | .0006734 | .152 | .0014484 | .0012143 |
| .113 | .0007809 | .0006851 | .153 | .0014684 | .0012296 |
| .114 | .0007953 | .0006969 | .154 | .0014886 | .0012451 |
| 0.115 | 0.0008098 | 0.0007088 | 0.155 | 0.0015090 | 0.0012607 |
| .116 | .0008245 | .0007208 | .156 | .0015295 | .0012763 |
| .117 | .0008393 | .0007329 | .157 | .0015502 | .0012921 |
| .118 | .0008542 | .0007451 | .158 | .0015710 | .0013079 |
| .119 | .0008693 | .0007574 | .159 | .0015920 | .0013238 |
| .120 | .0008845 | .0007698 | .160 | .0016131 | .0013398 |

TABLE III. 19

| x or z | ξ | ζ | x or z | ξ | ζ |
|--------|-----|-----|--------|-----|-----|
| 0.160 | 0.0016131 | 0.0013398 | 0.200 | 0.0025877 | 0.0020507 |
| .161 | .0016344 | .0013559 | .201 | .0026154 | .0020702 |
| .162 | .0016559 | .0013721 | .202 | .0026433 | .0020897 |
| .163 | .0016775 | .0013883 | .203 | .0026713 | .0021094 |
| .164 | .0016992 | .0014047 | .204 | .0026995 | .0021292 |
| 0.165 | 0.0017211 | 0.0014211 | 0.205 | 0.0027278 | 0.0021490 |
| .166 | .0017432 | .0014377 | .206 | .0027564 | .0021689 |
| .167 | .0017654 | .0014543 | .207 | .0027851 | .0021889 |
| .168 | .0017878 | .0014710 | .208 | .0028139 | .0022090 |
| .169 | .0018103 | .0014878 | .209 | .0028429 | .0022291 |
| 0.170 | 0.0018330 | 0.0015047 | 0.210 | 0.0028722 | 0.0022494 |
| .171 | .0018558 | .0015216 | .211 | .0029015 | .0022697 |
| .172 | .0018788 | .0015387 | .212 | .0029311 | .0022901 |
| .173 | .0019020 | .0015558 | .213 | .0029608 | .0023106 |
| .174 | .0019253 | .0015730 | .214 | .0029907 | .0023311 |
| 0.175 | 0.0019487 | 0.0015903 | 0.215 | 0.0030207 | 0.0023518 |
| .176 | .0019724 | .0016077 | .216 | .0030509 | .0023725 |
| .177 | .0019961 | .0016252 | .217 | .0030814 | .0023932 |
| .178 | .0020201 | .0016428 | .218 | .0031119 | .0024142 |
| .179 | .0020442 | .0016604 | .219 | .0031427 | .0024352 |
| 0.180 | 0.0020685 | 0.0016782 | 0.220 | 0.0031736 | 0.0024562 |
| .181 | .0020929 | .0016960 | .221 | .0032047 | .0024774 |
| .182 | .0021175 | .0017139 | .222 | .0032359 | .0024986 |
| .183 | .0021422 | .0017319 | .223 | .0032674 | .0025199 |
| .184 | .0021671 | .0017500 | .224 | .0032990 | .0025412 |
| 0.185 | 0.0021922 | 0.0017681 | 0.225 | 0.0033308 | 0.0025627 |
| .186 | .0022174 | .0017864 | .226 | .0033627 | .0025842 |
| .187 | .0022428 | .0018047 | .227 | .0033949 | .0026058 |
| .188 | .0022683 | .0018231 | .228 | .0034272 | .0026275 |
| .189 | .0022941 | .0018416 | .229 | .0034597 | .0026493 |
| 0.190 | 0.0023199 | 0.0018602 | 0.230 | 0.0034924 | 0.0026711 |
| .191 | .0023460 | .0018789 | .231 | .0035252 | .0026931 |
| .192 | .0023722 | .0018976 | .232 | .0035582 | .0027151 |
| .193 | .0023985 | .0019165 | .233 | .0035914 | .0027371 |
| .194 | .0024251 | .0019354 | .234 | .0036248 | .0027593 |
| 0.195 | 0.0024518 | 0.0019544 | 0.235 | 0.0036584 | 0.0027816 |
| .196 | .0024786 | .0019735 | .236 | .0036921 | .0028039 |
| .197 | .0025056 | .0019926 | .237 | .0037260 | .0028263 |
| .198 | .0025328 | .0020119 | .238 | .0037601 | .0028487 |
| .199 | .0025602 | .0020312 | .239 | .0037944 | .0028713 |
| .200 | .0025877 | .0020507 | .240 | .0038289 | .0028939 |

# TABLE III.

| x or z | $\xi$ | $\zeta$ | x or z | $\xi$ | $\zeta$ |
|--------|-------|---------|--------|-------|---------|
| 0.240 | 0.0038289 | 0.0028939 | 0.270 | 0.0049485 | 0.0036087 |
| .241 | .0038635 | .0029166 | .271 | .0049888 | .0036337 |
| .242 | .0038983 | .0029394 | .272 | .0050292 | .0036587 |
| .243 | .0039333 | .0029623 | .273 | .0050699 | .0036839 |
| .244 | .0039685 | .0029852 | .274 | .0051107 | .0037091 |
| 0.245 | 0.0040039 | 0.0030083 | 0.275 | 0.0051517 | 0.0037344 |
| .246 | .0040394 | .0030314 | .276 | .0051930 | .0037598 |
| .247 | .0040752 | .0030545 | .277 | .0052344 | .0037852 |
| .248 | .0041111 | .0030778 | .278 | .0052760 | .0038107 |
| .249 | .0041472 | .0031011 | .279 | .0053118 | .0038363 |
| 0.250 | 0.0041835 | 0.0031245 | 0.280 | 0.0053598 | 0.0038620 |
| .251 | .0042199 | .0031480 | .281 | .0054020 | .0038877 |
| .252 | .0042566 | .0031716 | .282 | .0054444 | .0039135 |
| .253 | .0042934 | .0031952 | .283 | .0054870 | .0039394 |
| .254 | .0043305 | .0032189 | .284 | .0055298 | .0039654 |
| 0.255 | 0.0043677 | 0.0032427 | 0.285 | 0.0055728 | 0.0039914 |
| .256 | .0044051 | .0032666 | .286 | .0056160 | .0040175 |
| .257 | .0044427 | .0032905 | .287 | .0056594 | .0040437 |
| .258 | .0044804 | .0033146 | .288 | .0057030 | .0040700 |
| .259 | .0045184 | .0033387 | .289 | .0057468 | .0040963 |
| 0.260 | 0.0045566 | 0.0033628 | 0.290 | 0.0057908 | 0.0041227 |
| .261 | .0045949 | .0033871 | .291 | .0058350 | .0041491 |
| .262 | .0046334 | .0034114 | .292 | .0058795 | .0041757 |
| .263 | .0046721 | .0034358 | .293 | .0059241 | .0042023 |
| .264 | .0047111 | .0034603 | .294 | .0059689 | .0042290 |
| 0.265 | 0.0047502 | 0.0034848 | 0.295 | 0.0060139 | 0.0042557 |
| .266 | .0047894 | .0035094 | .296 | .0060591 | .0042826 |
| .267 | .0048289 | .0035341 | .297 | .0061045 | .0043095 |
| .268 | .0048686 | .0035589 | .298 | .0061502 | .0043364 |
| .269 | .0049085 | .0035838 | .299 | .0061960 | .0043635 |
| .270 | .0049485 | .0036087 | .300 | .0062421 | .0043906 |

TABLE I*a*. 21

| A | ELLIPSE. | | | | HYPERBOLA. | | | |
|---|---|---|---|---|---|---|---|---|
| | Log E$_v$ | Log diff. | Log E$_r$ | Log diff. | Log E$_v$ | Log diff. | Log E$_r$. | Log diff. |
| 0.000 | 0.0000000 | 9.2401 | 0.0000000 | 9.6378 | 0.0000000 | 9.2398 | 0.0000000 | 9.6378 |
| .001 | .0001738 | .2403 | 9.9995656 | .6381 | 9.9998263 | .2395 | .0004341 | .6375 |
| .002 | .0003477 | .2406 | .9991309 | .6384 | .9996528 | .2392 | .0008680 | .6372 |
| .003 | .0005217 | .2408 | .9986959 | .6386 | .9994794 | .2389 | .0013017 | .6370 |
| .004 | .0006958 | .2413 | .9982607 | .6389 | .9993061 | .2386 | .0017350 | .6367 |
| 0.005 | 0.0008701 | 9.2416 | 9.9978252 | 9.6391 | 9.9991329 | 9.2383 | 0.0021682 | 9.6365 |
| .006 | .0010445 | .2418 | .9973895 | .6394 | .9989598 | .2381 | .0026010 | .6362 |
| .007 | .0012190 | .2420 | .9969535 | .6396 | .9987869 | .2378 | .0030337 | .6360 |
| .008 | .0013936 | .2423 | .9965173 | .6399 | .9986141 | .2375 | .0034660 | .6357 |
| .009 | .0015683 | .2428 | .9960807 | .6402 | .9984414 | .2372 | .0038981 | .6354 |
| 0.010 | 0.0017432 | 9.2430 | 9.9956439 | 9.6405 | 9.9982688 | 9.2369 | 0.0043299 | 9.6352 |
| .011 | .0019182 | .2433 | .9952068 | .6407 | .9980963 | .2366 | .0047615 | .6349 |
| .012 | .0020933 | .2435 | .9947695 | .6410 | .9979240 | .2363 | .0051928 | .6347 |
| .013 | .0022685 | .2438 | .9943319 | .6412 | .9977517 | .2360 | .0056239 | .6344 |
| .014 | .0024438 | .2443 | .9938941 | .6414 | .9975796 | .2357 | .0060547 | .6342 |
| 0.015 | 0.0026193 | 9.2445 | 9.9934560 | 9.6417 | 9.9974076 | 9.2354 | 0.0064853 | 9.6339 |
| .016 | .0027949 | .2448 | .9930176 | .6420 | .9972357 | .2351 | .0069156 | .6336 |
| .017 | .0029706 | .2453 | .9925789 | .6423 | .9970639 | .2348 | .0073456 | .6334 |
| .018 | .0031465 | .2455 | .9921400 | .6425 | .9968923 | .2345 | .0077754 | .6331 |
| .019 | .0033225 | .2458 | .9917008 | .6428 | .9967207 | .2342 | .0082049 | .6329 |
| 0.020 | 0.0034986 | 9.2460 | 9.9912614 | 9.6430 | 9.9965493 | 9.2339 | 0.0086342 | 9.6326 |
| .021 | .0036748 | .2460 | .9908217 | .6433 | .9963780 | .2336 | .0090632 | .6323 |
| .022 | .0038510 | .2465 | .9903817 | .6436 | .9962068 | .2333 | .0094920 | .6321 |
| .023 | .0040274 | .2470 | .9899415 | .6438 | .9960357 | .2330 | .0099205 | .6318 |
| .024 | .0042040 | .2472 | .9895010 | .6441 | .9958648 | .2328 | .0103487 | .6316 |
| 0.025 | 0.0043807 | 9.2475 | 9.9890602 | 9.6444 | 9.9956939 | 9.2325 | 0.0107767 | 9.6313 |
| .026 | .0045575 | .2477 | .9886192 | .6446 | .9955232 | .2322 | .0112045 | .6311 |
| .027 | .0047344 | .2480 | .9881779 | .6449 | .9953526 | .2319 | .0116320 | .6308 |
| .028 | .0049114 | .2485 | .9877363 | .6452 | .9951821 | .2316 | .0120592 | .6306 |
| .029 | .0050886 | .2487 | .9872945 | .6454 | .9950117 | .2313 | .0124862 | .6303 |
| 0.030 | 0.0052659 | 9.2490 | 9.9868524 | 9.6457 | 9.9948414 | 9.2310 | 0.0129130 | 9.6301 |
| .031 | .0054433 | .2494 | .9864100 | .6459 | .9946712 | .2307 | .0133395 | .6298 |
| .032 | .0056209 | .2497 | .9859674 | .6462 | .9945012 | .2304 | .0137657 | .6295 |
| .033 | .0057986 | .2499 | .9855245 | .6465 | .9943313 | .2301 | .0141917 | .6293 |
| .034 | .0059764 | .2502 | .9850813 | .6468 | .9941615 | .2298 | .0146175 | .6290 |
| 0.035 | 0.0061543 | 9.2504 | 9.9846378 | 9.6471 | 9.9939918 | 9.2295 | 0.0150430 | 9.6288 |
| .036 | .0063323 | .2509 | .9841940 | .6474 | .9938222 | .2292 | .0154683 | .6285 |
| .037 | .0065105 | .2512 | .9837499 | .6476 | .9936528 | .2290 | .0158933 | .6283 |
| .038 | .0066888 | .2514 | .9833056 | .6478 | .9934834 | .2287 | .0163180 | .6280 |
| .039 | .0068672 | .2516 | .9828610 | .6481 | .9933142 | .2284 | .0167426 | .6278 |
| .040 | .0070457 | .2519 | .9824161 | .6484 | .9931450 | .2281 | .0171668 | .6275 |

| A | ELLIPSE. | | | | HYPERBOLA. | | | |
|---|---|---|---|---|---|---|---|---|
| | Log E$_v$ | Log diff. | Log E$_r$ | Log diff. | Log E$_v$ | Log diff. | Log E$_r$. | Log Diff. |
| 0.040 | 0.0070457 | 9.2519 | 9.9824161 | 9.6484 | 9.9931450 | 9.2281 | 0.0171668 | 9.6275 |
| .041 | .0072243 | .2524 | .9819709 | .6487 | .9929760 | .2278 | .0175908 | .6273 |
| .042 | .0074031 | .2526 | .9815255 | .6489 | .9928071 | .2275 | .0180146 | .6270 |
| .043 | .0075820 | .2531 | .9810798 | .6492 | .9926383 | .2272 | .0184381 | .6267 |
| .044 | .0077611 | .2533 | .9806339 | .6494 | .9924696 | .2269 | .0188614 | .6265 |
| 0.045 | 0.0079403 | 9.2536 | 9.9801877 | 9.6497 | 9.9923010 | 9.2266 | 0.0192844 | 9.6262 |
| .046 | .0081196 | .2538 | .9797412 | .6500 | .9921325 | .2263 | .0197072 | .6260 |
| .047 | .0082990 | .2543 | .9792944 | .6502 | .9919642 | .2260 | .0201297 | .6257 |
| .048 | .0084786 | .2546 | .9788474 | .6505 | .9917960 | .2258 | .0205520 | .6255 |
| .049 | .0086583 | .2548 | .9784001 | .6508 | .9916279 | .2255 | .0209740 | .6252 |
| 0.050 | 0.0088381 | 9.2550 | 9.9779525 | 9.6511 | 9.9914599 | 9.2252 | 0.0213958 | 9.6250 |
| .051 | .0090180 | .2555 | .9775046 | .6514 | .9912920 | .2249 | .0218174 | .6247 |
| .052 | .0091981 | .2558 | .9770564 | .6516 | .9911242 | .2246 | .0222387 | .6245 |
| .053 | .0093783 | .2560 | .9766079 | .6519 | .9909565 | .2243 | .0226597 | .6242 |
| .054 | .0095586 | .2565 | .9761592 | .6521 | .9907890 | .2240 | .0230805 | .6240 |
| 0.055 | 0.0097391 | 9.2567 | 9.9757102 | 9.6524 | 9.9906215 | 9.2237 | 0.0235011 | 9.6237 |
| .056 | .0099197 | .2570 | .9752609 | .6527 | .9904542 | .2235 | .0239214 | .6235 |
| .057 | .0101004 | .2572 | .9748113 | .6529 | .9902869 | .2232 | .0243415 | .6232 |
| .058 | .0102812 | .2577 | .9743615 | .6532 | .9901198 | .2229 | .0247614 | .6230 |
| .059 | .0104622 | .2579 | .9739114 | .6535 | .9899528 | .2226 | .0251810 | .6227 |
| 0.060 | 0.0106433 | 9.2582 | 9.9734611 | 9.6538 | 9.9897859 | 9.2223 | 0.0256003 | 9.6225 |
| .061 | .0108245 | .2584 | .9730103 | .6541 | .9896191 | .2220 | .0260194 | .6222 |
| .062 | .0110058 | .2589 | .9725593 | .6543 | .9894525 | .2217 | .0264383 | .6220 |
| .063 | .0111873 | .2591 | .9721080 | .6546 | .9892859 | .2214 | .0268570 | .6217 |
| .064 | .0113689 | .2594 | .9716565 | .6548 | .9891195 | .2211 | .0272753 | .6215 |
| 0.065 | 0.0115506 | 9.2598 | 9.9712047 | 9.6551 | 9.9889531 | 9.2208 | 0.0276935 | 9.6212 |
| .066 | .0117325 | .2601 | .9707526 | .6554 | .9887869 | .2206 | .0281114 | .6210 |
| .067 | .0119145 | .2603 | .9703002 | .6557 | .9886208 | .2203 | .0285291 | .6207 |
| .068 | .0120966 | .2606 | .9698475 | .6560 | .9884548 | .2200 | .0289465 | .6205 |
| .069 | .0122788 | .2610 | .9693945 | .6562 | .9882889 | .2197 | .0293637 | .6202 |
| 0.070 | 0.0124612 | 9.2613 | 9.9689413 | 9.6565 | 9.9881231 | 9.2194 | 0.0297807 | 9.6200 |
| .071 | .0126437 | .2617 | .9684878 | .6567 | .9879574 | .2191 | .0301974 | .6197 |
| .072 | .0128264 | .2620 | .9680340 | .6570 | .9877918 | .2189 | .0306139 | .6195 |
| .073 | .0130092 | .2622 | .9675799 | .6573 | .9876263 | .2186 | .0310301 | .6192 |
| .074 | .0131921 | .2625 | .9671255 | .6576 | .9874610 | .2183 | .0314461 | .6190 |
| 0.075 | 0.0133751 | 9.2629 | 9.9666708 | 9.6578 | 9.9872957 | 9.2180 | 0.0318618 | 9.6187 |
| .076 | .0135583 | .2632 | .9662159 | .6581 | .9871306 | .2177 | .0322773 | .6185 |
| .077 | .0137416 | .2634 | .9657606 | .6584 | .9869655 | .2174 | .0326926 | .6182 |
| .078 | .0139250 | .2638 | .9653051 | .6587 | .9868006 | .2172 | .0331076 | .6180 |
| .079 | .0141086 | .2641 | .9648492 | .6590 | .9866358 | .2169 | .0335224 | .6177 |
| .080 | .0142923 | .2643 | .9643931 | .6592 | .9864711 | .2166 | .0339370 | .6175 |

TABLE I*a*.                                                    23

| A | ELLIPSE. | | | | HYPERBOLA. | | | |
|---|---|---|---|---|---|---|---|---|
| | Log E_v | Log diff. | Log E_r | Log diff. | Log E_v | Log diff. | Log E_r. | Log Diff. |
| 0.080 | 0.0142923 | 9.2643 | 9.9643931 | 9.6592 | 9.9864711 | 9.2166 | 0.0339370 | 9.6175 |
| .081 | .0144761 | .2646 | .9639367 | .6595 | .9863065 | .2163 | .0343513 | .6172 |
| .082 | .0146601 | .2649 | .9634800 | .6598 | .9861420 | .2160 | .0347654 | .6170 |
| .083 | .0148442 | .2652 | .9630230 | .6600 | .9859776 | .2157 | .0351793 | .6167 |
| .084 | .0150284 | .2655 | .9625657 | .6603 | .9858133 | .2155 | .0355930 | .6165 |
| 0.085 | 0.0152128 | 9.2659 | 9.9621081 | 9.6606 | 9.9856491 | 9.2152 | 0.0360064 | 9.6163 |
| .086 | .0153973 | .2662 | .9616503 | .6609 | .9854850 | .2149 | .0364196 | .6160 |
| .087 | .0155819 | .2665 | .9611922 | .6611 | .9853210 | .2146 | .0368325 | .6158 |
| .088 | .0157667 | .2668 | .9607337 | .6614 | .9851572 | .2143 | .0372452 | .6155 |
| .089 | .0159516 | .2671 | .9602749 | .6617 | .9849934 | .2140 | .0376577 | .6153 |
| 0.090 | 0.0161367 | 9.2674 | 9.9598159 | 9.6620 | 9.9848298 | 9.2138 | 0.0380699 | 9.6150 |
| .091 | .0163218 | .2677 | .9593566 | .6623 | .9846663 | .2135 | .0384819 | .6148 |
| .092 | .0165071 | .2680 | .9588970 | .6625 | .9845028 | .2132 | .0388937 | .6145 |
| .093 | .0166925 | .2684 | .9584371 | .6628 | .9843395 | .2129 | .0393052 | .6143 |
| .094 | .0168781 | .2687 | .9579769 | .6631 | .9841763 | .2126 | .0397165 | .6141 |
| 0.095 | 0.0170638 | 9.2690 | 9.9575164 | 9.6634 | 9.9840132 | 9.2123 | 0.0401276 | 9.6138 |
| .096 | .0172497 | .2693 | .9570556 | .6636 | .9838502 | .2121 | .0405385 | .6136 |
| .097 | .0174357 | .2696 | .9565945 | .6639 | .9836873 | .2118 | .0409491 | .6133 |
| .098 | .0176218 | .2700 | .9561331 | .6642 | .9835245 | .2115 | .0413595 | .6131 |
| .099 | .0178081 | .2703 | .9556714 | .6645 | .9833618 | .2112 | .0417696 | .6128 |
| 0.100 | 0.0179945 | 9.2706 | 9.9552095 | 9.6648 | 9.9831992 | 9.2109 | 0.0421796 | 9.6126 |
| .101 | .0181810 | .2708 | .9547472 | .6650 | .9830367 | .2107 | .0425893 | .6123 |
| .102 | .0183677 | .2712 | .9542847 | .6653 | .9828743 | .2104 | .0429988 | .6121 |
| .103 | .0185545 | .2715 | .9538218 | .6656 | .9827121 | .2101 | .0434080 | .6118 |
| .104 | .0187414 | .2718 | .9533586 | .6659 | .9825499 | .2098 | .0438170 | .6116 |
| 0.105 | 0.0189285 | 9.2722 | 9.9528951 | 9.6662 | 9.9823879 | 9.2095 | 0.0442258 | 9.6114 |
| .106 | .0191157 | .2725 | .9524314 | .6664 | .9822259 | .2093 | .0446343 | .6111 |
| .107 | .0193030 | .2728 | .9519673 | .6666 | .9820641 | .2090 | .0450426 | .6109 |
| .108 | .0194905 | .2731 | .9515030 | .6670 | .9819023 | .2087 | .0454507 | .6106 |
| .109 | .0196781 | .2734 | .9510383 | .6673 | .9817407 | .2084 | .0458585 | .6104 |
| 0.110 | 0.0198659 | 9.2738 | 9.9505734 | 9.6676 | 9.9815791 | 9.2081 | 0.0462661 | 9.6101 |
| .111 | .0200538 | .2741 | .9501081 | .6678 | .9814177 | .2079 | .0466735 | .6099 |
| .112 | .0202418 | .2744 | .9496425 | .6681 | .9812563 | .2076 | .0470807 | .6096 |
| .113 | .0204300 | .2747 | .9491766 | .6684 | .9810951 | .2073 | .0474876 | .6094 |
| .114 | .0206183 | .2750 | .9487105 | .6687 | .9809340 | .2070 | .0478943 | .6092 |
| 0.115 | 0.0208067 | 9.2754 | 9.9482440 | 9.6690 | 9.9807730 | 9.2067 | 0.0483008 | 9.6089 |
| .116 | .0209953 | .2757 | .9477772 | .6692 | .9806121 | .2065 | .0487071 | .6087 |
| .117 | .0211840 | .2760 | .9473101 | .6695 | .9804513 | .2062 | .0491131 | .6084 |
| .118 | .0213729 | .2763 | .9468428 | .6698 | .9802905 | .2059 | .0495189 | .6082 |
| .119 | .0215619 | .2767 | .9463751 | .6701 | .9801299 | .2056 | .0499245 | .6080 |
| .120 | .0217511 | .2770 | .9459071 | .6704 | .9799694 | .2054 | .0503298 | .6077 |

| A | ELLIPSE. | | | | HYPERBOLA. | | | |
|---|---|---|---|---|---|---|---|---|
| | Log $E_v$ | Log diff. | Log $E_r$ | Log diff. | Log $E_v$ | Log diff. | Log $E_r$. | Log Diff. |
| 0.120 | 0.0217511 | 9.2770 | 9.9459071 | 9.6704 | 9.9799694 | 9.2054 | 0.0503298 | 9.6077 |
| .121 | .0219404 | .2773 | .9454388 | .6707 | .9798090 | .2051 | .0507349 | .6075 |
| .122 | .0221298 | .2776 | .9449702 | .6709 | .9796487 | .2048 | .0511399 | .6072 |
| .123 | .0223193 | .2779 | .9445013 | .6712 | .9794885 | .2045 | .0515446 | .6070 |
| .124 | .0225091 | .2783 | .9440321 | .6715 | .9793284 | .2043 | .0519490 | .6068 |
| 0.125 | 0.0226990 | 9.2786 | 9.9435626 | 9.6718 | 9.9791684 | 9.2040 | 0.0523533 | 9.6065 |
| .126 | .0228889 | .2789 | .9430927 | .6721 | .9790085 | .2037 | .0527573 | .6063 |
| .127 | .0230791 | .2792 | .9426226 | .6724 | .9788487 | .2034 | .0531611 | .6061 |
| .128 | .0232693 | .2795 | .9421521 | .6727 | .9786890 | .2032 | .0535647 | .6058 |
| .129 | .0234597 | .2799 | .9416813 | .6729 | .9785294 | .2029 | .0539681 | .6056 |
| 0.130 | 0.0236503 | 9.2802 | 9.9412103 | 9.6732 | 9.9783699 | 9.2026 | 0.0543712 | 9.6053 |
| .131 | .0238410 | .2805 | .9407389 | .6735 | .9782105 | .2023 | .0547741 | .6051 |
| .132 | .0240318 | .2808 | .9402672 | .6738 | .9780512 | .2021 | .0551768 | .6049 |
| .133 | .0242228 | .2812 | .9397952 | .6741 | .9778920 | .2018 | .0555793 | .6046 |
| .134 | .0244139 | .2815 | .9393229 | .6744 | .9777329 | .2015 | .0559816 | .6044 |
| 0.135 | 0.0246052 | 9.2818 | 9.9388503 | 9.6747 | 9.9775739 | 9.2012 | 0.0563836 | 9.6041 |
| .136 | .0247966 | .2822 | .9383773 | .6749 | .9774150 | .2010 | .0567854 | .6039 |
| .137 | .0249882 | .2825 | .9379041 | .6752 | .9772562 | .2007 | .0571870 | .6037 |
| .138 | .0251799 | .2828 | .9374305 | .6755 | .9770975 | .2004 | .0575884 | .6034 |
| .139 | .0253717 | .2831 | .9369567 | .6758 | .9769390 | .2001 | .0579895 | .6032 |
| 0.140 | 0.0255637 | 9.2834 | 9.9364824 | 9.6761 | 9.9767805 | 9.1998 | 0.0583904 | 9.6029 |
| .141 | .0257558 | .2838 | .9360079 | .6764 | .9766221 | .1996 | .0587911 | .6027 |
| .142 | .0259481 | .2841 | .9355331 | .6767 | .9764638 | .1993 | .0591916 | .6025 |
| .143 | .0261405 | .2844 | .9350580 | .6770 | .9763057 | .1990 | .0595919 | .6022 |
| .144 | .0263331 | .2848 | .9345825 | .6773 | .9761476 | .1988 | .0599919 | .6020 |
| 0.145 | 0.0265258 | 9.2851 | 9.9341067 | 9.6775 | 9.9759896 | 9.1985 | 0.0603917 | 9.6018 |
| .146 | .0267187 | .2854 | .9336307 | .6778 | .9758317 | .1982 | .0607913 | .6015 |
| .147 | .0269117 | .2857 | .9331543 | .6781 | .9756739 | .1979 | .0611907 | .6013 |
| .148 | .0271048 | .2861 | .9326775 | .6784 | .9755162 | .1977 | .0615899 | .6010 |
| .149 | .0272981 | .2864 | .9322005 | .6787 | .9753586 | .1974 | .0619888 | .6008 |
| 0.150 | 0.0274915 | 9.2867 | 9.9317231 | 9.6790 | 9.9752011 | 9.1971 | 0.0623876 | 9.6006 |
| .151 | .0276851 | .2871 | .9312455 | .6793 | .9750437 | .1969 | .0627861 | .6003 |
| .152 | .0278789 | .2874 | .9307675 | .6796 | .9748864 | .1966 | .0631844 | .6001 |
| .153 | .0280728 | .2877 | .9302892 | .6798 | .9747292 | .1963 | .0635825 | .5999 |
| .154 | .0282668 | .2880 | .9298106 | .6801 | .9745721 | .1960 | .0639804 | .5996 |
| 0.155 | 0.0284610 | 9.2884 | 9.9293317 | 9.6804 | 9.9744151 | 9.1958 | 0.0643780 | 9.5994 |
| .156 | .0286553 | .2887 | .9288524 | .6807 | .9742582 | .1955 | .0647755 | .5992 |
| .157 | .0288498 | .2890 | .9283728 | .6810 | .9741014 | .1952 | .0651727 | .5989 |
| .158 | .0290444 | .2893 | .9278929 | .6813 | .9739447 | .1949 | .0655697 | .5987 |
| .159 | .0292392 | .2897 | .9274127 | .6816 | .9737881 | .1946 | .0659665 | .5985 |
| .160 | .0294341 | .2900 | .9269321 | .6819 | .9736316 | .1944 | .0663631 | .5982 |

TABLE I*a*. 25

| | ELLIPSE. | | | | HYPERBOLA. | | | |
|---|---|---|---|---|---|---|---|---|
| A | Log $E_v$ | Log diff. | Log $E_r$ | Log diff. | Log $E_v$ | Log diff. | Log E | Log diff. |
| 0.160 | 0.0294341 | 9.2900 | 9.9269321 | 9.6819 | 9.9736316 | 9.1944 | 0.0663631 | 9.5982 |
| .161 | .0296292 | .2903 | .9264512 | .6822 | .9734752 | .1941 | .0667595 | .5980 |
| .162 | .0298243 | .2906 | .9259700 | .6825 | .9733189 | .1938 | .0671556 | .5978 |
| .163 | .0300197 | .2910 | .9254885 | .6828 | .9731627 | .1936 | .0675516 | .5975 |
| .164 | .0302152 | .2913 | .9250067 | .6831 | .9730066 | .1933 | .0679473 | .5973 |
| 0.165 | 0.0304109 | 9.2916 | 9.9245245 | 9.6833 | 9.9728506 | 9.1930 | 0.0683428 | 9.5971 |
| .166 | .0306067 | .2920 | .9240421 | .6836 | .9726947 | .1928 | .0687381 | .5968 |
| .167 | .0308026 | .2923 | .9235592 | .6839 | .9725389 | .1925 | .0691332 | .5966 |
| .168 | .0309987 | .2926 | .9230761 | .6842 | .9723831 | .1922 | .0695281 | .5963 |
| .169 | .0311949 | .2930 | .9225926 | .6845 | .9722275 | .1920 | .0699228 | .5961 |
| 0.170 | 0.0313913 | 9.2933 | 9.9221089 | 9.6848 | 9.9720719 | 9.1917 | 0.0703172 | 9.5959 |
| .171 | .0315879 | .2936 | .9216247 | .6851 | .9719165 | .1914 | .0707114 | .5956 |
| .172 | .0317846 | .2940 | .9211403 | .6854 | .9717611 | .1912 | .0711055 | .5954 |
| .173 | .0319815 | .2943 | .9206555 | .6857 | .9716059 | .1909 | .0714993 | .5952 |
| .174 | .0321784 | .2946 | .9201704 | .6860 | .9714507 | .1906 | .0718929 | .5949 |
| 0.175 | 0.0323756 | 9.2950 | 9.9196850 | 9.6863 | 9.9712957 | 9.1904 | 0.0722863 | 9.5947 |
| .176 | .0325729 | .2953 | .9191992 | .6866 | .9711407 | .1901 | .0726795 | .5945 |
| .177 | .0327704 | .2956 | .9187131 | .6869 | .9709859 | .1898 | .0730724 | .5942 |
| .178 | .0329680 | .2960 | .9182266 | .6872 | .9708311 | .1895 | .0734652 | .5940 |
| .179 | .0331657 | .2963 | .9177399 | .6875 | .9706764 | .1893 | .0738578 | .5938 |
| 0.180 | 0.0333636 | 9.2966 | 9.9172528 | 9.6878 | 9.9705218 | 9.1890 | 0.0742501 | 9.5935 |
| .181 | .0335617 | .2970 | .9167654 | .6881 | .9703673 | .1887 | .0746422 | .5933 |
| .182 | .0337599 | .2973 | .9162776 | .6884 | .9702129 | .1885 | .0750341 | .5931 |
| .183 | .0339582 | .2977 | .9157895 | .6886 | .9700587 | .1882 | .0754259 | .5928 |
| .184 | .0341568 | .2980 | .9153011 | .6889 | .9699045 | .1879 | .0758173 | .5926 |
| 0.185 | 0.0343555 | 9.2983 | 9.9148123 | 9.6892 | 9.9697504 | 9.1877 | 0.0762086 | 9.5924 |
| .186 | .0345543 | .2987 | .9143232 | .6895 | .9695964 | .1874 | .0765997 | .5922 |
| .187 | .0347533 | .2990 | .9138338 | .6898 | .9694425 | .1871 | .0769906 | .5919 |
| .188 | .0349524 | .2993 | .9133441 | .6901 | .9692887 | .1869 | .0773812 | .5917 |
| .189 | .0351517 | .2997 | .9128540 | .6904 | .9691350 | .1866 | .0777717 | .5915 |
| 0.190 | 0.0353511 | 9.3000 | 9.9123635 | 9.6907 | 9.9689813 | 9.1863 | 0.0781619 | 9.5912 |
| .191 | .0355507 | .3003 | .9118727 | .6910 | .9688278 | .1861 | .0785520 | .5910 |
| .192 | .0357505 | .3007 | .9113816 | .6913 | .9686743 | .1858 | .0789418 | .5908 |
| .193 | .0359504 | .3010 | .9108901 | .6916 | .9685210 | .1855 | .0793315 | .5906 |
| .194 | .0361505 | .3014 | .9103983 | .6919 | .9683678 | .1853 | .0797209 | .5903 |
| 0.195 | 0.0363507 | 9.3017 | 9.9099062 | 9.6922 | 9.9682146 | 9.1850 | 0.0801102 | 9.5901 |
| .196 | .0365511 | .3020 | .9094138 | .6925 | .9680615 | .1847 | .0804992 | .5899 |
| .197 | .0367516 | .3024 | .9089210 | .6928 | .9679086 | .1845 | .0808881 | .5896 |
| .198 | .0369523 | .3027 | .9084278 | .6931 | .9677557 | .1842 | .0812767 | .5894 |
| .199 | .0371532 | .3031 | .9079343 | .6934 | .9676029 | .1839 | .0816651 | .5892 |
| .200 | .0373542 | .3034 | .9074405 | .6937 | .9674502 | .1837 | .0820533 | .5889 |

| | ELLIPSE. | | | | HYPERBOLA. | | | |
|---|---|---|---|---|---|---|---|---|
| A | Log $E_v$ | Log diff. | Log $E_r$ | Log diff. | Log $E_v$ | Log diff. | Log $E_r$. | Log Diff. |
| 0.200 | 0.0373542 | 9.3034 | 9.9074405 | 9.6937 | 9.9674502 | 9.1837 | 0.0820533 | 9.5889 |
| .201 | .0375554 | .3037 | .9069463 | .6940 | .9672976 | .1834 | .0824413 | .5887 |
| .202 | .0377567 | .3041 | .9064518 | .6943 | .9671451 | .1831 | .0828291 | .5885 |
| .203 | .0379582 | .3044 | .9059569 | .6946 | .9669927 | .1829 | .0832166 | .5882 |
| .204 | .0381598 | .3047 | .9054617 | .6949 | .9668404 | .1826 | .0836040 | .5880 |
| 0.205 | 0.0383616 | 9.3051 | 9.9049662 | 9.6952 | 9.9666882 | 9.1823 | 0.0839911 | 9.5878 |
| .206 | .0385635 | .3054 | .9044703 | .6955 | .9665361 | .1821 | .0843781 | .5876 |
| .207 | .0387656 | .3058 | .9039741 | .6958 | .9663841 | .1818 | .0847649 | .5873 |
| .208 | .0389679 | .3061 | .9034775 | .6961 | .9662321 | .1815 | .0851514 | .5871 |
| .209 | .0391703 | .3065 | .9029806 | .6964 | .9660803 | .1813 | .0855377 | .5869 |
| 0.210 | 0.0393729 | 9.3068 | 9.9024833 | 9.6967 | 9.9659285 | 9.1810 | 0.0859239 | 9.5867 |
| .211 | .0395757 | .3071 | .9019857 | .6970 | .9657768 | .1808 | .0863099 | .5864 |
| .212 | .0397786 | .3075 | .9014877 | .6974 | .9656253 | .1805 | .0866956 | .5862 |
| .213 | .0399817 | .3078 | .9009894 | .6977 | .9654738 | .1802 | .0870812 | .5860 |
| .214 | .0401849 | .3081 | .9004907 | .6980 | .9653224 | .1800 | .0874665 | .5858 |
| 0.215 | 0.0403883 | 9.3085 | 9.8999917 | 9.6983 | 9.9651711 | 9.1797 | 0.0878517 | 9.5855 |
| .216 | .0405918 | .3088 | .8994924 | .6986 | .9650199 | .1795 | .0882367 | .5853 |
| .217 | .0407955 | .3092 | .8989927 | .6989 | .9648687 | .1792 | .0886214 | .5851 |
| .218 | .0409994 | .3095 | .8984927 | .6992 | .9647177 | .1789 | .0890060 | .5849 |
| .219 | .0412034 | .3099 | .8979923 | .6995 | .9645667 | .1787 | .0893903 | .5846 |
| 0.220 | 0.0414076 | 9.3102 | 9.8974915 | 9.6998 | 9.9644159 | 9.1784 | 0.0897745 | 9.5844 |
| .221 | .0416120 | .3106 | .8969904 | .7001 | .9642651 | .1782 | .0901585 | .5842 |
| .222 | .0418165 | .3109 | .8964889 | .7004 | .9641145 | .1779 | .0905422 | .5839 |
| .223 | .0420211 | .3112 | .8959881 | .7007 | .9639639 | .1776 | .0909258 | .5837 |
| .224 | .0422260 | .3116 | .8954849 | .7010 | .9638134 | .1774 | .0913091 | .5835 |
| 0.225 | 0.0424310 | 9.3119 | 9.8949824 | 9.7013 | 9.9636630 | 9.1771 | 0.0916923 | 9.5833 |
| .226 | .0426362 | .3123 | .8944795 | .7016 | .9635127 | .1768 | .0920753 | .5830 |
| .227 | .0428415 | .3127 | .8939762 | .7019 | .9633625 | .1766 | .0924580 | .5828 |
| .228 | .0430470 | .3130 | .8934726 | .7022 | .9632123 | .1763 | .0928405 | .5826 |
| .229 | .0432527 | .3133 | .8929687 | .7025 | .9630623 | .1760 | .0932229 | .5823 |
| 0.230 | 0.0434585 | 9.3137 | 9.8924644 | 9.7028 | 9.9629124 | 9.1758 | 0.0936050 | 9.5821 |
| .231 | .0436645 | .3140 | .8919597 | .7031 | .9627625 | .1755 | .0939870 | .5819 |
| .232 | .0438707 | .3144 | .8914547 | .7035 | .9626128 | .1752 | .0943687 | .5817 |
| .233 | .0440770 | .3147 | .8909493 | .7038 | .9624631 | .1750 | .0947503 | .5814 |
| .234 | .0442835 | .3151 | .8904436 | .7041 | .9623136 | .1747 | .0951317 | .5812 |
| 0.235 | 0.0444902 | 9.3154 | 9.8899375 | 9.7044 | 9.9621641 | 9.1745 | 0.0955128 | 9.5810 |
| .236 | .0446970 | .3158 | .8894310 | .7047 | .9620147 | .1742 | .0958938 | .5808 |
| .237 | .0449040 | .3161 | .8889242 | .7050 | .9618654 | .1740 | .0962745 | .5806 |
| .238 | .0451111 | .3165 | .8884170 | .7053 | .9617162 | .1737 | .0966551 | .5803 |
| .239 | .0453184 | .3168 | .8879094 | .7056 | .9615670 | .1734 | .0970355 | .5801 |
| .240 | .0455259 | .3171 | .8874015 | .7059 | .9614180 | .1732 | .0974157 | .5799 |

TABLE I*a*. 27

| A | ELLIPSE. | | | | HYPERBOLA. | | | |
|---|---|---|---|---|---|---|---|---|
| | Log E$_v$ | Log diff. | Log E$_r$ | Log diff. | Log E$_v$ | Log diff. | Log E$_r$. | Log Diff. |
| 0.240 | 0.0455259 | 9.3171 | 9.8874015 | 9.7059 | 9.9614180 | 9.1732 | 0.0974157 | 9.5799 |
| .241 | .0457335 | .3175 | .8868932 | .7063 | .9612690 | .1729 | .0977957 | .5797 |
| .242 | .0459413 | .3179 | .8863846 | .7066 | .9611202 | .1727 | .0981755 | .5794 |
| .243 | .0461493 | .3182 | .8858756 | .7069 | .9609714 | .1724 | .0985551 | .5792 |
| .244 | .0463575 | .3186 | .8853663 | .7072 | .9608227 | .1722 | .0989345 | .5790 |
| 0.245 | 0.0465658 | 9.3189 | 9.8848566 | 9.7075 | 9.9606741 | 9.1719 | 0.0993137 | 9.5788 |
| .246 | .0467743 | .3193 | .8843465 | .7078 | .9605256 | .1716 | .0996927 | .5786 |
| .247 | .0469830 | .3196 | .8838360 | .7081 | .9603771 | .1714 | .1000716 | .5783 |
| .248 | .0471918 | .3200 | .8833252 | .7084 | .9602288 | .1711 | .1004502 | .5781 |
| .249 | .0474008 | .3203 | .8828140 | .7087 | .9600805 | .1709 | .1008287 | .5779 |
| 0.250 | 0.0476099 | 9.3207 | 9.8823025 | 9.7090 | 9.9599324 | 9.1706 | 0.1012069 | 9.5777 |
| .251 | .0478193 | .3210 | .8817906 | .7094 | .9597843 | .1704 | .1015850 | .5775 |
| .252 | .0480288 | .3214 | .8812783 | .7097 | .9596363 | .1701 | .1019628 | .5772 |
| .253 | .0482385 | .3217 | .8807657 | .7100 | .9594884 | .1698 | .1023405 | .5770 |
| .254 | .0484483 | .3221 | .8802526 | .7103 | .9593406 | .1696 | .1027180 | .5768 |
| 0.255 | 0.0486583 | 9.3224 | 9.8797392 | 9.7106 | 9.9591929 | 9.1693 | 0.1030953 | 9.5766 |
| .256 | .0488685 | .3226 | .8792254 | .7109 | .9590453 | .1691 | .1034724 | .5763 |
| .257 | .0490788 | .3231 | .8787113 | .7112 | .9588977 | .1688 | .1038493 | .5761 |
| .258 | .0492893 | .3235 | .8781968 | .7116 | .9587502 | .1685 | .1042259 | .5759 |
| .259 | .0495000 | .3238 | .8776819 | .7119 | .9586029 | .1683 | .1046024 | .5756 |
| 0.260 | 0.0497109 | 9.3242 | 9.8771666 | 9.7122 | 9.9584556 | 9.1680 | 0.1049787 | 9.5754 |
| .261 | .0499219 | .3245 | .8766510 | .7125 | .9583084 | .1678 | .1053548 | .5752 |
| .262 | .0501331 | .3249 | .8761350 | .7128 | .9581613 | .1675 | .1057308 | .5750 |
| .263 | .0503445 | .3252 | .8756186 | .7131 | .9580143 | .1673 | .1061065 | .5748 |
| .264 | .0505560 | .3256 | .8751019 | .7134 | .9578673 | .1670 | .1064821 | .5746 |
| 0.265 | 0.0507677 | 9.3260 | 9.8745848 | 9.7137 | 9.9577205 | 9.1668 | 0.1068574 | 9.5743 |
| .266 | .0509796 | .3263 | .8740673 | .7141 | .9575737 | .1665 | .1072326 | .5741 |
| .267 | .0511917 | .3267 | .8735495 | .7144 | .9574270 | .1662 | .1076076 | .5739 |
| .268 | .0514040 | .3270 | .8730312 | .7147 | .9572804 | .1660 | .1079824 | .5737 |
| .269 | .0516164 | .3274 | .8725126 | .7150 | .9571339 | .1657 | .1083570 | .5735 |
| 0.270 | 0.0518290 | 9.3277 | 9.8719936 | 9.7153 | 9.9569875 | 9.1655 | 0.1087314 | 9.5733 |
| .271 | .0520418 | .3281 | .8714742 | .7157 | .9568412 | .1652 | .1091056 | .5730 |
| .272 | .0522547 | .3284 | .8709544 | .7160 | .9566949 | .1650 | .1094797 | .5728 |
| .273 | .0524678 | .3288 | .8704343 | .7163 | .9565487 | .1647 | .1098536 | .5726 |
| .274 | .0526811 | .3292 | .8699137 | .7166 | .9564027 | .1644 | .1102272 | .5724 |
| 0.275 | 0.0528946 | 9.3295 | 9.8693928 | 9.7169 | 9.9562567 | 9.1642 | 0.1106007 | 9.5722 |
| .276 | .0531082 | .3299 | .8688715 | .7173 | .9561108 | .1639 | .1109740 | .5719 |
| .277 | .0533220 | .3303 | .8683498 | .7176 | .9559650 | .1637 | .1113471 | .5717 |
| .278 | .0535360 | .3306 | .8678278 | .7179 | .9558193 | .1634 | .1117200 | .5715 |
| .279 | .0537502 | .3310 | .8673053 | .7182 | .9556736 | .1632 | .1120927 | .5713 |
| .280 | .0539646 | .3313 | .8667825 | .7185 | .9555281 | .1629 | .1124652 | .5710 |

## TABLE I*a*.

| A | ELLIPSE. | | | | HYPERBOLA. | | | |
|---|---|---|---|---|---|---|---|---|
| | Log E$_v$ | Log diff. | Log E$_r$ | Log diff. | Log E$_v$ | Log diff. | Log E$_r$. | Log Diff. |
| 0.280 | 0.0539646 | 9.3313 | 9.8667825 | 9.7185 | 9.9555281 | 9.1629 | 0.1124652 | 9.5710 |
| .281 | .0541791 | .3317 | .8662593 | .7188 | .9553826 | .1627 | .1128375 | .5708 |
| .282 | .0543939 | .3320 | .8657357 | .7192 | .9552372 | .1624 | .1132097 | .5707 |
| .283 | .0546087 | .3324 | .8652117 | .7195 | .9550919 | .1622 | .1135817 | .5704 |
| .284 | .0548238 | .3327 | .8646873 | .7198 | .9549467 | .1619 | .1139534 | .5701 |
| 0.285 | 0.0550390 | 9.3331 | 9.8641625 | 9.7201 | 9.9548015 | 9.1617 | 0.1143250 | 9.5699 |
| .286 | .0552546 | .3335 | .8636374 | .7204 | .9546564 | .1614 | .1146964 | .5698 |
| .287 | .0554700 | .3338 | .8631118 | .7208 | .9545115 | .1612 | .1150677 | .5695 |
| .288 | .0556858 | .3342 | .8625859 | .7211 | .9543666 | .1609 | .1154387 | .5693 |
| .289 | .0559018 | .3345 | .8620596 | .7214 | .9542218 | .1606 | .1158096 | .5691 |
| 0.290 | 0.0561179 | 9.3349 | 9.8615329 | 9.7217 | 9.9540771 | 9.1604 | 0.1161803 | 9.5689 |
| .291 | .0563342 | .3353 | .8610058 | .7221 | .9539325 | .1601 | .1165508 | .5687 |
| .292 | .0565507 | .3356 | .8604783 | .7224 | .9537879 | .1599 | .1169211 | .5685 |
| .293 | .0567674 | .3360 | .8599504 | .7227 | .9536435 | .1596 | .1172913 | .5683 |
| .294 | .0569842 | .3364 | .8594221 | .7230 | .9534991 | .1594 | .1176612 | .5680 |
| 0.295 | 0.0572013 | 9.3367 | 9.8588935 | 9.7233 | 9.9533548 | 9.1591 | 0.1180310 | 9.5678 |
| .296 | .0574185 | .3371 | .8583644 | .7236 | .9532106 | .1589 | .1184006 | .5675 |
| .297 | .0576359 | .3375 | .8578349 | .7240 | .9530665 | .1586 | .1187699 | .5673 |
| .298 | .0578535 | .3379 | .8573051 | .7243 | .9529224 | .1584 | .1191391 | .5671 |
| .299 | .0580713 | .3383 | .8567748 | .7246 | .9527785 | .1581 | .1195081 | .5668 |
| .300 | .0582893 | .3387 | .8562442 | .7249 | .9526346 | .1578 | 0.1198768 | 9.5666 |

TABLE II*a*. 29

| $\tau_0$. | $v_0$. | Log $A_1$. | Log $A_2$. | Log $A_3$. |
|---|---|---|---|---|
| 0 | 0̊ 0′ 0″.00 | +3.7005216 | —0.00000 | —9.695 |
| 2 | 2 47 11.83 | 3.7000079 | 0.47160 | 9.691 |
| 4 | 5 34 0.00 | 3.6984710 | 0.76930 | 9.681 |
| 6 | 8 20 1.19 | 3.6959236 | 0.93987 | 9.664 |
| 8 | 11 4 52.82 | 3.6923863 | 1.05702 | 9.641 |
| 10 | 13 48 13.31 | +3.6878872 | —1.14430 | —9.610 |
| 12 | 16 29 42.39 | 3.6824613 | 1.21171 | 9.571 |
| 14 | 19 9 1.36 | 3.6761493 | 1.26497 | 9.525 |
| 16 | 21 45 53.23 | 3.6689972 | 1.30744 | 9.470 |
| 18 | 24 20 2.89 | 3.6610547 | 1.34135 | 9.405 |
| 20 | 26 51 17.15 | +3.6523748 | —1.36825 | —9.329 |
| 22 | 29 19 24.78 | 3.6430121 | 1.38929 | 9.239 |
| 24 | 31 44 16.52 | 3.6330224 | 1.40535 | 9.130 |
| 26 | 34 5 44.97 | 3.6224621 | 1.41714 | 8.994 |
| 28 | 36 23 44.51 | 3.6113863 | 1.42520 | 8.814 |
| 30 | 38 38 11.23 | +3.5998496 | —1.43003 | —8.538 |
| 32 | 40 49 2.74 | 3.5879044 | 1.43201 | —7.847 |
| 34 | 42 56 18.02 | 3.5756011 | 1.43149 | +8.237 |
| 36 | 44 59 57.33 | 3.5629877 | 1.42877 | 8.585 |
| 38 | 47 0 2.00 | 3.5501091 | 1.42410 | 8.753 |
| 40 | 48 56 34.33 | +3.5370077 | —1.41772 | +8.857 |
| 42 | 50 49 37.39 | 3.5237227 | 1.40983 | 8.928 |
| 44 | 52 39 14.95 | 3.5102905 | 1.40060 | 8.978 |
| 46 | 54 25 31.32 | 3.4967444 | 1.39020 | 9.013 |
| 48 | 56 8 31.24 | 3.4831149 | 1.37878 | 9.038 |
| 50 | 57 48 19.82 | +3.4694297 | —1.36645 | +9.056 |
| 52 | 59 25 2.41 | 3.4557140 | 1.35333 | 9.067 |
| 54 | 60 58 44.53 | 3.4419903 | 1.33952 | 9.073 |
| 56 | 62 29 31.82 | 3.4282790 | 1.32512 | 9.076 |
| 58 | 63 57 29.99 | 3.4145981 | 1.31021 | 9.075 |
| 60 | 65 22 44.74 | +3.4009637 | —1.29486 | +9.071 |
| 64 | 68 5 26.60 | 3.3738900 | 1.26308 | 9.056 |
| 68 | 70 38 21.86 | 3.3471520 | 1.23025 | 9.035 |
| 72 | 73 2 13.17 | 3.3208214 | 1.19672 | 9.008 |
| 76 | 75 17 40.91 | 3.2949510 | 1.16277 | 8.978 |
| 80 | 77 25 22.94 | +3.2695785 | —1.12863 | +8.945 |
| 84 | 79 25 54.44 | 3.2447291 | 1.09447 | 8.910 |
| 88 | 81 19 47.97 | 3.2204185 | 1.06044 | 8.874 |
| 92 | 83 7 33.52 | 3.1966546 | 1.02665 | 8.837 |
| 96 | 84 49 38.62 | 3.1734393 | 0.99319 | 8.798 |
| 100 | 86 26 28.52 | +3.1507694 | —0.96012 | +8.760 |
| 104 | 87 58 26.32 | 3.1286388 | 0.92749 | 8.721 |
| 108 | 89 25 53.18 | 3.1070382 | 0.89534 | 8.682 |
| 112 | 90 49 8.43 | 3.0859565 | 0.86370 | 8.643 |
| 116 | 92 8 29.76 | 3.0653811 | 0.83257 | 8.605 |

| $\tau_0$. | $v_0$. | | | Log $A_1$. | Log $A_2$. | Log $A_3$. |
|---|---|---|---|---|---|---|
| 116 | 92 | 8 | 29.76 | $+3.0653811$ | $-0.83257$ | $+8.605$ |
| 120 | 93 | 24 | 13.33 | 3.0452984 | 0.80199 | ·8.567 |
| 124 | 94 | 36 | 33.98 | 3.0256943 | 0.77194 | 8.529 |
| 128 | 95 | 45 | 45.25 | 3.0065544 | 0.74244 | 8.491 |
| 132 | 96 | 51 | 59.60 | 2.9878638 | 0.71347 | 8.454 |
| 136 | 97 | 55 | 28.43 | $+2.9696079$ | $-0.68505$ | $+8.418$ |
| 140 | 98 | 56 | 22.24 | 2.9517723 | 0.65716 | 8.382 |
| 144 | 99 | 54 | 50.68 | 2.9343427 | 0.62979 | 8.346 |
| 148 | 100 | 51 | 2.62 | 2.9173052 | 0.60293 | 8.311 |
| 152 | 101 | 45 | 6.25 | 2.9006462 | 0.57658 | 8.276 |
| 156 | 102 | 37 | 9.12 | $+2.8843526$ | $-0.55071$ | $+8.242$ |
| 160 | 103 | 27 | 18.23 | 2.8684116 | 0.52534 | 8.209 |
| 164 | 104 | 15 | 40.03 | 2.8528110 | 0.50043 | 8.176 |
| 168 | 105 | 2 | 20.49 | 2.8375388 | 0.47598 | 8.143 |
| 172 | 105 | 47 | 25.18 | 2.8225838 | 0.45198 | 8.111 |
| 176 | 106 | 30 | 59.23 | $+2.8079349$ | $-0.42841$ | $+8.080$ |
| 180 | 107 | 13 | 7.45 | 2.7935817 | 0.40526 | 8.049 |
| 184 | 107 | 53 | 54.28 | 2.7795141 | 0.38253 | 8.018 |
| 188 | 108 | 33 | 23.87 | 2.7657223 | 0.36020 | 7.988 |
| 192 | 109 | 11 | 40.10 | 2.7521971 | 0.33826 | 7.959 |
| 196 | 109 | 48 | 46.58 | $+2.7389297$ | $-0.31670$ | $+7.930$ |
| 200 | 110 | 24 | 46.69 | 2.7259114 | 0.29551 | 7.901 |
| 210 | 111 | 50 | 16.87 | 2.6944032 | 0.24407 | 7.831 |
| 220 | 113 | 9 | 55.67 | 2.6642838 | 0.19472 | 7.764 |
| 230 | 114 | 24 | 20.89 | 2.6354467 | 0.14732 | 7.700 |
| 240 | 115 | 34 | 4.97 | $+2.6077961$ | $-0.10174$ | $+7.637$ |
| 250 | 116 | 39 | 35.94 | 2.5812455 | 0.05786 | 7.577 |
| 260 | 117 | 41 | 18.16 | 2.5557170 | 0.01556 | 7.519 |
| 270 | 118 | 39 | 32.86 | 2.5311401 | 9.97476 | 7.463 |
| 280 | 119 | 34 | 38.67 | 2.5074507 | 9.93535 | 7.409 |
| 290 | 120 | 26 | 51.98 | $+2.4845910$ | $-9.89725$ | $+7.356$ |
| 300 | 121 | 16 | 27.30 | 2.4625078 | 9.86038 | 7.305 |
| 310 | 122 | 3 | 37.49 | 2.4411532 | 9.82467 | 7.256 |
| 320 | 122 | 48 | 34.01 | 2.4204831 | 9.79006 | 7.208 |
| 330 | 123 | 31 | 27.11 | 2.4004569 | 9.75648 | 7.161 |
| 340 | 124 | 12 | 25.97 | $+2.3810379$ | $-9.72387$ | $+7.116$ |
| 350 | 124 | 51 | 38.87 | 2.3621918 | 9.69219 | 7.072 |
| 360 | 125 | 29 | 13.25 | 2.3438873 | 9.66139 | 7.029 |
| 370 | 126 | 5 | 15.87 | 2.3260956 | 9.63142 | 6.987 |
| 380 | 126 | 39 | 52.85 | 2.3087898 | 9.60224 | 6.947 |
| 390 | 127 | 13 | 9.75 | $+2.2919450$ | $-9.57381$ | $+6.907$ |
| 400 | 127 | 45 | 11.66 | 2.2755384 | 9.54610 | 6.868 |
| 420 | 128 | 45 | 48.63 | 2.2439555 | 9.49269 | 6.794 |
| 440 | 129 | 42 | 16.43 | 2.2138871 | 9.44176 | 6.723 |
| 460 | 130 | 35 | 2.66 | 2.1851991 | 9.39310 | 6.655 |

TABLE II*a*.                                    31

| $\tau_0$. | $v_0$. | Log $A_1$. | Log $A_2$. | Log $A_3$. |
|---|---|---|---|---|
| 460 | 130° 35′ 2.66″ | +2.1851991 | —9.39310 | +96.655 |
| 480 | 131 24 30.82 | 2.1577741 | 9.34654 | 6.589 |
| 500 | 132 11 1.09 | 2.1315086 | 9.30188 | 6.527 |
| 520 | 132 54 50.84 | 2.1063114 | 9.25901 | 6.467 |
| 540 | 133 36 15.19 | 2.0821011 | 9.21777 | 6.409 |
| 560 | 134 15 27.33 | +2.0588051 | —9.17805 | +96.353 |
| 580 | 134 52 38.80 | 2.0363588 | 9.13976 | 6.299 |
| 600 | 135 27 59.81 | 2.0147037 | 9.10278 | 6.247 |
| 640 | 136 33 45.52 | 1.9735615 | 9.03246 | 6.148 |
| 680 | 137 33 45.39 | 1.9350140 | 8.96649 | 6.055 |
| 720 | 138 28 48.27 | +1.8987593 | —8.90438 | +95.968 |
| 760 | 139 19 33.81 | 1.8645446 | 8.84571 | 5.885 |
| 800 | 140 6 34.57 | 1.8321564 | 8.79012 | 5.807 |
| 850 | 141 0 45.22 | 1.7939648 | 8.72451 | 5.714 |
| 900 | 141 50 30.05 | 1.7580440 | 8.66275 | 5.627 |
| 950 | 142 36 24.37 | +1.7241428 | —8.60441 | +95.544 |
| 1000 | 143 18 57.20 | 1.6920492 | 8.54915 | 5.466 |
| 1050 | 143 58 32.66 | 1.6615826 | 8.49665 | 5.392 |
| 1100 | 144 35 30.95 | 1.6325881 | 8.44666 | 5.321 |
| 1150 | 145 10 9.20 | 1.6049315 | 8.39896 | 5.254 |
| 1200 | 145 42 41.98 | +1.5784963 | —8.35333 | +95.189 |
| 1250 | 146 13 21.82 | 1.5531804 | 8.30962 | 5.127 |
| 1300 | 146 42 19.55 | 1.5288937 | 8.26767 | 5.068 |
| 1350 | 147 9 44.57 | 1.5055568 | 8.22735 | 5.011 |
| 1400 | 147 35 45.11 | 1.4830989 | 8.18853 | 4.956 |
| 1450 | 148 0 28.40 | +1.4614567 | —8.15110 | +94.903 |
| 1500 | 148 24 0.83 | 1.4405738 | 8.11498 | 4.851 |
| 1600 | 149 7 55.10 | 1.4008865 | 8.04631 | 4.754 |
| 1700 | 149 48 6.25 | 1.3636849 | 7.98190 | 4.663 |
| 1800 | 150 25 5.10 | 1.3286785 | 7.92126 | 4.576 |
| 1900 | 150 59 16.75 | +1.2956243 | —7.86398 | +94.495 |
| 2000 | 151 31 1.89 | 1.2643177 | 7.80971 | 4.418 |
| 2100 | 152 0 37.76 | 1.2345845 | 7.75814 | 4.345 |
| 2200 | 152 28 18.85 | 1.2062750 | 7.70903 | 4.275 |
| 2300 | 152 54 17.45 | 1.1792601 | 7.66216 | 4.208 |
| 2400 | 153 18 44.05 | +1.1534272 | —7.61732 | +94.145 |
| 2500 | 153 41 47.70 | 1.1286779 | 7.57435 | 4.084 |
| 2600 | 154 3 36.21 | 1.1049254 | 7.53310 | 4.025 |
| 2700 | 154 24 16.39 | 1.0820930 | 7.49344 | 3.969 |
| 2800 | 154 43 54.21 | 1.0601125 | 7.45526 | 3.914 |
| 2900 | 155 2 34.93 | +1.0389230 | —7.41844 | +93.862 |
| 3000 | 155 20 23.19 | 1.0184698 | 7.38289 | 3.811 |
| 3200 | 155 53 38.39 | 0.9795803 | 7.31529 | 3.715 |
| 3400 | 156 24 7.80 | 0.9431040 | 7.25186 | 3.625 |
| 3600 | 156 52 14.00 | 0.9087603 | 7.19213 | 3.540 |

| $\tau_0$. | $v_0$. | Log A$_1$. | Log A$_2$. | Log A$_3$. |
|---|---|---|---|---|
| 3600 | 156° 52′ 14.00″ | +0.9087603 | —97.19213 | +93.540 |
| 3800 | 157 18 15.42 | 0.8763145 | 7.13568 | 3.459 |
| 4000 | 157 42 27.29 | 0.8455688 | 7.08218 | 3.383 |
| 4200 | 158 5 2.33 | 0.8163545 | 7.03133 | 3.311 |
| 4400 | 158 26 11.25 | 0.7885269 | 6.98289 | 3.242 |
| 4600 | 158 46 3.15 | +0.7619607 | —96.93664 | +93.176 |
| 4800 | 159 4 45.83 | 0.7365469 | 6.89238 | 3.113 |
| 5000 | 159 22 25.99 | 0.7121902 | 6.84996 | 3.053 |
| 5200 | 159 39 9.45 | 0.6888063 | 6.80923 | 2.995 |
| 5600 | 160 10 6.00 | 0.6446674 | 6.73234 | 2.885 |
| 6000 | 160 38 9.17 | +0.6036264 | —96.66082 | +92.783 |
| 6400 | 161 3 45.36 | 0.5652780 | 6.59398 | 2.688 |
| 6800 | 161 27 15.57 | 0.5292915 | 6.53125 | 2.599 |
| 7200 | 161 48 56.78 | 0.4953934 | 6.47215 | 2.514 |
| 7600 | 162 9 2.89 | 0.4633554 | 6.41629 | 2.435 |
| 8000 | 162 27 45.39 | +0.4329843 | —96.36332 | +92.359 |
| 8400 | 162 45 13.90 | 0.4041157 | 6.31297 | 2.287 |
| 8800 | 163 1 36.52 | 0.3766081 | 6.26499 | 2.219 |
| 9200 | 163 17 0.16 | 0.3503393 | 6.21916 | 2.154 |
| 9600 | 163 31 30.72 | 0.3252029 | 6.17531 | 2.091 |
| 10000 | 163 45 13.32 | +0.3011054 | —96.13326 | +92.031 |
| 10500 | 164 1 20.80 | 0.2723199 | 6.08303 | 1.959 |
| 11000 | 164 16 27.66 | 0.2448894 | 6.03516 | 1.891 |
| 11500 | 164 30 40.23 | 0.2186921 | 5.98944 | 1.826 |
| 12000 | 164 44 3.94 | 0.1936223 | 5.94568 | 1.764 |
| 13000 | 165 8 42.90 | +0.1465042 | —95.86343 | +91.646 |
| 14000 | 165 30 55.26 | 0.1029147 | 5.78733 | 1.538 |
| 15000 | 165 51 4.63 | 0.0623627 | 5.71652 | 1.437 |
| 16000 | 166 9 29.58 | 0.0244528 | 5.65032 | 1.342 |
| 17000 | 166 26 24.88 | 9.9888624 | 5.58817 | 1.254 |
| 18000 | 166 42 2.53 | +9.9553241 | —95.52959 | +91.170 |
| 19200 | 166 59 18.90 | 9.9174751 | 5.46348 | 1.076 |
| 20400 | 167 15 11.32 | 9.8819393 | 5.40141 | 90.987 |
| 21600 | 167 29 51.00 | 9.8484507 | 5.34290 | 90.904 |
| 22800 | 167 43 27.11 | 9.8167866 | 5.28758 | 90.825 |
| 24000 | 167 56 7.28 | +9.7867585 | —95.23512 | +90.750 |
| 26000 | 168 15 26.77 | 9.7399215 | 5.15328 | 90.633 |
| 28000 | 168 32 51.95 | 9.6965794 | 5.07755 | 90.525 |
| 30000 | 168 48 41.17 | 9.6562474 | 5.00706 | 90.424 |
| 32000 | 169 3 8.84 | 9.6185347 | 4.94116 | 90.330 |
| 34000 | 169 16 26.46 | +9.5831221 | —94.87926 | +90.242 |
| 36000 | 169 28 43.36 | 9.5497452 | 4.82093 | 90.159 |
| 38000 | 169 40 7.19 | 9.5181828 | 4.76576 | 90.080 |
| 40000 | 169 50 44.28 | 9.4882481 | 4.71343 | 90.005 |

TABLE III*a*. 33

| $\eta$ | Log $\mu$. | Log Diff. | $\eta$ | Log $\mu$. | Log Diff. | $\eta$ | Log $\mu$. | Log Diff. |
|------|-----------|-----------|------|-----------|-----------|------|-----------|-----------|
| 0.00 | 0.00000 00 |        | 0.30 | 0.00167 33 | 3.0594 | 0.60 | 0.00735 26 | 3.4468 |
| .01  | .00000 18  | 1.556  | .31  | .00179 01  | .0754  | .61  | .00763 61  | .4585  |
| .02  | .00000 72  | 1.857  | .32  | .00191 12  | .0910  | .62  | .00792 74  | .4703  |
| 0.03 | 0.00001 62 | 2.0354 | 0.33 | 0.00203 67 | 3.1062 | 0.63 | 0.00822 68 | 3.4822 |
| .04  | .00002 89  | .1614  | .34  | .00216 66  | .1211  | .64  | .00853 45  | .4941  |
| .05  | .00004 52  | .2589  | .35  | .00230 10  | .1356  | .65  | .00885 08  | .5061  |
| 0.06 | .00006 52  | 2.3385 | 0.36 | 0.00243 99 | 3.1498 | 0.66 | 0.00917 59 | 3.5182 |
| .07  | .00008 88  | .4057  | .37  | .00258 34  | .1638  | .67  | .00951 03  | .5304  |
| .08  | .00011 61  | .4639  | .38  | .00273 15  | .1774  | .68  | .00985 42  | 5427   |
| 0.09 | 0.00014 70 | 2.5152 | 0.39 | 0.00288 43 | 3.1911 | 0.69 | 0.01020 81 | 3.5551 |
| .10  | .00018 16  | .5617  | .40  | .00304 20  | .2044  | .70  | .01057 23  | .5677  |
| .11  | .00021 99  | .6031  | .41  | .00320 45  | .2175  | .71  | .01094 73  | .5805  |
| 0.12 | 0.00026 18 | 2.6410 | 0.42 | 0.00337 20 | 3.2304 | 0.72 | 0.01133 35 | 3.5934 |
| .13  | .00030 74  | .6767  | .43  | .00354 45  | .2433  | .73  | .01173 15  | .6066  |
| .14  | .00035 68  | .7097  | .44  | .00372 22  | .2557  | .74  | .01214 19  | .6200  |
| 0.15 | 0.00040 99 | 2.7404 | 0.45 | 0.00390 50 | 3.2681 | 0.75 | 0.01256 52 | 3.6336 |
| .16  | .00046 68  | .7694  | .46  | .00409 31  | .2807  | .76  | .01300 22  | .6476  |
| .17  | .00052 75  | .7966  | .47  | .00428 67  | .2930  | .77  | .01345 36  | .6618  |
| 0.18 | 0.00059 20 | 2.8222 | 0.48 | 0.00448 58 | 3.3053 | 0.78 | 0.01392 02 | 3.6765 |
| .19  | .00066 03  | .8466  | .49  | .00469 06  | ·3173  | .79  | .01440 31  | .6915  |
| .20  | .00073 25  | .8701  | .50  | .00490 11  | .3293  | .80  | .01490 32  | .7070  |
| 0.21 | 0.00080 86 | 2.8924 | 0.51 | 0.00511 75 | 3.3411 | 0.81 | 0.01542 18 | 3.7231 |
| .22  | .00088 86  | .9135  | .52  | .00533 98  | .3529  | .82  | .01596 03  | .7397  |
| .23  | .00097 25  | .9340  | .53  | .00556 83  | .3647  | .83  | .01652 02  | .7570  |
| 0.24 | 0.00106 04 | 2.9538 | 0.54 | 0.00580 30 | 3.3764 | 0.84 | 0.01710 33 | 3.7751 |
| .25  | .00115 23  | .9729  | .55  | .00604 41  | .3882  | .85  | .01771 19  | .7942  |
| .26  | .00124 83  | .9914  | .56  | .00629 19  | .4000  | .86  | .01834 86  | .8144  |
| 0.27 | .00134 84  | 3.0090 | 0.57 | 0.00654 65 | 3.4117 | 0.87 | 0.01901 65 | 3.8360 |
| .28  | .00145 25  | .0261  | .58  | .00680 80  | .4233  | .88  | .01971 95  | .8593  |
| .29  | .00156 08  | .0430  | .59  | .00707 66  | .4350  | .89  | .02046 29  | .8846  |
| 0.30 | 0.00167 33 | 3.0594 | 0.60 | 0.00735 26 | 3.4468 | 0.90 | 0.02125 29 | 3.9128 |
| .31  | .00179 01  | .0754  | .61  | .00763 61  | .4585  | .91  | .02209 92  | .9452  |
| .32  | .00191 12  | .0910  | .62  | .00792 74  | .4703  | .92  | .02301 60  |        |

# TABLE IV*a*.

| | | | $m \sin z^4 = \sin(z-q)$. | | $m$ and $q$ positive. | | | | | |
|---|---|---|---|---|---|---|---|---|---|---|

| | | | $z^{\mathrm{I}}$ | | $z^{\mathrm{II}}$ | | $z^{\mathrm{III}}$ | | $z^{\mathrm{IV}}$ | |
|---|---|---|---|---|---|---|---|---|---|---|
| $q$ | $\log m'$ | $\log m''$ | $m''$ | $m'$ | $m'$ | $m''$ | $m''$ | $m'$ | $m'$ | $m''$ |
| 1 | 4.2976 | 9.9999 | 1 0 | 1 20 | 1 20 | 89 40 | 89 40 | 177 37 | 180 55 | 181 0 |
| 2 | 3.3950 | 9.9996 | 2 0 | 2 40 | 2 40 | 89 20 | 89 20 | 175 14 | 181 51 | 182 0 |
| 3 | 2.8675 | 9.9992 | 3 0 | 4 0 | 4 0 | 89 0 | 89 0 | 172 52 | 182 46 | 183 0 |
| 4 | 2.4938 | 9.9986 | 4 0 | 5 20 | 5 20 | 88 40 | 88 40 | 170 28 | 183 42 | 184 0 |
| 5 | 2.2044 | 9.9978 | 5 0 | 6 41 | 6 41 | 88 19 | 88 19 | 168 5 | 184 37 | 185 0 |
| 6 | 1.9686 | 9.9968 | 6 0 | 8 1 | 8 1 | 87 59 | 87 59 | 165 41 | 185 32 | 186 0 |
| 7 | 1.7698 | 9.9957 | 7 1 | 9 22 | 9 22 | 87 38 | 87 38 | 163 18 | 186 28 | 186 59 |
| 8 | 1.5981 | 9.9943 | 8 1 | 10 42 | 10 42 | 87 18 | 87 18 | 160 52 | 187 23 | 187 59 |
| 9 | 1.4473 | 9.9928 | 9 2 | 12 3 | 12 3 | 86 57 | 86 57 | 158 28 | 188 18 | 188 58 |
| 10 | 1.3130 | 9.9911 | 10 3 | 13 25 | 13 25 | 86 35 | 86 35 | 156 3 | 189 13 | 189 57 |
| 11 | 1.1922 | 9.9892 | 11 5 | 14 46 | 14 46 | 86 14 | 86 14 | 153 37 | 190 9 | 190 56 |
| 12 | 1.0824 | 9.9871 | 12 7 | 16 8 | 16 8 | 85 52 | 85 52 | 151 10 | 191 4 | 191 54 |
| 13 | 0.9821 | 9.9848 | 13 9 | 17 31 | 17 31 | 85 29 | 85 29 | 148 43 | 191 59 | 192 52 |
| 14 | 0.8898 | 9.9823 | 14 12 | 18 53 | 18 53 | 85 7 | 85 7 | 146 14 | 192 54 | 193 49 |
| 15 | 0.8045 | 9.9796 | 15 16 | 20 17 | 20 17 | 84 43 | 84 43 | 143 45 | 193 49 | 194 46 |
| 16 | 0.7254 | 9.9767 | 16 20 | 21 40 | 21 40 | 84 20 | 84 20 | 141 14 | 194 44 | 195 42 |
| 17 | 0.6518 | 9.9736 | 17 26 | 23 5 | 23 5 | 83 55 | 83 55 | 138 42 | 195 39 | 196 38 |
| 18 | 0.5830 | 9.9702 | 18 33 | 24 30 | 24 30 | 83 30 | 83 30 | 136 9 | 196 33 | 197 33 |
| 19 | 0.5185 | 9.9667 | 19 41 | 25 56 | 25 56 | 83 4 | 83 4 | 133 34 | 197 28 | 198 28 |
| 20 | 0.4581 | 9.9629 | 20 51 | 27 23 | 27 23 | 82 37 | 82 37 | 130 58 | 198 23 | 199 22 |
| 21 | 0.4013 | 9.9588 | 22 2 | 28 50 | 28 50 | 82 10 | 82 10 | 128 19 | 199 17 | 200 15 |
| 22 | 0.3479 | 9.9545 | 23 15 | 30 19 | 30 19 | 81 41 | 81 41 | 125 38 | 200 11 | 201 8 |
| 23 | 0.2976 | 9.9499 | 24 31 | 31 49 | 31 49 | 81 11 | 81 11 | 122 55 | 201 6 | 202 0 |
| 24 | 0.2501 | 9.9451 | 25 49 | 33 20 | 33 20 | 80 40 | 80 40 | 120 9 | 202 0 | 202 51 |
| 25 | 0.2053 | 9.9400 | 27 10 | 34 53 | 34 53 | 80 7 | 80 7 | 117 20 | 202 54 | 203 42 |
| 26 | 0.1631 | 9.9345 | 28 35 | 36 28 | 36 28 | 79 32 | 79 32 | 114 27 | 203 47 | 204 32 |
| 27 | 0.1232 | 9.9287 | 30 4 | 38 5 | 38 5 | 78 55 | 78 55 | 111 30 | 204 41 | 205 22 |
| 28 | 0.0857 | 9.9226 | 31 38 | 39 45 | 39 45 | 78 15 | 78 15 | 108 27 | 205 35 | 206 11 |
| 29 | 0.0503 | 9.9161 | 33 18 | 41 27 | 41 27 | 77 33 | 77 33 | 105 19 | 206 28 | 207 0 |
| 30 | 0.0170 | 9.9092 | 35 5 | 43 13 | 43 13 | 76 47 | 76 47 | 102 3 | 207 21 | 207 48 |
| 31 | 9.9857 | 9.9019 | 37 1 | 45 4 | 45 4 | 75 56 | 75 56 | 98 37 | 208 14 | 208 36 |
| 32 | 9.9565 | 9.8940 | 39 9 | 47 1 | 47 1 | 74 59 | 74 59 | 95 0 | 209 6 | 209 24 |
| 33 | 9.9292 | 9.8856 | 41 33 | 49 6 | 49 6 | 73 54 | 73 54 | 91 6 | 209 58 | 210 11 |
| 34 | 9.9040 | 9.8765 | 44 21 | 51 22 | 51 22 | 72 38 | 72 38 | 86 49 | 210 50 | 210 58 |
| 35 | 9.8808 | 9.8665 | 47 47 | 53 58 | 53 58 | 71 2 | 71 2 | 81 53 | 211 41 | 211 46 |
| 36 | 9.8600 | 9.8555 | 52 31 | 57 13 | 57 13 | 68 47 | 68 47 | 75 40 | 212 32 | 212 33 |
| $q'$ | 9.8443 | 9.8443 | 63 26 | 63 26 | 63 26 | 63 26 | 63 26 | 63 26 | 213 15 | 213 15 |

$q' = 36° 52' 11.64''$ $\qquad\qquad$ $\sin q' = 0.6$

$$m \sin z^4 = \sin (z + q). \quad m \text{ and } q \text{ positive.}$$

| $q$ | $\log m'$. | $\log m''$. | $z^{\mathrm{I}}$ | | $z^{\mathrm{II}}$ | | $z^{\mathrm{III}}$ | | $z^{\mathrm{IV}}$ | |
|---|---|---|---|---|---|---|---|---|---|---|
| | | | $m'$ | $m''$ | $m''$ | $m'$ | $m'$ | $m''$ | $m''$ | $m'$ |
| 1 | 4.2976 | 9.9999 | 2 23 | 90 20 | 90 20 | 178 40 | 178 40 | 179 0 | 359 0 | 359 5 |
| 2 | 3.3950 | 9.9996 | 4 46 | 90 40 | 90 40 | 177 20 | 177 20 | 178 0 | 358 0 | 358 9 |
| 3 | 2.8675 | 9.9992 | 7 8 | 91 0 | 91 0 | 176 0 | 176 0 | 177 0 | 357 0 | 357 14 |
| 4 | 2.4938 | 9.9986 | 9 32 | 91 20 | 91 20 | 174 40 | 174 40 | 176 0 | 356 0 | 356 18 |
| 5 | 2.2044 | 9.9978 | 11 55 | 91 41 | 91 41 | 173 19 | 173 19 | 175 0 | 355 0 | 355 23 |
| 6 | 1.9686 | 9.9968 | 14 19 | 92 1 | 92 1 | 171 59 | 171 59 | 174 0 | 354 0 | 354 28 |
| 7 | 1.7698 | 9.9957 | 16 42 | 92 22 | 92 22 | 170 38 | 170 38 | 172 59 | 353 1 | 353 32 |
| 8 | 1.5981 | 9.9943 | 19 7 | 92 42 | 92 42 | 169 18 | 169 18 | 171 59 | 352 1 | 352 37 |
| 9 | 1.4473 | 9.9928 | 21 32 | 93 3 | 93 3 | 167 57 | 167 57 | 170 58 | 351 2 | 351 42 |
| 10 | 1.3130 | 9.9911 | 23 57 | 93 25 | 93 25 | 166 35 | 166 35 | 169 57 | 350 3 | 350 47 |
| 11 | 1.1922 | 9.9892 | 26 23 | 93 46 | 93 46 | 165 14 | 165 14 | 168 55 | 349 4 | 349 51 |
| 12 | 1.0824 | 9.9871 | 28 50 | 94 8 | 94 8 | 163 52 | 163 52 | 167 54 | 348 6 | 348 56 |
| 13 | 0.9821 | 9.9848 | 31 17 | 94 31 | 94 31 | 162 29 | 162 29 | 166 51 | 347 8 | 348 1 |
| 14 | 0.8898 | 9.9823 | 33 46 | 94 53 | 94 53 | 161 7 | 161 7 | 165 48 | 346 11 | 347 6 |
| 15 | 0.8045 | 9.9796 | 36 15 | 95 17 | 95 17 | 159 43 | 159 43 | 164 44 | 345 14 | 346 11 |
| 16 | 0.7254 | 9.9767 | 38 46 | 95 40 | 95 40 | 158 20 | 158 20 | 163 40 | 344 18 | 345 16 |
| 17 | 0.6518 | 9.9736 | 41 18 | 96 5 | 96 5 | 156 55 | 156 55 | 162 34 | 343 22 | 344 21 |
| 18 | 0.5830 | 9.9702 | 43 51 | 96 30 | 96 30 | 155 30 | 155 30 | 161 27 | 342 27 | 343 27 |
| 19 | 0.5185 | 9.9667 | 46 26 | 96 56 | 96 56 | 154 4 | 154 4 | 160 19 | 341 32 | 342 32 |
| 20 | 0.4581 | 9.9629 | 49 2 | 97 23 | 97 23 | 152 37 | 152 37 | 159 9 | 340 38 | 341 37 |
| 21 | 0.4013 | 9.9588 | 51 41 | 97 50 | 97 50 | 151 10 | 151 10 | 157 58 | 339 45 | 340 43 |
| 22 | 0.3479 | 9.9545 | 54 22 | 98 19 | 98 19 | 149 41 | 149 41 | 156 45 | 338 52 | 339 49 |
| 23 | 0.2976 | 9.9499 | 57 5 | 98 49 | 98 49 | 148 11 | 148 11 | 155 29 | 338 0 | 338 54 |
| 24 | 0.2501 | 9.9451 | 59 51 | 99 20 | 99 20 | 146 40 | 146 40 | 154 11 | 337 9 | 338 0 |
| 25 | 0.2053 | 9.9400 | 62 40 | 99 53 | 99 53 | 145 7 | 145 7 | 152 50 | 336 18 | 337 6 |
| 26 | 0.1631 | 9.9345 | 65 33 | 100 28 | 100 28 | 143 32 | 143 32 | 151 25 | 335 28 | 336 13 |
| 27 | 0.1232 | 9.9287 | 68 30 | 101 5 | 101 5 | 141 55 | 141 55 | 149 56 | 334 38 | 335 19 |
| 28 | 0.0857 | 9.9226 | 71 33 | 101 45 | 101 45 | 140 15 | 140 15 | 148 22 | 333 49 | 334 25 |
| 29 | 0.0503 | 9.9161 | 74 41 | 102 27 | 102 27 | 138 33 | 138 33 | 146 42 | 333 0 | 333 32 |
| 30 | 0.0170 | 9.9092 | 77 57 | 103 13 | 103 13 | 136 46 | 136 46 | 144 55 | 332 12 | 332 39 |
| 31 | 9.9857 | 9.9019 | 81 23 | 104 4 | 104 4 | 134 56 | 134 56 | 142 59 | 331 24 | 331 46 |
| 32 | 9.9565 | 9.8940 | 85 0 | 105 1 | 105 1 | 132 59 | 132 59 | 140 51 | 330 36 | 330 54 |
| 33 | 9.9292 | 9.8856 | 88 54 | 106 6 | 106 6 | 130 54 | 130 54 | 138 27 | 329 49 | 330 2 |
| 34 | 9.9040 | 9.8765 | 93 11 | 107 22 | 107 22 | 128 38 | 128 38 | 135 38 | 329 2 | 329 10 |
| 35 | 9.8808 | 9.8665 | 98 7 | 108 58 | 108 58 | 126 2 | 126 2 | 132 13 | 328 14 | 328 19 |
| 36 | 9.8600 | 9.8555 | 104 20 | 111 13 | 111 13 | 122 47 | 122 47 | 127 29 | 327 27 | 327 28 |
| $q'$ | 9.8443 | 9.8443 | 116 34 | 116 34 | 116 34 | 116 34 | 116 34 | 116 34 | 326 45 | 326 45 |

$$q' = 36° 52' 11.64'' \qquad\qquad \sin q' = 0.6$$

| x. | A. | Diff. | B. | Diff. | B′. | Diff. |
|---|---|---|---|---|---|---|
| °0 | — ″0.00 | —9.60 | —″0.000 | —11 | —″0.000 | —34 |
| 1 | 9.00 | 9.00 | 0.011 | 11 | 0.034 | 34 |
| 2 | 17.99 | 8.98 | 0.023 | 12 | 0.067 | 33 |
| 3 | 26.95 | 8.95 | 0.034 | 11 | 0.101 | 34 |
| 4 | 35.88 | 8.91 | 0.045 | 11 | 0.134 | 33 |
| 5 | — 44.77 | —8.87 | —0.057 | —12 | —0.167 | —33 |
| 6 | 53.61 | 8.80 | 0.068 | 11 | 0.200 | 33 |
| 7 | 62.37 | 8.73 | 0.080 | 12 | 0.232 | 32 |
| 8 | 71.07 | 8.65 | 0.092 | 12 | 0.263 | 31 |
| 9 | 79.67 | 8.56 | 0.104 | 12 | 0.294 | 31 |
| 10 | — 88.18 | —8.46 | —0.117 | —13 | —0.324 | —30 |
| 11 | 96.58 | 8.34 | 0.129 | 12 | 0.353 | 29 |
| 12 | 104.86 | 8.22 | 0.142 | 13 | 0.382 | 29 |
| 13 | 113.01 | 8.08 | 0.156 | 14 | 0.409 | 27 |
| 14 | 121.02 | 7.94 | 0.169 | 13 | 0.436 | 27 |
| 15 | —128.88 | —7.79 | —0.183 | —14 | —0.461 | —25 |
| 16 | 136.59 | 7.62 | 0.197 | 14 | 0.486 | 25 |
| 17 | 144.12 | 7.43 | 0.211 | 14 | 0.509 | 23 |
| 18 | 151.47 | 7.27 | 0.226 | 15 | 0.531 | 22 |
| 19 | 158.63 | 7.08 | 0.241 | 15 | 0.552 | 21 |
| 20 | —165.60 | —6.86 | —0.256 | —15 | —0.571 | —19 |
| 21 | 172.35 | 6.65 | 0.271 | 15 | 0.590 | 19 |
| 22 | 178.89 | 6.43 | 0.287 | 16 | 0.606 | 16 |
| 23 | 185.20 | 6.20 | 0.303 | 16 | 0.622 | 16 |
| 24 | 191.28 | 5.96 | 0.319 | 16 | 0.636 | 14 |
| 25 | —197.11 | —5.71 | —0.336 | —17 | —0.648 | —12 |
| 26 | 202.69 | 5.45 | 0.352 | 16 | 0.659 | 10 |
| 27 | 208.00 | 5.18 | 0.369 | 17 | 0.668 | 9 |
| 28 | 213.05 | 4.91 | 0.386 | 17 | 0.676 | 7 |
| 29 | 217.81 | 4.63 | 0.403 | 17 | 0.682 | 6 |
| 30 | —222.30 | —4.34 | —0.419 | —16 | —0.687 | — 4 |
| 31 | 226.48 | 4.04 | 0.436 | 17 | 0.690 | 3 |
| 32 | 230.37 | 3.74 | 0.453 | 17 | 0.692 | 1 |
| 33 | 233.95 | 3.42 | 0.470 | 17 | 0.692 | 0 |
| 34 | 237.21 | 3.10 | 0.486 | 16 | 0.691 | +- 2 |
| 35 | —240.15 | —2.78 | —0.502 | —16 | —0.688 | + 4 |
| 36 | 242.76 | 2.45 | 0.518 | 16 | 0.683 | 5 |
| 37 | 245.04 | 2.11 | 0.534 | 16 | 0.677 | 6 |
| 38 | 246.98 | 1.77 | 0.549 | 15 | 0.670 | 8 |
| 39 | 248.57 | 1.41 | 0.564 | 15 | 0.661 | 9 |
| 40 | —249.80 | —1.06 | —0.578 | —14 | —0.651 | +11 |
| 41 | 250.68 | 0.70 | 0.591 | 13 | 0.639 | 12 |
| 42 | 251.20 | 0.33 | 0.604 | 12 | 0.627 | 13 |

| x. | A. | Diff. | B. | Diff. | B′. | Diff. |
|----|----|-------|----|-------|-----|-------|
| 42 | −251″.20 | − 0.33 | −0″.604 | − 12 | −0″.627 | +13 |
| 43 | 251.34 | + 0.04 | 0.615 | 11 | 0.613 | 15 |
| 44 | 251.11 | 0.42 | 0.626 | 11 | 0.597 | 16 |
| 45 | 250.50 | 0.80 | 0.636 | 10 | 0.580 | 17 |
| 46 | 249.51 | 1.18 | 0.645 | 8 | 0.563 | 18 |
| 47 | −248.13 | + 1.57 | −0.652 | − 7 | −0.544 | +19 |
| 48 | 246.36 | 1.96 | 0.659 | 6 | 0.524 | 20 |
| 49 | 244.20 | 2.36 | 0.664 | 4 | 0.503 | 21 |
| 50 | 241.64 | 2.76 | 0.667 | 3 | 0.482 | 22 |
| 51 | 238.68 | 3.16 | 0.669 | 1 | 0.459 | 23 |
| 52 | −235.31 | + 3.57 | −0.669 | + 1 | −0.436 | +23 |
| 53 | 231.54 | 3.98 | 0.667 | 2 | 0.412 | 24 |
| 54 | 227.35 | 4.39 | 0.664 | 4 | 0.387 | 25 |
| 55 | 222.76 | 4.80 | 0.659 | 6 | 0.361 | 26 |
| 56 | 217.75 | 5.22 | 0.651 | 9 | 0.335 | 26 |
| 57 | −212.32 | + 5.64 | −0.641 | + 11 | −0.309 | +26 |
| 58 | 206.47 | 6.06 | 0.629 | 13 | 0.282 | 27 |
| 59 | 200.20 | 6.47 | 0.615 | 15 | 0.255 | 27 |
| 60 | 193.52 | 6.90 | 0.598 | 18 | 0.227 | 28 |
| 61 | 186.40 | 7.32 | 0.579 | 20 | 0.200 | 27 |
| 62 | −178.87 | + 7.74 | −0.557 | + 23 | −0.172 | +28 |
| 63 | 170.91 | 8.17 | 0.532 | 26 | 0.144 | 28 |
| 64 | 162.52 | 8.60 | 0.504 | 29 | 0.116 | 28 |
| 65 | 153.70 | 9.03 | 0.474 | 32 | 0.088 | 28 |
| 66 | 144.46 | 9.45 | 0.440 | 35 | 0.061 | 27 |
| 67 | −134.79 | + 9.88 | −0.403 | + 38 | −0.033 | +28 |
| 68 | 124.69 | 10.31 | 0.363 | 41 | −0.006 | 27 |
| 69 | 114.16 | 10.74 | 0.320 | 45 | +0.021 | 27 |
| 70 | 103.20 | 11.17 | 0.273 | 49 | 0.048 | 27 |
| 71 | 91.81 | 11.60 | 0.222 | 52 | 0.074 | 26 |
| 72 | − 80.00 | +12.03 | −0.168 | + 56 | +0.099 | +25 |
| 73 | 67.75 | 12.46 | 0.110 | 59 | 0.124 | 25 |
| 74 | 55.07 | 12.89 | 0.049 | 63 | 0.148 | 24 |
| 75 | 41.97 | 13.32 | +0.016 | 67 | 0.172 | 24 |
| 76 | 28.43 | 13.72 | 0.086 | 71 | 0.195 | 22 |
| 77 | − 14.47 | +14.18 | +0.159 | + 75 | +0.216 | +21 |
| 78 | 0.07 | 14.61 | 0.237 | 80 | 0.237 | 21 |
| 79 | + 14.76 | 15.04 | 0.319 | 84 | 0.257 | 20 |
| 80 | 30.02 | 15.47 | 0.405 | 88 | 0.276 | 19 |
| 81 | 45.70 | 15.89 | 0.496 | 93 | 0.294 | 18 |
| 82 | + 61.80 | +16.32 | +0.591 | + 97 | +0.311 | +16 |
| 83 | 78.34 | 16.76 | 0.691 | 102 | 0.326 | 15 |
| 84 | 95.32 | 17.19 | 0.795 | 106 | 0.340 | 13 |

# TABLE V*a*.

| x. | A. | Diff. | B. | Diff. | B'. | Diff. |
|---|---|---|---|---|---|---|
| 84 | + 95ʺ.32 | +17.19 | + 0ʺ.795 | +106 | +0ʺ.340 | + 13 |
| 85 | 112.72 | 17.62 | 0.904 | 111 | 0.352 | 12 |
| 86 | 130.56 | 18.06 | 1.018 | 116 | 0.363 | 10 |
| 87 | 148.84 | 18.49 | 1.137 | 121 | 0.373 | 9 |
| 88 | 167.54 | 18.92 | 1.261 | 126 | 0.381 | 7 |
| 89 | + 186.69 | +19.36 | + 1.390 | +132 | +0.386 | + 5 |
| 90 | 206.27 | 19.80 | 1.525 | 137 | 0.390 | 3 |
| 91 | 226.29 | 20.24 | 1.665 | 142 | 0.392 | 1 |
| 92 | 246.75 | 20.68 | 1.810 | 148 | 0.392 | — 1 |
| 93 | 267.65 | 21.13 | 1.961 | 154 | 0.390 | 3 |
| 94 | + 289.01 | +21.58 | + 2.118 | +159 | +0.385 | — 6 |
| 95 | 310.82 | 22.03 | 2.280 | 165 | 0.378 | 8 |
| 96 | 333.08 | 22.49 | 2.449 | 171 | 0.368 | 11 |
| 97 | 355.80 | 22.95 | 2.623 | 178 | 0.355 | 14 |
| 98 | 378.99 | 23.42 | 2.805 | 184 | 0.339 | 17 |
| 99 | + 402.65 | +23.89 | + 2.992 | +191 | +0.320 | — 21 |
| 100 | 426.78 | 24.37 | 3.187 | 198 | 0.297 | 25 |
| 101 | 451.40 | 24.86 | 3.388 | 204 | 0.270 | 28 |
| 102 | 476.51 | 25.36 | 3.596 | 212 | 0.240 | 32 |
| 103 | 502.12 | 25.86 | 3.812 | 220 | 0.205 | 37 |
| 104 | + 528.24 | +26.38 | + 4.036 | +227 | +0.165 | — 42 |
| 105 | 554.88 | 26.90 | 4.267 | 235 | 0.121 | 47 |
| 106 | 582.04 | 27.43 | 4.506 | 240 | 0.071 | 53 |
| 107 | 609.75 | 27.99 | 4.755 | 250 | +0.015 | 59 |
| 108 | 638.02 | 28.55 | 5.012 | 261 | —0.048 | 66 |
| 109 | + 666.85 | +29.11 | + 5.278 | +271 | —0.117 | — 72 |
| 110 | 696.27 | 29.72 | 5.554 | 281 | 0.193 | 80 |
| 111 | 726.29 | 30.33 | 5.841 | 292 | 0.278 | 89 |
| 112 | 756.93 | 30.96 | 6.138 | 302 | 0.371 | 98 |
| 113 | 788.21 | 31.61 | 6.446 | 314 | 0.474 | 108 |
| 114 | + 820.15 | +32.28 | + 6.766 | +326 | —0.587 | —119 |
| 115 | 852.77 | 32.98 | 7.099 | 339 | 0.712 | 131 |
| 116 | 886.11 | 33.70 | 7.445 | 353 | 0.849 | 144 |
| 117 | 920.18 | 34.45 | 8.806 | 368 | 1.000 | 158 |
| 118 | 955.02 | 35.22 | 8.181 | 383 | 1.166 | 174 |
| 119 | + 990.65 | +36.05 | + 8.572 | +399 | —1.348 | —191 |
| 120 | 1027.13 | 36.91 | 8.980 | 417 | 1.548 | 209 |
| 121 | 1064.47 | 37.79 | 9.407 | 436 | 1.767 | 230 |
| 122 | 1102.71 | 38.73 | 9.853 | 456 | 2.009 | 253 |
| 123 | 1141.93 | 39.71 | 10.320 | 478 | 2.274 | 278 |
| 124 | +1182.14 | +40.74 | +10.809 | +501 | —2.566 | —306 |
| 125 | 1223.41 | 41.82 | 11.323 | 527 | 2.886 | 336 |
| 126 | 1265.78 | 42.96 | 11.863 | 554 | 3.239 | 370 |

| x. | A. | Diff. | B. | Diff. | B'. | Diff. |
|---|---|---|---|---|---|---|
| 126 | +1263.78 | + 42.96 | + 11.863 | + 0.554 | − 3.239 | − 0.370 |
| 127 | 1309.33 | 44.16 | 12.431 | 0.584 | 3.627 | 0.408 |
| 128 | 1354.11 | 45.43 | 13.031 | 0.616 | 4.055 | 0.449 |
| 129 | 1400.20 | 46.78 | 13.663 | 0.651 | 4.526 | 0.496 |
| 130 | 1447.67 | 48.20 | 14.333 | 0.690 | 5.047 | 0.547 |
| 131 | +1496.61 | + 49.72 | + 15.043 | + 0.731 | − 5.621 | − 0.605 |
| 132 | 1547.11 | 51.33 | 15.796 | 0.777 | 6.257 | 0.669 |
| 133 | 1599.28 | 53.04 | 16.597 | 0.827 | 6.960 | 0.741 |
| 134 | 1653.20 | 54.87 | 17.451 | 0.883 | 7.739 | 0.821 |
| 135 | 1709.02 | 56.82 | 18.363 | 0.945 | 8.603 | 0.912 |
| 136 | +1766.84 | + 58.91 | + 19.341 | + 1.013 | − 9.563 | − 1.014 |
| 137 | 1826.84 | 61.15 | 20.389 | 1.088 | 10.631 | 1.128 |
| 138 | 1889.15 | 63.55 | 21.517 | 1.171 | 11.820 | 1.258 |
| 139 | 1953.95 | 66.14 | 22.732 | 1.265 | 13.148 | 1.406 |
| 140 | 2021.43 | 68.92 | 24.047 | 1.371 | 14.633 | 1.573 |
| 141 | +2091.79 | + 71.90 | + 25.475 | + 1.490 | − 16.295 | − 1.765 |
| 142 | 2165.28 | 75.15 | 27.027 | 1.623 | 18.163 | 1.984 |
| 143 | 2242.15 | 78.65 | 28.722 | 1.774 | 20.263 | 2.234 |
| 144 | 2322.68 | 82.47 | 30.576 | 1.946 | 22.631 | 2.523 |
| 145 | 2407.20 | 86.58 | 32.615 | 2.143 | 25.309 | 2.856 |
| 146 | +2496.06 | + 91.16 | + 34.862 | + 2.368 | − 28.344 | − 3.242 |
| 147 | 2589.66 | 96.11 | 37.351 | 2.626 | 31.794 | 3.713 |
| 148 | 2688.45 | 101.56 | 40.115 | 2.924 | 35.730 | 4.224 |
| 149 | 2792.96 | 107.54 | 43.199 | 3.272 | 40.233 | 4.836 |
| 150 | 2903.74 | 114.13 | 46.659 | 3.677 | 45.403 | 5.566 |
| 151 | +3021.46 | +121.43 | + 50.553 | + 4.153 | − 51.366 | − 6.437 |
| 152 | 3146.88 | 129.53 | 54.966 | 4.717 | 58.267 | 7.469 |
| 153 | 3280.84 | 138.56 | 59.987 | 5.385 | 66.295 | 8.705 |
| 154 | 3424.37 | 148.67 | 65.737 | 6.185 | 75.677 | 10.202 |
| 155 | 3578.59 | 160.01 | 72.357 | 7.155 | 86.700 | 12.024 |
| 156 | +3744.88 | +172.81 | + 80.042 | + 8.328 | − 99.726 | − 14.260 |
| 157 | 3924.79 | 187.33 | 89.014 | 9.767 | 115.221 | 17.023 |
| 158 | 4120.22 | 203.89 | 99.577 | 11.548 | 133.773 | 20.471 |
| 159 | 4333.38 | 222.87 | 112.111 | 13.777 | 156.174 | 24.815 |
| 160 | 4566.94 | 244.78 | 127.132 | 16.603 | 183.404 | 30.348 |
| 161 | +4824.14 | +244.78 | +145.317 | +20.209 | −216.860 | − 37.483 |
| 162 | 5108.93 | 270.26 | 167.550 | 24.869 | 258.371 | 46.802 |
| 163 | 5426.19 | 300.11 | 195.056 | 31.062 | 310.464 | 59.156 |
| 164 | 5782.01 | 335.39 | 229.674 | 39.353 | 376.683 | 75.318 |
| 165 | 6184.14 | 377.50 | 273.762 | 50.636 | 462.100 | 98.618 |
| 166 | +6642.49 | +428.33 | +330.946 | +66.405 | −574.089 | −130.816 |
| 167 | 7170.07 | 490.43 | 406.573 | 88.993 | 723.733 | 177.025 |
| 168 | 7784.18 | 567.43 | 508.933 | 122.256 | 928.140 | 246.403 |
| 169 | 8508.45 | | 651.086 | | 1214.530 | |

# CONSTANTS.

|  |  | Log. |
|---|---|---|
| Attractive force of the Sun, $k$ in terms of radius, | 0 .0172021 | 8.2355814 |
| $k$ in seconds, | 3548″.18761 | 3.5500066 |
| Length of the Sidereal Year (HANSEN and OLUFSEN), | 365$^d$.2563582 | 2.5625978 |
| Length of the Tropical Year, 1850, | 365$^d$.2422008 | 2.5625809 |
| Horizontal equatorial parallax of the Sun (ENCKE),* | 8″.5776 | 0.9333658 |
| Constant of Aberration (STRUVE), | 20″.4451 | 1.3105892 |
| Time required for light to pass from the Sun to the Earth, | 497$^s$.827 | 2.6970785 |
| Radius of Circle in Seconds of arc, | 206264″.806 | 5.3144251 |
| in Seconds of time, | 13750$^s$.987 | 4.1383339 |
| Sin 1″ | 0.000004848137 | 4.6855749 |
| Circumference of Circle in Seconds of arc, | 1296000″ | 6.1126050 |
| in Seconds of time, | 86400$^s$ | 4.9365137 |
| in terms of diameter, $\pi$ | 3.14159265 | 0.4971499 |

General Precession (STRUVE)  $50″.2411 + 0″.0002268\,t$

Obliquity of the ecliptic (STRUVE and PETERS), $23° 27′ 54″.22 - 0.4645\,t - .0000014\,t^2$
    in which $t$ is the number of years after 1800

| Daily precession, 1850, | 0″.1375837 | 9.1385669 |
|---|---|---|
| Modulus of Common Logarithms, $M$ | 0.4342945 | 9.6377843 |

---

* The Constants of Parallax, Aberration, etc., are those used in the *American Ephemeris*, and the authority for them may be found by reference to the volume for 1855.

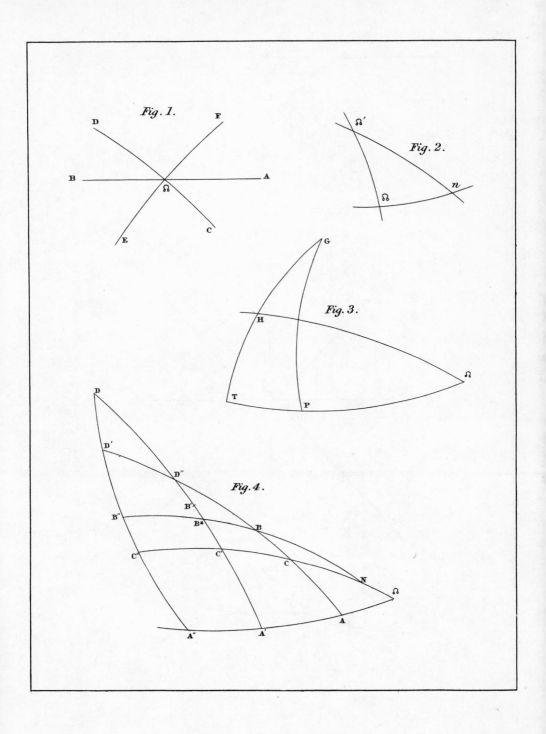

*Fig. 1.*

*Fig. 2.*

*Fig. 3.*

*Fig. 4.*

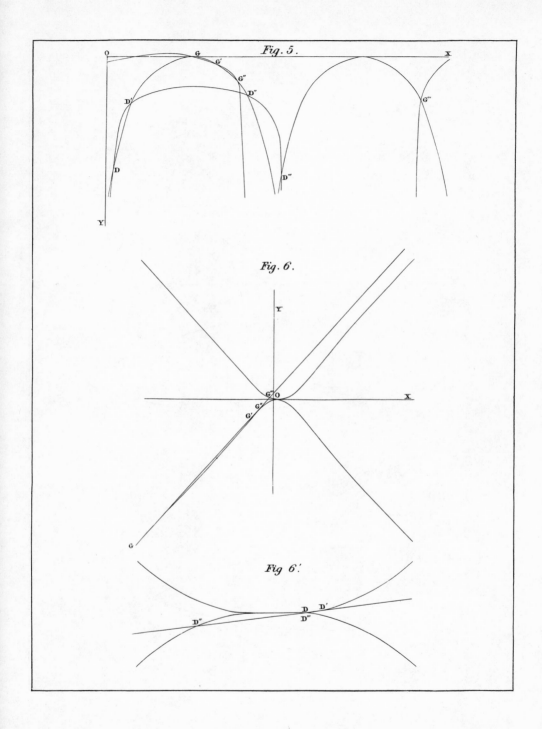

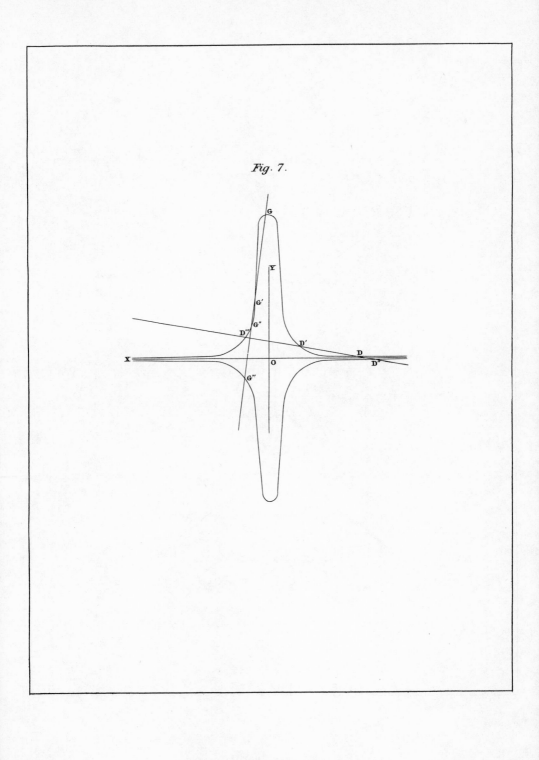

Fig. 7.

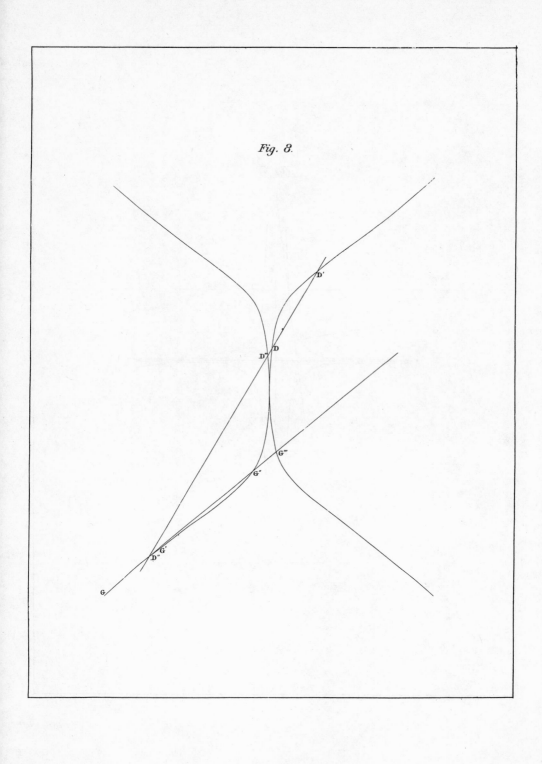

*Fig. 8.*

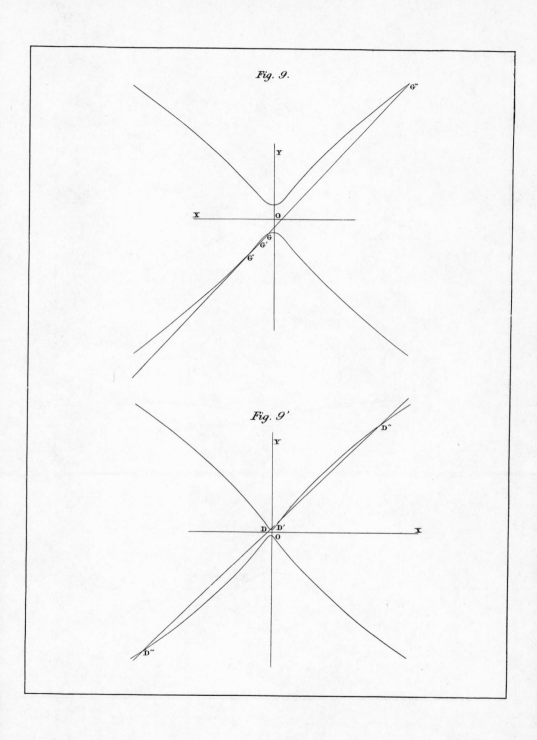

Fig. 9.

Fig. 9'

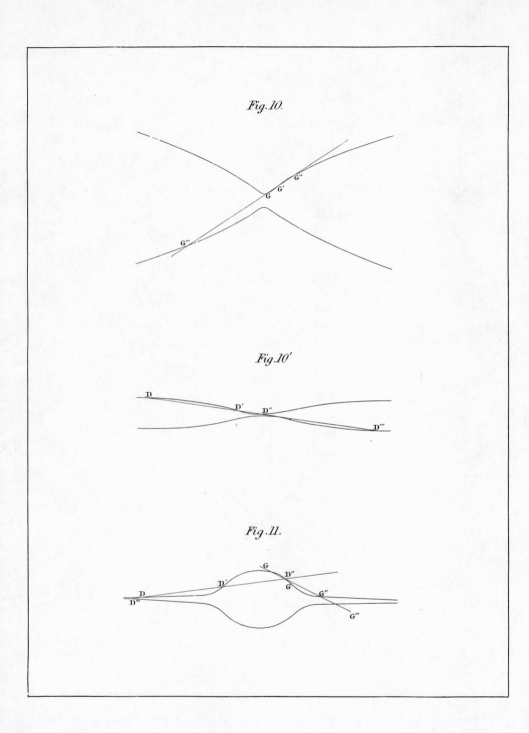

*Fig. 10.*

*Fig. 10'*

*Fig. 11.*

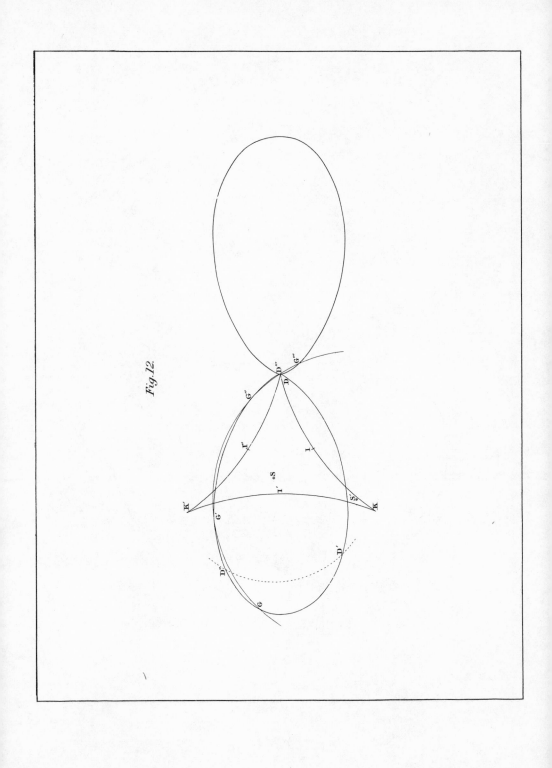

*Fig.12.*

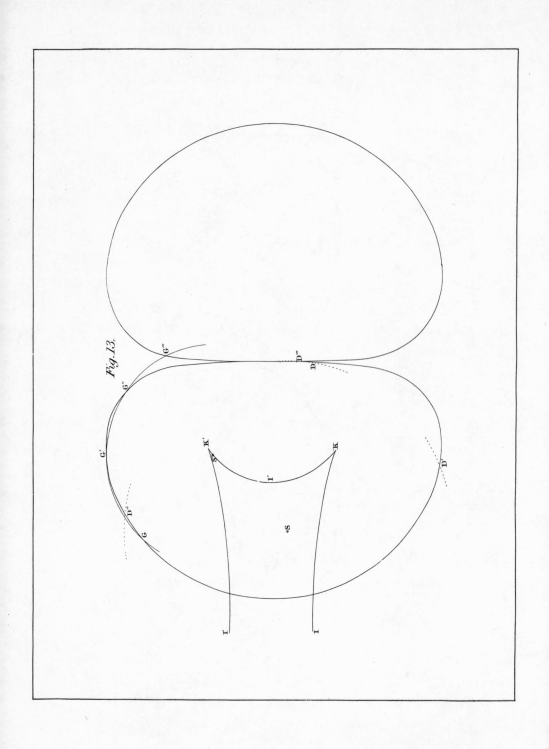

Fig.13.

# CATALOG OF DOVER BOOKS

# BOOKS EXPLAINING SCIENCE AND MATHEMATICS

**THE COMMON SENSE OF THE EXACT SCIENCES, W. K. Clifford.** Introduction by James Newman, edited by Karl Pearson. For 70 years this has been a guide to classical scientific and mathematical thought. Explains with unusual clarity basic concepts, such as extension of meaning of symbols, characteristics of surface boundaries, properties of plane figures, vectors, Cartesian method of determining position, etc. Long preface by Bertrand Russell. Bibliography of Clifford. Corrected, 130 diagrams redrawn. 249pp. 5⅜ x 8.
T61 Paperbound **$1.60**

**SCIENCE THEORY AND MAN, Erwin Schrödinger.** This is a complete and unabridged reissue of SCIENCE AND THE HUMAN TEMPERAMENT plus an additional essay: "What is an Elementary Particle?" Nobel Laureate Schrödinger discusses such topics as nature of scientific method, the nature of science, chance and determinism, science and society, conceptual models for physical entities, elementary particles and wave mechanics. Presentation is popular and may be followed by most people with little or no scientific training. "Fine practical preparation for a time when laws of nature, human institutions . . . are undergoing a critical examination without parallel," Waldemar Kaempffert, N. Y. TIMES. 192pp. 5⅜ x 8.
T428 Paperbound **$1.35**

**PIONEERS OF SCIENCE, O. Lodge.** Eminent scientist-expositor's authoritative, yet elementary survey of great scientific theories. Concentrating on individuals—Copernicus, Brahe, Kepler, Galileo, Descartes, Newton, Laplace, Herschel, Lord Kelvin, and other scientists—the author presents their discoveries in historical order adding biographical material on each man and full, specific explanations of their achievements. The clear and complete treatment of the post-Newtonian astronomers is a feature seldom found in other books on the subject. Index. 120 illustrations. xv + 404pp. 5⅜ x 8.
T716 Paperbound **$1.50**

**THE EVOLUTION OF SCIENTIFIC THOUGHT FROM NEWTON TO EINSTEIN, A. d'Abro.** Einstein's special and general theories of relativity, with their historical implications, are analyzed in non-technical terms. Excellent accounts of the contributions of Newton, Riemann, Weyl, Planck, Eddington, Maxwell, Lorentz and others are treated in terms of space and time, equations of electromagnetics, finiteness of the universe, methodology of science. 21 diagrams. 482pp. 5⅜ x 8.
T2 Paperound **$2.00**

**THE RISE OF THE NEW PHYSICS, A. d'Abro.** A half-million word exposition, formerly titled THE DECLINE OF MECHANISM, for readers not versed in higher mathematics. The only thorough explanation, in everyday language, of the central core of modern mathematical physical theory, treating both classical and modern theoretical physics, and presenting in terms almost anyone can understand the equivalent of 5 years of study of mathematical physics. Scientifically impeccable coverage of mathematical-physical thought from the Newtonian system up through the electronic theories of Dirac and Heisenberg and Fermi's statistics. Combines both history and exposition; provides a broad yet unified and detailed view, with constant comparison of classical and modern views on phenomena and theories. "A must for anyone doing serious study in the physical sciences," JOURNAL OF THE FRANKLIN INSTITUTE. "Extraordinary faculty . . . to explain ideas and theories of theoretical physics in the language of daily life," ISIS. First part of set covers philosophy of science, drawing upon the practice of Newton, Maxwell, Poincaré, Einstein, others, discussing modes of thought, experiment, interpretations of causality, etc. In the second part, 100 pages explain grammar and vocabulary of mathematics, with discussions of functions, groups, series, Fourier series, etc. The remainder is devoted to concrete, detailed coverage of both classical and quantum physics, explaining such topics as analytic mechanics, Hamilton's principle, wave theory of light, electromagnetic waves, groups of transformations, thermodynamics, phase rule, Brownian movement, kinetics, special relativity, Planck's original quantum theory, Bohr's atom, Zeeman effect, Broglie's wave mechanics, Heisenberg's uncertainty, Eigen-values, matrices, scores of other important topics. Discoveries and theories are covered for such men as Alembert, Born, Cantor, Debye, Euler, Foucault, Galois, Gauss, Hadamard, Kelvin, Kepler, Laplace, Maxwell, Pauli, Rayleigh, Volterra, Weyl, Young, more than 180 others. Indexed. 97 illustrations. ix + 982pp. 5⅜ x 8.
T3 Volume 1, Paperbound **$2.00**
T4 Volume 2, Paperbound **$2.00**

**CONCERNING THE NATURE OF THINGS, Sir William Bragg.** Christmas lectures delivered at the Royal Society by Nobel laureate. Why a spinning ball travels in a curved track; how uranium is transmuted to lead, etc. Partial contents: atoms, gases, liquids, crystals, metals, etc. No scientific background needed; wonderful for intelligent child. 32pp. of photos, 57 figures. xii + 232pp. 5⅜ x 8.
T31 Paperbound **$1.35**

**THE UNIVERSE OF LIGHT, Sir William Bragg.** No scientific training needed to read Nobel Prize winner's expansion of his Royal Institute Christmas Lectures. Insight into nature of light, methods and philosophy of science. Explains lenses, reflection, color, resonance, polarization, x-rays, the spectrum, Newton's work with prisms, Huygens' work with polarization, Crookes' with cathode ray, etc. Leads into clear statement of 2 major historical theories of light, corpuscle and wave. Dozens of experiments you can do. 199 illus., including 2 full-page color plates. 293pp. 5⅜ x 8.
S538 Paperbound **$1.85**

**PHYSICS, THE PIONEER SCIENCE, L. W. Taylor.** First thorough text to place all important physical phenomena in cultural-historical framework; remains best work of its kind. Exposition of physical laws, theories developed chronologically, with great historical, illustrative experiments diagrammed, described, worked out mathematically. Excellent physics text for self-study as well as class work. Vol. 1: Heat, Sound: motion, acceleration, gravitation, conservation of energy, heat engines, rotation, heat, mechanical energy, etc. 211 illus. 407pp. 5⅜ x 8. Vol. 2: Light, Electricity: images, lenses, prisms, magnetism, Ohm's law, dynamos, telegraph, quantum theory, decline of mechanical view of nature, etc. Bibliography. 13 table appendix. Index. 551 illus. 2 color plates. 508pp. 5⅜ x 8.

Vol. 1 S565 Paperbound **$2.00**
Vol. 2 S566 Paperbound **$2.00**
The set **$4.00**

**FROM EUCLID TO EDDINGTON: A STUDY OF THE CONCEPTIONS OF THE EXTERNAL WORLD, Sir Edmund Whittaker.** A foremost British scientist traces the development of theories of natural philosophy from the western rediscovery of Euclid to Eddington, Einstein, Dirac, etc. The inadequacy of classical physics is contrasted with present day attempts to understand the physical world through relativity, non-Euclidean geometry, space curvature, wave mechanics, etc. 5 major divisions of examination: Space; Time and Movement; the Concepts of Classical Physics; the Concepts of Quantum Mechanics; the Eddington Universe. 212pp. 5⅜ x 8. T491 Paperbound **$1.35**

**THE STORY OF ATOMIC THEORY AND ATOMIC ENERGY, J. G. Feinberg.** Wider range of facts on physical theory, cultural implications, than any other similar source. Completely non-technical. Begins with first atomic theory, 600 B.C., goes through A-bomb, developments to 1959. Avogadro, Rutherford, Bohr, Einstein, radioactive decay, binding energy, radiation danger, future benefits of nuclear power, dozens of other topics, told in lively, related, informal manner. Particular stress on European atomic research. "Deserves special mention . . . authoritative," Saturday Review. Formerly "The Atom Story." New chapter to 1959. Index. 34 illustrations. 251pp. 5⅜ x 8. T625 Paperbound **$1.45**

**THE STRANGE STORY OF THE QUANTUM, AN ACCOUNT FOR THE GENERAL READER OF THE GROWTH OF IDEAS UNDERLYING OUR PRESENT ATOMIC KNOWLEDGE, B. Hoffmann.** Presents lucidly and expertly, with barest amount of mathematics, the problems and theories which led to modern quantum physics. Dr. Hoffmann begins with the closing years of the 19th century, when certain trifling discrepancies were noticed, and with illuminating analogies and examples takes you through the brilliant concepts of Planck, Einstein, Pauli, de Broglie, Bohr, Schroedinger, Heisenberg, Dirac, Sommerfeld, Feynman, etc. This edition includes a new, long postscript carrying the story through 1958. "Of the books attempting an account of the history and contents of our modern atomic physics which have come to my attention, this is the best," H. Margenau, Yale University, in "American Journal of Physics." 32 tables and line illustrations. Index. 275pp. 5⅜ x 8. T518 Paperbound **$1.45**

**SPACE AND TIME, Emile Borel.** An entirely non-technical introduction to relativity, by world-renowned mathematician, Sorbonne Professor. (Notes on basic mathematics are included separately.) This book has never been surpassed for insight, and extraordinary clarity of thought, as it presents scores of examples, analogies, arguments, illustrations, which explain such topics as: difficulties due to motion; gravitation a force of inertia; geodesic lines; wave-length and difference of phase; x-rays and crystal structure; the special theory of relativity; and much more. Indexes. 4 appendixes. 15 figures. xvi + 243pp. 5⅜ x 8. T592 Paperbound **$1.45**

**THE RESTLESS UNIVERSE, Max Born.** New enlarged version of this remarkably readable account by a Nobel laureate. Moving from sub-atomic particles to universe, the author explains in very simple terms the latest theories of wave mechanics. Partial contents: air and its relatives, electrons & ions, waves & particles, electronic structure of the atom, nuclear physics. Nearly 1000 illustrations, including 7 animated sequences. 325pp. 6 x 9. T412 Paperbound **$2.00**

**SOAP SUBBLES, THEIR COLOURS AND THE FORCES WHICH MOULD THEM, C. V. Boys.** Only complete edition, half again as much material as any other. Includes Boys' hints on performing his experiments, sources of supply. Dozens of lucid experiments show complexities of liquid films, surface tension, etc. Best treatment ever written. Introduction. 83 illustrations. Color plate. 202pp. 5⅜ x 8. T542 Paperbound **95¢**

**SPINNING TOPS AND GYROSCOPIC MOTION, John Perry.** Well-known classic of science still unsurpassed for lucid, accurate, delightful exposition. How quasi-rigidity is induced in flexible and fluid bodies by rapid motions; why gyrostat falls, top rises; nature and effect on climatic conditions of earth's precessional movement; effect of internal fluidity on rotating bodies, etc. Appendixes describe practical uses to which gyroscopes have been put in ships, compasses, monorail transportation. 62 figures. 128pp. 5⅜ x 8. T416 Paperbound **$1.00**

**MATTER & LIGHT, THE NEW PHYSICS, L. de Broglie.** Non-technical papers by a Nobel laureate explain electromagnetic theory, relativity, matter, light and radiation, wave mechanics, quantum physics, philosophy of science. Einstein, Planck, Bohr, others explained so easily that no mathematical training is needed for all but 2 of the 21 chapters. Unabridged. Index. 300pp. 5⅜ x 8. T35 Paperbound **$1.60**

**A SURVEY OF PHYSICAL THEORY, Max Planck.** One of the greatest scientists of all time, creator of the quantum revolution in physics, writes in non-technical terms of his own discoveries and those of other outstanding creators of modern physics. Planck wrote this book when science had just crossed the threshold of the new physics, and he communicates the excitement felt then as he discusses electromagnetic theories, statistical methods, evolution of the concept of light, a step-by-step description of how he developed his own momentous theory, and many more of the basic ideas behind modern physics. Formerly "A" Survey of Physics." Bibliography. Index. 128pp. 5⅜ x 8.                    S650 Paperbound **$1.15**

**THE NATURE OF LIGHT AND COLOUR IN THE OPEN AIR, M. Minnaert.** Why is falling snow sometimes black? What causes mirages, the fata morgana, multiple suns and moons in the sky? How are shadows formed? Prof. Minnaert of the University of Utrecht answers these and similar questions in optics, light, colour, for non-specialists. Particularly valuable to nature, science students, painters, photographers. Translated by H. M. Kremer-Priest, K. Jay. 202 illustrations, including 42 photos. xvi + 362pp. 5⅜ x 8.                    T196 Paperbound **$1.95**

**THE STORY OF X-RAYS FROM RONTGEN TO ISOTOPES, A. R. Bleich.** Non-technical history of x-rays, their scientific explanation, their applications in medicine, industry, research, and art, and their effect on the individual and his descendants. Includes amusing early reactions to Röntgen's discovery, cancer therapy, detections of art and stamp forgeries, potential risks to patient and operator, etc. Illustrations show x-rays of flower structure, the gall bladder, gears with hidden defects, etc. Original Dover publication. Glossary. Bibliography. Index. 55 photos and figures. xiv + 186pp. 5⅜ x 8.                    T662 Paperbound **$1.35**

**TEACH YOURSELF ELECTRICITY, C. W. Wilman.** Electrical resistance, inductance, capacitance, magnets, chemical effects of current, alternating currents, generators and motors, transformers, rectifiers, much more. 230 questions, answers, worked examples. List of units. 115 illus. 194pp. 6⅞ x 4¼.                    Clothbound **$2.00**

**TEACH YOURSELF HEAT ENGINES, E. De Ville.** Measurement of heat, development of steam and internal combustion engines, efficiency of an engine, compression-ignition engines, production of steam, the ideal engine, much more. 318 exercises, answers, worked examples. Tables. 76 illus. 220pp. 6⅞ x 4¼.                    Clothbound **$2.00**

**TEACH YOURSELF MECHANICS, P. Abbott.** The lever, centre of gravity, parallelogram of force, friction, acceleration, Newton's laws of motion, machines, specific gravity, gas, liquid pressure, much more. 280 problems, solutions. Tables. 163 illus. 271pp. 6⅞ x 4¼.
Clothbound **$2.00**

**GREAT IDEAS OF MODERN MATHEMATICS: THEIR NATURE AND USE, Jagjit Singh.** Reader with only high school math will understand main mathematical ideas of modern physics, astronomy, genetics, psychology, evolution, etc., better than many who use them as tools, but comprehend little of their basic structure. Author uses his wide knowledge of non-mathematical fields in brilliant exposition of differential equations, matrices, group theory, logic, statistics, problems of mathematical foundations, imaginary numbers, vectors, etc. Original publication. 2 appendixes. 2 indexes. 65 illustr. 322pp. 5⅜ x 8.                    S587 Paperbound **$1.55**

**MATHEMATICS IN ACTION, O. G. Sutton.** Everyone with a command of high school algebra will find this book one of the finest possible introductions to the application of mathematics to physical theory. Ballistics, numerical analysis, waves and wavelike phenomena, Fourier series, group concepts, fluid flow and aerodynamics, statistical measures, and meteorology are discussed with unusual clarity. Some calculus and differential equations theory is developed by the author for the reader's help in the more difficult sections. 88 figures. Index. viii + 236pp. 5⅜ x 8.                    T440 Clothbound **$3.50**

# FREE! All you do is ask for it!

**A DOVER SCIENCE SAMPLER,** edited by George Barkin. 64-page book, sturdily bound, containing excerpts from over 20 Dover books explaining science. Edwin Hubble, George Sarton, Ernst Mach, A. d'Abro, Galileo, Newton, others, discussing island universes, scientific truth, biological phenomena, stability in bridges, etc. Copies limited, no more than 1 to a customer.        FREE

**THE FOURTH DIMENSION SIMPLY EXPLAINED, edited by H. P. Manning.** 22 essays, originally Scientific American contest entries, that use a minimum of mathematics to explain aspects of 4-dimensional geometry: analogues to 3-dimensional space, 4-dimensional absurdities and curiosities (such as removing the contents of an egg without puncturing its shell), possible measurements and forms, etc. Introduction by the editor. Only book of its sort on a truly elementary level, excellent introduction to advanced works. 82 figures. 251pp. 5⅜ x 8.
T711 Paperbound **$1.35**

**FAMOUS BRIDGES OF THE WORLD, D. B. Steinman.** An up-to-the-minute revised edition of a book that explains the fascinating drama of how the world's great bridges came to be built. The author, designer of the famed Mackinac bridge, discusses bridges from all periods and all parts of the world, explaining their various types of construction, and describing the problems their builders faced. Although primarily for youngsters, this cannot fail to interest readers of all ages. 48 illustrations in the text. 23 photographs. 99pp. 6⅛ x 9¼.
T161 Paperbound **$1.00**

**BRIDGES AND THEIR BUILDERS, David Steinman and Sara Ruth Watson.** Engineers, historians, everyone who has ever been fascinated by great spans will find this book an endless source of information and interest. Dr. Steinman, recipient of the Louis Levy medal, was one of the great bridge architects and engineers of all time, and his analysis of the great bridges of history is both authoritative and easily followed. Greek and Roman bridges, medieval bridges, Oriental bridges, modern works such as the Brooklyn Bridge and the Golden Gate Bridge, and many others are described in terms of history, constructional principles, artistry, and function. All in all this book is the most comprehensive and accurate semipopular history of bridges in print in English. New, greatly revised, enlarged edition. 23 photographs, 26 line drawings. Index. xvii + 401pp. 5⅜ x 8.     T431 Paperbound **$2.00**

**FADS AND FALLACIES IN THE NAME OF SCIENCE, Martin Gardner.** Examines various cults, quack systems, frauds, delusions which at various times have masqueraded as science. Accounts of hollow-earth fanatics like Symmes; Velikovsky and wandering planets; Hoerbiger; Bellamy and the theory of multiple moons; Charles Fort; dowsing, pseudoscientific methods for finding water, ores, oil. Sections on naturopathy, iridiagnosis, zone therapy, food fads, etc. Analytical accounts of Wilhelm Reich and orgone sex energy; L. Ron Hubbard and Dianetics; A. Korzybski and General Semantics; many others. Brought up to date to include Bridey Murphy, others. Not just a collection of anecdotes, but a fair, reasoned appraisal of eccentric theory. Formerly titled IN THE NAME OF SCIENCE. Preface. Index. x + 384pp. 5⅜ x 8.     T394 Paperbound **$1.50**

See also: A PHILOSOPHICAL ESSAY ON PROBABILITIES, P. de Laplace; ON MATHEMATICS AND MATHEMATICIANS, R. E. Moritz; AN ELEMENTARY SURVEY OF CELESTIAL MECHANICS, Y. Ryabov; THE SKY AND ITS MYSTERIES, E. A. Beet; THE REALM OF THE NEBULAE, E. Hubble; OUT OF THE SKY, H. H. Nininger; SATELLITES AND SCIENTIFIC RESEARCH, D. King-Hele; HEREDITY AND YOUR LIFE, A. M. Winchester; INSECTS AND INSECT LIFE, S. W. Frost; PRINCIPLES OF STRATIGRAPHY, A. W. Grabau; TEACH YOURSELF SERIES.

# HISTORY OF SCIENCE AND MATHEMATICS

**DIALOGUES CONCERNING TWO NEW SCIENCES, Galileo Galilei.** This classic of experimental science, mechanics, engineering, is as enjoyable as it is important. A great historical document giving insights into one of the world's most original thinkers, it is based on 30 years' experimentation. It offers a lively exposition of dynamics, elasticity, sound, ballistics, strength of materials, the scientific method. "Superior to everything else of mine," Galileo. Trans. by H. Crew, A. Salvio. 126 diagrams. Index. xxi + 288pp. 5⅜ x 8.
     S99 Paperbound **$1.65**

**A DIDEROT PICTORIAL ENCYCLOPEDIA OF TRADES AND INDUSTRY, Manufacturing and the Technical Arts in Plates Selected from "L'Encyclopédie ou Dictionnaire Raisonné des Sciences, des Arts, et des Métiers" of Denis Diderot. Edited with text by C. Gillispie.** This first modern selection of plates from the high point of 18th century French engraving is a storehouse of valuable technological information to the historian of arts and science. Over 2000 illustrations on 485 full page plates, most of them original size, show the trades and industries of a fascinating era in such great detail that the processes and shops might very well be reconstructed from them. The plates teem with life, with men, women, and children performing all of the thousands of operations necessary to the trades before and during the early stages of the industrial revolution. Plates are in sequence, and show general operations, closeups of difficult operations, and details of complex machinery. Such important and interesting trades and industries are illustrated as sowing, harvesting, beekeeping, cheesemaking, operating windmills, milling flour, charcoal burning, tobacco processing, indigo, fishing, arts of war, salt extraction, mining, smelting, casting iron, steel, extracting mercury, zinc, sulphur, copper, etc., slating, tinning, silverplating, gilding, making gunpowder, cannons, bells, shoeing horses, tanning, papermaking, printing, dyeing, and more than 40 other categories. Professor Gillispie, of Princeton, supplies a full commentary on all the plates, identifying operations, tools, processes, etc. This material, presented in a lively and lucid fashion, is of great interest to the reader interested in history of science and technology. Heavy library cloth. 920pp. 9 x 12.     T421 Two volume set **$18.50**

**DE MAGNETE, William Gilbert.** This classic work on magnetism founded a new science. Gilbert was the first to use the word "electricity", to recognize mass as distinct from weight, to discover the effect of heat on magnetic bodies; invent an electroscope, differentiate between static electricity and magnetism, conceive of the earth as a magnet. Written by the first great experimental scientist, this lively work is valuable not only as an historical landmark, but as the delightfully easy to follow record of a perpetually searching, ingenious mind. Translated by P. F. Mottelay. 25 page biographical memoir. 90 figures. lix + 368pp. 5⅜ x 8.     S470 Paperbound **$2.00**

**CHARLES BABBAGE AND HIS CALCULATING ENGINES, edited by P. Morrison and E. Morrison.** Babbage, leading 19th century pioneer in mathematical machines and herald of modern operational research, was the true father of Harvard's relay computer Mark I. His Difference Engine and Analytical Engine were the first machines in the field. This volume contains a valuable introduction on his life and work; major excerpts from his autobiography, revealing his eccentric and unusual personality; and extensive selections from "Babbage's Calculating Engines," a compilation of hard-to-find journal articles by Babbage, the Countess of Lovelace, L. F. Menabrea, and Dionysius Lardner. 8 illustrations, Appendix of miscellaneous papers. Index. Bibliography. xxxviii + 400pp. 5⅜ x 8. T12 Paperbound **$2.00**

**A HISTORY OF ASTRONOMY FROM THALES TO KEPLER, J. L. E. Dreyer.** (Formerly A HISTORY OF PLANETARY SYSTEMS FROM THALES TO KEPLER.) This is the only work in English to give the complete history of man's cosmological views from prehistoric times to Kepler and Newton. Partial contents: Near Eastern astronomical systems, Early Greeks, Homocentric Spheres of Eudoxus, Epicycles, Ptolemaic system, medieval cosmology, Copernicus, Kepler, etc. Revised, foreword by W. H. Stahl. New bibliography. xvii + 430pp. 5⅜ x 8.
S79 Paperbound **$1.98**

**A SHORT HISTORY OF ANATOMY AND PHYSIOLOGY FROM THE GREEKS TO HARVEY, Charles Singer.** Corrected edition of THE EVOLUTION OF ANATOMY, classic work tracing evolution of anatomy and physiology from prescientific times through Greek & Roman periods, Dark Ages, Renaissance, to age of Harvey and beginning of modern concepts. Centered on individuals, movements, periods that definitely advanced anatomical knowledge: Plato, Diocles, Aristotle, Theophrastus, Herophilus, Erasistratus, the Alexandrians, Galen, Mondino, da Vinci, Linacre, Sylvius, others. Special section on Vesalius; Vesalian atlas of nudes, skeletons, muscle tabulae. Index of names, 20 plates.. 270 extremely interesting illustrations of ancient, medieval, Renaissance, Oriental origin. xii + 209pp. 5⅜ x 8. T389 Paperbound **$1.75**

**FROM MAGIC TO SCIENCE, Charles Singer.** A great historian examines aspects of medical science from the Roman Empire through the Renaissance. Includes perhaps the best discussion of early herbals, and a penetrating physiological interpretation of "The Visions of Hildegarde of Bingen." Also examined are Arabian and Galenic influences; the Sphere of Pythagoras; Paracelsus; the reawakening of science under Leonardo da Vinci, Vesalius; the Lorica of Gildas the Briton; etc. Frequent quotations with translations. New Introduction by the author. New unabridged, corrected edition. 158 unusual illustrations from classical and medieval sources. Index. xxvii + 365pp. 5⅜ x 8. T390 Paperbound **$2.00**

**HISTORY OF MATHEMATICS, D. E. Smith.** Most comprehensive non-technical history of math in English. Discusses lives and works of over a thousand major and minor figures, with footnotes supplying technical information outside the book's scheme, and indicating disputed matters. Vol I: A chronological examination, from primitive concepts through Egypt, Babylonia, Greece, the Orient, Rome, the Middle Ages, the Renaissance, and up to 1900. Vol 2: The development of ideas in specific fields and problems, up through elementary calculus. Two volumes, total of 510 illustrations, 1355pp. 5⅜ x 8. Set boxed in attractive container. T429, 430 Paperbound, the set **$5.00**

**A SHORT ACCOUNT OF THE HISTORY OF MATHEMATICS, W. W. R. Ball.** Most readable non-technical history of mathematics treats lives, discoveries of every important figure from Egyptian, Phoenician mathematicians to late 19th century. Discusses schools of Ionia, Pythagoras, Athens, Cyzicus, Alexandria, Byzantium, systems of numeration; primitive arithmetic; Middle Ages, Renaissance, including Arabs, Bacon, Regiomontanus, Tartaglia, Cardan, Stevinus, Galileo, Kepler; modern mathematics of Descartes, Pascal, Wallis, Huygens, Newton, Leibnitz, d'Alembert, Euler, Lambert, Laplace, Legendre, Gauss, Hermite, Weierstrass, scores more. Index. 25 figures. 546pp. 5⅜ x 8. S630 Paperbound **$2.00**

**A SOURCE BOOK IN MATHEMATICS, D. E. Smith.** Great discoveries in math, from Renaissance to end of 19th century, in English translation. Read announcements by Dedekind, Gauss, Delamain, Pascal, Fermat, Newton, Abel, Lobachevsky, Bolyai, Riemann, De Moivre, Legendre, Laplace, others of discoveries about imaginary numbers, number congruence, slide rule, equations, symbolism, cubic algebraic equations, non-Euclidean forms of geometry, calculus, function theory, quaternions, etc. Succinct selections from 125 different treatises, articles, most unavailable elsewhere in English. Each article preceded by biographical, historical introduction. Vol. I: Fields of Number, Algebra. Index. 32 illus. 338pp. 5⅜ x 8. Vol. II: Fields of Geometry, Probability, Calculus, Functions, Quaternions. 83 illus. 432pp. 5⅜ x 8.
Vol. 1: S552 Paperbound **$1.85**
Vol. 2: S553 Paperbound **$1.85**
2 vol. set, boxed **$3.50**

**A HISTORY OF THE CALCULUS, AND ITS CONCEPTUAL DEVELOPMENT, Carl B. Boyer.** Provides laymen and mathematicians a detailed history of the development of the calculus, from early beginning in antiquity to final elaboration as mathematical abstractions. Gives a sense of mathematics not as a technique, but as a habit of mind, in the progression of ideas of Zeno, Plato, Pythagoras, Eudoxus, Arabic and Scholastic mathematicians, Newton, Leibnitz, Taylor, Descartes, Euler, Lagrange, Cantor, Weierstrass, and others. This first comprehensive critical history of the calculus was originally titled "The Concepts of the Calculus." Foreword by R. Courant. Preface. 22 figures. 25-page bibliography. Index. v + 364pp. 5⅜ x 8. S509 Paperbound **$2.00**

**A CONCISE HISTORY OF MATHEMATICS, D. Struik.** Lucid study of development of mathematical ideas, techniques from Ancient Near East, Greece, Islamic science, Middle Ages, Renaissance, modern times. Important mathematicians are described in detail. Treatment is not anecdotal, but analytical development of ideas. "Rich in content, thoughtful in interpretation," U.S. QUARTERLY BOOKLIST. Non-technical; no mathematical training needed. Index. 60 illustrations, including Egyptian papyri, Greek mss., portraits of 31 eminent mathematicians. Bibliography. 2nd edition. xix + 299pp. 5⅜ x 8. **T255 Paperbound $1.75**

See also: NON-EUCLIDEAN GEOMETRY, R. Bonola; THEORY OF DETERMINANTS IN HISTORICAL ORDER OF DEVELOPMENT, T. Muir; HISTORY OF THE THEORY OF ELASTICITY AND STRENGTH OF MATERIALS, I. Todhunter and K. Pearson; A SHORT HISTORY OF ASTRONOMY, A. Berry; CLASSICS OF SCIENCE.

# PHILOSOPHY OF SCIENCE AND MATHEMATICS

**FOUNDATIONS OF SCIENCE: THE PHILOSOPHY OF THEORY AND EXPERIMENT, N. R. Campbell.** A critique of the most fundamental concepts of science in general and physics in particular. Examines why certain propositions are accepted without question, demarcates science from philosophy, clarifies the understanding of the tools of science. Part One analyzes the presuppositions of scientific thought: existence of the material world, nature of scientific laws, multiplication of probabilities, etc.: Part Two covers the nature of experiment and the application of mathematics: conditions for measurement, relations between numerical laws and theories, laws of error, etc. An appendix covers problems arising from relativity, force, motion, space, and time. A classic in its field. Index. xiii + 565pp. 5⅝ x 8⅜. **S372 Paperbound $2.95**

**WHAT IS SCIENCE?, Norman Campbell.** This excellent introduction explains scientific method, role of mathematics, types of scientific laws. Contents: 2 aspects of science, science & nature, laws of science, discovery of laws, explanation of laws, measurement & numerical laws, applications of science. 192pp. 5⅜ x 8. **S43 Paperbound $1.25**

**THE VALUE OF SCIENCE, Henri Poincaré.** Many of the most mature ideas of the "last scientific universalist" covered with charm and vigor for both the beginning student and the advanced worker. Discusses the nature of scientific truth, whether order is innate in the universe or imposed upon it by man, logical thought versus intuition (relating to math, through the works of Weierstrass, Lie, Klein, Riemann), time and space (relativity, psychological time, simultaneity), Hertz's concept of force, interrelationship of mathematical physics to pure math, values within disciplines of Maxwell, Carnot, Mayer, Newton, Lorentz, etc. Index. iii + 147pp. 5⅜ x 8. **S469 Paperbound $1.35**

**SCIENCE AND METHOD, Henri Poincaré.** Procedure of scientific discovery, methodology, experiment, idea-germination—the intellectual processes by which discoveries come into being. Most significant and most interesting aspects of development, application of ideas. Chapters cover selection of facts, chance, mathematical reasoning, mathematics, and logic; Whitehead, Russell, Cantor; the new mechanics, etc. 288pp. 5⅜ x 8. **S222 Paperbound $1.35**

**SCIENCE AND HYPOTHESIS, Henri Poincaré.** Creative psychology in science. How such concepts as number, magnitude, space, force, classical mechanics were developed, and how the modern scientist uses them in his thought. Hypothesis in physics, theories of modern physics. Introduction by Sir James Larmor. "Few mathematicians have had the breadth of vision of Poincaré, and none is his superior in the gift of clear exposition," E. T. Bell. Index. 272pp. 5⅜ x 8. **S221 Paperbound $1.35**

**PHILOSOPHY AND THE PHYSICISTS, L. S. Stebbing.** The philosophical aspects of modern science examined in terms of a lively critical attack on the ideas of Jeans and Eddington. Discusses the task of science, causality, determinism, probability, consciousness, the relation of the world of physics to that of everyday experience. Probes the philosophical significance of the Planck-Bohr concept of discontinuous energy levels, the inferences to be drawn from Heisenberg's Uncertainty Principle, the implications of "becoming" involved in the 2nd law of thermodynamics, and other problems posed by the discarding of Laplacean determinism. 285pp. 5⅜ x 8. **T480 Paperbound $1.65**

**EXPERIMENT AND THEORY IN PHYSICS, Max Born.** A Nobel laureate examines the nature and value of the counterclaims of experiment and theory in physics. Synthetic versus analytical scientific advances are analyzed in the work of Einstein, Bohr, Heisenberg, Planck, Eddington, Milne, and others by a fellow participant. 44pp. 5⅜ x 8. **S308 Paperbound 60¢**

**THE NATURE OF PHYSICAL THEORY, P. W. Bridgman.** Here is how modern physics looks to a highly unorthodox physicist—a Nobel laureate. Pointing out many absurdities of science, and demonstrating the inadequacies of various physical theories, Dr. Bridgman weighs and analyzes the contributions of Einstein, Bohr, Newton, Heisenberg, and many others. This is a non-technical consideration of the correlation of science and reality. Index. xi + 138pp. 5⅜ x 8.
S33 Paperbound **$1.25**

**THE PHILOSOPHY OF SPACE AND TIME, H. Reichenbach.** An important landmark in the development of the empiricist conception of geometry, covering the problem of the foundations of geometry, the theory of time, the consequences of Einstein's relativity, including: relations between theory and observations; coordinate and metrical properties of space; the psychological problem of visual intuition of non-Euclidean structures; and many other important topics in modern science and philosophy. The majority of ideas require only a knowledge of intermediate math. Introduction by R. Carnap. 49 figures. Index. xviii + 296pp. 5⅜ x 8.
S443 Paperbound **$2.00**

**MATTER & MOTION, James Clerk Maxwell,** This excellent exposition begins with simple particles and proceeds gradually to physical systems beyond complete analysis: motion, force, properties of centre of mass of material system, work, energy, gravitation, etc. Written with all Maxwell's original insights and clarity. Notes by E. Larmor. 17 diagrams. 178pp. 5⅜ x 8.
S188 Paperbound **$1.35**

**THE ANALYSIS OF MATTER, Bertrand Russell.** How do our senses concord with the new physics? This volume covers such topics as logical analysis of physics, prerelativity physics, causality, scientific inference, physics and perception, special and general relativity, Weyl's theory, tensors, invariants and their physical interpretation, periodicity and qualitative series. "The most thorough treatment of the subject that has yet been published," THE NATION. Introduction by L. E. Denonn. 422pp. 5⅜ x 8.
T231 Paperbound **$1.95**

**SUBSTANCE AND FUNCTION, & EINSTEIN'S THEORY OF RELATIVITY, Ernst Cassirer.** Two books bound as one. Cassirer establishes a philosophy of the exact sciences that takes into consideration newer developments in mathematics, and also shows historical connections. Partial contents: Aristotelian logic, Mill's analysis, Helmholtz & Kronecker, Russell & cardinal numbers, Euclidean vs. non-Euclidean geometry, Einstein's relativity. Bibliography. Index. xxi + 465pp. 5⅜ x 8.
T50 Paperbound **$2.00**

**PRINCIPLES OF MECHANICS, Heinrich Hertz.** This last work by the great 19th century physicist is not only a classic, but of great interest in the logic of science. Creating a new system of mechanics based upon space, time, and mass, it returns to axiomatic analysis, to understanding of the formal or structural aspects of science, taking into account logic, observation, and a priori elements. Of great historical importance to Poincaré, Carnap, Einstein, Milne. A 20-page introduction by R. S. Cohen, Wesleyan University, analyzes the implications of Hertz's thought and the logic of science. Bibliography. 13-page introduction by Helmholtz. xlii + 274pp. 5⅜ x 8.
S316 Clothbound **$3.50**
S317 Paperbound **$1.85**

**THE PHILOSOPHICAL WRITINGS OF PEIRCE, edited by Justus Buchler.** (Formerly published as THE PHILOSOPHY OF PEIRCE.) This is a carefully balanced exposition of Peirce's complete system, written by Peirce himself. It covers such matters as scientific method, pure chance vs. law, symbolic logic, theory of signs, pragmatism, experiment, and other topics. Introduction by Justus Buchler, Columbia University. xvi + 368pp. 5⅜ x 8.
T217 Paperbound **$1.95**

**ESSAYS IN EXPERIMENTAL LOGIC, John Dewey.** This stimulating series of essays touches upon the relationship between inquiry and experience, dependence of knowledge upon thought, character of logic; judgments of practice, data and meanings, stimuli of thought, etc. Index. viii + 444pp. 5⅜ x 8.
T73 Paperbound **$1.95**

**LANGUAGE, TRUTH AND LOGIC, A. Ayer.** A clear introduction to the Vienna and Cambridge schools of Logical Positivism. It sets up specific tests by which you can evaluate validity of ideas, etc. Contents: Function of philosophy, elimination of metaphysics, nature of analysis, a priori, truth and probability, etc. 10th printing. "I should like to have written it myself," Bertrand Russell. Index. 160pp. 5⅜ x 8.
T10 Paperbound **$1.25**

**THE PSYCHOLOGY OF INVENTION IN THE MATHEMATICAL FIELD, J. Hadamard.** Where do ideas come from? What role does the unconscious play? Are ideas best developed by mathematical reasoning, word reasoning, visualization? What are the methods used by Einstein, Poincaré, Galton, Riemann? How can these techniques be applied by others? Hadamard, one of the world's leading mathematicians, discusses these and other questions. xiii + 145pp. 5⅜ x 8.
T107 Paperbound **$1.25**

**FOUNDATIONS OF GEOMETRY, Bertrand Russell.** Analyzing basic problems in the overlap area between mathematics and philosophy, Nobel laureate Russell examines the nature of geometrical knowledge, the nature of geometry, and the application of geometry to space. It covers the history of non-Euclidean geometry, philosophic interpretations of geometry—especially Kant—projective and metrical geometry. This is most interesting as the solution offered in 1897 by a great mind to a problem still current. New introduction by Prof. Morris Kline of N. Y. University. xii + 201pp. 5⅜ x 8.
S232 Clothbound **$3.25**
S233 Paperbound **$1.60**

# CHEMISTRY AND PHYSICAL CHEMISTRY

**ORGANIC CHEMISTRY, F. C. Whitmore.** The entire subject of organic chemistry for the practicing chemist and the advanced student. Storehouse of facts, theories, processes found elsewhere only in specialized journals. Covers aliphatic compounds (500 pages on the properties and synthetic preparation of hydrocarbons, halides, proteins, ketones, etc.), alicyclic compounds, aromatic compounds, heterocyclic compounds, organophosphorus and organometallic compounds. Methods of synthetic preparation analyzed critically throughout. Includes much of biochemical interest. "The scope of this volume is astonishing," INDUSTRIAL AND ENGINEERING CHEMISTRY. 12,000-reference index. 2387-item bibliography. Total of x + 1005pp. 5⅜ x 8.
Two volume set.
S700 Vol I Paperbound **$2.00**
S701 Vol II Paperbound **$2.00**
The set **$4.00**

**THE PRINCIPLES OF ELECTROCHEMISTRY, D. A. MacInnes.** Basic equations for almost every subfield of electrochemistry from first principles, referring at all times to the soundest and most recent theories and results; unusually useful as text or as reference. Covers coulometers and Faraday's Law, electrolytic conductance, the Debye-Hueckel method for the theoretical calculation of activity coefficients, concentration cells, standard electrode potentials, thermodynamic ionization constants, pH, potentiometric titrations, irreversible phenomena, Planck's equation, and much more. "Excellent treatise," AMERICAN CHEMICAL SOCIETY JOURNAL. "Highly recommended," CHEMICAL AND METALLURGICAL ENGINEERING. 2 Indices. Appendix. 585-item bibliography. 137 figures. 94 tables. ii + 478pp. 5⅝ x 8⅜.
S52 Paperbound **$2.35**

**THE CHEMISTRY OF URANIUM: THE ELEMENT, ITS BINARY AND RELATED COMPOUNDS, J. J. Katz and E. Rabinowitch.** Vast post-World War II collection and correlation of thousands of AEC reports and published papers in a useful and easily accessible form, still the most complete and up-to-date compilation. Treats "dry uranium chemistry," occurrences, preparation, properties, simple compounds, isotopic composition, extraction from ores, spectra, alloys, etc. Much material available only here. Index. Thousands of evaluated bibliographical references. 324 tables, charts, figures. xxi + 609pp. 5⅜ x 8.
S757 Paperbound **$2.95**

**KINETIC THEORY OF LIQUIDS, J. Frenkel.** Regarding the kinetic theory of liquids as a generalization and extension of the theory of solid bodies, this volume covers all types of arrangements of solids, thermal displacements of atoms, interstitial atoms and ions, orientational and rotational motion of molecules, and transition between states of matter. Mathematical theory is developed close to the physical subject matter. 216 bibliographical footnotes. 55 figures. xi + 485pp. 5⅜ x 8.
S94 Clothbound **$3.95**
S95 Paperbound **$2.45**

**POLAR MOLECULES, Pieter Debye.** This work by Nobel laureate Debye offers a complete guide to fundamental electrostatic field relations, polarizability, molecular structure. Partial contents: electric intensity, displacement and force, polarization by orientation, molar polarization and molar refraction, halogen-hydrides, polar liquids, ionic saturation, dielectric constant, etc. Special chapter considers quantum theory. Indexed. 172pp. 5⅜ x 8.
S64 Paperbound **$1.50**

**ELASTICITY, PLASTICITY AND STRUCTURE OF MATTER, R. Houwink.** Standard treatise on rheological aspects of different technically important solids such as crystals, resins, textiles, rubber, clay, many others. Investigates general laws for deformations; determines divergences from these laws for certain substances. Covers general physical and mathematical aspects of plasticity, elasticity, viscosity. Detailed examination of deformations, internal structure of matter in relation to elastic and plastic behavior, formation of solid matter from a fluid, conditions for elastic and plastic behavior of matter. Treats glass, asphalt, gutta percha, balata, proteins, baker's dough, lacquers, sulphur, others. 2nd revised, enlarged edition. Extensive revised bibliography in over 500 footnotes. Index. Table of symbols. 214 figures. xviii + 368pp. 6 x 9¼.
S385 Paperbound **$2.45**

**THE PHASE RULE AND ITS APPLICATION, Alexander Findlay.** Covering chemical phenomena of 1, 2, 3, 4, and multiple component systems, this "standard work on the subject" (NATURE, London), has been completely revised and brought up to date by A. N. Campbell and N. O. Smith. Brand new material has been added on such matters as binary, tertiary liquid equilibria, solid solutions in ternary systems, quinary systems of salts and water. Completely revised to triangular coordinates in ternary systems, clarified graphic representation, solid models, etc. 9th revised edition. Author, subject indexes. 236 figures. 505 footnotes, mostly bibliographic. xii + 494pp. 5⅜ x 8.
S91 Paperbound **$2.45**

**TERNARY SYSTEMS: INTRODUCTION TO THE THEORY OF THREE COMPONENT SYSTEMS, G. Masing.** Furnishes detailed discussion of representative types of 3-components systems, both in solid models (particularly metallic alloys) and isothermal models. Discusses mechanical mixture without compounds and without solid solutions; unbroken solid solution series; solid solutions with solubility breaks in two binary systems; iron-silicon-aluminum alloys; allotropic forms of iron in ternary system; other topics. Bibliography. Index. 166 illustrations. 178pp. 5⅝ x 8⅜.                                                            S631 Paperbound **$1.45**

**THE STORY OF ALCHEMY AND EARLY CHEMISTRY, J. M. Stillman.** An authoritative, scholarly work, highly readable, of development of chemical knowledge from 4000 B.C. to downfall of phlogiston theory in late 18th century. Every important figure, many quotations. Brings alive curious, almost incredible history of alchemical beliefs, practices, writings of Arabian Prince Oneeyade, Vincent of Beauvais, Geber, Zosimos, Paracelsus, Vitruvius, scores more. Studies work, thought of Black, Cavendish, Priestley, Van Helmont, Bergman, Lavoisier, Newton, etc. Index. Bibliography. 579pp. 5⅜ x 8.                                S628 Paperbound **$2.45**

See also: **ATOMIC SPECTRA AND ATOMIC STRUCTURE,** G. Herzberg; **INVESTIGATIONS ON THE THEORY OF THE BROWNIAN MOVEMENT,** A. Einstein; **TREATISE ON THERMODYNAMICS,** M. Planck.

# ASTRONOMY AND ASTROPHYSICS

**AN ELEMENTARY SURVEY OF CELESTIAL MECHANICS, Y. Ryabov.** Elementary exposition of gravitational theory and celestial mechanics. Historical introduction and coverage of basic principles, including: the elliptic, the orbital plane, the 2- and 3-body problems, the discovery of Neptune, planetary rotation, the length of the day, the shapes of galaxies, satellites (detailed treatment of Sputnik I), etc. First American reprinting of successful Russian popular exposition. Elementary algebra and trigonometry helpful, but not necessary; presentation chiefly verbal. Appendix of theorem proofs. 58 figures. 165pp. 5⅜ x 8.
T756 Paperbound **$1.25**

**THE SKY AND ITS MYSTERIES, E. A. Beet.** One of most lucid books on mysteries of universe; deals with astronomy from earliest observations to latest theories of expansion of universe, source of stellar energy, birth of planets, origin of moon craters, possibility of life on other planets. Discusses effects of sunspots on weather; distances, ages of several stars; master plan of universe; methods and tools of astronomers; much more. "Eminently readable book," London Times. Extensive bibliography. Over 50 diagrams. 12 full-page plates, fold-out star map. Introduction. Index, 238pp. 5¼ x 7½.                        T627 Clothbound **$3.00**

**THE REALM OF THE NEBULAE, E. Hubble.** One of the great astronomers of our time records his formulation of the concept of "island universes," and its impact on astronomy. Such topics are covered as the velocity-distance relation; classification, nature, distances, general field of nebulae; cosmological theories; nebulae in the neighborhood of the Milky Way. 39 photos of nebulae, nebulae clusters, spectra of nebulae, and velocity distance relations shown by spectrum comparison. "One of the most progressive lines of astronomical research," The Times (London). New introduction by A. Sandage. 55 illustrations. Index. iv + 201pp. 5⅜ x 8.                                                                S455 Paperbound **$1.50**

**OUT OF THE SKY, H. H. Nininger.** A non-technical but comprehensive introduction to "meteoritics", the young science concerned with all aspects of the arrival of matter from outer space. Written by one of the world's experts on meteorites, this work shows how, despite difficulties of observation and sparseness of data, a considerable body of knowledge has arisen. It defines meteors and meteorites; studies fireball clusters and processions, meteorite composition, size, distribution, showers, explosions, origins, craters, and much more. A true connecting link between astronomy and geology. More than 175 photos, 22 other illustrations. References. Bibliography of author's publications on meteorites. Index. viii + 336pp. 5⅜ x 8.                                                                 T519 Paperbound **$1.85**

**SATELLITES AND SCIENTIFIC RESEARCH, D. King-Hele.** Non-technical account of the manmade satellites and the discoveries they have yielded up to the spring of 1959. Brings together information hitherto published only in hard-to-get scientific journals. Includes the life history of a typical satellite, methods of tracking, new information on the shape of the earth, zones of radiation, etc. Over 60 diagrams and 6 photographs. Mathematical appendix. Bibliography of over 100 items. Index. xii + 180pp. 5⅜ x 8½.                              T703 Clothbound **$4.00**

**HOW TO MAKE A TELESCOPE, Jean Texereau.** Enables the most inexperienced to choose, design, and build an f/6 or f/8 Newtonian type reflecting telescope, with an altazimuth Couder mounting, suitable for lunar, planetary, and stellar observation. A practical step-by-step course covering every operation and every piece of equipment. Basic principles of geometric and physical optics are discussed (though unnecessary to construction), and the merits of reflectors and refractors compared. A thorough discussion of eyepieces, finders, grinding, installation, testing, using the instrument, etc. 241 figures and 38 photos show almost every operation and tool. Potential errors are anticipated as much as possible. Foreword by A. Couder. Bibliography and sources of supply listing. Index. xiii + 191pp. 6¼ x 10.                                                                 T464 Clothbound **$3.50**

**AN INTRODUCTORY TREATISE ON DYNAMICAL ASTRONOMY, H. C. Plummer.** Unusually wide connected and concise coverage of nearly every significant branch of dynamical astronomy, stressing basic principles throughout: determination of orbits, planetary theory, lunar theory, precession and nutation, and many of their applications. Hundreds of formulas and theorems worked out completely, important methods thoroughly explained. Covers motion under a central attraction, orbits of double stars and spectroscopic binaries, the libration of the moon, and much more. Index. 8 diagrams. xxi + 343pp. 5⅝ x 8⅜. S689 Paperbound **$2.35**

**A COMPENDIUM OF SPHERICAL ASTRONOMY, S. Newcomb.** Long a standard collection of basic methods and formulas most useful to the working astronomer, and clear full text for students. Includes the most important common approximations; 40 pages on the method of least squares; general theory of spherical coordinates; parallax; aberration; astronomical refraction; theory of precession; proper motion of the stars; methods of deriving positions of stars; and much more. Index. 9 Appendices of tables, formulas, etc. 36 figures. xviii + 444pp. 5⅜ x 8.
S690 Paperbound **$2.25**

**AN INTRODUCTORY TREATISE ON THE LUNAR THEORY, E. W. Brown.** Indispensable for all scientists and engineers interested in orbital calculation, satellites, or navigation of space. Only work in English to explain in detail 5 major mathematical approaches to the problem of 3 bodies, those of Laplace, de Pontécoulant, Hansen, Delaunay, and Hill. Covers expressions for mutual attraction, equations of motion, forms of solution, variations of the elements in disturbed motion, the constants and their interpretations, planetary and other disturbing influences, etc. Index. Bibliography. Tables. xvi + 292pp. 5⅝ x 8⅜.
S666 Paperbound **$2.00**

**LES METHODES NOUVELLES DE LA MECANIQUE CELESTE, H. Poincaré.** Complete text (in French) of one of Poincaré's most important works. This set revolutionized celestial mechanics: first use of integral invariants, first major application of linear differential equations, study of periodic orbits, lunar motion and Jupiter's satellites, three body problem, and many other important topics. "Started a new era . . . so extremely modern that even today few have mastered his weapons," E. T. Bell. Three volumes. Total 1282pp. 6⅛ x 9¼.
Vol. 1. S401 Paperbound **$2.75**
Vol. 2. S402 Paperbound **$2.75**
Vol. 3. S403 Paperbound **$2.75**
The set **$7.50**

**SPHERICAL AND PRACTICAL ASTRONOMY, W. Chauvenet.** First book in English to apply mathematical techniques to astronomical problems is still standard work. Covers almost entire field, rigorously, with over 300 examples worked out. Vol. 1, spherical astronomy, applications to nautical astronomy; determination of hour angles, parallactic angle for known stars; interpolation; parallax; laws of refraction; predicting eclipses; precession, nutation of fixed stars; etc. Vol. 2, theory, use, of instruments; telescope; measurement of arcs, angles in general; electro-chronograph; sextant, reflecting circles; zenith telescope; etc. 100-page appendix of detailed proof of Gauss' method of least squares. 5th revised edition. Index. 15 plates, 20 tables. 1340pp. 5⅜ x 8.
Vol. 1 S618 Paperbound **$2.75**
Vol. 2 S619 Paperbound **$2.75**
The set **$5.50**

**THE INTERNAL CONSTITUTION OF THE STARS, Sir A. S. Eddington.** Influence of this has been enormous; first detailed exposition of theory of radiative equilibrium for stellar interiors, of all available evidence for existence of diffuse matter in interstellar space. Studies quantum theory, polytropic gas spheres, mass-luminosity relations, variable stars, etc. Discussions of equations paralleled with informal exposition of intimate relationship of astrophysics with great discoveries in atomic physics, radiation. Introduction. Appendix. Index. 421pp. 5⅜ x 8.
S563 Paperbound **$2.25**

**ASTRONOMY OF STELLAR ENERGY AND DECAY, Martin Johnson.** Middle level treatment of astronomy as interpreted by modern atomic physics. Part One is non-technical, examines physical properties, source of energy, spectroscopy, fluctuating stars, various models and theories, etc. Part Two parallels these topics, providing their mathematical foundation. "Clear, concise, and readily understandable," American Library Assoc. Bibliography. 3 indexes. 29 illustrations. 216pp. 5⅜ x 8. S537 Paperbound **$1.50**

**RADIATIVE TRANSFER, S. Chandrasekhar.** Definitive work in field provides foundation for analysis of stellar atmospheres, planetary illumination, sky radiation; to physicists, a study of problems analogous to those in theory of diffusion of neutrons. Partial contents: equation of transfer, isotropic scattering, H-functions, diffuse reflection and transmission, Rayleigh scattering, X, Y functions, radiative equilibrium of stellar atmospheres. Extensive bibliography. 3 appendices. 35 tables. 35 figures. 407pp. 5⅝ x 8⅜. S599 Paperbound **$2.25**

**AN INTRODUCTION TO THE STUDY OF STELLAR STRUCTURE, Subrahmanyan Chandrasekhar.** Outstanding treatise on stellar dynamics by one of world's greatest astrophysicists. Uses classical & modern math methods to examine relationship between loss of energy, the mass, and radius of stars in a steady state. Discusses thermodynamic laws from Caratheodory's axiomatic standpoint; adiabatic, polytropic laws; work of Ritter, Emden, Kelvin, others; Stroemgren envelopes as starter for theory of gaseous stars; Gibbs statistical mechanics (quantum); degenerate stellar configuration & theory of white dwarfs, etc. "Highest level of scientific merit," BULLETIN, AMER. MATH. SOC. Bibliography. Appendixes. Index. 33 figures. 509pp. 5⅜ x 8. S413 Paperbound **$2.75**

**PRINCIPLES OF STELLAR DYNAMICS, S. Chandrasekhar.** A leading astrophysicist here presents the theory of stellar dynamics as a branch of classical dynamics, clarifying the fundamental issues and the underlying motivations of the theory. He analyzes the effects of stellar encounters in terms of the classical 2-body problem, and investigates problems centering about Liouville's theorem and the solutions of the equations of continuity. This edition also includes 4 important papers by the author published since "Stellar Dynamics," and equally indispensable for all workers in the field: "New Methods in Stellar Dynamics" and "Dynamical Friction," Parts I, II, and III. Index. 3 Appendixes. Bibliography. 50 illustrations. x + 313pp. 5⅜ x8.
S659 Paperbound **$2.00**

**A SHORT HISTORY OF ASTRONOMY, A. Berry.** Popular standard work for over 50 years, this thorough and accurate volume covers the science from primitive times to the end of the 19th century. After the Greeks and the Middle Ages, individual chapters analyze Copernicus, Brahe, Galileo, Kepler, and Newton, and the mixed reception of their discoveries. Post-Newtonian achievements are then discussed in unusual detail: Halley, Bradley, Lagrange, Laplace, Herschel, Bessel, etc. 2 Indexes. 104 illustrations, 9 portraits. xxxi + 440pp. 5⅜ x 8.
T210 Paperbound **$2.00**

**THREE COPERNICAN TREATISES, translated with notes by Edward Rosen.** 3 papers available nowhere else in English: "The Commentariolus" and "Letter against Werner" of Copernicus; the "Narratio prima" of Rheticus. The "Commentariolus" is Copernicus's most lucid exposition of his system. The "Letter against Werner" throws light on development of Copernicus's thought. The "Narratio prima" is earliest printed presentation of the new astronomy. "Educational and enjoyable," Astrophysical Journal. Corrected edition. Biographical introduction. 877-item bibliography of virtually every book, article, on Copernicus published 1939-1958. Index. 19 illustrations. 218pp. 5⅜ x 8.          S585 Paperbound **$1.75**

# EARTH SCIENCES

**PRINCIPLES OF STRATIGRAPHY, A. W. Grabau.** Classic of 20th century geology, unmatched in scope and comprehensiveness. Nearly 600 pages cover the structure and origins of every kind of sedimentary, hydrogenic, oceanic, pyroclastic, atmoclastic, hydroclastic, marine hydroclastic, and bioclastic rock; metamorphism; erosion; etc. Includes also the constitution of the atmosphere; morphology of oceans, rivers, glaciers; volcanic activities; faults and earthquakes; and fundamental principles of paleontology (nearly 200 pages). New introduction by Prof. M. Kay, Columbia U. 1277 bibliographical entries. 264 diagrams. Tables, maps, etc. Two volume set. Total of xxxii + 1185pp. 5⅜ x 8.                          S686 Vol I Paperbound **$2.50**
S687 Vol II Paperbound **$2.50**
The set **$5.00**

**THE GEOLOGICAL DRAMA, H. and G. Termier.** Unusual work by 2 noted French geologists: not the usual survey of geological periods, but general principles; continent formation, the influence of ice-ages and earth movements in shaping the present-day land masses, the creation and advance of life, the position of man. Readable and authoritative survey for the layman; excellent supplement for the student of geology; important collection of recent European theories for the American geologist. Much material appears here for the first time in a non-technical work. Index. 30 photographs, 5 diagrams. 5 maps. 144pp. 6 x 9.          T702 Clothbound **$3.95**

**THE EVOLUTION OF THE IGNEOUS ROCKS, N. L. Bowen.** Invaluable serious introduction applies techniques of physics and chemistry to explain igneous rock diversity in terms of chemical composition and fractional crystallization. Discusses liquid immiscibility in silicate magmas, crystal sorting, liquid lines of descent, fractional resorption of complex minerals, petrogenesis, etc. Of prime importance to geologists & mining engineers, also to physicists, chemists working with high temperatures and pressures. "Most important," TIMES, London. 3 indexes. 263 bibliographic notes. 82 figures. xviii + 334pp. 5⅜ x 8.          S311 Paperbound **$1.85**

**INTERNAL CONSTITUTION OF THE EARTH, edited by Beno Gutenberg.** Completely revised. Brought up-to-date, reset. Prepared for the National Research Council this is a complete & thorough coverage of such topics as earth origins, continent formation, nature & behavior of the earth's core, petrology of the crust, cooling forces in the core, seismic & earthquake material, gravity, elastic constants, strain characteristics and similar topics. "One is filled with admiration . . . a high standard . . . there is no reader who will not learn something from this book," London, Edinburgh, Dublin, Philosophic Magazine. Largest bibliography in print: 1127 classified items. Indexes. Tables of constants. 43 diagrams. 439pp. 6⅛ x 9¼.
S414 Paperbound **$2.45**

**HYDROLOGY, edited by Oscar E. Meinzer.** Prepared for the National Research Council. Detailed complete reference library on precipitation, evaporation, snow, snow surveying, glaciers, lakes, infiltration, soil moisture, ground water, runoff, drought, physical changes produced by water, hydrology of limestone terranes, etc. Practical in application, especially valuable for engineers. 24 experts have created "the most up-to-date, most complete treatment of the subject," AM. ASSOC. of PETROLEUM GEOLOGISTS. Bibliography. Index. 165 illustrations. xi + 712pp. 6⅛ x 9¼.                          S191 Paperbound **$2.95**

**THE BIRTH AND DEVELOPMENT OF THE GEOLOGICAL SCIENCES, F. D. Adams.** Most thorough history of the earth sciences ever written. Geological thought from earliest times to the end of the 19th century, covering over 300 early thinkers & systems: fossils & their explanation, vulcanists vs. neptunists, figured stones & paleontology, generation of stones, dozens of similar topics. 91 illustrations, including medieval, renaissance woodcuts, etc. Index. 632 footnotes, mostly bibliographical. 511pp. 5⅜ x 8. **T5 Paperbound $2.00**

**DE RE METALLICA, Georgius Agricola.** 400-year old classic translated, annotated by former President Herbert Hoover. The first scientific study of mineralogy and mining, for over 200 years after its appearance in 1556, it was the standard treatise. 12 books, exhaustively annotated, discuss the history of mining, selection of sites, types of deposits, making pits, shafts, ventilating, pumps, crushing machinery; assaying, smelting, refining metals; also salt, alum, nitre, glass making. Definitive edition, with all 289 16th century woodcuts of the original. Biographical, historical introductions, bibliography, survey of ancient authors. Indexes. A fascinating book for anyone interested in art, history of science, geology, etc. Deluxe edition. 289 illustrations. 672pp. 6¾ x 10¾. Library cloth. **S6 Clothbound $10.00**

**GEOGRAPHICAL ESSAYS, William Morris Davis.** Modern geography & geomorphology rest on the fundamental work of this scientist. 26 famous essays presenting most important theories, field researches. Partial contents: Geographical Cycle, Plains of Marine and Subaerial Denudation, The Peneplain, Rivers and Valleys of Pennsylvania, Outline of Cape Cod, Sculpture of Mountains by Glaciers, etc. "Long the leader & guide," ECONOMIC GEOGRAPHY. "Part of the very texture of geography . . . models of clear thought," GEOGRAPHIC REVIEW. Index. 130 figures. vi + 777pp. 5⅜ x 8. **S383 Paperbound $2.95**

**A HISTORY OF ANCIENT GEOGRAPHY, E. H. Bunbury.** Standard study, in English, of ancient geography; never equalled for scope, detail. First full account of history of geography from Greeks' first world picture based on mariners, through Ptolemy. Discusses every important map, discovery, figure, travel, expedition, war, conjecture, narrative, bearing on subject. Chapters on Homeric geography, Herodotus, Alexander expedition, Strabo, Pliny, Ptolemy, would stand alone as exhaustive monographs. Includes minor geographers, men not usually regarded in this context: Hecataeus, Pythea, Hipparchus, Artemidorus, Marinus of Tyre, etc. Uses information gleaned from military campaigns such as Punic wars, Hannibal's passage of Alps, campaigns of Lucullus, Pompey, Caesar's wars, the Trojan war. New introduction by W. H. Stahl, Brooklyn College. Bibliography. Index. 20 maps. 1426pp. 5⅜ x 8. **T570-1, clothbound, 2 volume set $12.50**

**URANIUM PROSPECTING, H. L. Barnes.** For immediate practical use, professional geologist considers uranium ores, geological occurrences, field conditions, all aspects of highly profitable occupation. Index. Bibliography. x + 117pp. 5⅜ x 8. **T309 Paperbound $1.00**

# BIOLOGICAL SCIENCES

**THE ORIGIN OF LIFE, A. I. Oparin.** A classic of biology. This is the first modern statement of the theory of gradual evolution of life from nitrocarbon compounds. A brand-new evaluation of Oparin's theory in light of later research, by Dr. S. Morgulis, University of Nebraska. xxv +270pp. 5⅜ x8. **S213 Paperbound $1.75**

**HEREDITY AND YOUR LIFE, A. M. Winchester.** Authoritative, concise explanation of human genetics, in non-technical terms. What factors determine characteristics of future generations, how they may be altered; history of genetics, application of knowledge to control health, intelligence, number of entire populations. Physiology of reproduction, chromosomes, genes, blood types, Rh factor, dominant, recessive traits, birth by proxy, sexual abnormalities, radiation, much more. Index. 75 illus. 345pp. 5⅜ x 8. **T598 Paperbound $1.45**

**MATHEMATICAL BIOPHYSICS: PHYSICO-MATHEMATICAL FOUNDATIONS OF BIOLOGY, N. Rashevsky.** One of most important books in modern biology, now revised, expanded with new chapters, to include most significant recent contributions. Vol. 1: Diffusion phenomena, particularly diffusion drag forces, their effects. Old theory of cell division based on diffusion drag forces, other theoretical approaches, more exhaustively treated than ever. Theories of excitation, conduction in nerves, with formal theories plus physico-chemical theory. Vol. 2: Mathematical theories of various phenomena in central nervous system. New chapters on theory of color vision, of random nets. Principle of optimal design, extended from earlier edition. Principle of relational mapping of organisms, numerous applications. Introduces into mathematical biology such branches of math as topology, theory of sets. Index. 236 illustrations. Total of 988pp. 5⅜ x 8. **S574 Vol. 1 (Books 1, 2) Paperbound $2.50**
**S575 Vol. 2 (Books 3, 4) Paperbound $2.50**
**2 vol. set $5.00**

**ELEMENTS OF MATHEMATICAL BIOLOGY, A. J. Lotka.** A pioneer classic, the first major attempt to apply modern mathematical techniques on a large scale to phenomena of biology, biochemistry, psychology, ecology, similar life sciences. Partial Contents: Statistical meaning of irreversibility; Evolution as redistribution; Equations of kinetics of evolving systems; Chemical, inter-species equilibrium; parameters of state; Energy transformers of nature, etc. Can be read with profit even by those having no advanced math; unsurpassed as study-reference. Formerly titled ELEMENTS OF PHYSICAL BIOLOGY. 72 figures. xxx + 460pp. 5⅜ x 8.                                                  S346 Paperbound **$2.45**

**FRESHWATER MICROSCOPY, W. J. Garnett.** Non-technical, practical book for the layman and student. Contains only information directly confirmed by the distinguished British scientist's personal observation. Tells how to collect and examine specimens, describes equipment and accessories, mounting, staining, correct illumination, measuring, the microprojector, etc. Describes hundreds of different plant and animal species, over 200 illustrated by microphotos. Many valuable suggestions on the work amateurs can do to throw new light on the field. Index. 51 full-page plates. 50 diagrams. Bibliography. 2 Appendices. Glossary of scientific terms. xii + 300pp. 6 x 9.                           S790 Clothbound **$5.95**

**CULTURE METHODS FOR INVERTEBRATE ANIMALS, P. S. Galtsoff, F. E. Lutz, P. S. Welch, J. G. Needham, eds.** A compendium of practical experience of hundreds of scientists and technicians, covering invertebrates from protozoa to chordata, in 313 articles on 17 phyla. Explains in great detail food, protection, environment, reproduction conditions, rearing methods, embryology, breeding seasons, schedule of development, much more. Includes at least one species of each considerable group. Half the articles are on class insecta. Introduction. 97 illustrations. Bibliography. Index. xxix + 590pp. 5⅜ x 8.              S526 Paperbound **$2.75**

**THE BIOLOGY OF THE LABORATORY MOUSE, edited by G. D. Snell.** 1st prepared in 1941 by the staff of the Roscoe B. Jackson Memorial Laboratory, this is still the standard treatise on the mouse, assembling an enormous amount of material for which otherwise you spend hours of research. Embryology, reproduction, histology, spontaneous tumor formation, genetics of tumor transplantation, endocrine secretion & tumor formation, milk, influence & tumor formation, inbred, hybrid animals, parasites, infectious diseases, care & recording. Classified bibliography of 1122 items. 172 figures, including 128 photos. ix + 497pp. 6⅛ x 9¼.
S248 Clothbound **$6.00**

**THE BIOLOGY OF THE AMPHIBIA, G. K. Noble,** Late Curator of Herpetology at the Am. Mus. of Nat. Hist. Probably the most used text on amphibia, unmatched in comprehensiveness, clarity, detail. 19 chapters plus 85-page supplement cover development; heredity; life history; speciation; adaptation; sex, integument, respiratory, circulatory, digestive, muscular, nervous systems; instinct, intelligence, habits, environment, economic value, relationships, classification, etc. "Nothing comparable to it," C. H. Pope, Curator of Amphibia, Chicago Mus. of Nat. Hist. 1047 bibliographic references. 174 illustrations. 600pp. 5⅜ x 8.
S206 Paperbound **$2.98**

**STUDIES ON THE STRUCTURE AND DEVELOPMENT OF VERTEBRATES, E. S. Goodrich.** A definitive study by the greatest modern comparative anatomist. Exceptional in its accounts of the ossicles of the ear, the separate divisions of the coelem and mammalian diaphragm, and the 5 chapters devoted to the head region. Also exhaustive morphological and phylogenetic expositions of skeleton, fins and limbs, skeletal visceral arches and labial cartilages, visceral clefts and gills, vascular, respiratory, excretory, and periphal nervous systems, etc., from fish to the higher mammals. 754 illustrations. 69 page biographical study by C. C. Hardy. Bibliography of 1186 references. "What an undertaking . . . to write a textbook which will summarize adequately and succinctly all that has been done in the realm of Vertebrate Morphology these recent years," Journal of Anatomy. Index. Two volumes. Total 906pp. 5⅜ x 8.                                     Two vol. set S449-50 Paperbound **$5.00**

**THE GENETICAL THEORY OF NATURAL SELECTION, R. A. Fisher.** 2nd revised edition of a vital reviewing of Darwin's Selection Theory in terms of particulate inheritance, by one of the great authorities on experimental and theoretical genetics. Theory is stated in mathematical form. Special features of particulate inheritance are examined: evolution of dominance, maintenance of specific variability, mimicry and sexual selection, etc. 5 chapters on man and his special circumstances as a social animal. 16 photographs. Bibliography. Index. x + 310pp. 5⅜ x 8.                                           S466 Paperbound **$1.85**

**THE AUTOBIOGRAPHY OF CHARLES DARWIN, AND SELECTED LETTERS, edited by Francis Darwin.** Darwin's own record of his early life; the historic voyage aboard the "Beagle"; the furor surrounding evolution, and his replies; reminiscences of his son. Letters to Henslow, Lyell, Hooker, Huxley, Wallace, Kingsley, etc., and. thoughts on religion and vivisection. We see how he revolutionized geology with his concept of ocean subsidence; how his great books on variation of plants and animals, primitive man, the expression of emotion among primates, plant fertilization, carnivorous plants, protective coloration, etc., came into being. Appendix. Index. 365pp. 5⅜ x 8.                T479 Paperbound **$1.65**

**THE LIFE OF PASTEUR, R. Vallery-Radot.** 13th edition of this definitive biography, cited in Encyclopaedia Britannica. Authoritative, scholarly, well-documented with contemporary quotes, observations; gives complete picture of Pasteur's personal life; especially thorough presentation of scientific activities with silkworms, fermentation, hydrophobia, innoculation, etc. Introduction by Sir William Osler. Index. 505pp. 5⅜ x 8.              T633 Paperbound **$2.00**

**ANTONY VAN LEEUWENHOEK AND HIS "LITTLE ANIMALS," edited by Clifford Dobell.** First book to treat extensively, accurately, life and works (relating to protozoology, bacteriology) of first microbiologist, bacteriologist, micrologist. Includes founding papers of protozoology, bacteriology; history of Leeuwenhoek's life; discussions of his microscopes, methods, language. His writing conveys sense of an enthusiastic, naive genius, as he looks at rainwater, pepper water, vinegar, frog's skin, rotifers, etc. Extremely readable, even for nonspecialists. "One of the most interesting and enlightening books I have ever read," Dr. C. C. Bass, former Dean, Tulane U. School of Medicine. Only authorized edition. 400-item bibliography. Index. 32 illust. 442pp. 5⅜ x 8. S594 Paperbound **$2.25**

**MICROGRAPHIA, Robert Hooke.** Hooke, 17th century British universal scientific genius, was a major pioneer in celestial mechanics, optics, gravity, and many other fields, but his greatest contribution was this book, now reprinted entirely from the original 1665 edition, which gave microscopy its first great impetus. With all the freshness of discovery, he describes fully his microscope, and his observations of cork, the edge of a razor, insects' eyes, fabrics, and dozens of other different objects. 38 plates, full-size or larger, contain all the original illustrations. This book is also a fundamental classic in the fields of combustion and heat theory, light and color theory, botany and zoology, hygrometry, and many other fields. It contains such farsighted predictions as the famous anticipation of artificial silk. The final section is concerned with Hooke's observations on the moon and stars. 323pp. 5⅜ x 8.
Paperbound **$2.00**

**CONDITIONED REFLEXES: AN INVESTIGATION OF THE PHYSIOLOGICAL ACTIVITIES OF THE CEREBRAL CORTEX, I. P. Pavlov.** Full, authorized translation of Pavlov's own survey of his work in experimental psychology reviews entire course of experiments, summarizes conclusions, outlines psychological system based on famous "conditioned reflex" concept. Details of technical means used in experiments, observations on formation of conditioned reflexes, function of cerebral hemispheres, results of damage, nature of sleep, typology of nervous system, significance of experiments for human psychology. Trans. by Dr. G. V. Anrep, Cambridge Univ. 235-item bibliography. 18 figures. 445pp. 5⅜ x 8. S614 Paperbound **$2.25**

**THE PRINCIPLES OF PSYCHOLOGY, William James.** The full long course, unabridged, of one of the great classics of Western science. Wonderfully lucid descriptions of human mental activity, consciousness, emotions, reason, abnormal phenomena, and similar topics. Examines motor zones, sensory aphasia, phosphorus and thought, cerebral thermometry, neural process in perception, ideo-motor action—in short, the entire spectrum of human mental activity. "Standard reading . . . a classic of interpretation," PSYCHIATRIC QUARTERLY. 94 illustrations. Two volume set. Total of 1408pp. 5⅜ x 8. T381 Vol I Paperbound **$2.50**
T382 Vol II Paperbound **$2.50**
The set **$5.00**

**THE TRAVELS OF WILLIAM BARTRAM, edited by Mark Van Doren.** This famous source-book of American anthropology, natural history, geography is the record kept by Bartram in the 1770's, on travels through the wilderness of Florida, Georgia, the Carolinas. Containing accurate and beautiful descriptions of Indians, settlers, fauna, flora, it is one of the finest pieces of Americana ever written. Introduction by Mark Van Doren. 13 original illustrations. Index. 448pp. 5⅜ x 8. T13 Paperbound **$2.00**

**FRUIT KEY AND TWIG KEY TO TREES AND SHRUBS (FRUIT KEY TO NORTHEASTERN TREES, TWIG TREE TO DECIDUOUS WOODY PLANTS OF EASTERN NORTH AMERICA), W. M. Harlow.** The only guides with photographs of every twig and fruit described—especially valuable to the novice. The fruit key (both deciduous trees and evergreens) has an introduction explaining seeding, organs involved, fruit types and habits. The twig key introduction treats growth and morphology. In the keys proper, identification is easy and almost automatic. This exceptional work, widely used in university courses, is especially useful for identification in winter, or from the fruit or seed only. Over 350 photos, up to 3 times natural size. Bibliography, glossary, index of common and scientific names, in each key. xvii + 125pp. 5⅝ x 8⅜. T511 Paperbound **$1.25**

**TREES OF THE EASTERN AND CENTRAL UNITED STATES AND CANADA, W. M. Harlow,** Professor of Wood Technology, College of Forestry, State University of N. Y., Syracuse, N. Y. This middle-level text is a serious work covering more than 140 native trees and important escapes, with information on general appearance, growth habit, leaf forms, flowers, fruit, bark, and other features. Commercial use, distribution, habitat, and woodlore are also given. Keys within the text enable you to locate various species with ease. With this book you can identify at sight almost any tree you are likely to encounter; you will know which trees have edible fruit, which are suitable for house planting, and much other useful and interesting information. More than 600 photographs and figures. xiii + 288pp. 4⅝ x 6½. T395 Paperbound **$1.35**

**HOW TO KNOW THE FERNS, F. T. Parsons.** Ferns, among our most lovely native plants, are all too little known. This modern classic of nature lore will enable the layman to identify any American fern he is likely to come across. After an introduction on the structure and life of ferns, the 57 most important ferns are fully pictured and described (arranged upon a simple identification key). Index of Latin and English names. 61 illustrations and 42 full-page plates. xiv + 215pp. 5⅜ x 8. T740 Paperbound **$1.25**

**INSECT LIFE AND INSECT NATURAL HISTORY, S. W. Frost.** Unusual for emphasizing habits, social life, and ecological relations of insects, rather than more academic aspects of classification and morphology. Prof. Frost's enthusiasm and knowledge are everywhere evident as he discusses insect associations, and specialized habits like leaf-mining, leaf-rolling, and case-making, the gall insects, the boring insects, aquatic insects, etc. He examines all sorts of matters not usually covered in general works, such as: insects as human food; insect music and musicians; insect response to electric and radio waves; use of insects in art and literature. The admirably executed purpose of this book, which covers the middle ground between elementary treatment and scholarly monographs, is to excite the reader to observe for himself. Over 700 illustrations. Extensive bibliography. x + 524pp. 5⅜ x 8.
T517 Paperbound **$2.25**

**COMMON SPIDERS OF THE UNITED STATES, J. H. Emerton.** Only non-technical, but thorough, reliable guide to spiders for the layman. Over 200 spiders from all parts of the country, arranged by scientific classification, are identified by shape and color, number of eyes, habitat and range, habits, etc. Full text, 501 line drawings and photographs, and valuable introduction explain webs, poisons, threads, capturing and preserving spiders, etc. Index. New synoptic key by S. W. Frost. xxiv + 225pp. 5⅜ x 8.
T223 Paperbound **$1.35**

**BEHAVIOR AND SOCIAL LIFE OF THE HONEYBEE, Ronald Ribbands.** Outstanding scientific study; a compendium of practically everything known about social life of the honeybee. Stresses behavior of individual bees in field, hive. Extends Frisch's experiments on communication among bees. Covers perception of temperature, gravity, distance, vibration; sound production; glands; structural differences; wax production; temperature regulation; recognition, communication; drifting, mating behavior, other highly interesting topics. Bibliography of 690 references. Indexes. 127 diagrams, graphs, sections of bee anatomy, fine photographs. 352pp. 5½ x 8½.
S410 Clothbound **$4.50**

**ANIMALS IN MOTION, Eadweard Muybridge.** Largest, most comprehensive selection of Muybridge's famous action photos of animals, from his ANIMAL LOCOMOTION. 3919 high-speed shots of 34 different animals and birds in 123 different types of action: horses, mules, oxen, pigs, goats, camels, elephants, dogs, cats, guanacos, sloths, lions, tigers, jaguars, raccoons, baboons, deer, elk, gnus, kangaroos, many others, in different actions — walking, running, flying, leaping. Horse alone shown in more than 40 different ways. Photos taken against ruled backgrounds; most actions taken from 3 angles at once: 90°, 60°, rear. Most plates original size. Of considerable interest to scientists as a classic of biology, as a record of actual facts of natural history and physiology. "A really marvellous series of plates," NATURE (London). "A monumental work," Waldemar Kaempffert. Photographed by E. Muybridge. Edited by L. S. Brown, American Museum of Natural History. 74-page introduction on mechanics of motion. 340 pages of plates, 3919 photographs. 416pp. Deluxe binding, paper. (Weight 4½ lbs.) 7⅞ x 10⅝.
T203 Clothbound **$10.00**

**THE HUMAN FIGURE IN MOTION. Eadweard Muybridge.** This new edition of a great classic in the history of science and photography is the largest selection ever made from the original Muybridge photos of human action: 4789 photographs, illustrating 163 types of motion: walking, running, lifting, etc. in time-exposure sequence photos of speeds up to 1/6000th of a second. Men, women, children, mostly undraped, showing bone and muscle positions against ruled backgrounds, mostly taken at 3 angles at once. Not only was this a great work of photography, acclaimed by contemporary critics as a work of genius, it was also a great 19th century landmark in biological research. Historical introduction by Prof. Robert Taft, U. of Kansas. Plates original size, full detail. Over 500 action strips. 407pp. 7¾ x 10⅝. Deluxe edition.
T204 Clothbound **$10.00**

See also: **ANALYSIS OF SENSATIONS, E. Mach; ON THE SENSATIONS OF TONE, H. Helmholtz; FROM MAGIC TO SCIENCE, C. Singer; A SHORT HISTORY OF ANATOMY AND PHYSIOLOGY FROM THE GREEKS TO HARVEY, C. Singer; ELEMENTARY STATISTICS, WITH APPLICATIONS IN MEDICINE AND THE BIOLOGICAL SCIENCES, F. E. Croxton.**

# MEDICINE

**CLASSICS OF CARDIOLOGY, F. A. Willius and T. E. Keys.** Monumental collection of 52 papers by 51 great researchers and physicians on the anatomy, physiology, and pathology of the heart and the circulation, and the diagnosis and therapy of their diseases. These are the original writings of Harvey, Sénac, Auenbrugger, Withering, Stokes, Einthoven, Osler, and 44 others from 1628 to 1912. 27 of the papers are complete, the rest in major excerpts; all are in English. The biographical notes and introductory essays make this a full history of cardiology —with exclusively first-hand material. 103 portraits, diagrams, and facsimiles of title pages. Chronological table. Total of xx + 858pp. 5⅝ x 8⅜. Two volume set.
T912 Vol I Paperbound **$2.00**
T913 Vol II Paperbound **$2.00**
The set **$4.00**